OXIDATION IN ORGANIC CHEMISTRY

Part A

ORGANIC CHEMISTRY

A SERIES OF MONOGRAPHS

Edited by

ALFRED T. BLOMQUIST

Department of Chemistry, Cornell University, Ithaca, New York

Volume 1. Wolfgang Kirmse. CARBENE CHEMISTRY. 1964

Volume 2. Brandes H. Smith. BRIDGED AROMATIC COMPOUNDS. 1964

Volume 3. Michael Hanack. CONFORMATION THEORY. 1965

Volume 4. Donald J. Cram. FUNDAMENTALS OF CARBANION CHEMISTRY. 1965

Volume 5. Kenneth B. Wiberg (Editor).
OXIDATION IN ORGANIC CHEMISTRY, PART A. 1965
PART B. *In preparation.*

Volume 6. R. F. Hudson. STRUCTURE AND MECHANISM IN ORGANO-PHOSPHORUS CHEMISTRY. 1965

IN PREPARATION
Jan Hamer (Editor). 1,4-CYCLOADDITION REACTIONS
A. William Johnson. YLID CHEMISTRY

OXIDATION IN
ORGANIC CHEMISTRY

Edited by KENNETH B. WIBERG

DEPARTMENT OF CHEMISTRY
YALE UNIVERSITY
NEW HAVEN, CONNECTICUT

PART A

1965

ACADEMIC PRESS   *New York and London*

ACADEMIC PRESS INC.
111 Fifth Avenue New York, New York 10003

United Kingdom Edition published by
ACADEMIC PRESS INC. (LONDON) LTD.
Berkeley Square House, London W. 1

LIBRARY OF CONGRESS CATALOG CARD NUMBER: 65-26047

PRINTED IN THE UNITED STATES OF AMERICA

Contributors

C. A. Bunton, *Department of Chemistry, University of California, Santa Barbara, California*

Rudolf Criegee, *Laboratorium für Organische Chemie, Technische Hochschule Karlsruhe, Karlsruhe, Germany*

J. S. Littler, *Department of Organic Chemistry, The University, Bristol, England*

William H. Richardson, *Department of Chemistry, San Diego State College, San Diego, California*

Ross Stewart, *Department of Chemistry, University of British Columbia, Vancouver, Canada*

W. A. Waters, *Dyson Perrins Laboratory, Oxford University, Oxford, England*

Kenneth B. Wiberg, *Department of Chemistry, Yale University, New Haven, Connecticut*

Preface

Reactions involving oxidation and reduction are among the most common of chemical processes. However, in contrast to many other types of reactions which have received continued attention for many years, it is only relatively recently that oxidations have been subjected to detailed study. The data concerning these reactions have not been extensively reviewed, and thus it seemed particularly appropriate to devote these volumes to a detailed discussion of most of the important examples.

The first volume is concerned with the reactions of two of the most common oxidants, permanganate and chromic acid; with oxidation by the transition metal ions, cerium(IV), cobalt(III), manganese(III), and vanadium(IV); with the reactions of the versatile oxidant, lead tetraacetate; and with the important subject of oxidative cleavage of diols and related compounds. Each of the reviews was written by a chemist who is actively studying the subject being reviewed.

We believe that an understanding of a chemical reaction can be achieved only through an investigation of the mechanism by which the change occurs. Thus, a considerable emphasis has been placed on mechanistic considerations throughout this work. Because of the importance of many of these reactions in synthetic work, tables of yields obtained in the oxidation of typical compounds have been included, where appropriate, as well as typical procedures for effecting the reactions. We hope this information will be found to be useful to those engaged in the preparation of organic compounds.

New Haven, Connecticut   KENNETH B. WIBERG
August, 1965

Contents

Contributors v

Preface vii

Contents of Part B xii

CHAPTER I

Oxidation by Permanganate

Ross Stewart

   I. Properties of Permanganate and Its Reduction
      Products 2
  II. Permanganate Exchange Reactions 23
 III. Permanganate Oxidation of Inorganic Substrates 25
 IV. Permanganate Oxidation of Organic Substrates 35
  V. Rate Data for Permanganate Oxidations 68

CHAPTER II

Oxidation by Chromic Acid and Chromyl Compounds

Kenneth B. Wiberg

    I. Introduction 69
   II. The Nature of Chromium in Its Higher
      Oxidation States 69
  III. Oxidation of Inorganic Species 75
  IV. Oxidations at Saturated Carbon-Hydrogen Bonds 82
   V. Oxidation at Carbon–Carbon Double Bonds 125
  VI. Oxidation of Alcohols 142
 VII. Oxidation of Diols 170
VIII. Oxidation of Aldehydes 172
  IX. Oxidation of Ketones 178
   X. Oxidation of Carboxylic Acids 180
  XI. Oxidation at Sulfur 182
 XII. Miscellaneous Oxidation Reactions 183

CHAPTER III

Oxidation by Vanadium(V), Cobalt(III), and Manganese(III)

W. A. Waters and J. S. Littler

I. Introduction 186
II. The Chemical Natures of the Oxidizing Species 188
III. Reduction by Inorganic Species 195
IV. Oxidation of Alcohols and Related Compounds 198
V. The Oxidation of Glycols and Related Compounds 204
VI. Aldehydes 211
VII. Ketones 223
VIII. Carboxylic Acids 228
IX. Other Oxidations 235
X. Biochemical Significance 240

CHAPTER IV

Ceric Ion Oxidation of Organic Compounds

William H. Richardson

I. Introduction 244
II. Inorganic Chemistry of Ceric Ion 244
III. Oxidation of Alcohols 247
IV. Oxidation of Vicinal Glycols and Other
     Polyhydric Alcohols 250
V. Oxidation of Aldehydes and Ketones 255
VI. Oxidation of Carboxylic Acids 264
VII. Oxidation of Hydroperoxides 267
VIII. Oxidation of Nitrogen-Containing Compounds 269
IX. Oxidation of Sulfur-Containing Compounds 270
X. Oxidation of Stable Free Radicals 271
XI. Oxidation of Hydrocarbons 271
XII. Indirect Oxidations with Ceric Ions 272

CHAPTER V

Oxidations with Lead Tetraacetate

Rudolf Criegee

I. Introduction 278
II. Reactions with Hydroxyl Groups 284
III. Reactions with C–H Bonds 305
IV. Reactions with C–C Bonds in Saturated Systems 334
V. Reactions with Olefins and Acetylenes 335
VI. Reactions with Compounds of Sulfur, Nitrogen,
     and Phosphorus 351
VII. Reactions with Organometallic Compounds 363
     Appendix: Oxidations with Thallic Acetate and
     Iodoso Acetates 365

CHAPTER VI

Glycol Cleavage and Related Reactions

C. A. Bunton

I. Introduction 367
II. Periodic Acid 368
III. Lead Tetraacetate 398
IV. Iodoso Compounds 405
V. Sodium Bismuthate 406
VI. Xenic Acid 406

Author Index . . . . , . . . 409

Subject Index 433

Contents of Part B
(Tentative)

P. BAILEY, Oxidation by Ozone

J. G. WALLACE, Hydrogen Peroxide Oxidation

M. ANBAR, Oxidation by Hypohalites

A. SCOTT, Oxidation of Phenols

H. MALTZ, Ferricyanide Oxidation

W. G. NIGH, Cupric Ion Oxidation

AUTHOR INDEX—SUBJECT INDEX

CHAPTER **I**

Oxidation by Permanganate

Ross Stewart

I.	Properties of Permanganate and Its Reduction Products	2
	A. Oxidation States of Manganese	2
	B. Oxidation Potentials	10
	C. Spectra of Permanganate and Related Ions	11
	D. Detection and Analysis of Permanganate	13
	E. Decomposition of Permanganate	20
	F. Permanganic Acid	22
II.	Permanganate Exchange Reactions	23
	A. Oxygen Exchange	23
	B. Electron Exchange with Manganese(VI)	24
	C. Manganese(VII), Manganese(IV), and Manganese(II) Reactions	25
III.	Permanganate Oxidation of Inorganic Substrates	25
	A. Derivatives of Ammonia	26
	B. Borane Derivatives	27
	C. Sulfur Ions	28
	D. Halides	29
	E. Metal Ions	30
	F. Hydrogen	30
	G. Hydrogen Peroxide	31
	H. Cyanide Ion	32
	I. Carbon Monoxide	33
IV.	Permanganate Oxidation of Organic Substrates	35
	A. Hydrocarbons	36
	B. Alcohols	47
	C. Aldehydes and Ketones	52
	D. Phenols	59
	E. Organic Nitrogen Compounds	60
	F. Organic Sulfur Compounds	63
	G. Bifunctional Compounds	64
	H. Miscellaneous Reactions	68
V.	Rate Data for Permanganate Oxidations	68

The vigor of permanganate ion as an oxidizing agent assures it an important role in the chemical laboratory. Its reactions are the more interesting because

1

of the several oxidation states to which it can be reduced, the fate of the manganese being largely determined by the reaction conditions, in particular, the acidity of the medium. The mechanism of these reactions, on the other hand, is determined both by reaction conditions and by the characteristics of the particular substrate with which it reacts. Considerable work has been done over the past 10 years in elucidating the mechanisms of permanganate oxidations of both organic and inorganic substrates and many of these are now well understood. The present chapter deals with various facets, both practical and theoretical, of the chemistry of permanganate oxidation reactions.

I. Properties of Permanganate and Its Reduction Products

A. OXIDATION STATES OF MANGANESE

Manganese species having oxidation numbers between $+1$ and $+7$ are all known, but of these the $+2$, $+4$, and $+7$ states are the only ones which are stable over wide ranges of acidity. Manganese(VI) and manganese(V), particularly the latter, undergo disproportionation to manganese(VII) and manganese(IV) in all but strongly basic solution. Manganese(III) on the other hand disproportionates to manganese(II) and manganese(IV) in all but strongly acid solution. There is evidence for the existence of manganese(I) in certain complexes.[1]

The chemistry of manganese(VII) is the principal concern of the remainder of the chapter; the present section will describe more briefly the chemistry of other oxidation states of manganese.

1. MANGANESE(VI) (MANGANATE)[2]

Manganese(VI) exists in basic solution as the green manganate ion, MnO_4^{2-}. (Its absorption spectrum is considered in the next section.) The stability and oxidizing action of manganate has been investigated by Waters,[3,4] Stamm,[5] Symons,[6,7] Duke,[8] and others. In basic solutions which are less than $1 M$ in hydroxide ion, manganate ion slowly disproportionates to permanganate and manganese dioxide[9]:

$$3 \, MnO_4^{2-} + 2 \, H_2O \rightarrow 2 \, MnO_4^- + MnO_2 + 4 \, OH^-$$

---

[1] See for example, A. Sacco and L. Naldini, *Gazz. Chim. Ital.* **86**, 207 (1956).
[2] The name manganate(VI) is recommended by *Chemical Abstracts*.
[3] J. S. F. Pode and W. A. Waters, *J. Chem. Soc.* p. 717 (1956).
[4] A. Y. Drummond and W. A. Waters, *J. Chem. Soc.* p. 435 (1953).
[5] H. Stamm, "Die Reduktion von Permanganat zu Manganat als Grundlage eines neuen Titrationsvervahrens." Akad. Verlagsges., Leipzig, Germany, 1937.
[6] A. Carrington and M. C. R. Symons, *J. Chem. Soc.* p. 3373 (1956).
[7] A. Carrington, D. Schonland, and M. C. R. Symons, *J. Chem. Soc.* p. 659 (1957).
[8] F. R. Duke, *J. Am. Chem. Soc.* **70**, 3975 (1948).
[9] F. R. Duke, *J. Phys. Chem.* **56**, 882 (1952).

In neutral and acid solution the disproportionation is instantaneous. An equilibrium value for the above reaction has been measured [10]

$$K = \frac{[MnO_4^-]^2 [OH^-]^4}{[MnO_4^{2-}]^3} = 16 \pm 7$$

but this quantity is not actually constant because of the varying activity of manganese dioxide. Fresh and aged manganese dioxide precipitates have quite different reactivities.

Carrington and Symons [6] have pointed out that the disproportionation of manganate in acid may involve a condensation similar to that which is well known to occur with the analogous acid chromate ion:

$$2 HMnO_4^- \rightarrow Mn_2O_7^{2-} + H_2O$$

Further polymerization might occur and be accompanied by the separation of MnO_4^- and the formation of MnO_2 polymers.

Potassium manganate solutions are conveniently prepared by the method of Pode and Waters [3] which involves heating potassium permanganate in concentrated potassium hydroxide solution and then extracting the product with carbonate-free solution of alkali. The great spectral differences of the permanganate and manganate ions (see next section) can be used to show the absence of permanganate in these solutions. Solid potassium manganate of 96% purity can be conveniently prepared by the method of Rigby.[11]

Permanganate oxidations in alkaline solution normally produce manganese dioxide; this is a three-equivalent change. In the presence of barium ions, however, insoluble barium manganate, $BaMnO_4$, precipitates, resulting in a one-equivalent reduction of the manganese. This technique was used by Stamm as a volumetric procedure for alkaline permanganate titrations.[12] The teal-blue barium manganate has a low solubility, about $10^{-5} M$. However, the precipitation of manganate by barium ions as it is formed in a reaction is no guarantee that reduction of manganese(VII) to manganese(VI) has proceeded by a one-equivalent step. A two-equivalent reduction to manganese(V) may be taking place followed by a rapid manganese(V)–manganese(VII) reaction. The latter process is, indeed, known to be very fast [6]:

$$MnO_4^- + MnO_4^{3-} \rightarrow 2 MnO_4^{2-}$$

Early work on the manganate–water exchange reaction showed that manganate exchanged its oxygen atoms with the solvent much more rapidly than did permanganate.[13] Subsequent work, however, indicates that the

[10] H. I. Schlesinger and H. B. Siems, *J. Am. Chem. Soc.* **46**, 1965 (1924).
[11] W. Rigby, *J. Chem. Soc.* p. 2452 (1956).
[12] H. Stamm, *Angew. Chem.* **47**, 791 (1934).
[13] M. C. R. Symons, *J. Chem. Soc.* p. 3676 (1954).

exchange occurs during the isolation of the manganate (as insoluble barium manganate) and that the uncatalyzed exchange is slow.[14]

Oxidations by manganate are almost always much slower than those of permanganate. A rare exception to this generalization is the oxidation of aromatic aldehydes; the rates of manganate and permanganate oxidation are virtually the same for these compounds at the same pH.[15] By contrast, alcohols are oxidized much more slowly by manganate (benzhydrol is oxidized by this reagent at only one-fortieth the permanganate rate).[16] Cyanide ion is oxidized by manganate at about one-eightieth the permanganate rate.[17]

1,2-Diols undergo rather rapid cleavage by manganate, apparently producing manganese dioxide directly since in $10\,N$ alkali no trace of the characteristic blue manganese(V) color appears in the solution.[3] Phenol oxidation by manganate on the other hand produces a blue solution, and Pode and Waters argue that these observations indicate a two-equivalent oxidation step for the glycol and a one-equivalent oxidation step for the phenol. These would certainly be reasonable reaction paths for these two substrates:

$$
\begin{array}{c}
\text{ArO}^- \\
\text{MnO}_4{}^{2-} \quad
\begin{array}{l}
\longrightarrow \ \text{MnO}_4{}^{3-} \\
\longrightarrow \ \text{MnO}_2
\end{array}
\end{array}
$$

$$
\begin{array}{cc}
\text{OH} & \text{OH} \\
| & | \\
-\text{C} & -\text{C}- \\
| & |
\end{array}
$$

Alkenes undergo dihydroxylatiosn by aqueous manganate and the mode of addition is cis,[3,11] as it is with permanganate (see Section IV,A,2):

$$
\begin{array}{ccc}
\text{H}-\text{C}-\text{CO}_2\text{H} & & \text{HOCHCO}_2\text{H} \\
\parallel & \xrightarrow[\text{H}_2\text{O}]{\text{MnO}_4{}^{2-}} & | \\
\text{H}-\text{C}-\text{CO}_2\text{H} & & \text{HOCHCO}_2\text{H}
\end{array}
$$

$$
\text{Maleic acid} \qquad\qquad\qquad meso\text{-Tartaric acid}
$$

Moderate yields of glycol are obtained in this way but the osmium tetroxide method is usually superior.

Manganate is oxidized to permanganate by reagents such as sodium bismuthate and periodate. The mechanism of the latter's reaction,

$$
2\,\text{MnO}_4{}^{2-} + \text{H}_3\text{IO}_6{}^{2-} \ \rightarrow\ 2\,\text{MnO}_4{}^- + \text{IO}_3{}^- + 3\,\text{OH}^-
$$

has been studied by Lister and Yoshino,[18] who conclude that the mechanism

[14] H. O. McDonald, *Dissertation Abstr.* **21**, 454 (1960).
[15] K. B. Wiberg and R. Stewart, *J. Am. Chem. Soc.* **77**, 1786 (1955).
[16] R. Stewart, *J. Am. Chem. Soc.* **79**, 3057 (1957).
[17] R. Stewart and R. Van der Linden, *Can. J. Chem.* **38**, 2237 (1960).
[18] M. W. Lister and Y. Yoshino, *Can. J. Chem.* **38**, 2342 (1960).

involves periodate oxidation of the small amount of manganese(V) formed in the disproportionation equilibrium:

$$2\,MnO_4{}^{2-} \rightleftharpoons MnO_4{}^- + MnO_4{}^{3-}$$

$$MnO_4{}^{3-} + H_3IO_6{}^{2-} \rightarrow MnO_4{}^- + IO_3{}^- + 3\,OH^-$$

Periodate-permanganate is a useful reagent for the cleavage of alkenes (see Section IV,A,2).

2. MANGANESE(V) (HYPOMANGANATE)[19]

The blue salt, potassium hypomanganate, K_3MnO_4,[20] was first prepared by Lux in 1946.[21] He fused manganese dioxide, potassium hydroxide, and sodium nitrite. Hypomanganate can also be prepared by fusion of potassium permanganate and sodium hydroxide and by reduction of manganate in strongly basic solution by such oxidants as sulfite and thiosulfate.[22]

The isomorphism of hypomanganate, orthophosphate, and vanadate salts is in agreement with the formula $MnO_4{}^{3-}$ rather than $MnO_3{}^-$.[23]

Hypomanganate solutions are fairly stable in the cold for a few days in concentrated alkali but slowly deposit manganese dioxide. In $4N$ alkali disproportionation occurs within a few minutes.

$$2\,MnO_4{}^{3-} + 2\,H_2O \rightarrow MnO_4{}^{2-} + MnO_2 + 4\,OH^-$$

As pointed out earlier, hypomanganate is instantaneously oxidized by permanganate.

The oxidizing vigor of hypomanganate is less than that of manganate which, as we have seen, is generally less than that of permanganate. The reactivity toward reductants thus varies inversely with the charge on the oxidant.

$$MnO_4{}^- > MnO_4{}^{2-} > MnO_4{}^{3-}$$

As will be seen in subsequent discussion, many permanganate oxidations in basic and neutral solution proceed via reactions between permanganate ion and the anions of the substrates. If manganate and hypomanganate oxidation mechanisms are similar, the effect of charge accumulation on the oxidant accounts for the above reactivity order.

Pode and Waters showed that hypomanganate oxidizes primary and secondary alcohols slowly but has little effect on alkenes, tertiary alcohols, or phenols.[24]

[19] The name manganate(V) is recommended by *Chemical Abstracts*.

[20] W. Klemm, *Proc. Intern. Symp. Reactivity Solids, Gothenburg* **1**, 173 (1952); *Chem. Abstr.* **48**, 12602 (1954).

[21] H. Lux, *Z. Naturforsch.* **1**, 281 (1946).

[22] R. Scholder and H. Waterstradt, *Z. Anorg. Allgem. Chem.* **277**, 172 (1954).

[23] A. Carrington and M. C. R. Symons, *J. Chem. Soc.* p. 3373 (1956).

[24] J. S. F. Pode and W. A. Waters, *J. Chem. Soc.* p. 717 (1956).

Hypomanganate can be detected as an intermediate in the oxidation of hydrogen peroxide by strongly alkaline permanganate. The color of the solution changes from purple (MnO_4^-) to green (MnO_4^{2-}) to light blue (MnO_4^{3-}) to deep green ($MnO_4^{3-} + MnO_2$) to a brown turbidity (MnO_2). Filtration of the deep green solution removes the manganese dioxide and reveals the blue hypomanganate component.

3. MANGANESE(IV)

Manganese dioxide, the brown insoluble material whose degree of hydration varies, is the normal form of manganese(IV). However, under certain circumstances soluble forms can exist. Manganese dioxide is the normal end product of permanganate oxidation except in strongly alkaline solution where manganate is stable enough to be the terminal stage and in certain oxidations in acid solution, notably with oxalic acid, where reduction to the manganous state occurs.

Manganese dioxide is sometimes rather slowly precipitated, particularly in the presence of phosphate ions, and a neutral solution containing a yellow-brown manganese(IV) species, attributed to $H_2MnO_4^{2-}$, has been found to obey Beer's Law.[25]

Manganese dioxide can be dissolved in fuming sulfuric acid to give a clear blue solution.[26] The latter is identical to one produced by the spontaneous decomposition of potassium permanganate in fuming sulfuric acid.[26-28] It is suggested that the species responsible for the color is the neutral sulfate, $Mn(SO_4)_2$.[28] Manganese dioxide is also dissolved with reduction by sodium bisulfite either as the powder or in solution. This is, in fact, the most convenient way of removing the brown stains which those who work with permanganate frequently find on both their glassware and their skin.

The decomposition of permanganate in 60% sulfuric acid is slower but is clearly autocatalytic since a sudden evolution of oxygen occurs after the solution has been standing for a few minutes.[29] A clear brown solution (shoulder at 290 mμ, long absorption in the visible) results, and this solution obeys Beer's Law. Interestingly enough, as the sulfuric acid concentration of this solution is increased to 97% the brown color changes slowly to blue (broad

[25] B. Jezowska-Trzebiatowska and J. Kalecinski, *Bull. Acad. Polon. Sci. Ser. Sci. Chim. Geol. Geograph.* **9**, 791 (1961).

[26] M. M. Mocek, Ph. D. Thesis, University of British Columbia, Vancouver, Canada, 1962.

[27] F. R. Lankshear, *Z. Anorg. Allgem. Chem.* **82**, 97 (1913).

[28] H. C. Mishra and M. C. R. Symons, *Proc. Chem. Soc.* p. 23 (1962); *J. Chem. Soc.* p. 4490 (1963).

[29] Manganese dioxide also promotes the decomposition of permanganate in neutral solution, but this autocatalytic reaction is very much slower. See H. N. Morse, A. J. Hopkins, and M. S. Walker, *Am. Chem. J.* **18**, 401 (1896).

absorption band centered near 570 mμ) and the spectrum becomes identical to that obtained by decomposing permanganate in fuming acid or dissolving MnO_2 in fuming acid. The condition of the manganese dioxide is critical, however, since it will not dissolve in 97% sulfuric acid.[26]

The brown-to-blue color change may involve a dehydration of the type,

$$MnO(OH)_2 + 2\,H^+ \rightarrow MnO_2H^+ + H_3O^+$$

or one of them may be a complex sulfate as suggested by Mishra and Symons.[28]

Both the brown and the blue solutions are able to oxidize hydrogen peroxide and sulfur dioxide rapidly and homogeneously.

Manganese dioxide dispersed in organic solvents such as ligroin, chloroform, acetone, and ether has become a favored oxidant for α,β-unsaturated alcohols.[30] Alkenes and alkynes are unaffected by the reaction as can be seen from this example[31]:

$$HC\equiv CCH=C-CH_2OH \xrightarrow{MnO_2} HC\equiv CCH=C-CHO$$
$$\qquad\qquad\quad | \qquad\qquad\qquad\qquad\qquad |$$
$$\qquad\qquad\ CH_3 \qquad\qquad\qquad\qquad\qquad CH_3$$

The vicinal unsaturated linkage is required for activation of the alcohol group since saturated alcohols are usually unaffected by the reagent. The condition of the manganese dioxide and its method of preparation (usually the Guyard reaction) have an effect on the oxidant's activity. Active samples, for example, are able to oxidize benzyl alcohols to aldehydes.[32]

This reagent has proved to be extremely useful in isoprenoid and steroid syntheses.[33, 34] Little information on the mechanism of this heterogeneous reaction is available, however.

Oxidation of aryl alcohols to ketones[35] and diarylmethanes to tetra-arylethanes[36] can be brought about by manganese dioxide dispersed in aromatic hydrocarbon solvents. Radical formation through hydrogen abstraction by the oxidant appears to be the reaction mechanism in the second case, at least:

$$Ar_2CH_2 \xrightarrow[-H\cdot]{MnO_2} Ar_2CH\cdot$$

$$2\,Ar_2CH\cdot \longrightarrow Ar_2CHCHAr_2$$

[30] R. M. Evans, *Quart. Rev.* p. 61 (1959).

[31] R. Ahmed and B. C. L. Weedon, *J. Chem. Soc.* p. 3286 (1953).

[32] M. Harfenist, A. Bavley, and W. A. Lazier, *J. Org. Chem.* **19**, 1608 (1954). See also I. T. Harrison, *Proc. Chem. Soc.* p. 110 (1964).

[33] H. R. Cama, P. D. Dalvi, R. A. Morton, M. K. Salah, G. R. Steinberg, and A. L. Stubbs, *Biochem. J.* **52**, 535 (1952).

[34] F. Sondheimer, C. Amendolla, and G. Rosenkranz, *J. Am. Chem. Soc.* **75**, 5930 (1953).

[35] E. F. Pratt and J. F. Van de Castle, *J. Org. Chem.* **26**, 2973 (1961).

[36] E. F. Pratt and S. P. Suskind, *J. Org. Chem.* **28**, 638 (1963).

4. Manganese(III) (Manganic Ion)

Trivalent manganese exists as the red manganic ion, Mn^{III}, in concentrated acid solution. At low acidities it undergoes disproportionation[37] unless it is stabilized by being complexed with such groups as fluoride[38] or pyrophosphate:

$$2\,Mn^{III} \rightleftharpoons Mn^{II} + Mn^{IV}$$

Sulfate complexes to some extent with manganese(III), but perchlorate is without effect. However, in the presence of a large excess of manganous ion, fairly stable solutions of manganese(III) in perchloric acid can be prepared with the molarity of acid being as low as $1.5\,M$.[39]

Pyrophosphate is a particularly effective complexing agent and the ion $Mn(H_2P_2O_7)_3{}^{3-}$ has found use as an oxidant in quantitative inorganic analysis[40, 41] and as a glycol cleaving reagent in organic chemistry[42] and is stable to disproportionation even in neutral solution. In more acidic solution the complex ion exists in the protonated form. The fluoride complex is believed to be $MnF_4{}^-$,[38] and even in sulfuric acid the complex ion $Mn(SO_4)_2{}^-$ is believed to be the major species.[43]

Waters *et al.* have examined the mechanism of the oxidation of various organic compounds with manganic pyrophosphate. Aldehydes and ketones which can enolize are degraded by this reagent, and the rate-controlling step in the oxidation proves to be the enolization itself[44]:

$$\underset{RCH_2CR}{\overset{O}{\overset{\|}{}}} \xrightarrow[\text{slow}]{H^+} \underset{RCH=CR}{\overset{OH}{\overset{|}{}}} \xrightarrow[\text{fast}]{Mn^{III}} \underset{RCH-CR}{\overset{OH\ \ O}{\overset{|\ \ \ \|}{}}} \xrightarrow{Mn^{III}} \text{further oxidation}$$

1,2-Diols are cleaved by manganic pyrophosphate and the oxidation in this case is first order in oxidant.[45] A cyclic complex is believed to form by displacement of a pyrophosphato ligand by one of the hydroxyls of the diol. This complex then decomposes to ketone, manganese(II), and a radical. The latter suffers rapid oxidation to a second mole of ketone.

The cyclic nature of this cleavage is similar to the mechanisms established

---

[37] R. G. Selim and J. J. Lingane, *Anal. Chim. Acta* **21**, 536 (1959).

[38] H. F. Launer, *J. Am. Chem. Soc.* **54**, 2597 (1932).

[39] D. R. Rosseinsky, *J. Chem. Soc.* p. 1181 (1963).

[40] R. Belcher and T. S. West, *Anal. Chim. Acta* **6**, 322 (1952).

[41] I. M. Kolthoff and R. Belcher, "Volumetric Analysis," Vol. III, p. 649. Wiley (Interscience), New York, 1957.

[42] W. A. Waters, *Quart. Rev.* p. 277 (1958).

[43] A. R. J. P. Ubbelohde, *J. Chem. Soc.* p. 1605 (1935).

[44] A. Y. Drummond and W. A. Waters, *J. Chem. Soc.* p. 440 (1953); p. 497 (1955).

[45] A. Y. Drummond and W. A. Waters, *J. Chem. Soc.* p. 3119 (1953).

$$R-\underset{\underset{R}{|}}{\overset{\overset{R}{|}}{C}}-OH \;\;\; + Mn(H_2P_2O_7)_3{}^{3-} \;\rightleftharpoons\; R-\underset{\underset{R}{|}}{\overset{\overset{R}{|}}{C}}-O \underset{R-\underset{R}{|}}{\overset{R}{\diagdown}} Mn^{III} \;\longrightarrow\; \underset{R_2\overset{\cdot}{C}OH}{R_2C{=}O} + Mn^{II}$$

$$R_2\overset{\cdot}{C}OH \;\xrightarrow{\;Mn^{III}\;}\; R_2C{=}O + H^+$$

for the periodic acid and other glycol cleavage reactions. However, there appear to be some important differences in the reaction mechanisms.[46]

Ordinary alcohols and alkenes are inert to manganic oxidation. Oxalic acid is degraded by manganic ion and this reaction is involved in the permanganate–oxalic acid reaction described elsewhere.

5. Manganese(II) (Manganous Ion)

Manganous ion is the end product of permanganate oxidation only in acid solution and only when fairly good reducing agents like iodide or ferrous ions are used. Most organic compounds reduce permanganate to manganese dioxide even in acid solution. Oxalic acid is exceptional in that it is able to effect a five-equivalent reduction of permanganate to the manganous state. The mechanism of this reaction is discussed in Section IV,G,2.

In weakly acid and neutral solution, manganous ion reacts with permanganate to form manganese dioxide:

$$2\ MnO_4{}^- + 3\ Mn^{2+} + 4\ OH^- \;\rightarrow\; 5\ MnO_2 + 2\ H_2O$$

This oxidation, usually known as the Guyard reaction,[47, 48] has been used for the volumetric determination of manganese.[49] If the reaction is conducted in the presence of fluoride ions[50] to stabilize manganese(III), the stoichiometry of the reaction becomes

$$4\ Mn^{II} + Mn^{VII} \;\rightarrow\; 5\ Mn^{III}$$

The extensive work by Tompkins,[51] Polissar,[52] and Adamson[53] on the

[46] See P. Levesley, W. A. Waters, and A. N. Wright, *J. Chem. Soc.* p. 840 (1956); R. Stewart. "Oxidation Mechanisms: Application to Organic Chemistry." Benjamin, New York. 1964.

[47] A. Guyard, *Bull. Soc. Chim. France* **6**, 89 (1864); see also P. Gorgeau, *Ann. Chim. Phys.* **66**, 153 (1962).

[48] J. Volhard, *Ann.* **198**, 318 (1879).

[49] I. M. Kolthoff and R. Belcher, "Volumetric Analysis," Vol. III, p. 97. Wiley (Interscience), New York, 1957.

[50] V. M. Zvenigorodskaya, *Zavodsk. Lab.* **12**, 152 (1946); *Chem. Abstr.* **40**, 5662 (1946).

[51] F. C. Tompkins, *Trans. Faraday Soc.* **38**, 131 (1942).

[52] M. J. Polissar, *J. Am. Chem. Soc.* **58**, 1372 (1936) and earlier papers.

[53] A. W. Adamson, *J. Phys. & Colloid Chem.* **55**, 293 (1951).

mechanism of the Guyard reaction has been reviewed in detail by Ladbury and Cullis.[54] The reaction is autocatalytic and exhibits a lengthy induction period. The latter can be further extended by the addition of fluoride ions and there seems little doubt that manganic ions, which are complexed by fluoride, are reactive intermediates.

B. OXIDATION POTENTIALS

In the previous section the six important oxidation states of manganese [manganese(II) to (VII)] were described.[55] This multiplicity of oxidation states gives rise to a total of fifteen possible half-cell reactions although not all of these have been examined. The manganese(VI)–manganese(III) couple, for example, cannot be measured because manganese(VI) is stable only in basic solution and manganese(III) in acid solution.

One can compute the over-all potential for the five-equivalent reduction of permanganate to manganous ion to be 1.51 volts. Despite the importance of this reaction in analytical chemistry, one finds that a great many reductants are unable to bring about this change.

If one then considers the one-electron half-cell reactions involving manganese ions, only the following three potentials are found[56, 57]:

		$E°$, volts
Mn^{VII}–Mn^{VI}	$e + MnO_4^- \rightarrow MnO_4^{2-}$	$+0.558 \pm 0.002$
Mn^{VI}–Mn^{V}	$e + MnO_4^{2-} \rightarrow MnO_4^{3-}$	$+0.285 \pm 0.01$
Mn^{III}–Mn^{II}	$e + Mn^{3+} \rightarrow Mn^{2+}$	$+1.51$

Of these three systems only the Mn^{VII}–Mn^{VI} couple can be considered to refer to the standard state. The Mn^{VI}–Mn^{V} couple was, perforce, measured in concentrated alkaline solution, and extrapolation to the standard state was not possible. The Mn^{III}–Mn^{II} couple is strongly dependent on the presence of anions which can complex with the manganese(III). Even the value listed above, which was obtained in fairly concentrated sulfuric acid solution, may not refer to free manganic ions but rather to ones partly complexed by sulfate. In the presence of strongly complexing ions the potential drops drastically, as expected.

When one examines the potentials of the systems in which manganese dioxide is a component, two factors must be considered. First, it must be realized that it is difficult to obtain reproducible values of the measured couple because of the nonuniform activity of different preparations of solid manganese dioxide. (Consistent results seem to be obtained using pyrolusite

[54] J. W. Ladbury and C. F. Cullis, *Chem. Rev.* **58**, 403 (1958).
[55] Thermodynamic data for compounds and ions of manganese are given by W. M. Latimer, "Oxidation Potentials," p. 235. Prentice-Hall, Englewood Cliffs, New Jersey, 1952.
[56] A. Carrington and M. C. R. Symons, *Chem. Rev.* **63**, 443 (1963).
[57] G. Grube and H. Metzger, *Z. Elektrochem.* **29**, 17 (1923).

prepared by heating manganous nitrate.[58]) Second, the potentials, assuming they can be measured precisely, depend on whether the reaction is conducted in acidic or basic solution. Thus the Mn^{VII}–Mn^{IV} couple has the values[58,59]:

$$E°, \text{ volts}$$

$$3\,e + MnO_4^- + 4\,H^+ \ \rightarrow\ MnO_2 + 2\,H_2O \qquad +1.70$$
$$3\,e + MnO_4^- + 2\,H_2O \ \rightarrow\ MnO_2 + 4\,OH^- \qquad +0.59$$

The higher potential for the reaction in acid solution is, of course, a consequence of the free energy change corresponding to the reaction,

$$4\,H^+ + 4\,OH^- \ \rightarrow\ 2\,H_2O$$

by which the two equations differ.

The corresponding couples, measurable only in basic solution, involving manganate and manganese dioxide have the values[58,59]:

$$2\,e + MnO_4^{2-} + 2\,H_2O \ \rightarrow\ MnO_2 + 4\,OH^- \qquad E° = +0.60 \text{ volts}$$

Manganese dioxide, as an oxidant, has a fairly large potential for reduction to manganous ion:

$$2\,e + MnO_2 + 4\,H^+ \ \rightarrow\ Mn^{2+} + 2\,H_2O \qquad E° = +1.23 \text{ volts}$$

The potential of the Mn^{VII}–Mn^{II} couple is somewhat larger, 1.51 volts.

The vigor with which oxidation of various substrates is brought about by the oxidants whose potentials are given above (MnO_4^-, MnO_4^{2-}, and MnO_2) is only remotely related to the magnitude of these potentials in most cases. With organic substrates, in particular, mechanistic factors are of major importance; the over-all free energy change of the oxidant (determined by its potential) is of minor importance. Thus, despite the lower potential of permanganate in basic solution than in acid solution, the oxidation rates of alcohols, hydrogen cyanide, and formic acid, for example, are all considerably greater at, say, pH 12 than at pH 2. The mechanisms of these reactions are discussed in later sections of the chapter.

C. SPECTRA OF PERMANGANATE AND RELATED IONS

1. ULTRAVIOLET AND VISIBLE SPECTRA

The three manganese oxy-anions, MnO_4^-, MnO_4^{2-}, and MnO_4^{3-}, all absorb strongly in the visible[56,60–62]; the colors produced are purple, green, and blue, respectively. Figure 1 shows the visible and ultraviolet spectra of aqueous solutions of permanganate, manganate, and hypomanganate salts, the latter two being obtained in alkaline solution (see page 14).

[58] W. M. Latimer, "Oxidation Potentials," pp. 238–239. Prentice-Hall, Englewood Cliffs, New Jersey, 1952.

[59] L. V. Andrews and D. J. Brown, *J. Am. Chem. Soc.* **57**, 254 (1935).

[60] M. C. R. Symons and P. A. Trevalion, *J. Chem. Soc.* p. 3503 (1962).

[61] R. M. Bennett and O. G. Holmes, *Can. J. Chem.* **41**, 108 (1963).

[62] J. Halpern and A. C. Harkness, *J. Phys. Chem.* **31**, 1147 (1959).

The absorption maxima data are collected in Table I.

TABLE I

SPECTRAL DATA FOR PERMANGANATE, MANGANATE,
AND HYPOMANGANATE IONS

MnO_4^-		MnO_4^{2-}		MnO_4^{3-}	
λ_{max} (mμ)	$e \times 10^{-3}$	λ_{max} (mμ)	$e \times 10^{-3}$	λ_{max} (mμ)	$e \times 10^{-3}$
546	2.38	606	1.71	667	0.90
526	2.40	439	1.38	313	3.90
311	1.80	347	1.83		
		299	1.66		

The visible spectrum of permanganate is unaltered by changes in solvent and temperature.[60, 63] However, in aqueous silver perchlorate the permanganate spectrum is altered[64] and there seems little doubt that a silver permanganate complex, $AgMnO_4$, is formed.[60] Ferrous, mercuric, aluminum, cadmium, or zinc ions have no effect on the permanganate spectrum, however.

The spectrum of permanganate in various solid environments has been studied by Symons and Trevalion[60] and the spectrum of manganate and hypomanganate in sodium nitrate and potassium nitrate melts has been studied by Bennett and Holmes.[61]

Increased pressure on potassium permanganate causes a blue shift in the absorption maxima.[65] This has been attributed to an $n - \pi^*$ transition from a t_1 level on oxygen to an e^* level on the metal. For a theoretical discussion of the electronic transitions responsible for the color in manganese oxy-anions see the papers of Symons et al., Halpern and Harkness, Wolfsberg and Helmholz, and Carrington et al.[60, 63, 66–68]

2. INFRARED SPECTRA

The infrared spectra of several permanganate salts have been obtained by Miller et al. over a very wide frequency range.[69, 70] A very strong absorption

[63] M. Smith and M. C. R. Symons, J. Chem. Phys. 25, 1074 (1956).

[64] J. Teltow, Z. Physik. Chem. (Leipzig) B40, 397 (1938); B43, 198 (1939).

[65] W. H. Bentley and H. G. Drickamer, J. Chem. Phys. 34, 2200 (1961).

[66] M. Wolfsberg and L. Helmholz, J. Chem. Phys. 20, 837 (1952).

[67] A. Carrington and D. S. Schonland, Mol. Phys. 3, 331 (1960).

[68] A. Carrington and Ch. K. Joergensen, Mol. Phys. 4, 395 (1961).

[69] F. A. Miller and C. H. Williams, Anal. Chem. 24, 1253 (1952).

[70] F. A. Miller, G. L. Carlson, F. F. Bentley, and W. H. Jones, Spectrochim. Acta 16, 135 (1960). See also C. J. Ballhausen, Theoret. Chim. Acta 1, 285 (1963).

band, whose assignment is in doubt, occurs near 900 cm^{-1} in all the salts that were examined. At lower frequency, in the cesium bromide region, a doublet at 380 and 400 cm^{-1} occurs in most cases.

The principal bands of three permanganate salts are listed in Table II. In the case of sodium permanganate trihydrate, the water bands obscure some of the bands of the permanganate.

TABLE II

PRINCIPAL INFRARED BANDS OF PERMANGANATE SALTS

Salt	Frequency (cm^{-1})	Intensity	Characteristics
KMnO$_4$	387	Medium	Sharp
	402	Strong	Sharp
	845	Weak	
	900	Very strong	
	1725	Weak	
NaMnO$_4 \cdot 3$ H$_2$O	420–640	Very strong	Very broad
	812	Weak	
	857	Strong	
	896	Very strong	
	1625	Strong	Sharp
Ba(MnO$_4$)$_2$	378	Medium	Sharp
	400	Weak	Sharp
	844	Weak	
	877	Strong	
	913	Strong	
	935	Medium	

D. DETECTION AND ANALYSIS OF PERMANGANATE

Permanganate is an extremely important volumetric reagent in quantitative analysis and this aspect of its chemistry has been very adequately treated in other books and treatises. The present section has a somewhat different emphasis since it is devoted to a discussion of the determination of permanganate under various conditions and during the course of various reactions.

Several organic indicators whose colors depend upon their states of oxidation and whose redox reactions are readily reversible can be used to detect the presence of small amounts of oxidizing agents such as permanganate[71] but they are specific only in so far as their redox potential places a lower limit on the strength of oxidant which they will detect.

[71] See for example E. Ruzicka and M. Kotoucek, *Z. Anal. Chem.* **183**, 351 (1961).

Paper chromatography has been used to resolve several of the ions of manganese, including permanganate.[72]

1. Spectrophotometry

The characteristic color of permanganate (and manganate and hypomanganate) can be used to detect the ion in small concentration, and its ultraviolet and visible spectrum, which was described in the previous section, serves for more specific identification. The problem of analyzing solutions containing both permanganate and manganate is one which can often be handled better by this means than by the conventional iodometric method discussed later. The spectra shown in Fig. 1 reveal distinctly different absorp-

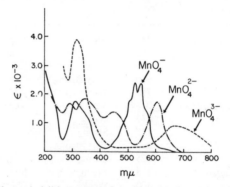

Fig. 1. Ultraviolet and visible spectra of the ions, MnO_4^-, MnO_4^{2-}, and MnO_4^{3-}.

tion maxima for the two ions, but in each case the other ion also absorbs to some extent at the particular wavelength. The analysis for both ions can be conveniently made by taking measurements at two wavelengths.

Suitable wavelengths for measurements of the permanganate and manganate concentration in a solution are 522 and 426 mμ. The absorption at the former wavelength is due mainly to permanganate and at the latter mainly to manganate.[73] At 522 mμ the extinction coefficient of permanganate is 2370 and of manganate 387. At 426 mμ the extinction coefficient of permanganate is 77 and of manganate 1370. For a 1 cm light path we have:

$$D_{522} = 2370[MnO_4^-] + 387[MnO_4^{2-}]$$

$$D_{426} = 77[MnO_4^-] + 1370[MnO_4^{2-}]$$

Elimination of manganate from these equations gives the expression

$$[MnO_4^-] = \frac{D_{522} - 0.282 D_{426}}{2348}$$

[72] H. M. Stevens, *Anal. Chim. Acta* **16**, 435 (1957).
[73] G. L. Zimmerman, Ph. D. Thesis, University of Chicago, Illinois, 1949.

Solutions containing permanganate and suspended manganese dioxide cannot be analyzed in this way since the suspended matter scatters the light and gives spurious optical density values. If the manganese dioxide is removed by filtration or centrifugation, the analysis of the permanganate becomes straightforward. However, colloidal manganese dioxide is sometimes difficult to remove by these means.

In concentrated sulfuric acid, manganese(IV) remains in solution (see Section I,A), and in this case the permanganate concentration can be determined spectrophotometrically by measurements in the 525 $m\mu$ region. Manganese(IV) does have a small absorption in this region, however, and correction is required if accurate measurements are desired.

2. VOLUMETRIC DETERMINATION

There are many reducing agents which can be used in the standardization of aqueous permanganate—potassium iodate, sodium oxalate, oxalic acid, potassium ferrocyanide, ferrous ammonium sulfate, and others—and the reader is referred to standard works on volumetric analysis for a discussion of these reactions. When the amount of permanganate in a reaction mixture requires volumetric determination, however, this is almost always done by iodometry. (The use of spectrophotometry, which is also an important method, was described in the previous section.)

The addition of an excess of acidified potassium iodide to a solution of permanganate reduces the latter to the manganese(II) state immediately:

$$2\ MnO_4^- + 10\ I^- + 16\ H^+ \rightarrow 2\ Mn^{2+} + 5\ I_2 + 8\ H_2O$$

The liberated iodine can then be titrated to the starch endpoint with standard thiosulfate solution:

$$I_2 + 2\ S_2O_3^{2-} \rightarrow 2\ I^- + S_4O_6^{2-}$$

Since acidified iodide solution is subject to air oxidation, particularly under the influence of light, it is customary to add small quantities (of the order of 100 mg) of sodium bicarbonate to the acidified iodide solution to displace the dissolved air. Addition of carbonate to a solution containing both iodide and liberated iodine may cause some of the latter to be lost by volatilization.

The iodometric determination of permanganate reaction mixtures involves reduction of permanganate *and* any of its reduction products of intermediate valence to the manganese(II) condition. Since most permanganate oxidations result in the formation of manganese(IV) [except in strongly basic solution where manganese(VI) may be formed and in acid solution with certain efficient reductants where manganese(II) is formed] the iodometric method determines not simply the permanganate concentration but rather the total oxidizing power of the system. Thus, if permanganate has been completely reduced to manganese dioxide by, for example, sodium formate in neutral solution, the resulting solution still retains two-fifths of its original oxidizing power and the volume of thiosulfate solution used in the titration of the iodine liberated by this mixture will be two-fifths of that required for the permanganate before reaction:

$$2\ MnO_4^- + 3\ HCO_2^- + H_2O \longrightarrow 2\ MnO_2 + 3\ CO_2 + 5\ OH^-$$

$$2\ MnO_2 + 4\ I^- + 8\ H^+ \longrightarrow 2\ Mn^{2+} +\ \boxed{2\ I_2}\ + 4\ H_2O$$

$$2\ MnO_4^- + 10\ I^- + 16\ H^+ \longrightarrow 2\ Mn^{2+} +\ \boxed{5\ I_2}\ + 8\ H_2O$$

If permanganate has been completely reduced to manganate by, for example, sodium formate in strongly alkaline solution, the resulting solution still retains four-fifths of its original oxidizing power:

$$2\ MnO_4^+ + HCO_2^- + OH^- \longrightarrow 2\ MnO_4^{2-} + CO_2 + H_2O$$

$$2\ MnO_4^{2-} + 8\ I^- + 16\ H^+ \longrightarrow 2\ Mn^{2+} +\ \boxed{4\ I_2}\ + 8\ H_2O$$

$$2\ MnO_4^- + 10\ I^- + 16\ H^+ \longrightarrow 2\ Mn^{2+} +\ \boxed{5\ I_2}\ + 8\ H_2O$$

An iodometric determination of permanganate in a manganate–permanganate mixture is likely to be somewhat imprecise because of the relatively small change in the thiosulfate titer. In this case the spectrophotometric method, however, can be applied with considerable precision since both permanganate and manganate absorb strongly in the visible (see previous section).

Permanganate, like many other anions, forms an insoluble tetraphenylarsonium salt. Tetraphenylarsonium chloride or perchlorate is frequently used to remove permanganate from solution. Tetraphenylarsonium permanganate can be extracted into nitrobenzene and other organic solvents.[74]

3. APPLICATION TO KINETICS

Kinetic studies of permanganate oxidations have contributed greatly to our knowledge of the mechanistic pathways by which this reagent reacts with many organic and inorganic substrates. The two major analytical methods described in the previous two sections—spectrophotometry and iodometry— are both applicable to kinetic studies. In the case of spectrophotometry, the method is straightforward since the permanganate concentration is obtained directly from the use of the equation which appears in Section I,D,1. When iodometry is used, however, the concentration of permanganate remaining at

[74] J. M. Matuszek, Jr. and T. T. Sugihara, *Anal. Chem.* **33**, 35 (1961).

any time can only be calculated if the oxidation state of the reduced form of manganese is known.

a. *Stoichiometric Ratio of Oxidant to Reductant.* If permanganate reacts with a substrate H_2Z and oxidizes this to Z in neutral, acidic, or mildly basic solution, the oxidation state to which the manganese is reduced will, in most cases, be $+4$:

$$2 \, MnO_4^- + 3 \, H_2Z \rightarrow 2 \, MnO_2 + Z + 2 \, OH^- + 2 \, H_2O$$

If equivalent amounts of permanganate and substrate react, i.e., a $2:3$ molar ratio, then the following derivation can be made, beginning with the rate law:

$$-\frac{d[Mn^{VII}]}{dt} = k[Mn^{VII}][H_2Z] \tag{1}$$

Since $[H_2Z] = \frac{3}{2}[Mn^{VII}]$ throughout the reaction,

$$-\frac{d[Mn^{VII}]}{dt} = \frac{3}{2} k[Mn^{VII}]^2$$

Integration gives

$$\tfrac{3}{2} kt = \frac{1}{[Mn^{VII}]} - \frac{1}{[Mn^{VII}]_0}$$

for time t and time zero, respectively.

$$\tfrac{3}{2} kt[Mn^{VII}]_0 = \frac{[Mn^{VII}]_0}{[Mn^{VII}]} - 1 = kt[H_2Z]_0 \tag{2}$$

But

$$[Mn^{VII}]_0 = \frac{V_0 N}{5} \cdot \frac{1000}{5} \tag{3}$$

where N = normality of thiosulfate and V_0 = volume of thiosulfate required for titration at time zero.

The concentration of permanganate at time t is related to the quantity of thiosulfate required to titrate the iodine that it liberates *and* which the manganese dioxide liberates and is given by the expression,

$$[Mn^{VII}] = \frac{N}{5} \cdot \frac{1000}{v}[V_t - \tfrac{2}{3}(V_0 - V_t)] \tag{4}$$

where V_t is the volume at time t and v is the volume in milliliters of the aliquot. Substituting the value of $[Mn^{VII}]_0$ from Eq. (3) and the value of $[Mn^{VII}]$ from Eq. (4) into Eq. (2) and simplifying produces the result:

$$kt[H_2Z]_0 = \frac{V_0}{V_t - \tfrac{2}{3}(V_0 - V_t)} - 1$$

$$= \frac{V_0 - V_t}{V_t - \tfrac{2}{5}V_0}$$

Plotting the quotient $(V_0 - V_t)/(V_t - \frac{2}{5}V_0)$ against t yields a straight line of slope $k[H_2Z]_0$, provided the rate law shown in Eq. (1) is valid.

If the substrate H_2Z is oxidized by permanganate in strongly alkaline solution, the oxidation state to which the manganese is reduced will, in most cases, be $+6$:

$$2\,MnO_4^- + H_2Z + 2\,OH^- \rightarrow 2\,MnO_4^{2-} + Z + H_2O$$

If equivalent amounts of permanganate and substrate react, i.e., a $1:2$ ratio, it can be shown by means of a derivation similar to that shown above that the following expression holds:

$$kt[H_2Z]_0 = \frac{V_0 - V_t}{V_t - \frac{4}{5}V_0}$$

If manganate, rather than permanganate, is used as an oxidant, the reaction will in most cases be found to be much slower:

$$MnO_4^{2-} + H_2Z \rightarrow MnO_2 + 2\,OH^-$$

For this case, the following expression can be derived:

$$kt[H_2Z]_0 = \frac{V_0 - V_t}{V_t - \frac{1}{2}V_0}$$

b. *Nonstoichiometric Ratio of Oxidant to Reductant.* When nonstoichiometric ratios of permanganate and substrate are used, other relations must be developed.[75] For example, if permanganate is reduced by the substrate to manganate only, and if an equimolar ratio of permanganate and substrate is used (a 100% excess of substrate), then the rate expression can be derived as follows:

$$-\frac{d[Mn^{VII}]}{dt} = k[Mn^{VII}][H_2Z]$$

Let $x = [Mn^{VII}]$ and $y = [H_2Z]$ at any time t and x_0 and y_0 be the corresponding quantities at time zero:

$$-\frac{dx}{dt} = kxy$$

Since

$$x_0 = y_0, \qquad y = \tfrac{1}{2}y_0 + \tfrac{1}{2}x$$

and

$$-\frac{dx}{dt} = \tfrac{1}{2}kx(y_0 - x)$$

$$-\tfrac{1}{2}kt = \int \frac{dx}{x(y_0 - x)}$$

$$= -\frac{1}{y_0}\ln\!\left(\frac{y_0 - x}{x}\right) \tag{5}$$

[75] R. Stewart, *J. Am. Chem. Soc.* **79**, 3057 (1957).

Now the concentration which relates the thiosulfate titer and the Mn^{VII} concentration [corresponding to Eq. (4)] is:

$$[Mn^{VII}] = x = \frac{N}{5} \cdot \frac{1000}{v} [V_t - 4(V_0 - V_t)]$$

Substituting for x in Eq. (5) and simplifying gives

$$\tfrac{1}{2}kty_0 = \tfrac{1}{2}kt[H_2Z]_0 = \ln \frac{V_t - \tfrac{3}{5}V_0}{V_t - \tfrac{4}{5}V_0}$$

$$\frac{kt[H_2Z]_0}{4.61} = \log \frac{V_t - \tfrac{3}{5}V_0}{V_t - \tfrac{4}{5}V_0}$$

A plot of the logarithmic quantity against time produces a straight line of slope

$$\frac{k[H_2Z]_0}{4.61}$$

If a molar ratio of permanganate to substrate of 4:1 is used and if the reduction proceeds only to the manganate stage (a 100% excess of permanganate), then a similar derivation to that given above yields the equation:

$$-\frac{kt[H_2Z]_0}{2.30} = \log \frac{V_t - \tfrac{9}{10}V_0}{V_t - \tfrac{4}{5}V_0}$$

c. *Acidity Changes Accompanying Reaction.* In all permanganate oxidations, either acid or base is produced and since the oxidation rate of most substrates is strongly pH dependent, it is obvious that any meaningful rate study must be carried out in buffered solution. In strongly acid or strongly alkaline solution the concentration of acid or base may be much larger than the concentration of oxidant and reductant, and in these cases acidity changes caused by the oxidation are likely to be small.

Oxidation of aldehydes by permanganate in unbuffered neutral solution causes a drop in pH (to a point approximately 0.3 pH units above the pK of the acid produced), whereas oxidation of a secondary alcohol to a ketone causes a rise in pH.[76] The stoichiometry of these two oxidations reveals the difference in the two cases:

$$3\ RCHO + 2\ MnO_4^- \rightarrow \underline{2\ RCO_2^-} + RCO_2H + 2\ MnO_2 + H_2O$$

$$3\ R_2CHOH + 2\ MnO_4^- \rightarrow 3\ R_2C{=}O + \underline{2\ OH^-} + 2\ MnO_2 + 2\ H_2O$$

The oxidation of a weak acid may generate hydrogen ions, whereas the

[76] Contrary to suggestions appearing in the earlier literature, there is ample evidence that glass electrode measurements are reliable when made on solutions containing permanganate.

oxidation of the corresponding anion generates hydroxyl ions. The equations for the oxidation of sulfite and bisulfite illustrate this point:

$$3\ HSO_3^- + 2\ MnO_4^- \rightarrow 3\ SO_4^{2-} + \underline{H^+} + 2\ MnO_2 + H_2O$$

$$3\ SO_3^{2-} + 2\ MnO_4^- + H_2O \rightarrow 3\ SO_4^{2-} + \underline{2\ OH^-} + 2\ MnO_2$$

The initial pH of this reaction has, in fact, been found to have a profound effect on whether the solution becomes more acidic or more basic.[77] An added complication in the case of sulfite oxidation is the production of dithionate, $S_2O_6^{2-}$, as a minor by-product and intermediate (see Section III,C,2).

E. DECOMPOSITION OF PERMANGANATE

1. THERMAL DECOMPOSITION

Permanganate salts are stable to thermal decomposition in the solid state at room temperature[78] but in solution they decompose at widely different rates depending upon the particular solvent employed. Water is the only solvent which reduces permanganate very slowly[79], but even aqueous solutions that are very acidic or alkaline cause extensive decomposition to take place.

a. *Neutral Solution.* The decomposition of aqueous permanganate is autocatalytic since manganese dioxide is an effective catalyst for the process[80]:

$$2\ MnO_4^- + H_2O \xrightarrow{\ MnO_2\ } 2\ MnO_2 + 2\ OH^- + \tfrac{3}{2}\ O_2$$

It follows that even traces of dust or of other reducing materials will induce decomposition of permanganate solutions. The preparation of stable solutions is described in textbooks on quantitative analysis. It is estimated that a neutral $0.02\ M$ permanganate solution which has been carefully freed from impurities and kept in the dark will lose less than 0.2% of its titer in 6 months.[81]

b. *Acid Solution.* Dilute aqueous acid solutions of permanganate are less stable than neutral solutions, but the decomposition is still relatively slow unless the solutions are boiled. The decomposition rate is roughly proportional

---

[77] C. H. Sorum, F. S. Charlton, J. A. Neptune, and J. O. Edwards, *J. Am. Chem. Soc.* **74**, 219 (1952).

[78] The thermal decomposition of silver permanganate has been studied by G. A. Grant and M. Katz, *Can. J. Chem.* **32**, 1068 (1954).

[79] It has been reported that very dry acetone, in the dark, is stable to permanganate. B. Jezowska-Trzebiatowska, A. Bartecki, and M. Chrmielowska, *Bull. Acad. Polon. Sci. Ser. Sci. Chim. Geol. Geograph.* **7**, 485 (1959); *Chem. Abstr.* **54**, 19134 (1960).

[80] H. N. Morse, A. J. Hopkins and M. S. Walker, *Am. Chem. J.* **18**, 401 (1896); see also Section I,A,4.

[81] I. M. Kolthoff and R. Belcher, "Volumetric Analysis," Vol. III, p. 38. Wiley (Interscience), New York, 1957.

to the acidity, and manganese dioxide also promotes the decomposition in acid solution.[82]

In concentrated sulfuric acid or in oleum, permanganate decomposes rapidly to a soluble manganese(IV) species (see Section I,A,3).

c. *Alkaline Solution.* Concentrated alkaline solutions of permanganate slowly decompose to give oxygen and manganate. The mechanisms proposed by Symons and by Jezowska-Trzebiatowska *et al.* involve an initial electron abstraction from hydroxyl ion by permanganate[83-87]:

$$MnO_4^- + OH^- \rightarrow MnO_4^{2-} + \cdot OH$$

It is known that manganate retards the reaction and that the liberated oxygen comes from the solvent, not from the permanganate. The manganate inhibition is compatible with the above reaction being reversible, although others have concluded that this reaction is the rate-controlling step.[88]

In the Symons mechanism, subsequent one-electron abstractions by permanganate involve conversion of $\cdot OH$ to $\cdot O^-$ to HO_2^- to $\cdot O_2^-$ to O_2, and the manganate inhibition is believed the result of the reversibility of some of these steps.[89]

The presence of radicals in alkaline permanganate oxidations is indicated by polymerization and coupling reactions.[90, 91]

2. PHOTOLYTIC DECOMPOSITION

Light accelerates the decomposition of permanganate both in solution and in the solid state. Zimmerman showed that photolysis of permanganate solutions liberated oxygen and deposited manganese dioxide.[92] The isotopic

[82] A. Noll, *Z. Angew. Allgem. Chem.* **24**, 1509 (1911). See also P. G. Desideri, *J. Electroanal. Chem.* **6**, 344 (1963).

[83] M. C. R. Symons, *J. Chem. Soc.* p. 3956 (1953).

[84] M. C. R. Symons, *Research* **6**, 5S (1953).

[85] B. Jezowska-Trzebiatowska, J. Nawojska, and M. Wronska, *Bull. Acad. Polon. Sci. Classe (III)* **2**, 447 (1954); *Chem. Abstr.* **49**, 7939 (1955).

[86] B. Jezowska-Trzebiatowska and J. Kalecinski, *Bull. Acad. Polon. Sci. Ser. Sci. Chem. Geol. Geograph.* **7**, 405 (1959); *Chem. Abstr.* **54**, 19122 (1960).

[87] See also H. Stamm, "Newer Methods of Volumetric Analysis." Van Nostrand, Princeton, New Jersey, 1938; *Angew. Chem.* **47**, 791 (1934); J. Vepřek-Šiška, V. Ettel, and A. Regner, *J. Inorg. Nucl. Chem.* **26**, 1476 (1964); R. Landsberg and K.-H. Heckner, *Nature* **201**, 1123 (1964); M. Wronska and M. Baranowska, *in* "Theory and Structure of Complex Compounds" (B. Jezowska-Trzebiatowska, ed.), p. 645. Macmillan (Pergamon), New York, 1964; R. Landsberg and R. Thiele, *ibid.*, p. 637.

[88] R. Landsberg, W. Geissler, and S. Mueller, *Z. Chem.* **1**, 169 (1961).

[89] See also K. A. K. Lott, M. C. R. Symons, and P. A. Trevalion, *Proc. Chem. Soc.* p. 357 (1960).

[90] J. Kenyon and M. C. R. Symons, *J. Chem. Soc.* p. 3580 (1953).

[91] B. Jezowska-Trzebiatowska, J. Nawojska, and M. Wronska, *Rocznicki Chem.* **29**, 259 (1955); *Chem. Abstr.* **50**, 11781 (1956).

[92] G. L. Zimmerman, *J. Chem. Phys.* **23**, 825 (1955).

composition of the liberated oxygen was found to be independent of the isotopic composition of the water.

Photolysis of permanganate in rigid glasses at low temperature with ultraviolet light produces manganese(III) and oxygen.[93] Neither manganate nor hypomanganate nor chromate nor vanadate decompose under these conditions.

F. PERMANGANIC ACID

It has long been known that permanganate salts dissolve in sulfuric acid to give a green solution[94] which has been attributed to the presence of $(MnO_3)_2SO_4$,[95] permanganyl sulfate, or to Mn_2O_7, permanganic anhydride.[96]

Symons et al.[97] attribute the green color (λ_{max} at 458 mμ, a smaller absorption peak at 630 mμ) to the presence of permanganic acid and have shown that the color changes which result from gradual acidification of a permanganate solution—purple to red to brown to green—probably accompany the simple protonation process. That is, the brown color of a 60% sulfuric acid solution of permanganate is the color of the mixture of permanganate (purple) and permanganic acid (green), although colloidal manganese dioxide, formed by reduction or decomposition, gives a very similar spectrum.

Using a spectrophotometric method and the Hammett acidity function, H_0, Symons et al, determined the pK_a of permanganic acid to be -2.25 in perchloric acid. That is, the equilibrium,

$$H^+ + MnO_4^- \rightleftharpoons HMnO_4$$

is at the midpoint in 39% perchloric acid. (The appropriate function for the protonation of an anion base is actually H_- which has only recently been determined for aqueous acids.[98,99])

Stewart and Mocek found that the pK_a of permanganic acid is considerably more negative in sulfuric acid than in perchloric acid.[100] A similar situation occurs with chromic acid, and it appears that the protonation of inorganic oxy-anions cannot be precisely described with the aid of conventional acidity functions and a single pK_a value. Using the H_0 function, a pK_a of -4.6 was obtained in sulfuric acid, corresponding to half-ionization in 61% sulfuric acid. Using the H_- function, a pK_a of -5.1 was obtained, corresponding, again, to half-ionization in 61% sulfuric acid.

[93] U. Klaning and M. C. R. Symons, *J. Chem. Soc.* p. 3269 (1959).

[94] H. J. Aschoff, *J. Prakt. Chem.* **81** (1), 29 (1860).

[95] B. Franke, *J. Prakt. Chem.* **36** (2), 31 (1887).

[96] F. Ephraim, "Inorganic Chemistry," p. 486. Gurney and Jackson, London, 1948.

[97] N. Bailey, A. Carrington, K. A. K. Lott and M. C. R. Symons, *J. Chem. Soc.* p. 290 (1960).

[98] R. H. Boyd, *J. Am. Chem. Soc.* **83**, 4288 (1961).

[99] J. N. Phillips, *Australian J. Chem.* **14**, 183 (1961).

[100] R. Stewart and M. M. Mocek, *Can. J. Chem.* **41**, 1160 (1963).

Further spectral changes, which are less dramatic, occur as the permanganic acid solutions are made more acidic. Royer[101] used cryoscopy and conductivity to study the green solution of potassium permanganate in 99.9% sulfuric acid and interpreted his results in terms of the ionization:

$$KMnO_4 + 3\ H_2SO_4 \rightarrow K^+ + MnO_3^+ + H_3O^+ + 3\ HSO_4^-$$

On the other hand, Mishra and Symons,[102] on the basis of independent conductivity measurements and a theoretical analysis of the absorption spectra, believe the following reaction occurs:

$$KMnO_4 + 3\ H_2SO_4 \rightarrow O_3MnOSO_3H + H_3O^+ + K^+ + 2\ HSO_4^-$$

Both groups point out that the conductivity and cryoscopy data are equivocal and it may be that partly dissociated permanganyl bisulfate is the form in which manganese(VII) is present in the system:

$$O_3MnOSO_3H \rightleftharpoons MnO_3^+ + HSO_4^-$$

It is very unlikely that the process which is half complete in 61% sulfuric acid and 39% perchloric acid is the production of the permanganyl ion, MnO_3^+, since such an ionization should be better described by the H_R (C_0, J_0)[103] acidity function than by either the H_0 or H_- functions. In fact, the H_R function gives a very unsatisfactory ionization curve when fitted to the spectral data for these solutions and it is probable that the process being observed is protonation of permanganate ion to give permanganic acid.

The anhydride of permanganic acid, Mn_2O_7, is believed to be the oil that separates from cold concentrated solutions of potassium permanganate in sulfuric acid. Distillation produces a dark green substance which decomposes to manganese dioxide, oxygen, and water at room temperature.[104]

II. Permanganate Exchange Reactions

A. OXYGEN EXCHANGE

Permanganate ion exchanges its oxygen atoms only slowly with aqueous solvent in neutral solution.[105] The exchange is faster in base and becomes very fast in acid. The rate law for the exchange in mildly acid media shows the

---

[101] D. J. Royer, *J. Inorg. Nucl. Chem.* **17**, 159 (1961).

[102] H. C. Mishra and M. C. R. Symons, *J. Chem. Soc.* p. 4411 (1962).

[103] N. C. Deno, H. E. Berkheimer, W. L. Evans, and H. J. Peterson, *J. Am. Chem. Soc.* **81**, 2344 (1959).

[104] A. Simon and F. Feher, *Z. Elektrochem.* **38**, 137 (1932).

[105] G. A. Mills, *J. Am. Chem. Soc.* **62**, 2833 (1940); N. F. Hall and O. R. Alexander, *J. Am. Chem. Soc.* **62**, 3455 (1940).

presence of an acid-independent and an acid-dependent term, the latter involving the square of the hydrogen ion concentration[106]:

$$\text{rate} = k_1[MnO_4^-] + k_2[MnO_4^-][H^+]^2$$

The second order acid catalysis implicates permanganic acidium ion, $H_2MnO_4^+$, as a reactive intermediate:

$$MnO_4^- + 2\,H^+ \rightleftharpoons H_2MnO_4^+$$

This may undergo a displacement of a molecule of water by a solvent water molecule:

$$H_2{}^*O + H_2MnO_4^+ \rightarrow [H_2{}^*O\cdots MnO_3\cdots OH_2]^+ \rightarrow H_2MnO_3{}^*O^+ + H_2O$$

Or it may reversibly dehydrate to permanganyl ion:

$$H_2MnO_4^+ \underset{\longleftarrow}{\overset{H_2{}^*O}{\longrightarrow}} MnO_3^+ + H_2O$$

It has been suggested that the exchange in basic solution may be caused by the presence of small amounts of manganate ion, which is known to be formed by the decomposition of alkaline permanganate.[107] Manganate and permanganate undergo a rapid electron transfer reaction (see next section), and experiments in which the manganate–water exchange reaction was studied by means of precipitation and analysis of barium manganate suggested that the manganate–water exchange reaction was also fast. However, the latter reaction appears to be catalyzed by the presence of barium manganate, and experiments in which labeled manganate was used and the water enrichment was followed indicate that manganate–water exchange is actually very slow.[106]

Symons points out that the vacant d-orbitals of the metal atom may provide an exchange route involving a pentacoordinated manganese intermediate or transition state. In support of this idea is the fact that bromate and iodate undergo quite rapid oxygen exchange, whereas chlorate and perchlorate, which would not be expected to expand their valence shell in this way, do not.

B. ELECTRON EXCHANGE WITH MANGANESE(VI)

The very fast exchange between manganate and permanganate has been studied in detail by Wahl *et al.*[108-110] This reaction proceeds via an outer-sphere complex; that is, the first coordination sphere of each metal ion remains

106 H. O. McDonald, *Dissertation Abstr.* 21, 454 (1960).
107 M. C. R. Symons, *J. Chem. Soc.* p. 3676 (1954).
108 J. C. Sheppard and A. C. Wahl, *J. Am. Chem. Soc.* 79, 1020 (1957); O. E. Myers and J. C. Sheppard, *J. Am. Chem. Soc.* 83, 4739 (1961); see also A. D. Britt and W. M. Yen, *J. Am. Chem. Soc.* 83, 4516 (1961).
109 A. C. Wahl, *Z. Elektrochem.* 64, 90 (1960).
110 L. Gjertsen and A. C. Wahl, *J. Am. Chem. Soc.* 81, 1572 (1959).

intact as the two complex ions exchange their identity.[111] The transfer of one electron which produces this exchange is facile because of the rather small changes in the manganese–oxygen bond distances and in the ion–solvent interactions which accompany the reaction.

$$*MnO_4^- + MnO_4^{2-} \rightleftharpoons *MnO_4^{2-} + MnO_4^-$$

The specific effect of metal cations on this exchange reaction is interesting.[109,110] Alkali metal ions all catalyze the reaction, and their order of effectiveness is $Cs^+ > K^+ > Na^+ > Li^+$. This catalysis probably proceeds via symmetrical bridged species such as[111]:

$$[O_3Mn—Cs—MnO_3]^{2-}$$

C. MANGANESE(VII), MANGANESE(IV), AND MANGANESE(II) REACTIONS

The exchange between permanganate ion and manganese dioxide, containing radioactive manganese, is very slow, although the age of the manganese dioxide sample undoubtedly has some effect on the rate.[112] The homogeneous exchange reaction between manganese(VII) and manganese(IV) which could be studied in strongly acid solution would be expected to be very much faster.

During the course of the Guyard reaction,

$$2 MnO_4^- + 3 Mn^{2+} + 2 H_2O \rightarrow 5 MnO_2 + 4 H^+$$

some exchange between the manganese(VII) and manganese(II) takes place.[113–115] The reaction is fractionally dependent on the concentrations of the manganese ions and on the hydrogen ion concentration. Adamson concludes that the rate-controlling step is between manganese(III) and (IV) oxy-cations:

$$*MnO^+ + MnO^{2+} \rightleftharpoons *MnO^{2+} + MnO^+$$

III. Permanganate Oxidation of Inorganic Substrates

Permanganate can operate as both a one- and two-equivalent oxidizing agent. The classification of oxidants in this way is credited to Kirk and Browne, who recognized that most reagents could be grouped in one of two categories, depending on whether they tended to cause the oxidation state of a substrate to change by one or by two units.[116] They used the terms mono- and di-delectronators for these classes, and others have used the terms one- and two-electron transfer reagents, but as Higginson and Marshall point out these

[111] J. Halpern, *Quart. Rev.* p. 207 (1961).
[112] E. Broda and J. Erber, *Monatsh.* **81**, 53 (1950).
[113] M. J. Polissar, *J. Am. Chem. Soc.* **58**, 1372 (1936).
[114] A. W. Adamson, *J. Phys. & Colloid Chem.* **55**, 293 (1951).
[115] J. A. Happe and D. S. Martin, *J. Am. Chem. Soc.* **77**, 4212 (1955).
[116] R. E. Kirk and A. W. Browne, *J. Am. Chem. Soc.* **50**, 337 (1928).

terms suggest that the reactions necessarily occur by electron transfer processes.[117, 118]

Cerium(IV) and cobalt(III) are typical one-equivalent oxidants, and thallium(III) and hypochlorite ion are typical two-equivalent oxidants. It is not surprising that the stable reduction products of cerium and cobalt ions are one oxidation level removed, whereas those of thallium and hypochlorite ions are two oxidation levels removed from the oxidants.

$$\left.\begin{array}{l} Ce^{IV} \rightarrow Ce^{III} \\ Co^{III} \rightarrow Co^{II} \end{array}\right\} \text{One-equivalent oxidants}$$

$$\left.\begin{array}{l} Tl^{III} \rightarrow Tl^{I} \\ OCl^{-} \rightarrow Cl^{-} \end{array}\right\} \text{Two-equivalent oxidants}$$

The basis for classifying oxidants in this way depends on the type of products formed when certain substrates, in particular hydrazine and sulfite, are oxidized. Most oxidants, when in excess, oxidize hydrazine to nitrogen. If the oxidation is incomplete, it is found that one-equivalent oxidants tend to produce ammonia as the only by-product, whereas two-equivalent oxidants produce some hydrazoic acid as well. Similarly, one-equivalent reagents convert sulfite to dithionate, $S_2O_6^{2-}$ (presumably via the radical anion SO_3^-), whereas two-equivalent oxidants tend to produce sulfate.

Permanganate is an oxidant with manifold reaction paths, and it is not surprising that it can function as either a one- or a two-equivalent oxidant depending on the characteristics of the substrate that it is attacking.

A. DERIVATIVES OF AMMONIA

Ammonia itself is slowly oxidized by permanganate to a mixture of products, chiefly nitrogen, nitrites, and nitrates. Derivatives of ammonia are almost all oxidized more rapidly than the parent compound. In particular, aromatic primary amines suffer immediate ring degradation when treated with permanganate.

1. HYDRAZINE

This substance's oxidation pattern, as has been pointed out earlier, reveals something of the reaction paths available to various oxidants. Permanganate, in accordance with its versatility, is both a one- and a two-equivalent oxidant and converts hydrazine to mixtures of nitrogen, ammonia, and hydrazoic acid, the latter in smaller amount.[119-121] The distribution of products will depend

[117] W. C. E. Higginson and J. W. Marshall, *J. Chem. Soc.* p. 447 (1957..

[118] For a discussion of one- and two-equivalent reactions see W. C. E. Higginson, D. Sutton, and P. Wright, *J. Chem. Soc.* p. 1380 (1953); J. Halpern, *Can. J. Chem.* 37, 148 (1959); and J. H. Baxendale, *Chem. Soc. (London) Spec. Publ.* 1, 40 (1954).

[119] A. W. Browne and F. F. Shetterly, *J. Am. Chem. Soc.* 31, 221 (1909).

[120] J. Petersen, *Z. Anorg. Chem.* 5, 1 (1894).

[121] W. C. E. Higginson and D. Sutton, *J. Chem. Soc.* p. 1402 (1953).

on the conditions and on the presence or absence of an excess of the oxidant since hydrazoic acid, for example, will itself undergo oxidation to nitrogen by permanganate.[122]

In basic solution the reaction appears to be simpler, and hydrazine is smoothly oxidized to nitrogen:

$$4\,KMnO_4 + 3\,NH_2NH_2 \rightarrow 3\,N_2 + 4\,MnO_2 + 4\,KOH + 4\,H_2O$$

2. HYDROXYLAMINE

Like hydrazine, this substrate gives a variety of oxidation products when acted on by permanganate. Kurtenacker and Neusser state that in strongly alkaline solution nitrite is the principal product and nitrous oxide the major by-product. In weakly alkaline solution, where the rate is at a minimum, nitrogen is the major product, with nitrite and nitrous oxide being the by-products. In neutral and acid solution, nitrous oxide and nitric acid are formed, the proportion of the latter increasing as the solution is made more acidic.[123]

Undoubtedly the composition of the products depends not only on the acidity of the medium but also on the stoichiometry of the reactants and the reaction time, since nitrous oxide and nitrite can be made to undergo some oxidation themselves by permanganate.

B. BORANE DERIVATIVES

Boron hydride and borohydride ion are both oxidized by permanganate to borates.[124] The oxidation of pyridine–borane complex illustrates this:

$$2\,MnO_4^- + BH_3 \cdot pyridine \rightarrow 2\,MnO_2 + BO_2^- + pyridine + OH^- + H_2O$$

The oxidation of borohydride to borate is accompanied by the production of smaller quantities of hydrogen gas.[125,126] As might be expected for a reaction between such reagents, the reaction is very fast. The mechanisms of several permanganate oxidations, particularly of organic substrates, have been assumed to occur by hydride transfer from the substrate anion to permanganate. This would be a particularly attractive mechanism for the borohydride–permanganate reaction:

$$BH_4^- + MnO_4^- \rightarrow BH_3 + HMnO_4^{2-}$$

The BH_3 molecule is still a good reductant and the boron will eventually be converted to borate, although it is difficult to predict the exact course of these

[122] J. H. van der Meulen, *Rec. Trav. Chim.* **67**, 600 (1948).

[123] A. Kurtenacker and R. Neusser, *Z. Anorg. Allgem. Chem.* **131**, 27 (1923); **130**, 199 (1923).

[124] V. I. Mikheeva, N. N. Mal'tseva, and E. M. Fedneva, *Zh. Neorgan. Khim.* **3**, 2225 (1958).

[125] E. H. Jensen, "A Study of Sodium Borohydride." Nyt Nordisk. Forlang, Copenhagen, 1954.

[126] T. Freund and N. Nuenke, *J. Am. Chem. Soc.* **83**, 3378 (1961).

steps. The hypomanganate ion, $HMnO_4^{2-}$, can be oxidized to manganate in strongly basic solution or can disproportionate in neutral or acid solution:

$$BH_3 \xrightarrow[\text{H}_2\text{O}]{\text{Mn}^{\text{VII}}} BO_2^-$$

$$HMnO_4^{2-} + MnO_4^- + OH^- \rightarrow 2\,MnO_4^{2-} + H_2O \qquad \text{in basic solution}$$

$$3\,HMnO_4^{2-} + H_2O \rightarrow 2\,MnO_2 + MnO_4^- + 5\,OH^- \qquad \text{in neutral or acid solution}$$

In addition, the hypomanganate may react with borohydride (or one of its oxidation products still containing reactive hydrogen), since borohydride is a very reactive substrate. Freund and Nuenke conclude that this side reaction is the source of the hydrogen which is liberated during the course of the reaction[126]:

$$BH_4^- + 2\,Mn^V \rightarrow (BH_2^-) + H_2 + 2\,Mn^{IV}$$

They showed that the hydrogen atoms in the liberated gas came from the borohydride, not from the aqueous solvent. This is in sharp contrast to the borohydride hydrolysis reaction in which one of the two hydrogen atoms in the hydrogen molecule comes from the solvent.[127]

C. SULFUR IONS

1. SULFIDE ION

In basic solution, excess permanganate oxidizes sulfide to sulfate[128]:

$$8\,MnO_4^- + 3\,S^{2-} + 4\,H_2O \rightarrow 8\,MnO_2 + 3\,SO_4^{2-} + 8\,OH^-$$

In neutral or acid media, the reaction tends to be incomplete, with sulfur and tetrathionate being by-products.[129]

2. SULFITE ION

The products formed when sulfite is oxidized are diagnostic of the character of the oxidant; one-equivalent oxidants tend to produce dithionate, whereas two-equivalent oxidants tend to produce sulfate (see introduction to Section III). Permanganate, in keeping with its versatile character, can produce both products but with an excess of permanganate, or, in basic solution, sulfate formation is almost quantitative[130]:

$$2\,MnO_4^- + 3\,SO_3^{2-} + H_2O \rightarrow 2\,MnO_2 + 3\,SO_4^{2-} + 2\,OH^-$$

$$2\,MnO_4^- + 6\,SO_3^{2-} + 4\,H_2O \rightarrow 2\,MnO_2 + 3\,S_2O_6^{2-} + 8\,OH^-$$

[127] T. Freund, *J. Inorg. Nucl. Chem.* **9**, 246 (1959).
[128] M. Hönig and E. Zatzek, *Monatsh.* **4**, 738 (1883).
[129] S. Mohammad and S. N. Bedi, *J. Indian Chem. Soc.* **21**, 55 (1944).
[130] J. Pinnow, *Z. Anal. Chem.* **43**, 91 (1904).

Halperin and Taube used oxygen-18 labeled permanganate to oxidize sulfite and showed that partial transfer of oxygen (0.2 atoms of oxygen per mole of sulfate formed) from permanganate occurred during the oxidation.[131] This is a further indication that multiple reaction paths exist for this reaction.

3. THIOSULFATE AND THIOCYANATE IONS

Alkaline permanganate oxidizes both thiosulfate[132] and thiocyanate[133] to sulfate. Cyanate is formed, in addition, in the latter case:

$$3\ S_2O_3{}^{2-} + 8\ MnO_4{}^- + H_2O\ \rightarrow\ 6\ SO_4{}^{2-} + 8\ MnO_2 + 2\ OH^-$$

$$3\ SCN^- + 8\ MnO_4{}^- + H_2O\ \rightarrow\ 3\ SO_4{}^{2-} + 3\ CNO^- + 8\ MnO_2 + 2\ OH^-$$

In acid and neutral solution, the oxidations tend to be incomplete.[134] Dithionate and cyanide ions are the major by-products, cyanide oxidation by permanganate being very slow in acid (see Section III,H).

D. HALIDES

Permanganate oxidizes chloride, bromide, and iodide but at greatly different rates. In basic solution, chloride ion is virtually inert to permanganate. Iodide ion, on the other hand, is readily oxidized to iodate in basic or neutral solution[135, 136]:

$$2\ MnO_4{}^- + I^- + H_2O\ \rightarrow\ IO_3{}^- + 2\ MnO_2 + 2\ OH^-$$

In alkaline solution containing barium ions to precipitate manganate as it is formed, Stamm has shown that periodate is produced[137]:

$$8\ MnO_4{}^- + 8\ Ba^{2+} + I^- + 8\ OH^-\ \rightarrow\ 8\ BaMnO_4 + IO_4{}^- + 4\ H_2O$$

In acid solution, all the halides are fairly readily oxidized, but again iodide is the most reactive. Indeed, the reduction of manganese(VII) to manganese(II) by acidified iodide is rapid and quantitative and is used in the standard volumetric method for determining permanganate (see Section I,D,2). It is probable that the neutral hydrogen halides, HCl, HBr, and HI, are the reactive substrates in these reactions.

Hydrochloric acid, if concentrated and in excess, will also reduce manganese(IV) to manganese(II). (Concentrated hydrochloric acid will dissolve

[131] J. Halperin and H. Taube, *J. Am. Chem. Soc.* **74**, 380 (1952).

[132] G. Lunge and J. H. Smith, *J. Soc. Chem. Ind.* **2**, 463 (1883); G. Lunge and D. Segaller, *ibid.* **19**, 221 (1900).

[133] H. Stamm, *Z. Angew. Chem.* **47**, 791 (1934).

[134] K. Schröder, *Z. Anal. Chem.* **81**, 308 (1930).

[135] Y. K. Gupta, *J. Inorg. Nucl. Chem.* **19**, 179 (1961).

[136] A. Schwicker, *Z. Anal. Chem.* **110**, 161 (1937).

[137] H. Stamm, *Z. Angew. Chem.* **47**, 791 (1934).

and reduce manganese dioxide.) Under milder conditions, manganese dioxide is the reduction product[138]:

$$2\ KMnO_4 + 8\ HCl\ \rightarrow\ 3\ Cl_2 + 2\ MnO_2 + 4\ H_2O + 2\ KCl$$

$$2\ KMnO_4 + 16\ HCl\ \rightarrow\ 5\ Cl_2 + 2\ MnCl_2 + 8\ H_2O + 2\ KCl$$

E. METAL IONS

The very high potential of the several permanganate couples (Section I,B) means that most metal ions which exhibit multiple oxidation states will be oxidized from the lower to the upper state by this reagent. These reactions are primarily the concern of the analytical chemist and it does not seem appropriate to duplicate here the extensive discussions of these reactions found in standard works on analytical chemistry.[139]

A partial list of metal ions which undergo clean oxidation by permanganate is the following: ferrous ion, ferrocyanide ion, chromium(III), vanadyl ion [VO^{2+}, vanadium(IV)], stannous ion, antimony(III), uranium(IV), tungsten(IV), thallium(I), and platinum(II).

Acid permanganate solutions have occasionally been used to dissolve metals by direct oxidation.[140]

A few oxidants are able to oxidize manganous ion to permanganate. Solid sodium bismuthate in acid is a powerful enough oxidant to accomplish this:

$$2\ Mn^{2+} + 5\ NaBiO_3 + 14\ H^+\ \rightarrow\ 2\ MnO_4^- + 5\ Na^+ + 5\ Bi^{3+} + 7\ H_2O$$

Ammonium persulfate, lead dioxide, argentic oxide (AgO),[141] potassium periodate, and ozone[142] also oxidize manganese(II) to manganese(VII).

F. HYDROGEN

Hydrogen is smoothly oxidized by aqueous permanganate under homogeneous conditions.[143] In neutral and acid solution manganese dioxide is the product, whereas in alkaline solution manganate is the product:

$$2\ MnO_4^- + 3\ H_2 + 2\ H^+\ \rightarrow\ 2\ MnO_2 + 4\ H_2O$$

$$2\ MnO_4^- + H_2 + 2\ OH^-\ \rightarrow\ 2\ MnO_4^{2-} + 2\ H_2O$$

Webster and Halpern showed that the reaction rate is virtually independent of

[138] F. P. Venable and D. H. Jackson, *J. Am. Chem. Soc.* **42**, 237 (1920).

[139] See for example I. M. Kolthoff and R. Belcher "Volumetric Analysis," Vol. III, Chapters 1 and 2. Wiley (Interscience), New York, 1957.

[140] W. Foster, *Chem. News* **115**, 73 (1917).

[141] M. Tanaka, *Bull. Chem. Soc. (Japan)* **26**, 299 (1953); **27**, 10 (1954).

[142] H. H. Willard and L. L. Merritt, Jr., *Ind. Eng. Chem. Anal. Ed.* **14**, 486 (1942).

[143] A. H. Webster and J. Halpern, *Trans. Faraday Soc.* **53**, 51 (1957); see also G. Just and Y. Kauko, *Z. Physik. Chem. (Leipzig)* **76**, 601 (1911); E. Wilke and H. Kuhn, *ibid.* **113**, 313 (1924).

the acidity but is first order in both permanganate and hydrogen. The reaction appears to be a simple bimolecular one in which a two-equivalent reduction of the manganese(VII) probably occurs:

$$MnO_4^- + H_2 \rightarrow HMnO_4^{2-} + H^+$$

This reaction has an activation energy of 15 kcal mole^{-1}.

The reduction of permanganate by hydrogen is catalyzed by silver ion. The reaction kinetics are third order in this case and the reaction is between a hydrogen molecule and a silver permanganate molecule formed in a rapid equilibrium step. It is known that silver permanganate complex formation does occur in solution (see Section I,C,1):

$$Ag^+ + MnO_4^- \rightleftharpoons AgMnO_4$$

$$AgMnO_4 + H_2 \longrightarrow AgH^+ + HMnO_4^-$$

$$AgH^+ \xrightarrow[\text{fast}]{MnO_4^-} Ag^+ + H^+$$

There is evidence for the existence of the ion AgH$^+$ in other systems.[144]

The silver catalyzed reaction has a low activation energy (9 kcal mole^{-1}) and this suggests that reactions in which the permanganate undergoes a one-equivalent reduction will be favored over those in which a two-equivalent reduction occurs, other things being equal. In the case of the uncatalyzed reaction, a one-equivalent step is energetically unfavorable because of the high energy of atomic hydrogen; that is, the following reaction is highly endothermic:

$$H_2 + MnO_4^- \rightarrow H\cdot + HMnO_4^-$$

When the permanganate–hydrogen reaction is conducted in D$_2$O as solvent the rate is virtually identical with that in H$_2$O.[145]

G. HYDROGEN PEROXIDE

Permanganate rapidly oxidizes hydrogen peroxide to water and oxygen. In acid solution manganous ion is the reduction product:

$$2\,MnO_4^- + 5\,H_2O_2 + 6\,H^+ \rightarrow 2\,Mn^{2+} + 5\,O_2 + 8\,H_2O$$

In the neutral region manganese dioxide is formed and in alkaline solution manganate is formed.

Cahill and Taube[146] and Baertschi[147] showed that the oxygen which was liberated by the acid permanganate oxidation of hydrogen peroxide was

[144] A. H. Webster and J. Halpern, *J. Phys. Chem.* **60**, 280 (1956).
[145] J. F. Harrod and J. Halpern, *J. Phys. Chem.* **65**, 563 (1961).
[146] A. E. Cahill and H. Taube, *J. Am. Chem. Soc.* **74**, 2312 (1952).
[147] P. Baertschi, *Experientia* **7**, 215 (1951).

derived completely from the peroxide itself. The oxidation of D_2O_2 in D_2O proceeds at only one-seventh the rate of the corresponding protio system.[148] The oxygen–oxygen bond in the peroxide clearly remains intact during the reaction.

The reaction is catalyzed by manganous ions and by manganese dioxide.[149–151] The hydrogen peroxide molecule or the corresponding anions, HO_2^- and O_2^{2-},[152] probably reacts with permanganate and with manganese ions of lower valence.

H. CYANIDE ION

In alkaline solution permanganate oxidizes cyanide ion quantitatively to cyanate[153, 154]:

$$2\ MnO_4^- + CN^- + 2\ OH^- \rightarrow 2\ MnO_4^{2-} + CNO^- + H_2O$$

Drummond and Waters made use of this reaction as an analytical tool in their studies of permanganate oxidation mechanisms.[155] If an alkaline permanganate oxidation is conducted in the presence of barium ion, insoluble barium manganate is formed and manganese(VI) is prevented from participating in further oxidation. The dark colored precipitate makes a volumetric determination of the oxidizing power of the solution difficult, however, and so Drummond and Waters added an excess of cyanide ion to quench the reaction. The permanganate rapidly converts cyanide to cyanate and, after filtration, a Liebig determination can be made of the unreacted cyanide in the filtrate.

In solutions less basic than about pH 12 other products, in particular cyanogen and carbon dioxide, are also formed. Cyanogen hydrolyzes to cyanate and cyanide quite rapidly in solutions more basic than about pH 9 and so is difficult to detect:

$$2\ MnO_4^- + 6\ CN^- + 4\ H_2O \rightarrow 3\ (CN)_2 + 2\ MnO_2 + 8\ OH^-$$

$$(CN)_2 + 2\ OH^- \rightarrow CN^- + CNO^- + H_2O$$

The carbon dioxide results from oxidation of cyanogen and its hydrolysis products.

The permanganate–cyanide reaction is very slow in acid solution. The reaction rate rises rapidly as the solution is made slightly basic and it reaches a maximum near pH 9. It then falls somewhat, but remains quite rapid through

148 T.-L. Chang, *Science* **100**, 29 (1944).
149 F. Fouinat and M. Magat, *J. Chim. phys.* **47**, 514 (1950).
150 E. Abel, *Monatsh.* **86**, 462, 952 (1955).
151 E. H. Riesenfeld and T.-L. Chang, *Z. Anorg. Allgem. Chem.* **230**, 239 (1937).
152 J. S. F. Pode and W. A. Waters, *J. Chem. Soc.* p. 717 (1956).
153 H. Stamm, *Angew. Chem.* **47**, 791 (1934).
154 R. Gaugin, *Bull. Soc. Chim. France* p. 1048 (1948).
155 A. Y. Drummond and W. A. Waters, *J. Chem. Soc.* p. 435 (1953).

the strongly basic region. Stewart and Van der Linden concluded that there were two reaction paths involved.[156] One is first order in cyanide ion and first order in permanganate. This reaction, which was also studied by Freund,[157] appears to be the dominant one in the alkaline region. It has a low activation energy, about 9 kcal mole^{-1}, and the use of oxygen-18 labeled permanganate shows that the newly acquired oxygen atom in the cyanate comes chiefly from the permanganate, not from the solvent. The most reasonable mechanism for this reaction is a bimolecular one in which an oxygen atom is transferred from permanganate to cyanide:

$$MnO_4^- + CN^- \longrightarrow [O_3Mn\cdots O\cdots CN]^{2-} \rightarrow MnO_3^- + OCN^-$$

$$MnO_3^- + MnO_4^- + 2\,OH^- \xrightarrow{\text{fast}} 2\,MnO_4^{2-} + H_2O$$

The second path is somewhat more complicated. It is of higher kinetic order and it is pH dependent. The kinetic form of the reaction appears to be:

$$-\frac{d[MnO_4^-]}{dt} = k[MnO_4^-][CN^-]^2[H^+] = k'[MnO_4^-][CN^-][HCN]$$

At high reactant concentrations and in less basic solutions, it becomes the dominant reaction path. The rate maximum near pH 9 (the pK_a of HCN is 9.1) and the kinetic order suggest that the transition state is composed of one permanganate ion, one cyanide ion, and one hydrogen cyanide molecule. Very little oxygen-18 is found in the cyanate isolated under these conditions, i.e., in the pH region 8–12, and the mechanism for this path probably involves direct cyanogen formation, possibly via a reaction sequence such as:

$$HCN + CN^- \rightleftharpoons H(CN)_2^-$$

$$MnO_4^- + H(CN)_2^- \longrightarrow (CN)_2 + H^+ + MnO_4^{3-}$$

$$3\,MnO_4^{3-} + 4\,H_2O \xrightarrow{\text{fast}} 2\,MnO_2 + MnO_4^- + 8\,OH^-$$

Much of the cyanogen will then be hydrolyzed but the cyanate formed as one of the hydrolysis products will have acquired its oxygen from the solvent.

I. CARBON MONOXIDE

The homogeneous oxidation of carbon monoxide in aqueous solution by permanganate has been studied by Just and Kauko[158] and by Halpern and Harkness.[159] The reaction is first order in both carbon monoxide and per-

[156] R. Stewart and R. Van der Linden, *Can. J. Chem.* **38**, 2237 (1960).

[157] T. Freund, *J. Inorg. Nucl. Chem.* **15**, 371 (1960).

[158] G. Just and Y. Kauko, *Z. Physik. Chem.* (*Leipzig*) **82**, 71 (1913).

[159] J. Halpern and A. C. Harkness, personal communication; A. C. Harkness, Ph. D. Thesis, University of British Columbia, Vancouver, Canada, 1963; see also F. C. Phillips, *Am. Chem. J.* **16**, 255 (1894).

manganate and is not markedly dependent on changes in acidity or ionic strength.

$$3\ CO + 2\ MnO_4^- + H_2O \rightarrow 3\ CO_2 + 2\ MnO_2 + 2\ OH^-$$

As in almost all cases, manganate is the reduction product in alkaline solution since it is, in general, a less reactive oxidant than permanganate (see Section IV,C,2, however). The alkaline reaction can be written:

$$CO + 2\ MnO_4^- + 4\ OH^- \rightarrow CO_3^{2-} + 2\ MnO_4^{2-} + 2\ H_2O$$

The reaction parameters at pH 7 have the following values[159] (the values in acid and basic solution are not markedly different):

$$\left.\begin{array}{l} k_2 = 1.1 \text{ liter mole}^{-1} \text{ sec}^{-1} \\ \Delta S^{\ddagger} = -15.2 \text{ e.u.} \\ \Delta H^{\ddagger} = 14.0 \text{ kcal mole}^{-1} \end{array}\right\} \text{at } 25^\circ \text{C} \right\} \text{ for uncatalyzed reaction}$$

The mechanism of this reaction is probably a nucleophilic attack by a permanganate oxygen on the carbon atom of the carbon monoxide. This intermediate might then hydrolyze with either carbon–oxygen or manganese–oxygen bond fission:

$$MnO_4^- + CO \rightarrow O_3MnO\text{---}CO^-$$

$$O_3MnO\text{---}CO^- + H_2O \rightarrow MnO_4^{3-} + CO_2 + 2\ H^+$$

There is a dramatic catalytic effect of silver(I) and mercury(II) ions on this reaction. Silver ion, in particular, in very small amounts accelerates the reaction. This effect is particularly marked at lower temperatures since the activation enthalpy is extraordinarily low:

$$\left.\begin{array}{l} k_3 = 1.1 \times 10^5 \text{ liters}^2 \text{ mole}^{-2} \text{ sec}^{-1} \\ \Delta S^{\ddagger} = -30.4 \text{ e.u.} \\ \Delta H^{\ddagger} = 1.3 \text{ kcal mole}^{-1} \end{array}\right\} \text{at } 0^\circ \right\} \text{ for Ag}^+ \text{ catalyzed reaction}$$

The catalyzed reaction is believed to involve the formation of an insertion complex:

$$Ag^+ + CO + MnO_4^- \longrightarrow Ag\text{---}\overset{\overset{\displaystyle O}{\|}}{C}\text{---}OMnO_3 \qquad \text{rate-determining}$$

$$Ag\text{---}\overset{\overset{\displaystyle O}{\|}}{C}\text{---}OMnO_3 + H_2O \longrightarrow Ag^+ + CO_2 + MnO_4^{3-} + 2\ H^+ \qquad \text{fast}$$

An insertion complex, rather similar to the above, is known to form between carbon monoxide and mercury(II).[160, 161]

[160] W. Schoeller, W. Schrauth, and W. Essers, *Ber.* **46**, 2864 (1913).
[161] J. Halpern and S. F. A. Kettle, *Chem. & Ind.* (*London*) p. 668 (1961).

IV. Permanganate Oxidation of Organic Substrates

Permanganate is a vigorous, and in some cases a drastic, oxidant which has long been used in the organic laboratory. The reactivity of this reagent depends to a great extent on whether the reaction conditions are neutral, acidic, or basic. Permanganate oxidations of organic compounds are often, but by no means always, considerably faster in alkaline than in neutral solution. This is usually due to a change in the organic substrate that occurs when the solution is made basic, e.g., ionization of an alcohol, rather than to any alteration in the permanganate ion. The increase in oxidation rate that invariably occurs when reaction conditions are strongly acidic (30–50 % sulfuric acid) is caused mainly by conversion of permanganate ion to the still more active oxidant, permanganic acid (Section I,F).

An appreciation of the ionization patterns of organic compounds such as alcohols, amines, carboxylic acids, and even aldehydes and ketones is very helpful in predicting the ease with which permanganate ion will oxidize a particular group. As a general rule one can state that anions are oxidized more readily by permanganate ion than are neutral molecules which, in turn, are oxidized more readily than cations. The oxidation of alcohols (Section IV,A,2) illustrates the first of these points, and the oxidation of amines (Section IV,E) the second. Further, dianions are oxidized more readily than monoanions and this is illustrated by the oxidation of fluoral hydrate (Section IV,C,4), i.e., in general

$$Z^{2-} > HZ^- > H_2Z > H_3Z^+$$

Since permanganate anion is the oxidant in all but the most acidic systems (where the more powerful oxidant $HMnO_4$ is formed), one might have expected that repulsions between the permanganate anion and an anionic substrate would hinder the reaction. The permanganate reactions usually reflect this only in their highly negative entropies of activation, however, and the low enthalpies of activation commonly found more than compensate for this (Section V).

Aqueous solutions of permanganate are quite stable except when they are strongly basic or strongly acidic (Section I,E,1). Many organic solvents either are readily oxidized by potassium permanganate or do not dissolve the salt in appreciable amounts. This somewhat reduces the effectiveness of permanganate as an oxidant for organic compounds since heterogeneous conditions are sometimes required.[161a]

Neutral acetone solutions of permanganate have a reasonable stability, particularly when the system is very dry, but even these solutions, unless very carefully prepared, soon begin to deposit manganese dioxide (Section I,E,1). These solutions are frequently satisfactory for effecting organic oxidations.

[161a] See, however, N. A. Gibson and J. W. Hosking, *Australian J. Chem.* **18**, 123 (1965).

Acetic acid dissolves reasonable amounts of potassium permanganate and is fairly inert to the latter's oxidizing action. Tertiary butyl alcohol can also be used.

Degradation to carbon dioxide occurs with most organic compounds on prolonged heating with aqueous permanganate, although in basic solution oxalate is frequently isolated as a major reaction product. This is because oxalate suffers further rapid oxidation only in acid solution.

A. HYDROCARBONS

1. ALKANES

Little is known about the oxidation by aqueous permanganate of saturated hydrocarbons, per se, chiefly because of low mutual solubility. Reactions can be studied, however, with saturated chains containing an inert functional group such as carboxyl. The latter, particularly in basic solution, provides the desired water solubility.

The oxidation by both manganate and permanganate of branched chain carboxylic acids to the tertiary hydroxy acids was studied by Kenyon and Symons[162]:

$$R_2CH(CH_2)_nCO_2H \rightarrow R_2C(OH)(CH_2)_nCO_2H$$

Their results indicated participation of the carboxylate group in the oxidation. The oxidation of optically active 4-methylhexanoic acid by both manganate and permanganate in dilute alkali produced the 4-hydroxylactone which retained some optical activity.[163] Racemic product was obtained with strongly alkaline permanganate.

These authors assumed that an inversion of configuration at C-4 had occurred with the dilute alkaline reagent, with the carboxylate group displacing a hydride to the oxidant. The racemization in concentrated alkali was thought to be due to hydrogen atom abstraction by hydroxyl radicals.

A more detailed study of the permanganate oxidation of 4-methylhexanoic acid has been made by Wiberg and Fox who have shown that this reaction actually proceeds with partial retention (40%) of configuration at C-4[164]:

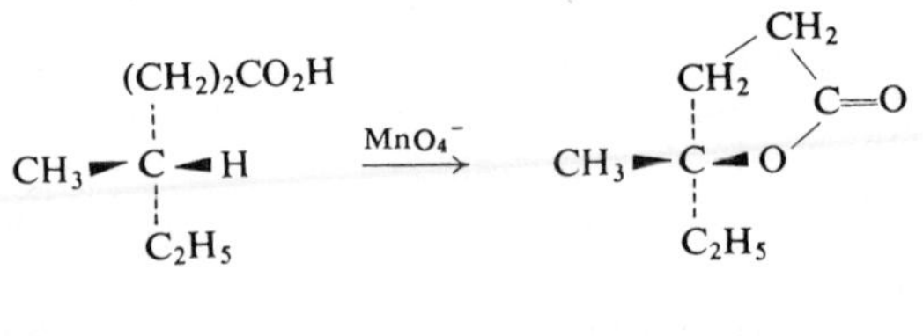

[162] J. Kenyon and M. C. R. Symons, *J. Chem. Soc.* p. 2129 (1953).
[163] J. Kenyon and M. C. R. Symons, *J. Chem. Soc.* p. 3580 (1953).
[164] K. B. Wiberg and A. S. Fox, *J. Am. Chem. Soc.* **85**, 3487 (1963).

The yields of hydroxy acid are rather poor in this reaction both at pH 7 and at pH 13. When permanganate–O^{18} was used in the oxidation, a minimum of 25% oxygen transfer was found, i.e., the oxygen in the new hydroxyl group at C-4 came partly from the oxidant. Carboxyl participation is not completely absent, however, since a small amount of oxygen-18 (corresponding to 7–9% transfer) is found at the 4-position when the *carboxyl*-labeled compound is oxidized.

Wiberg and Fox point out that the increased rate of permanganate oxidation of a tertiary benzylic hydrogen compared to an ordinary tertiary hydrogen is small compared with that expected if a carbonium ion is formed. To accommodate this fact, and the oxygen-18 and stereochemical data, they suggest that alkanes are oxidized in the following way. The permanganate ion abstracts a hydrogen atom from the tertiary position, giving a radical pair trapped briefly in a solvent cage. Recombination yields the alkyl hypomanganate ester:

$$R_3CH + MnO_4^- \rightarrow [R_3C \cdot MnO_4H^-] \rightarrow R_3C—O—MnO_3H^-$$

This ester may decompose in several ways. The most important route, judging from the oxygen-18 and stereochemical data, is hydrolysis to the alcohol and manganese(V), which quickly disproportionates. This path will result in retention of configuration and oxygen-transfer from permanganate:

$$R_3C—O—MnO_3H^- + H_2O \longrightarrow R_3COH + H_2MnO_4^- \text{ (Mn}^V)$$

A second decomposition route of the ester might be ionization at the carbon–oxygen bond leading to racemization but not to oxygen transfer:

$$R_3C—O—MnO_3H^- \longrightarrow R_3C^+ + HMnO_4^{2-} \text{ (Mn}^V)$$

$$R_3C^+ \longrightarrow R_3COH$$

Finally, to account for the small amount of oxygen transfer from carboxyl to C-4, a minor decomposition path involving carboxyl participation is invoked:

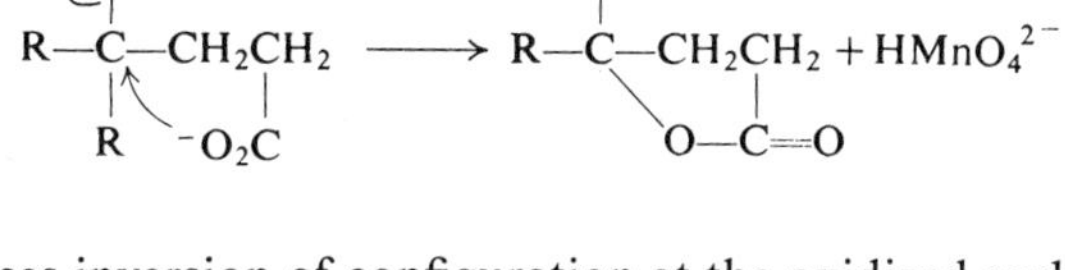

$$R—\underset{\underset{R}{|}}{\overset{\overset{OMnO_3H^-}{|}}{C}}—CH_2CH_2 \longrightarrow R—\underset{\underset{O—C=O}{|}}{\overset{\overset{R}{|}}{C}}—CH_2CH_2 + HMnO_4^{2-}$$

This path causes inversion of configuration at the oxidized carbon.

Oxidation also occurs at the tertiary position (α in this case) with norbornanecarboxylic acid. Both the *endo* and *exo* isomers of this compound react with alkaline permanganate to give the same product, the 2-*exo*-hydroxy-2-*endo*-carboxylic acid. The *endo* isomer is much more reactive, however, whereas the closely related compound, isocamphenilanic acid, is inert[165]:

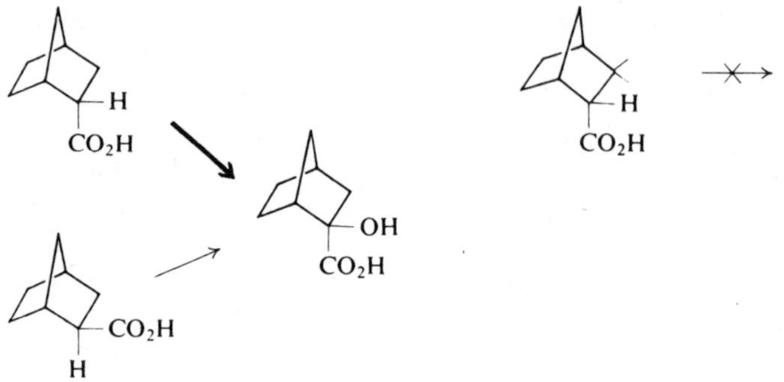

The α-carbon atom is also the point of oxidation in the reaction of alkaline permanganate with isobutyric acid[166]:

$$(CH_3)_2CHCO_2H \xrightarrow[OH^-]{MnO_4^-} (CH_3)_2\overset{\overset{\displaystyle OH}{|}}{C}CO_2H$$

The permanganate oxidation of dihydro-α-terpineol in basic solution converts the tertiary hydrogen to hydroxyl with *retention* of configuration. This is in agreement with the conclusions of Wiberg and Fox:

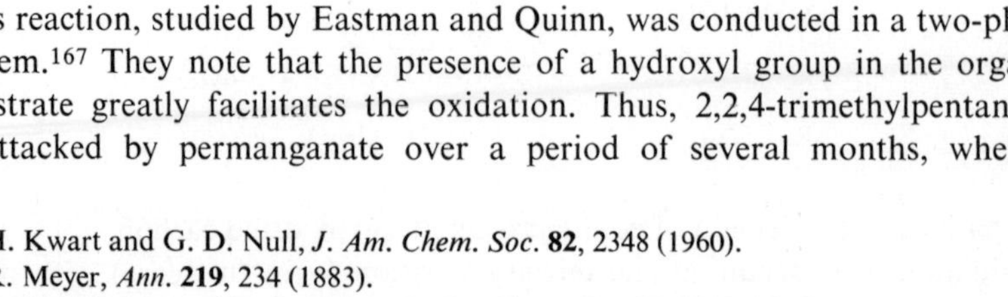

This reaction, studied by Eastman and Quinn, was conducted in a two-phase system.[167] They note that the presence of a hydroxyl group in the organic substrate greatly facilitates the oxidation. Thus, 2,2,4-trimethylpentane is unattacked by permanganate over a period of several months, whereas

[165] H. Kwart and G. D. Null, *J. Am. Chem. Soc.* **82**, 2348 (1960).
[166] R. Meyer, *Ann.* **219**, 234 (1883).
[167] R. H. Eastman and R. A. Quinn, *J. Am. Chem. Soc.* **82**, 4249 (1960),

2,4-dimethylpentan-2-ol is converted to the ditertiary glycol in 30–50% yield in 5 days.

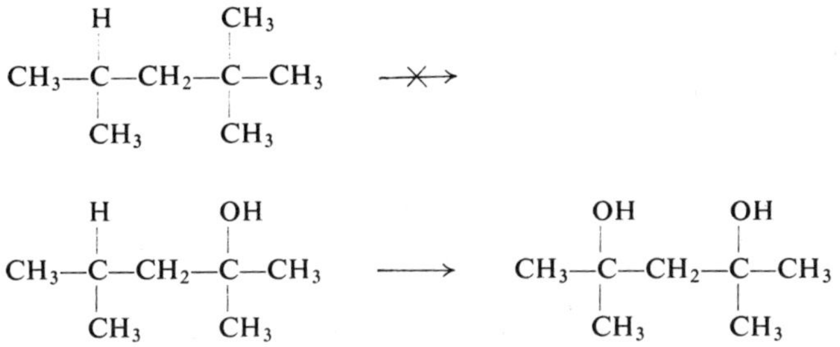

$$CH_3-\underset{\underset{CH_3}{|}}{\overset{\overset{H}{|}}{C}}-CH_2-\underset{\underset{CH_3}{|}}{\overset{\overset{CH_3}{|}}{C}}-CH_3 \quad \xrightarrow{\quad\times\quad}$$

$$CH_3-\underset{\underset{CH_3}{|}}{\overset{\overset{H}{|}}{C}}-CH_2-\underset{\underset{CH_3}{|}}{\overset{\overset{OH}{|}}{C}}-CH_3 \quad \longrightarrow \quad CH_3-\underset{\underset{CH_3}{|}}{\overset{\overset{OH}{|}}{C}}-CH_2-\underset{\underset{CH_3}{|}}{\overset{\overset{OH}{|}}{C}}-CH_3$$

The solubilizing effect of the hydroxyl group may be important here.

Alkyl groups attached to aromatic rings are oxidized more readily than the ring in most cases (Section IV,A,4). Complete oxidation to the carboxylic acid usually occurs, but some compounds containing a tertiary hydrogen can be oxidized to the corresponding tertiary alcohol in excellent yield:

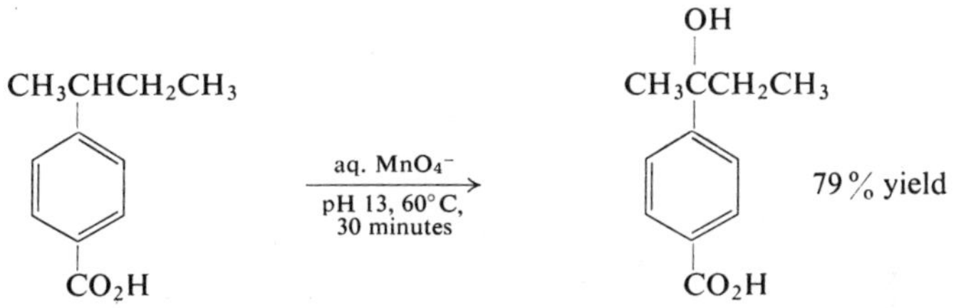

$$\text{CH}_3\text{CHCH}_2\text{CH}_3 \xrightarrow[\substack{\text{pH 13, 60°C,}\\ \text{30 minutes}}]{\text{aq. MnO}_4^-} \text{CH}_3\overset{\overset{\text{OH}}{|}}{\text{C}}\text{CH}_2\text{CH}_3 \qquad 79\% \text{ yield}$$

with benzene rings bearing CO$_2$H substituents.

Terephthalic acid and *p*-acetylbenzoic acid are minor products in this reaction. In neutral solution the yield of alcohol was much less.

The oxidation of substituted toluenes to the corresponding benzoic acid has been studied in acetic acid solution.[168, 169] Electron withdrawing groups in the ring decrease the oxidation rate, but a satisfactory mechanism is difficult to arrive at because of uncertainty as to the identity of the active oxidant. Both permanganate ion and manganese ions of lower valence seem to be involved.

The three isomeric chlorotoluenes are oxidized chiefly to the benzoic acids in water[170] or acetic acid solution but are degraded to carbon dioxide in sulfuric acid solution[169] where, presumably, the more vigorous oxidant, permanganic acid, is formed.

The greater vigor of manganese(VII) compared with chromium(VI) is

[168] C. F. Cullis and J. W. Ladbury, *J. Chem. Soc.* pp. 555, 1407, 2850 (1955).
[169] G. Speroni and R. Barchielli, *Gazz. Ital. Chim.* **71**, 765 (1941).
[170] H. T. Clarke and E. R. Taylor, *Org. Syn. Coll. Vol.* **II**, 135 (1943).

illustrated by the effect of these reagents on xylene derivatives. Both alkyl groups are oxidized by permanganate but only one by chromic acid[171]:

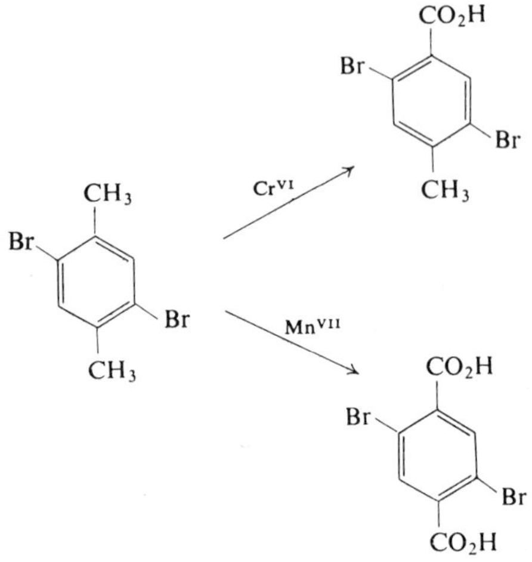

A typical procedure for the degradation of a sidechain of an aromatic compound follows.

Isonicotinic Acid.[172] Potassium permanganate (190 gm, 1.20 moles) was added in 20 gm portions to a stirred, boiling solution of 46 gm (0.50 mole) of 4-methyl-pyridine in 750 ml water. After 15 minutes of boiling the solution was filtered to remove the manganese dioxide, the latter was washed with hot water, and the combined filtrates were reduced in volume to about 275 ml. The residue was acidified with 75 ml acetic acid, cooled to 20° C, and the precipitated isonicotinic acid removed by filtration (yield, approximately 50%). Somewhat higher yields have been obtained with other aryl alkanes.

Alkylthiophenes and alkylpyridines (but not alkylfurans[173]) can usually be oxidized to the corresponding carboxyl compounds without extensive degradation of the ring occurring.[172, 174]

The autoxidation of aryl alkanes at benzylic positions can be initiated by permanganate. There seems little doubt that resonance-stabilized benzyl radicals are intermediates in these reactions but whether the initiating hydrogen

[171] B. Schultz, *Ber.* **18**, 1762 (1885).

[172] C. F. Koelsch, *J. Am. Chem. Soc.* **65**, 2460 (1943).

[173] T. Reichstein, H. R. Rosenberg, and R. Eberhardt, *Helv. Chim. Acta* **18**, 721 (1935).

[174] A. W. Singer and S. M. McElvain, *Org. Syn. Coll. Vol.* **III**, 740 (1955); G. Black, E. Depp, and B. B. Corson, *J. Org. Chem.* **14**, 14 (1949); R. L. Malan and P. M. Dean, *J. Am. Chem. Soc.* **69**, 1797 (1947).

atom abstraction is done by permanganate ion or by a manganese ion of lower valence is not known[175]:

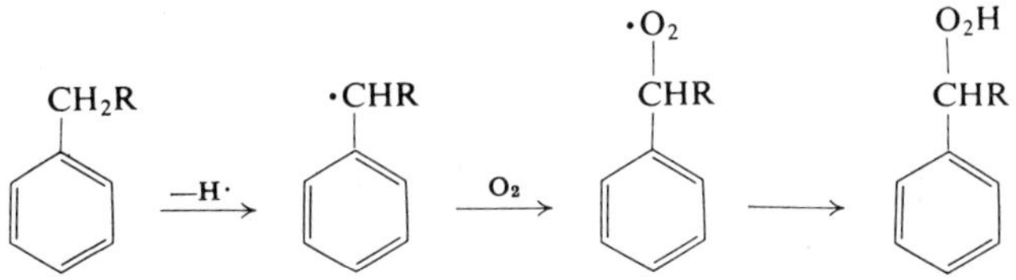

Similarly, radical coupling reactions can be brought about by permanganate; for example,

$$C_6H_5CH_2CH_2CH_3 \xrightarrow{Mn^{VII}} CH_3CH_2CH—CHCH_2CH_3$$

with C_6H_5 groups on the two central carbons.

2. ALKENES

The Baeyer test for unsaturation in organic compounds involves the decoloration of a permanganate solution. Aqueous solutions are commonly used because of their stability, but solutions in organic solvents are more convenient because of the usually greater solubility of the organic substrate. Ethanol is preferable to acetone in this connection.[176] Many negative tests with olefins were found when acetone was used.

The dihydroxylation of alkenes by aqueous permanganate is a well-known reaction but one which frequently requires carefully controlled conditions if good yields of product are to be obtained:

$$3 \ —CH{=}CH— + 2 \ MnO_4^- + 4 \ H_2O \longrightarrow 3 \ \overset{OH}{\underset{|}{—CH}}\overset{OH}{\underset{|}{—CH}}— + 2 \ MnO_2 + 2 \ OH^-$$

Cleavage of the chain to produce aldehydes, ketones, or carboxylic acids frequently occurs. In neutral or only slightly basic solution hydroxy ketones are also produced and, if the glycol is the desired product, basic conditions are to be preferred:

$$RCH{=}CR_2 \longrightarrow RCHOHC(OH)R_2$$

$$\longrightarrow RCHO \ (or \ RCO_2H) + R_2C{=}O$$

$$\longrightarrow R—\overset{O}{\overset{\|}{C}}—\overset{OH}{\underset{|}{C}}R_2$$

[175] W. A. Waters, *Trans. Faraday Soc.* **42**, 184 (1946).
[176] V. N. Ipatieff, W. W. Thompson, and H. Pines, *J. Am. Chem. Soc.* **70**, 1658 (1948).

There is no doubt that a cyclic manganese ester is formed first in this reaction.[177] The mode of addition of the hydroxyl groups is *cis* as shown by the conversion of maleic acid to *meso*-tartaric acid and fumaric acid to *dl*-tartaric acid. The use of oxygen-18 has confirmed the cyclic mechanism since oxygen transfer from permanganate to substrate occurs.[178]

At low hydroxyl ion concentrations, larger amounts of α-hydroxy ketones are formed and the following branching reaction path has been suggested.[179] Competition between ring opening by hydroxyl ion and further oxidation by permanganate accounts for the effect of basicity on the distribution of products:

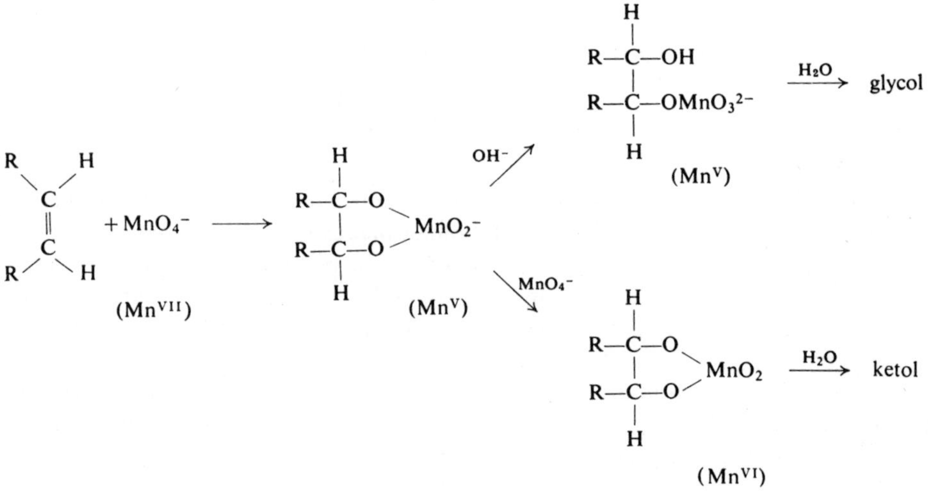

Glycol path:

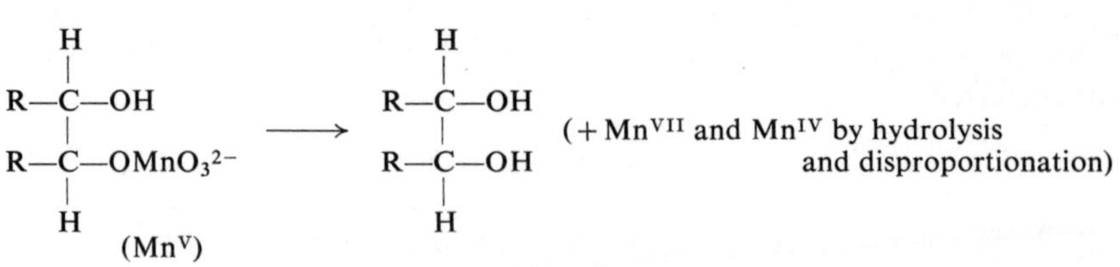

[177] G. Wagner, *J. Russ. Phys. Chem. Soc.* **27**, 219 (1895); J. Boeseken, *Rec. Trav. chim.* **41**, 199 (1922); **47**, 683 (1928).

[178] K. B. Wiberg and K. A. Saegebarth, *J. Am. Chem. Soc.* **79**, 2822 (1957).

[179] K. B. Wiberg, personal communication.

Ketol path:

$$\begin{array}{c}
\text{H} \\
\mid \\
\text{R—C—O} \\
\mid \qquad \text{MnO}_2 \\
\text{R—C—O} \\
\mid \\
\text{H} \qquad (\text{Mn}^{\text{VI}}) \\
\text{H}_2\text{O:} \\
\end{array}
\quad \longrightarrow \quad
\begin{array}{c}
\text{H} \\
\mid \\
\text{R—C—OMnO}_2^- \\
\mid \qquad\quad \text{H}_2\text{O} \\
\text{R—C=O} \\
\\
(\text{Mn}^{\text{IV}})
\end{array}
\quad \longrightarrow \quad
\begin{array}{c}
\text{H} \\
\mid \\
\text{R—C—OH} \\
\mid \qquad\quad + \text{MnO}_2 \\
\text{R—C=O} \\
\\
(\text{Mn}^{\text{IV}})
\end{array}$$

Lapworth and Mottram[180] have examined the conversion of oleic acid to dihydroxystearic acid by permanganate. They find that an almost quantitative yield can be obtained if the temperature is kept between 0 and 10° C, the aqueous permanganate concentration is kept below 1 %, the reaction time is less than 5 minutes, the concentration of the sodium or potassium salt of oleic acid is kept below 0.1 %, and there is a slight excess of base present to prevent the formation of hydroxy ketone.

The dihydroxylation of alkenes can be accomplished in acetone solution, in neutral aqueous solution, in aqueous magnesium sulfate, in alcoholic magnesium sulfate, and in aqueous base. Table III gives some examples of this reaction.[181–188]

A typical procedure for the dihydroxylation of a double bond follows.

Phenylglyceric Acid.[181] A solution of 24 gm of potassium permanganate (0.15 mole) in 80 ml of water was added to a solution of 20 gm of methyl cinnamate (0.12 mole) dissolved in 1.5 liters of ethanol at −40° C, and the solution was stirred vigorously for 4 hours. The manganese dioxide was filtered off and the filtrate concentrated to 200 ml. Solid potassium hydroxide (20 gm) was added and the mixture allowed to stand for a few hours to saponify the methyl phenylglycerate. The solution was then acidified with dilute sulfuric acid and extracted repeatedly with a total of 3 liters of ether. After removal of the ether, about 15 gm (67 %) of impure phenylglyceric acid remained as a white crystalline mass. Recrystallization gives the pure compound, m.p. 141° C.

[180] A. Lapworth and E. N. Mottram, *J. Chem. Soc.* p. 1628 (1925).
[181] C. N. Riiber, *Ber.* **48**, 823 (1915).
[182] P. D. Bartlett and A. Bavley, *J. Am. Chem. Soc.* **60**, 2416 (1938); see also H. Z. Sable, T. Adamson, B. Tolbert, and Th. Posternak, *Helv. Chim. Acta* **46**, 1157 (1963).
[183] M. F. Clarke and L. N. Owen, *J. Chem. Soc.* p. 315 (1949).
[184] E. M. Stoddard, *J. Chem. Soc.* p. 1874 (1931).
[185] G. Wagner, *Ber.* **21**, 1230, 3347 (1888).
[186] E. J. Witzemann, W. L. Evans, H. Hass, and E. F. Schroeder, *Org. Syn. Coll. Vol.* **II**, 307 (1943).
[187] J. C. Sheean and B. M. Bloom, *J. Am. Chem. Soc.* **74**, 3825 (1952).
[188] C. Harries and X. Pappos, *Ber.* **34**, 2979 (1901).

TABLE III

Dihydroxylation of Alkenes by Permanganate

Reactant	Product	Conditions	Yield (%)	Reference
1,2-Dimethylcyclopentene	cis-1,2-Dimethylcyclopentane-1,2-diol	Aq acetone	45	182
Cyclohexene	cis-Cyclohexane-1,2-diol	Aq ethanol	33	183
Cinnamic acid	Benzaldehyde	Aq neutral soln, 100° C	87	184
	Phenylglyceric acid		13	
Methyl cinnamate	Phenylglyceric acid	Aq ethanol, −40° C	67	181
3-Methyl-1-butene	3-Methylbutane-1,2-diol	Aq neutral soln	50	185
Acrolein diethyl acetal	Glyceraldehyde diethyl acetal	Aq soln, 5° C	67	186
Oleic acid	Dihydroxystearic acid	Dil aq soln, 0–10° C	100	180
2,5-Dimethoxy-2,5-dihydrofuran	2,5-Dimethoxy-3,4-dihydroxy-2,5-dihydrofuran	Aq ethanol, MgSO$_4$, 0° C	37	187
Mesityl oxide	2-Methylpentane-2,3-diol-4-one	Acetone, 20–25° C	60	188

Styrene can be converted to phenylglyoxylic acid in 55–69% yield by alkaline permanganate,[189] with the hydroxy ketone the probable intermediate:

$$C_6H_5CH{=}CH_2 \longrightarrow C_6H_5\overset{\overset{\displaystyle O}{\|}}{C}{-}CO_2H$$

Epoxidation of certain alkenes has been brought about by the use of permanganate in acetic acid solution:

Cleavage to carboxylic acids or ketones always competes with the reactions above—glycol, ketol, and epoxide formation—and an excess of oxidant or a higher temperature will almost always result in cleavage.[190] One of the few alkenes that is inert to permanganate is 1,1-dineopentylethylene,

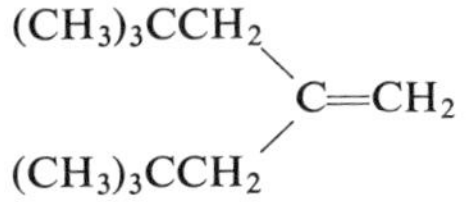

It can be recovered after prolonged treatment with hot concentrated alkaline permanganate.[191]

Electron-withdrawing groups on an alkene appear to facilitate its oxidation since fluoro-olefins suffer rapid degradation and cleavage.[192] Oxidation of a cyanoalkene in the steroid series produces a good yield of ketol[193]:

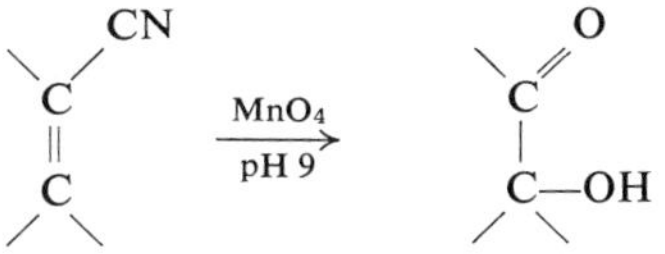

A curious result is observed in the oxidation of a styrene derivative. The

[189] C. D. Hurd, R. W. McNamee, and F. O. Green, *J. Am. Chem. Soc.* **61**, 2979 (1939).

[190] P. H. Begemann, J. G. Keppler, and H. A. Boekenoogen, *Rec. Trav. Chim.* **69**, 439 (1950); J. G. Keppler, *Rev. Trav. Chim.* **76**, 49 (1957); A. T. James and J. Webb, *Biochem. J.* **66**, 515 (1957); A. T. Blomquist and C. G. Bottomley, *J. Am. Chem. Soc.* **87**, 86 (1965).

[191] P. D. Bartlett, G. L. Fraser, and R. B. Woodward, *J. Am. Chem. Soc.* **63**, 495 (1941).

[192] J. Burdon and J. C. Tatlow, *J. Appl. Chem.* (*London*) **8**, 293 (1958); see also H. Suzuki, *Bull. Chem. Soc. Japan* **33**, 406 (1960).

[193] R. Tull, R. E. Jones, S. A. Robinson, and M. Tishler, *J. Am. Chem. Soc.* **77**, 196 (1955).

cleavage produces a product with a two carbon side chain in addition to the expected cleavage product[194]:

$$ArCH{=}CHCH_2OCH_3 \xrightarrow{Mn^{VII}} ArCHO + ArCH_2CHO$$

The second product probably results from a condensation between the initially produced pair of aldehydes, followed by a second cleavage, decarboxylation, vinyl ether hydrolysis, and ketonization:

$$ArCHO + CH_3OCH_2CHO \longrightarrow ArCH{=}\underset{\underset{OCH_3}{|}}{C}{-}CHO \xrightarrow{oxidation} ArCH{=}\underset{\underset{OCH_3}{|}}{C}{-}CO_2H \xrightarrow{-CO_2}$$

$$ArCH{=}CHOCH_3 \xrightarrow{H_2O} ArCH{=}CHOH \longrightarrow ArCH_2CHO$$

Oxidation of alkenes takes place smoothly with periodate and catalytic amounts of permanganate in neutral solution. The permanganate is the active oxidant and is regenerated continuously by the periodate. Lemieux and von Rudloff[195–197] have shown that oleic acid is cleaved to give a quantitative yield of azelaic and pelargonic acids. Compounds containing isopropylidene groups likewise give a quantitative yield of acetone. Compounds containing terminal methylenes give a high, but not quantitative, yield of formaldehyde:

$$RCH{=}CHR \xrightarrow[IO_4^-]{MnO_4^-} 2\,RCO_2H$$

$$(CH_3)_2C{=}CHR \xrightarrow[IO_4^-]{MnO_4^-} (CH_3)_2C{=}O + RCO_2H$$

$$RCH{=}CH_2 \xrightarrow[IO_4^-]{MnO_4^-} RCO_2H + CH_2O$$

The periodate–permanganate cleavage of alkenes is finding wide application as a means of determining the position of double bonds in unsaturated compounds.[198]

3. ALKYNES

Carbon–carbon triple bonds are usually oxidized by permanganate to form diketo or cleavage products but little is known about the mechanism or the

[194] L. Bert, *Compt. Rend. Acad. Sci.* **215**, 276 (1942).
[195] R. U. Lemieux and E. von Rudloff, *Can. J. Chem.* **33**, 1701, 1710 (1955).
[196] E. von Rudloff, *Can. J. Chem.* **33**, 1714 (1955).
[197] E. von Rudloff, *Can. J. Chem.* **34**, 1413 (1956).
[198] A. P. Tulloch and G. A. Ledingham, *Can. J. Microbiol.* **6**, 625 (1960); F. D. Gunstone and P. J. Sykes, *J. Chem. Soc.* p. 3058 (1962); E. von Rudloff, *J. Am. Oil Chemists Soc.* **33**, 126 (1956).

optimum reaction conditions. Electrophiles often react more slowly with alkynes than alkenes and this appears to be so for permanganate.

The following reaction occurs in very high yield (92–96%)[199]:

$$CH_3(CH_2)_7C\equiv C(CH_2)_7CO_2H \xrightarrow[\text{pH 7·5}]{\text{aq. MnO}_4^-} CH_3(CH_2)_7\overset{\displaystyle O}{\overset{\displaystyle \|}{C}}-\overset{\displaystyle O}{\overset{\displaystyle \|}{C}}(CH_2)_7CO_2H$$

4. AROMATIC RINGS

Aromatic compounds with electron-donating groups in the ring are subject to ring rupture by permanganate. Phenols and anilines are very rapidly degraded to carbon dioxide whereas xylenes, toluene, and benzene, itself, are progressively more stable. Even benzene is degraded slowly by boiling alkaline permanganate.[200] The stabilizing effect of an electron-withdrawing group such as nitro is illustrated by the pattern of oxidation of 1-nitronaphthalene:

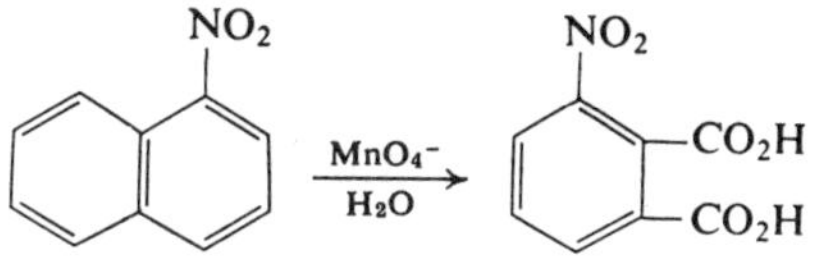

The destabilizing effect of an amino or hydroxyl group is illustrated by the oxidation of 1-naphthylamine:

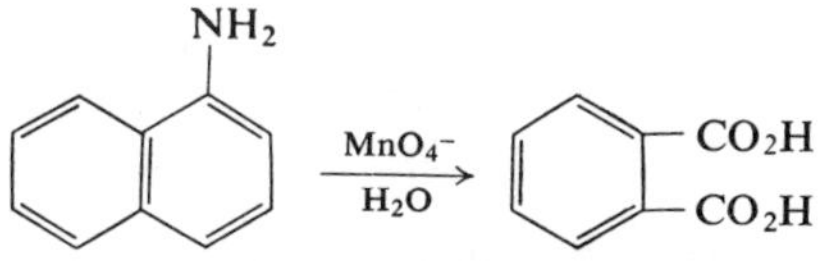

Other condensed polynuclear hydrocarbons, such as pyrene and naphthacene, are degraded by alkaline permanganate to various carboxylic acids. Triphenylene forms mellitic acid[200]:

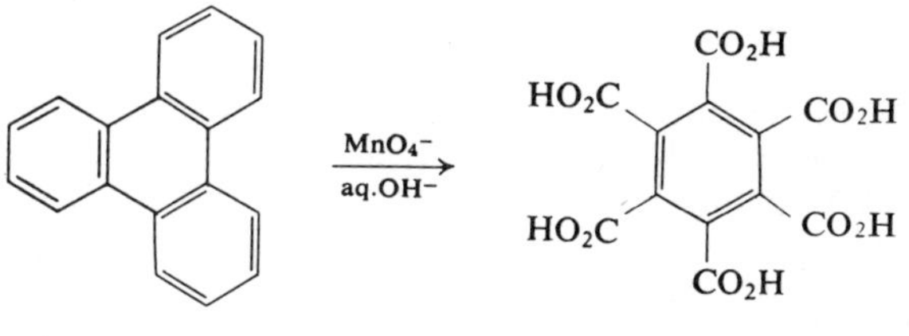

B. ALCOHOLS

Primary and secondary alcohols are oxidized rapidly by permanganate in basic solution, whereas tertiary alcohols are stable unless extreme conditions

[199] N. A. Khan and M. S. Newman, *J. Org. Chem.* **17**, 1063 (1952).
[200] J. J. Ward, W. R. Kirner, and H. C. Howard, *J. Am. Chem. Soc.* **67**, 246 (1945).

are used to degrade the molecule. The subsequent discussion, then, applies only to primary and secondary alcohols.

In neutral and mildly acidic solution, alcohols are much more stable to permanganate ion than in basic solution.[201,202] The faster oxidation rate in more concentrated acid (10–30% sulfuric acid) is probably due to protonation of the oxidant, although induced oxidation involving manganese(III) and (IV) may be important.[203] The base catalysis, however, is clearly due to the ionization of the alcohol[204,205]:

$$R_2CHOH + OH^- \rightleftharpoons R_2CHO^- + H_2O$$

$$R_2CHO^- \xrightarrow{Mn^{VII}} R_2C{=}O$$

Figure 2 shows the variation of rate with acidity for the permanganate

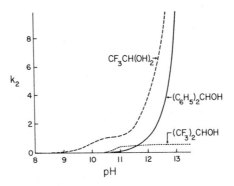

FIG. 2. Rate of the permanganate oxidation of benzhydrol, hexafluoro-2-propanol and fluoral hydrate as a function of pH.

oxidation of benzhydrol, $(C_6H_5)_2CHOH$,[204] fluoral hydrate, $CF_3CH(OH)_2$,[236] and hexafluoro-2-propanol, $(CF_3)_2CHOH$.[206]

[201] In 1 N sulfuric acid, however, ethanol and 1-propanol are oxidized quantitatively to acetic and propionic acids in 24 hours at room temperature. I. M. Kolthoff and R. Belcher, "Volumetric Analysis," Vol. III, p. 118. Wiley (Interscience), New York, 1957.

[202] Secondary alcohols seems to be more readily oxidized in acid solution than do primary alcohols. F. O. Ritter, *J. Chem. Educ.* **30**, 395 (1953).

[203] Induced oxidation of primary and secondary alcohols occurs in acid. These compounds are oxidized by mixtures of permanganate and hydrogen peroxide in acid solution very much more rapidly than by these reagents separately. J. H. Merz, G. Stafford, and W. A. Waters, *J. Chem. Soc.* p. 638 (1951).

[204] R. Stewart, *J. Am. Chem. Soc.* **79**, 3057 (1957).

[205] R. Stewart and R. Van der Linden, *Discussions Faraday Soc.* p. 211 (1960).

[206] R. Stewart and R. Van der Linden, *Tetrahedron Letters* **2**, 28 (1960).

The midpoint of the oxidation curve for the fluoro alcohol corresponds to the pK_a for its ionization ($pK_a = 10.0$). Benzhydrol, being a much weaker acid, is incompletely ionized in the accessible region of the pH scale.

Secondary alcohols give ketones on oxidation, and if these can enolize they will be partially cleaved by alkaline permanganate (Section IV,C,1). Ketones that do not enolize are stable to alkaline permanganate, and excellent yields of products may be obtained.

Primary alcohols give aldehydes, and these too may be partly degraded via their enol forms. Those aldehydes which do not enolize are subject to further oxidation to the carboxylic acid:

$$RCH_2CH_2OH \xrightarrow[OH^-]{Mn^{VII}} RCH_2CHO \xrightarrow[Mn^{VII}]{OH^-} RCH{=}CHOH \xrightarrow{Mn^{VII}} RCO_2H + CO_2$$

$$\searrow RCH_2CO_2H$$

It is interesting to compare the relative rates of permanganate oxidation of alcohols and aldehydes. Alcohols are oxidized very slowly in neutral solution but rapidly in base, with the rate in most cases being proportional to the hydroxyl ion concentration[204, 205]:

$$v = k[R_2CHOH][MnO_4^-][OH^-]$$

Aldehydes, on the other hand, are oxidized at reasonable rates even in neutral solution and, although the rate increases, in most cases, as the solution is made basic, it does so less rapidly than for alcohols; that is, the rate is proportional to a smaller power of the hydroxyl ion concentration (Section IV,C,2). Accordingly, aldehydes cannot be isolated as products of primary alcohol oxidation in the neutral or mildly basic region although this may be possible in strongly basic solution.

The mechanism of the alcohol–permanganate reaction has been shown by Stewart *et al.* to involve hydrogen abstraction, either as hydride ion or as a hydrogen atom, by the permanganate ion from the anion of the alcohol.

$$R_2CHO^- + MnO_4^- \longrightarrow R_2C{=}O + HMnO_4^{2-}$$

$$\searrow R_2C{-}O^- + HMnO_4^-$$

The rate-controlling step is clearly between the alkoxide ion and the permanganate ion, as shown by the reaction kinetics, and it involves a scission of the carbon–hydrogen bond as shown by the presence of a substantial kinetic isotope effect for the oxidation of R_2CDOH. Indeed, with highly fluorinated alcohols such as $C_6H_5CDOHCF_3$[206] and $(CF_3)_2CDOH$[207] isotope effects of 16:1 and 19:1, respectively, are found at 25° C. These are very much larger than those found in most reactions and cannot be attributed simply to loss of the stretching modes in the transition state. It is possible that changes in the bending vibrations occur on going from initial state to transition state, but why adjacent fluorine atoms should cause this is not clear.

Hydride ion abstraction by permanganate from the alkoxide ion, R_2CHO^-, would at first glance appear to be the most attractive mechanism for the rate-controlling step. However, substituting electron-donating or electron-withdrawing groups in the phenyl group of phenyltrifluoromethylcarbinol has only a small effect *on the rate-controlling step* and this seems unlikely if hydride is being expelled in the process.[208] [It should be made clear that the over-all oxidation rate may be quite sensitive to substitution in the alcohol. This effect, however, is chiefly in the pre-equilibrium ionization step. That is, $(CF_3)_2CHOH$ is oxidized much more rapidly than $C_6H_5CHOHCF_3$ at pH 9 but only because the anion of the former is present in larger concentration than that of the latter. The effect is actually in the reverse order at pH 13 where ionization is complete (see Fig. 2).]

Hydrogen atom abstraction from alkoxide ion would produce the radical anion, $R_2\overset{.}{C}-O^-$, which would be subject to further rapid oxidation to the ketone:

$$R_2\overset{.}{C}-O^- \xrightarrow{\text{Mn}^{\text{VII}}} R_2C{=}O$$

Supposing hydrogen abstraction occurs, the greater ease of abstraction from the alkoxide ion than from the neutral alcohol is due to the relatively greater stability of the radical anion, $R_2\overset{.}{C}-O^-$, compared with the neutral ketyl, $R_2\overset{.}{C}-OH$.[209] Ketyls are stronger acids than the corresponding alcohol by a factor of possibly 10^6; this means that if the transition states for the permanganate oxidations resemble the products, the conversion of alkoxide to radical anion will be very much faster than the conversion of alcohol to ketyl. The problem of distinguishing hydride ion and hydrogen atom abstraction in these systems has been examined by Kurz.[209a]

From the preparative point of view permanganate is a readily available and

[207] M. M. Mocek and R. Stewart, unpublished results.

[208] Until reliable values of the ionization constants of ordinary alcohols, such as benzhydrol, are known it is not possible to calculate the rate of the reaction between their anions and permanganate. If benzhydrol. $(C_6H_5)_2CHOH$, has a pK_a of 15 or higher, one can show that the reaction between $(C_6H_5)_2CHO^-$ and MnO_4^- is faster by a factor of at least 100

$$\overset{O^-}{\underset{|}{}}$$

than the reaction between $C_6H_5CHCF_3$ and MnO_4^-.

[209] G. Porter and F. Wilkinson, *Trans. Faraday Soc.* **57**, 1686 (1961).

[209a] J. L. Kurz, *J. Am. Chem. Soc.* **86**, 2229 (1964).

TABLE IV

OXIDATION OF PRIMARY AND SECONDARY ALCOHOLS WITH PERMANGANATE

Reactant	Product	Conditions	Yield (%)	Reference
C₆H₅OCH₂CH₂CH₂OH	C₆H₅OCH₂CH₂CO₂H	Aq MgSO₄, 15–25° C	45	212
C₆H₅C(=O)NHC(CH₃)₂CH₂OH	C₆H₅C(=O)NH(CH₃)₂CO₂H	Aq NaOH, 40° C	92	213
C₂H₅CH(CH₂)₄CH₂OH (CH₃)	C₂H₅CH(CH₂)₄CO₂H (CH₃)	Aq H₂SO₄, 25° C	66	214
CH₃(CH₂)₃CHCH₂OH (C₂H₅)	CH₃(CH₂)₃CHCO₂H (C₂H₅)	Aq NaOH, 20–25° C	74	210
n-C₄H₉CHOHC₆H₅	n-C₄H₉C(=O)C₆H₅	Glacial HOAc, 25–30° C	96	211
iso-C₃H₇-CHOHC₆H₅	iso-C₃H₇-C(=O)C₆H₅	Glacial HOAc, 25–30° C	71	211
t-C₄H₉CHOHC₆H₅	t-C₄H₉C(=O)C₆H₅	Glacial HOAc, 25–30° C	34[a]	211
C₆H₅CHOHCO₂H	C₆H₅CCO₂H	Aq NaOH[b]	50–72	215, 216
(C₆H₅)₂CHOH	(C₆H₅)₂C=O	Aq NaOH	65	204

[a] Benzaldehyde is the major product in this case.   [b] Benzaldehyde is the major product in acid solution.

easily used reagent for the conversion of primary alcohols to carboxylic acids and secondary alcohols to ketones (Table IV).[210-216]

A typical procedure for the oxidation of a primary alcohol to a carboxylic acid follows.

2-*Ethylhexanoic Acid*.[210] A solution of 340 gm (2.15 moles) of potassium permanganate dissolved in 3 liters water was added with stirring to a mixture of 130 gm (1.0 mole) of 2-ethylhexanol-1 and 30 gm of sodium hydroxide dispersed in 250 ml of water. After 12 hours of stirring, the mixture was acidified with sulfuric acid, sodium bisulfite was added to dissolve the manganese dioxide formed, and the solution was extracted with ether. Evaporation of the ether layer gave 107 gm (74%) of 2-ethylhexanoic acid. (The reaction times can usually be sharply reduced from that given in this procedure without greatly affecting the yield of product.)

A typical procedure for the oxidation of a secondary alcohol to a ketone follows.

Isobutyrophenone.[211] A solution of 14.2 gm (0.09 mole) of potassium permanganate dissolved in 400 ml of glacial acetic acid and 125 ml of water was added dropwise to a stirred solution of 21.4 gm of phenylisopropylcarbinol (0.14 mole) over a period of 3 hours with the temperature being maintained at 25–30° C. The reaction mixture was then steam distilled, and from the distillate an oil layer consisting of 14.6 gm (71%) of isobutyrophenone was obtained. (Basic conditions similar to those used in the previous procedure can also be used to oxidize secondary alcohols to ketones.)

C. ALDEHYDES AND KETONES

1. ALIPHATIC ALDEHYDES AND KETONES

Aliphatic aldehydes are oxidized readily by permanganate in acid, neutral, and basic solution, whereas ketones react rapidly only in alkali or concentrated acid. The ketone oxidations result, of necessity, in the molecule being degraded

[210] J. Kenyon and B. C. Platt, *J. Chem. Soc.* p. 633 (1939).
[211] H. A. Neidig, D. L. Funck, R. Uhrich, R. Baker, and W. Kreiser, *J. Am. Chem. Soc.* **72**, 4617 (1950).
[212] S. G. Powell, *J. Am. Chem. Soc.* **45**, 2707 (1923).
[213] J. H. Billman and E. E. Parker, *J. Am. Chem. Soc.* **66**, 538 (1944).
[214] L. Crombie and S. H. Harper, *J. Chem. Soc.* p. 2685 (1950).
[215] S. F. Acree, *Am. Chem. J.* **50**, 389 (1913).
[216] C. D. Hurd and R. W. McNamee, *Org. Syn. Coll. Vol.* **I**, 244 (1941).

to smaller fragments, and there seems little doubt that enolization precedes carbon–carbon bond cleavage:

$$\underset{\substack{\parallel \\ \text{O}}}{\text{RCCHR}_2} \xrightarrow{\text{OH}^-} \underset{\substack{| \\ \text{OH}}}{\text{RC}=\text{CR}_2} \xrightarrow{\text{Mn}^{\text{VII}}} \text{RCO}_2\text{H} + \text{R}_2\text{C}=\text{O}$$

In one experiment, Drummond and Waters showed that acetone in cold alkaline solution reduced 12.1 equivalents of permanganate in 40 minutes, although simple cleavage to acetic acid and carbon dioxide would require only 8 equivalents.[190] (Conversion to oxalate and carbon dioxide would require 14 equivalents and to carbon dioxide, alone, 16.) Considerable quantities of oxalate are probably formed via acetaldehyde enol as intermediate. Aliphatic ketones, in fact, may suffer stepwise degradation via successive enol intermediates.[217] Phenyl alkyl ketones, such as acetophenone, are degraded to benzoic acids and carbon dioxide,[218] although phenylglyoxylic acids can be isolated as intermediates in basic solution.[219] In fact, tolylglyoxylic acid can be obtained in 70 % yield by the careful oxidation of *p*-methylacetophenone by alkaline permanganate.[219]

Aliphatic aldehydes are oxidized to carboxylic acids in neutral solution, but in alkali or concentrated acid, competition between this reaction and carbon–carbon bond fission occurs. The latter undoubtedly proceeds via cleavage of the enol.

TABLE V

OXIDATION OF ALDEHYDES TO CORRESPONDING CARBOXYLIC ACID WITH PERMANGANATE

Aldehyde	Conditions	Yield (%)	Reference
(C$_6$H$_5$)$_2$CCHO | CH$_3$	Aq Na$_2$CO$_3$	55	221
CH$_3$(CH$_2$)$_3$CHCHO | C$_2$H$_5$	Aq NaOH	78	210
CH$_3$(CH$_2$)$_5$CHO	Aq H$_2$SO$_4$, T < 20° C	75	222
3,4-CH$_2$O$_2$C$_6$H$_3$CHO	Aq soln, 70–80° C	90	223

[217] A. Y. Drummond and W. A. Waters, *J. Chem. Soc.* p. 435 (1953).
[218] C. F. Koelsch, *Org. Syn. Coll. Vol.* **III**, 791 (1955).
[219] A. Claus and W. Neukranz, *J. Prakt. Chem.* [2] **44**, 77 (1891).

It can be assumed that the direct oxidation of aliphatic aldehydes to carboxylic acids, which occurs without carbon–carbon bond cleavage, follows the
same reaction path as the oxidation of aromatic aldehydes for which enolization is impossible. The oxidation of these compounds is discussed in the next
section. Trimethylacetaldehyde, which cannot enolize, has an oxidation
pattern similar to benzaldehyde but is oxidized approximately ten times as
fast.[220] Table V gives representative yields of carboxylic acids formed by
aldehyde oxidation.[221–223]

2. AROMATIC ALDEHYDES

The course of the permanganate oxidation of aromatic aldehydes has been
studied by Tronov,[224] by Tompkins,[225] and by Wiberg and Stewart.[226]
Figure 3 shows the rate of permanganate oxidation of benzaldehyde and

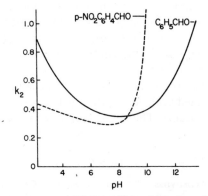

FIG. 3. Rate of the permanganate oxidation of benzaldehyde and p-nitrobenzaldehyde as
a function of pH.

p-nitrobenzaldehyde as a function of the pH of the solution. The effect of both
structure of the aldehyde and acidity of the medium is apparent.

The oxidation in alkaline solution is strongly accelerated by electron withdrawing groups as revealed by the Hammett rho value of $+1.83$ for the reaction
at pH 12.6:

$$ArCHO + 2\ MnO_4^- + 3\ OH^- \rightarrow ArCO_2^- + 2\ MnO_4^{2-} + 2\ H_2O$$

[220] D. G. Fleming and R. Stewart, unpublished results.
[221] D. E. Bateman and C. S. Marvel, *J. Am. Chem. Soc.* **49**, 2914 (1927).
[222] J. R. Ruhoff, *Org. Syn. Coll. Vol.* **II**, 315 (1943).
[223] R. L. Shriner and E. C. Kleiderer, *Org. Syn. Coll. Vol.* **II**, 538 (1943).
[224] B. V. Tronov, *J. Russ. Phys. Chem. Soc.* **59**, 1155 (1927).
[225] F. C. Tompkins, *Trans. Faraday Soc.* **39**, 280 (1943).
[226] K. B. Wiberg and R. Stewart, *J. Am. Chem. Soc.* **77**, 1786 (1955).

Although the reaction of most aromatic aldehydes is base catalyzed, the reaction shows only a fractional dependence on the hydroxyl ion concentration. It seems likely that the anion of the hydrate of the aldehyde,

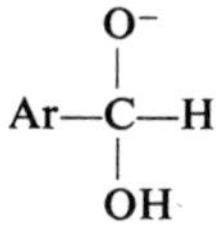

$$\begin{array}{c} O^- \\ | \\ Ar-C-H \\ | \\ OH \end{array}$$

or the corresponding radical,

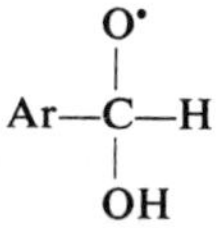

$$\begin{array}{c} O^{\bullet} \\ | \\ Ar-C-H \\ | \\ OH \end{array}$$

is involved in the oxidation, but further work is required to elucidate the mechanism completely.

It is interesting that manganate oxidizes aromatic aldehydes at approximately the same rate as does permanganate. Manganate oxidizes the vast majority of compounds at a much slower rate than does permanganate.

In neutral and acid solution, the effect of substituents is fairly small and in the opposite direction to that found in alkaline solution. Wiberg and Stewart showed that the oxidation in neutral solution is accompanied by transfer of oxygen from permanganate to the substrate, i.e., when permanganate–O^{18} was used as the oxidant, the benzoic acid isolated from the reaction contained oxygen-18. The oxidation of deuteriated aldehydes, ArCDO, produced substantial isotope effects and it is clear that the C—H bond is cleaved in the rate-controlling step. There is also general acid catalysis observed when the reaction is conducted in phosphate and carbonate buffers. These facts are all accomodated by the following mechanism involving a manganese ester intermediate [226]:

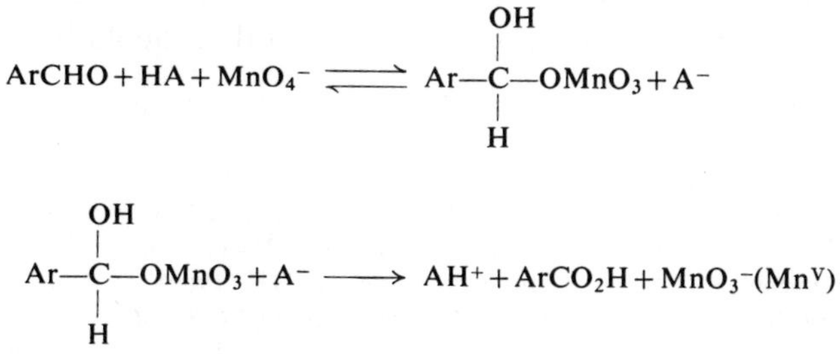

$$ArCHO + HA + MnO_4^- \rightleftharpoons \begin{array}{c} OH \\ | \\ Ar-C-OMnO_3 \\ | \\ H \end{array} + A^-$$

$$\begin{array}{c} OH \\ | \\ Ar-C-OMnO_3 \\ | \\ H \end{array} + A^- \longrightarrow AH^+ + ArCO_2H + MnO_3^- (Mn^V)$$

$$3\ Mn^V \xrightarrow{\text{fast}} 2\ Mn^{IV} + Mn^{VII}$$

It might be argued that electron-withdrawing substituents should facilitate both the pre-equilibrium step and the rate-controlling step and, since these groups clearly decrease the observed oxidation rate, the following mechanism should also be considered:

$$ArC\overset{O}{\underset{H}{\diagup}} + OMnO_3^- + HA \longrightarrow \left[ArC\overset{O}{\diagup}\cdots O\cdots MnO_3^- \cdots HA \right] \longrightarrow$$

$$ArCO_2H + MnO_3^- + HA$$

Hydrogen bonding to the permanganate anion by an acid molecule would increase the former's electron-withdrawing character. Saturated groups, as in alcohols, would not be attacked by permanganate because of the difficulties of bonding to a tetracoordinated carbon atom as compared with the tricoordinated carbon of aldehydes.

3. FORMIC ACID

The oxidation of formic acid to carbon dioxide by permanganate has received considerable study.[227–232] The reaction rate is almost independent of pH in solutions more basic than pH 5, and formate ion is clearly the reactant[233]:

$$3\,HCO_2^- + 2\,MnO_4^- + 5\,H^+ \;\rightarrow\; 3\,CO_2 + 2\,MnO_2 + 4\,H_2O$$

or

$$3\,HCO_2^- + 2\,MnO_4^- + OH^- \;\rightarrow\; 3\,CO_3^{2-} + 2\,MnO_2 + 2\,H_2O$$

Below this point the rate drops off and it is easy to show that the rate follows the ionization curve of formic acid. The rate continues to decrease with added acid until, when sulfuric acid is used, the solution is approximately 20% in sulfuric acid. Beyond this point the rate rises again and this has been attributed to protonation of the permanganate ion.[207] There are thus three, and possibly four, different regions of the acid–base spectrum that should be considered.

[227] J. Holluta, Z. Physik. Chem. (Leipzig) **102**, 32, 276 (1922); **106**, 276, 324 (1923); **113**, 464 (1924).

[228] D. R. Mann and F. C. Tompkins, Trans. Faraday Soc. **37**, 201 (1941).

[229] L. M. Hill and F. C. Tompkins, Trans. Roy. Soc. S. Africa **29**, 309 (1942); **30**, 59 (1943).

[230] K. B. Wiberg and R. Stewart, J. Am. Chem. Soc. **78**, 1214 (1956).

[231] S. M. Taylor and J. Halpern, J. Am. Chem. Soc. **81**, 2933 (1959).

[232] H. Aebi, W. Buser, and Ch. Lüthi, Helv. Chim. Acta **39**, 944 (1956).

[233] Formate ion reacts rapidly enough with permanganate that it can be determined by direct titration in hot solution. F. Oberhauser and W. Hensinger, Z. Angew. Chem. **47**, 791 (1934).

Above pH 5 the reaction clearly is between the two anions, formate and permanganate. There is a substantial isotope effect (~ 7 at $25°$ C)[230-232] for the oxidation of DCO_2^-, a substantial solvent isotope effect when D_2O is used ($k_{H_2O}/k_{D_2O} = 0.38$),[231] and when permanganate–O^{18} is used the carbon dioxide that is formed is found to contain considerable amounts of oxygen-18.[230]

In view of the arguments presented later about the oxidation of the cobalt(III)–formate complex, the following one-equivalent mechanism can be considered [compare with the hydrogen abstraction mechanism suggested for alkoxide ions (Section IV,B) and aldehyde hydrates (Section IV,C,4)]:

$$HCO_2^- + MnO_4^- \longrightarrow CO_2^{\cdot-} + HMnO_4^- \qquad \text{rate controlling}$$

$$CO_2^{\cdot-} \xrightarrow[\text{or Mn}^{VI}]{\text{Mn}^{VII}} CO_2 \qquad \text{fast}$$

The oxygen transfer could result from the combination of the initially formed radical pair, followed by hydrolysis to carbonate and manganese(V):

$$CO_2^{\cdot-} + HMnO_4^- \rightarrow O_2C\text{—}OMnO_3H^{2-} \rightarrow CO_3^{2-} + Mn^V$$

The reaction between unionized formic acid and permanganate ion is very slow and becomes the dominant path in a very narrow acidity range, near 20% sulfuric acid. It is interesting to note that both the solvent isotope effect (when D_2O is used) and the reactant isotope effect (when DCO_2H is used) are small for this path.[231]

The increased reaction rate beyond 20% sulfuric acid is probably due to formation of the stronger oxidant, permanganic acid, since the reaction rate becomes proportional to h_- in this region[207]:

$$H^+ + MnO_4^- \rightleftharpoons HMnO_4$$

$$HMnO_4 + HCO_2H \rightarrow \text{products}$$

Above 50% sulfuric acid the reaction rate undergoes a still more rapid increase and this may be due to formation of MnO_3^+. Both this reaction and the one involving $HMnO_4$ exhibit substantial reactant isotope effects.[207]

Certain transition metal ions have interesting effects on the formate–permanganate reaction. Ferric ion, but not silver, cupric, or cobaltous ions, catalyzes the reaction markedly, and formate, when complexed to cobalt(III), appears to be oxidized by two different paths. Candlin and Halpern[234] have shown that in one of these paths the oxidation of formate to CO_2 is accomplished by permanganate *and* cobalt(III) and thus each is a one-equivalent step. In the presence of excess permanganate both oxidation steps are brought about by permanganate ion. The first step is probably the abstraction of a

[234] J. P. Candlin and J. Halpern, *J. Am. Chem. Soc.* **85**, 2518 (1963).

hydrogen atom of the cobalt–formate complex by permanganate (an isotope effect of 10 is found at 25° C):

$$(NH_3)_5Co^{III}—O_2CH + MnO_4^- \rightarrow (NH_3)_5Co^{III}—CO_2\cdot + HMnO_4^-$$

The radical complex can then either decompose to CO_2 and cobalt(II) or react with a second permanganate ion to form $(NH_3)_5Co^{III}H_2O, CO_2$, and Mn^{VI}.

4. ALDEHYDE HYDRATES

Those aldehydes that are extensively hydrated in aqueous solution, such as formaldehyde and the trihaloacetaldehydes, have a somewhat different oxidation pattern than those of ordinary aldehydes. In basic solution the anions,

$$\overset{\displaystyle O^-}{\underset{\displaystyle OH}{R—\overset{|}{\underset{|}{C}}—H}}$$

are generated and these are rapidly oxidized just as are the anions of alcohols (Section IV,B). Formaldehyde is also oxidized in neutral solution but more

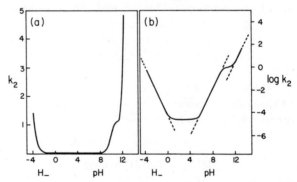

FIG. 4. Rate of the permanganate oxidation of fluoral hydrate as a function of pH: (a) k_2 versus pH; (b) $\log k_2$ versus pH.

slowly,[235] and this may involve the unhydrated molecule, which is in equilibrium with the hydrate. Fluoral, CF_3CHO, on the other hand, is oxidized extremely slowly in neutral solution and this reflects the stability of the hydrate. Chloral, CCl_3CHO, is also oxidized slowly in neutral solution and rapidly in base but in this case the oxidation process actually involves formate ion formed from the rapid hydrolysis of chloral:

$$CCl_3CH(OH)_2 + OH^- \rightarrow HCO_2^- + CHCl_3 + H_2O$$

$$3\,HCO_2^- + 2\,MnO_4^- + H_2O \rightarrow 3\,CO_2 + 2\,MnO_2 + 5\,OH^-$$

[235] J. Holluta and A. Mutschin, Z. Physik. Chem. (Leipzig) **150**, 381 (1930).

Stewart and Mocek[236] have studied the permanganate–fluoral oxidation over a very wide range of acidities with the results shown in Fig. 4. There are clearly four different reaction paths for the oxidation. Each is a bimolecular reaction between a fluoral and a manganese(VII) species and each dominates a certain region of the acid–base spectrum. The principal reactants are:

$$\text{(a) above pH 12} \qquad CF_3-\overset{\displaystyle O^-}{\underset{\displaystyle O_-}{C}}-H + MnO_4^-$$

$$\text{(b) pH 6–11} \qquad CF_3-\overset{\displaystyle O^-}{\underset{\displaystyle OH}{C}}-H + MnO_4^-$$

$$\text{(c) pH 1–4} \qquad CF_3-\overset{\displaystyle OH}{\underset{\displaystyle OH}{C}}-H + MnO_4^-$$

$$\text{(d) } H_- \text{ 0 to } -4 \qquad CF_3-\overset{\displaystyle OH}{\underset{\displaystyle OH}{C}}-H + HMnO_4$$

Since the isotope effects for the oxidation of $CF_3CD(OH)_2$ are substantial in all these cases, scission of the carbon–hydrogen bond occurs in the transition state. Either a hydride ion or a hydrogen atom abstraction process is occurring here, and the mechanism is probably the same as that for alcohols, which aldehyde hydrates resemble structurally (Section IV,B). The enormous increase in rate in basic solution that results from the second ionization of fluoral hydrate is a further indication of the importance of negative charge in facilitating hydrogen abstraction by permanganate.

D. PHENOLS

Phenols are readily oxidized by permanganate and, given sufficient oxidant, are degraded to carbon dioxide and water. Electron withdrawing groups, such as nitro, help stabilize the phenol to attack by permanganate, but this simply means that the oxidation of di- and trinitrophenols is slow enough to be

[236] R. Stewart and M. M. Mocek, *Can. J. Chem.* **41**, 1160 (1963).

measured.[237-240] Quantitative conversion of the mononitrophenols to carbon dioxide and water can be readily achieved.

The first step in the reaction of phenols, as might be expected, controls the rate of those oxidations that are slow enough to be measured, and this is followed by rapid degradation of the intermediate products.[239] The nature of the first step is still uncertain since added manganous ions accelerate, and added fluoride ions decelerate, the reaction (Sections I,A,5 and IV,G,2).

E. ORGANIC NITROGEN COMPOUNDS

1. AMINES

Most aromatic primary amines are oxidized almost instantaneously by neutral or basic permanganate to give ring cleavage products and eventually carbon dioxide and ammonia.

The conjugate acids of amines are oxidized more slowly than the free bases and this also applies to amino acids.[241] Metal ions such as bismuth(III),[242] chromium(III),[242] and copper(II)[243] also help stabilize amines by complexing and in some cases they appear to stabilize the amino group to permanganate oxidation more effectively than do protons.

Aliphatic amines are oxidized by permanganate to a variety of products. The reactions are sometimes incomplete and give a multiplicity of products; for example, diethylamine is oxidized to a mixture of acetic acid, ammonia, ethanol, and acetohydroxamic acid.[244] On the other hand, benzylamine and N,N-dimethylbenzylamine can be oxidized to benzaldehyde by aqueous permanganate at pH 10.3 in yields of 80% and 90%, respectively[245]:

$$C_6H_5CH_2N(CH_3)_2 \xrightarrow{MnO_4^-} C_6H_5CHO$$

Alkylation does not protect an amine from oxidation by permanganate in the way that alkylation of an alcohol (to form an ether) does.

Shechter et al. have shown that benzylamines are oxidized by buffered

[237] B. V. Tronov and M. Y. Grigor'ev, Izv. Tomsk. Ind. Inst. 60 (3), 37 (1940); Chem. Abstr, 37, 1029 (1943).
[238] F. F. Musgrave and E. A. Moelwyn-Hughes, Trans. Faraday Soc. 29, 1162 (1933).
[239] C. N. Hinshelwood and C. A. Winkler, J. Chem. Soc. p. 368 (1936).
[240] E. A. Alexander and F. C. Tompkins, Trans. Faraday Soc. 35, 1156 (1939).
[241] O. G. Pokrovskaya, Izv. Sibirsk. Otd. Akad. Nauk. SSSR 8, 50 (1959); Chem. Abstr. 54, 7307 (1960).
[242] M. T. Beck and O. Kling, Acta Chem. Scand. 15, 453 (1961).
[243] G. Martin, Compt. Rend. Acad. Sci. 232, 1213 (1951); 236, 2517 (1953).
[244] V. S. Smirnov and E. A. Shklyaruk, J. Gen. Chem. (USSR) (Eng. Transl.) 16, 1443, 1687 (1946); Chem. Abstr. 41, 5435, 6202 (1947).
[245] M.-M. Wei and R. Stewart, unpublished results.

permanganate to substituted *N*-[α-(benzylideneamino)-benzyl]-benzamides and *N,N'*-(iminodibenzylidene)-bis[benzamides].[245a]

$$\underset{\displaystyle ArCH{=}NCH(Ar)NHCAr}{\overset{\displaystyle \overset{O}{\|}}{}} \quad \text{and} \quad \underset{\displaystyle ArCNHCH(Ar)NHCH(Ar)NHCAr}{\overset{\displaystyle \overset{O}{\|}}{}}$$

These products arise from condensation of the initially formed imine, $ArCH{=}NH$, with unreacted amine, followed by further oxidation.

Trialkylcarbinylamines can be oxidized by permanganate in aqueous or aqueous–acetone solution to tertiary nitroalkanes in very good yield:

$$R_3CNH_2 \xrightarrow{\;MnO_4^-\;} R_3CNO_2$$

t-Butylamine gives 83 % of *t*-nitrobutane, for example. Kornblum has recently reviewed this reaction.[246] The oxidation of $(CH_3)_3CNH_2$ to the nitro compound is much slower than the oxidation of the amine $(CH_3)_3N$. The initial attack in the latter case occurs at the C—H bond adjacent to the nitrogen,[245] and the former compound lacks such a bond.

2. Nitro Compounds

When aromatic nitro compounds are degraded by permanganate, the nitro unit ends up as nitrate ion. The protective influence of the nitro group on an aromatic ring has been mentioned previously (Section IV,A,1).

TABLE VI

Permanganate Oxidation of Nitroalkane Salts to Carbonyl Compounds

Reactant	Product	Yield (%)	Reference
1-Nitrobutane	Butyraldehyde	83–97	247
Cyclobutylnitromethane	Cyclobutylcarboxaldehyde	91	247
2,2-Dimethyl-1-nitropropane	Trimethylacetaldehyde	69	247
Nitrocyclohexane	Cyclohexanone	84	250
1-Nitrodecalin	1-Decalone	51	251
Nitrocyclobutane	Cyclobutanone	94	247
2,2-Dimethyl-3-nitrobutane	*t*-Butyl methyl ketone	66	247
2-Nitrobutane	Ethyl methyl ketone	94	247

[245a] H. Shechter, S. S. Rawalay, and M. Tubis, *J. Am. Chem. Soc.* **86**, 1701 (1964); H. Shechter and S. S. Rawalay, *ibid.* p. 1706 (1964).

[246] N. Kornblum, *in* "Organic Reactions" (A. C. Cope, ed.), Vol. XII, p. 116. Wiley, New York, 1962; see also N. Kornblum and W. J. Jones, *Org. Syn.* **43**, 87 (1963).

The salts of aliphatic nitro compounds are oxidized by weakly basic permanganate to aldehydes and ketones and this is a reaction of considerable synthetic value [247-251] (see Table VI):

$$R_2CHNO_2 + KOH \rightarrow R_2C\!\!=\!\!NO_2K + H_2O$$

$$3\,R_2C\!\!=\!\!NO_2K + 2\,KMnO_4 + H_2O \rightarrow 3\,R_2C\!\!=\!\!O + 2\,MnO_2 + 3\,KNO_2 + 2\,KOH$$

3. HETEROCYCLIC COMPOUNDS

There are many natural products containing heterocyclic rings that have been degraded with permanganate as part of their structure proofs.[252] Pyridine rings are more stable to the action of permanganate than are pyrrole or pyrimidine rings. Pyrimidines are cleaved to urea or N-substituted ureas,[253] urea itself being very stable, indeed, to the action of both acidic and basic permanganate. This reaction can be used to oxidize the cytosine and similar groups in deoxyribonucleic acids to the corresponding ureido compounds in very high yield[254]:

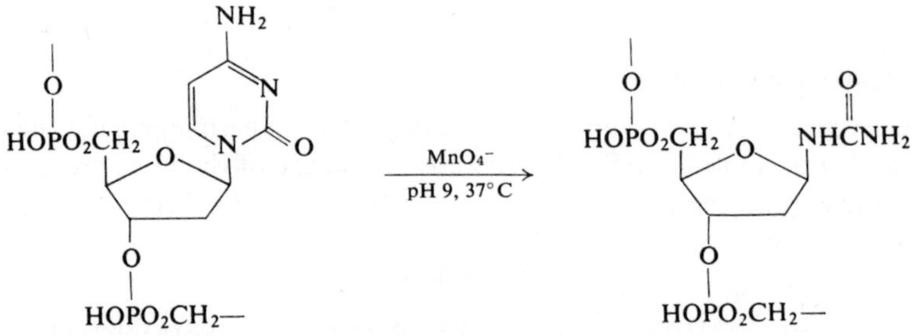

Uric acid is oxidized by alkaline permanganate to allantoin in good yield and it was suggested by Behrend that this took place through formation of the symmetrical intermediate[255, 256]:

[247] H. Shechter and F. T. Williams, Jr., *J. Org. Chem.* **27**, 3699 (1962).

[248] S. Nametkin and A. Zabrodina, *Ber.* **69**, 1789 (1936) and earlier papers.

[249] S. Nametkin, *J. Russ. Phys. Chem. Soc.* **47**, 1590 (1915) and earlier papers.

[250] S. Nametkin and E. I. Posdnjakova, *J. Russ. Phys. Chem. Soc.* **45**, 1420 (1913).

[251] S. Nametkin and O. Madaeff-Ssitscheff, *Ber.* **59**, 370 (1926).

[252] See for example H. Leuchs and G. Schwaebel, *Ber.* **46**, 3693 (1913).

[253] B. Chatamra and A. S. Jones, *J. Chem. Soc.* p. 811 (1963); see also A. S. Jones and R. T. Walker, *J. Chem. Soc.* p. 3554 (1963).

[254] A. S. Jones, G. W. Ross, S. Takemura, T. W. Thompson, and R. T. Walker, *J. Chem. Soc.* p. 373 (1964).

[255] R. Behrend, *Ann.* **333**, 141 (1904).

[256] W. H. Hartman, E. W. Moffet, and J. B. Dickey, *Org. Syn. Coll. Vol.* **II**, 21 (1943).

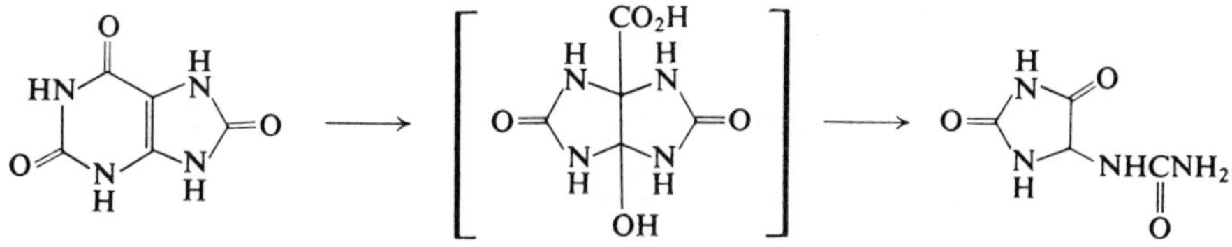

Uric Acid   Allantoin

Cavalieri and Brown used N^{15} to confirm this reaction path.[257] They showed that the nitrogens in the uric acid became scrambled during the reaction, indicating formation of a symmetrical intermediate.

F. ORGANIC SULFUR COMPOUNDS

Sulfides are oxidized by permanganate to sulfones in good yield. The latter are virtually inert to the action of permanganate, and solutions of permanganate in either acetic acid[258, 259] or aqueous base[260] are excellent reagents for this conversion:

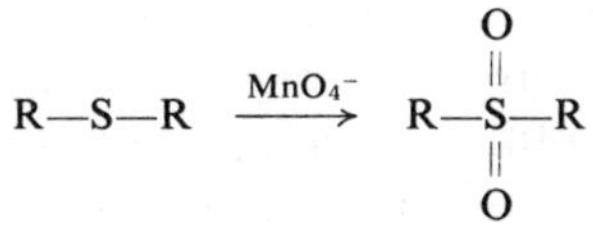

Both aliphatic and aromatic sulfides react in this way. Sulfoxides can also be conveniently oxidized to sulfones by permanganate[261, 262] and they are intermediates, presumably, in the sulfide to sulfone reaction. Dinitrodithienyl sulfides can be oxidized at the acyclic sulfur, the thiophene rings remaining unattacked[263]:

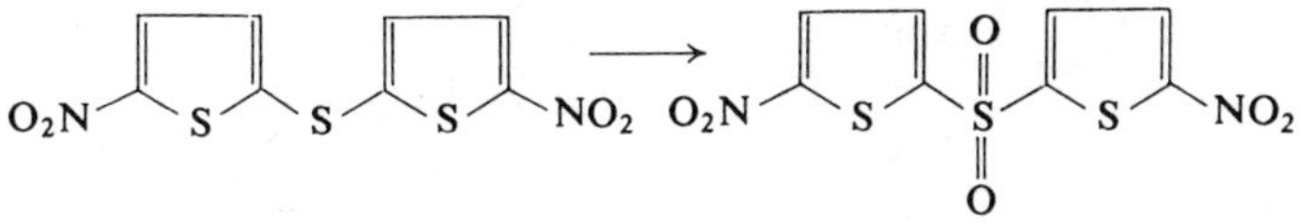

[257] L. F. Cavelieri and G. B. Brown, *J. Am. Chem. Soc.* **70**, 1242 (1948).
[258] G. W. Fenton and C. K. Ingold, *J. Chem. Soc.* p. 3127 (1928).
[259] E. Bourgeois and J. Henrion, *Bull. Soc. Chim. France* **51**, 1416 (1932).
[260] F. G. Bordwell and G. D. Cooper, *J. Am. Chem. Soc.* **74**, 1058 (1952).
[261] E. O. Beckmann, *J. Prakt. Chem.* [2] **17**, 439 (1878).
[262] T. P. Hilditch, *J. Chem. Soc.* p. 1618 (1908).
[263] O. Dann and E. F. Möller, *Ber.* **80**, 23 (1947); **82**, 76 (1949).

Thiols[264,265] and sulfinic acids[266,267] are converted to sulfonic acids by alkaline permanganate:

$$ArSH \xrightarrow[OH^-]{MnO_4^-} ArSO_3H$$

$$ArSO_2H \xrightarrow[OH^-]{MnO_4^-} ArSO_3H$$

Indeed, permanganate is one of the most commonly used oxidants for these purposes.[268]

G. BIFUNCTIONAL COMPOUNDS

1. HYDROXY COMPOUNDS

Glycols are cleaved by permanganate but this reaction is considerably slower than the corresponding reaction of alkenes.[269] This suggests that the C—C cleavage of alkenes, which always accompanies the dihydroxylation reaction, involves not the glycol which is formed but, rather, a manganese-containing precursor. Alcohols in general are subject to base catalyzed oxidation by permanganate. However, little detailed information is available on the glycol–permanganate reaction and it is possible, though not likely, that a cyclic ester is an intermediate in this case, as it is with some chromic acid[270] and some lead tetraacetate glycol cleavage reactions.[271] Such an intermediate would require oxygen substitution on manganese, and oxygen-18 exchange experiments with water as the substituting agent suggest that this is not a rapid process.

It should be pointed out that the cyclic manganese ester that has been confirmed as an intermediate in the alkene–permanganate reaction (A) is distinctly different from any that might form in the glycol–permanganate reaction (B). The latter would be pentacoordinated and contain manganese(VII):

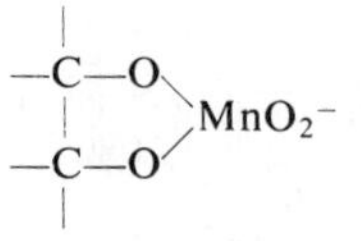

(A) 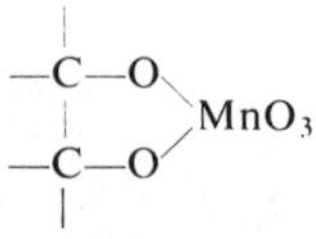   (B)

[264] A. F. Holleman and P. Caland, *Ber.* **44**, 2504 (1911).
[265] W. P. Wynne and J. Bruce, *J. Chem. Soc.* p. 731 (1898).
[266] J. Moschner, *Ber.* **34**, 1257 (1901).
[267] S. Smiles and R. Le Rossignol, *J. Chem. Soc.* p. 745 (1908).
[268] C. M. Suter, "Organic Chemistry of Sulfur," p. 366. Wiley, New York, 1944.
[269] W. L. Evans, *J. Am. Chem. Soc.* **45**, 171 (1923).
[270] J. Roček and F. H. Westheimer, *J. Am. Chem. Soc.* **84**, 2241 (1962).
[271] R. Criegee, *Angew. Chem.* **70**, 173 (1958).

α-Hydroxy acids are oxidized by permanganate to give two sets of products. In basic solution the keto acids are the principal products although these can be subject to further oxidation.[272] Mandelic acid is oxidized to phenylglyoxylic acid by alkaline permanganate in good yield, however[216]:

$$C_6H_5CHOHCO_2H \xrightarrow[OH^-]{MnO_4^-} C_6H_5\overset{\overset{\displaystyle O}{\|}}{C}CO_2H$$

In acid permanganate, oxidative decarboxylation occurs to a great extent, producing benzaldehyde and carbon dioxide:

$$C_6H_5CHOHCO_2H \xrightarrow[H^+]{MnO_4^-} C_6H_5CHO + CO_2$$

Benzilic acid is inert to alkaline permanganate[3] but is converted to benzophenone by acid permanganate (and also by manganese dioxide)[273]:

$$(C_6H_5)_2COHCO_2H \xrightarrow[H^+]{MnO_4^-} (C_6H_5)_2C{=}O + CO_2$$

The reaction is autocatalytic and it has been shown that lower oxidation states of manganese, i.e., Mn^{IV} and Mn^{III}, are much more effective oxidants than permanganate itself. The rates of this oxidative decarboxylation are identical in H_2O and D_2O.

β-Hydroxy acids can be decarboxylated by the action of alkaline permanganate and this is probably a straightforward alcohol oxidation to produce a β-keto acid which eliminates carbon dioxide spontaneously[274]:

$$RCHOHCH_2CO_2H \longrightarrow R\overset{\overset{\displaystyle O}{\|}}{C}CH_2CO_2H \longrightarrow CO_2 + R\overset{\overset{\displaystyle O}{\|}}{C}CH_3$$

2. OXALIC ACID

The reaction between permanganate and oxalate has been the subject of study for close to a century. Several extensive reviews have appeared in the past few years recounting the work of scores of investigators on this reaction.[275–277] The reaction is very complex and the mechanism is not completely

[272] S. Senent-Perez, L. Ramos, and H. Sanz-Garcia, *Anales Real Soc. Espan. Fis. Quim. (Madrid) Ser.* **B53**, 573 (1957); *Chem. Abstr.* **54**, 1992 (1960); see also Y. K. Gupta and R. Dutta, *Proc. Natl. Acad. Sci. India* **A28**, 236 (1959); *Chem. Abstr.* **54**, 17019 (1960); G. V. Bakore and R. Dayal, *Current Sci. (India)* **28**, 279 (1959); G. V. Bakore, R. Shanker, and U. Goyal, *Indian J. Chem.* **1**, 331 (1963).

[273] J. M. Pink and R. Stewart, unpublished results.

[274] A. M. Unrau and D. J. Canvin, *Can. J. Chem.* **41**, 607 (1963).

[275] R. M. Noyes, *Trans. N. Y. Acad. Sci.* **13**, 314 (1951).

[276] E. Abel, *Monatsh.* **83**, 695 (1952).

[277] J. W. Ladbury and C. F. Cullis, *Chem. Rev.* **58**, 403 (1958).

understood even yet. Nevertheless, it is a reaction of sufficiently precise stoichiometry to be used as a standard volumetric procedure.

Oxalic acid in acid solution is one of those reagents that reduces permanganate to the manganese(II) state:

$$5 MnO_4^- + 5 C_2O_4^{2-} + 16 H^+ \rightarrow 2 Mn^{2+} + 10 CO_2 + 8 H_2O$$

The direct reaction between permanganate and oxalate is extremely slow, however, since Launer and Yost showed that these reagents showed essentially no reaction in a week if lower oxidation states of manganese were scavenged by the addition of fluoride ions to the solution.[278] There is no doubt that manganese ions of lower oxidation state are involved since the induction period is sharply reduced by the addition of manganous salts to the reaction mixture.

The most recent study of the mechanism of the reaction is by Adler and Noyes who suggest that the first step is the one-electron reaction between a permanganate ion and a manganese(II)–oxalate complex:

$$MnO_4^- + MnC_2O_4 \rightarrow MnO_4^{2-} + MnC_2O_4^+$$

The manganate will disproportionate rapidly in acid solution or will be reduced if sufficient manganous ion is present. The cation, $MnC_2O_4^+$, is a manganese(III)–oxalate complex and it is known that such complexes exist; the trioxalato complex, $Mn(C_2O_4)_3^{3-}$, is red and the dioxolato complex, $Mn(C_2O_4)_2^-$, is yellow. With oxalate and manganous ion in excess, the formation of a mixture of these manganese(III)–oxalate complexes is almost instantaneous. The decomposition of these complexes was studied by Taube and by Adler and Noyes and this appears to occur as follows (using the trioxalato complex as the example)[279–281]:

$$Mn(C_2O_4)_3^{3-} \rightarrow Mn^{2+} + 2 C_2O_4^{2-} + CO_2 + CO_2^-$$

The radical anion, CO_2^- (Section IV,C,3), is further oxidized in a second step to carbon dioxide. Others have preferred to write the radical anion intermediate as $C_2O_4^-$ (rather than as $CO_2^- + CO_2$).[282–284]

In the presence of air some induced oxidation of oxalate by oxygen occurs.

In basic solution oxalate is fairly stable to the action of permanganate and, indeed, is often found as a reaction product when organic molecules are

[278] H. J. Launer and D. M. Yost, *J. Am. Chem. Soc.* **56**, 2571 (1934).

[279] H. Taube, *J. Am. Chem. Soc.* **70**, 1216 (1948).

[280] S. J. Adler and R. M. Noyes, *J. Am. Chem. Soc.* **77**, 2036 (1955).

[281] See also S. Yamashita, T. Hayakawa, and O. Toyama, *Bull. Univ. Osaka Prefect. Ser.* A5, 131 (1957); *Chem. Abstr.* **51**, 15226 (1957).

[282] E. Abel, *Z. Elektrochem.* **43**, 629 (1937).

[283] J. Weiss, *Discussions Faraday Soc.* **2**, 188 (1947).

[284] L. Malaprade and J. Coulombeau, *Compt. Rend. Acad. Sci.* **238**, 2322 (1954).

TABLE VII
RATE DATA FOR PERMANGANATE OXIDATIONS[a]

Reactant	Product	pH	k_2 (liters mole^{-1} sec^{-1})	$\Delta H^{\ddagger}$ (kcal mole^{-1})	$\Delta S^{\ddagger}$ (e.u.)[b]	Remarks	Reference
$(C_6H_5)_2CHOH$	$(C_6H_5)_2C{=}O$	12.3	1.5	5.7	-38.4	$(C_6H_5)_2CHO^-$ is reductant	204
$C_6H_5CHOHCF_3$	$C_6H_5COCF_3$	13	7.6	9.1	-24.3^*	$C_6H_5\overset{O^-}{C}HCF_3$ is reductant	205
$m\text{-}NO_2C_6H_4CHOHCF_3$	$m\text{-}NO_2C_6H_4COCF_3$	13	7.7	9.6	-23.8^*	$m\text{-}NO_2C_6H_5\overset{O^-}{C}HCF_3$ is reductant	205
C_6H_5CHO	$C_6H_5CO_2H$	6.5	0.32	10.3	-26.2	—	226
		12.0	0.57				
$p\text{-}CH_3OC_6H_4CHO$	$p\text{-}CH_3OC_6H_4CO_2H$	6.5	0.39	10.0	-26.8	—	226
$p\text{-}NO_2C_6H_4CHO$	$p\text{-}NO_2C_6H_4CO_2H$	6.5	0.22	11.1	-24.3	—	226
		12.0	16				
$CF_3CH(OH)_2$	CF_3CO_2H	4.0	0.0001	—	—	O^-	236
		10.2	0.8	12.4	-18.4^*	CF_3CHOH is reductant	
		12.8	22.5	6.6	-30	$CF_3CHO_2^{2-}$ is reductant	
$2,4,6\text{-}(NO_2)_3C_6H_2OH$	—		—	11.6	—		239
$C_6H_5CH_3$	$C_6H_5CO_2H$		0.26	12.6	-23	In 54% acetic acid, 50° C	168
$C_5H_5CO_2H$	—		0.01	11.2	-34	In 54% acetic acid, 50° C	168
HCO_2H	CO_2		0.001	16.4	-19^*	—	231
HCO_2^-	CO_2		2.0	13.0	-15^*	—	231
CO	CO_2	1–13	1–2	13	-17^*	50° C	158, 159
CN^-	CNO^-	13.3	4	9	-27^*	—	156, 157
H_2	H_2O	1–13	0.2	14.7	-13^*	30° C	143

[a] Aqueous homogeneous solution at 25° C, except where noted.
[b] Asterisk indicates entropy of activation for what is believed to be the rate-controlling step.

degraded by alkaline permanganate. The instability of manganese(III) ions in basic solution undoubtedly is an important factor in this connection.

H. MISCELLANEOUS REACTIONS

The oxidizing action of permanganate can give rise to radicals and electron deficient entities. The ability of certain permanganate–substrate mixtures to initiate polymerization of olefins has been mentioned earlier (Section I,E,1,c). Studies of the acrylonitrile polymerization catalyzed by the permanganate–oxalate reaction have been made.[285] Radicals produced in the oxidation reaction are undoubtedly responsible for initiating the polymerization chain.

Other polymerizations, such as that of certain siloxanes, may involve electrophilic intermediates.[286] Electrophile generation apparently occurs in the reported sulfonation of a naphthalene derivative which can be brought about by a mixture of sodium sulfate and permanganate.[287]

The formation of electron-deficient intermediates (carbonium ions or electron-deficient oxygen cations) is probably also responsible for the molecular rearrangements of organic substrates that occasionally accompany their oxidation. Levitt has discussed possible mechanisms for these rearrangements.[288]

V. Rate Data for Permanganate Oxidations

Table VII lists rate constants, activation enthalpies, and activation entropies for those permanganate oxidations for which this data is available. The reactions as a whole are characterized by rather low energies of activation and quite negative entropies of activation. In many cases the measured activation parameters include the enthalpy and entropy of a pre-equilibrium step. In some cases in which the mechanism is believed known, the listed entropy of activation is starred and refers to the rate-controlling step alone.

The reactions in all cases, except where noted, refer to aqueous homogeneous solution at 25° C.

[285] S. Yuguchi and M. Watanabe, *Kobunshi Kagaku* **18**, 273 (1961).
[286] V. N. Gruber and L. S. Mukhina, *Vysokomolekul. Soedin.* **3**, 174 (1961); *Chem. Abstr.* **55**, 27957 (1961).
[287] S. V. Bogdanov and I. B. Migacheva, *J. Gen. Chem. USSR (Engl. Transl.)* **20**, 124 (1950).
[288] L. S. Levitt, *J. Org. Chem.* **20**, 1297 (1955); see also G. C. Buzby, Jr., A. J. Castro, and E. B. Reid, *J. Org. Chem.* **28**, 1082 (1963); H. A. Neidig, D. L. Funck, R. Uhrich, R. Baker, and W. Kreiser, *J. Am. Chem. Soc.* **72**, 4617 (1950).

CHAPTER **II**

Oxidation by Chromic Acid and Chromyl Compounds

Kenneth B. Wiberg

I. Introduction 69
II. The Nature of Chromium in Its Higher Oxidation States 69
III. Oxidation of Inorganic Species 75
IV. Oxidation at Saturated Carbon–Hydrogen Bonds 82
   A. Oxidation of Aryl Alkanes 83
   B. Allylic Oxidation 105
   C. Oxidation of Alkanes 109
V. Oxidation of Carbon–Carbon Double Bonds 125
VI. Oxidation of Alcohols 142
VII. Oxidation of Diols 170
VIII. Oxidation of Aldehydes 172
IX. Oxidation of Ketones 178
X. Oxidation of Carboxylic Acids 180
XI. Oxidation at Sulfur 182
XII. Miscellaneous Oxidation Reactions 183

I. Introduction

Chromic acid is one of the most versatile of the available oxidizing agents, reacting with almost all types of oxidizable groups. The reactions often may be controlled to yield largely one product, and this makes chromic acid oxidation a useful synthetic tool. As a result of the pioneering work of Westheimer and his collaborators, and of the many investigations which followed, the details of the mechanisms of these reactions are in many cases fairly well understood. The following discussion will concentrate largely on the synthetic usefulness of the reactions, and on the mechanisms of the reactions. (Figures, tables, and references will be numbered according to Section in this chapter.)

II. The Nature of Chromium in Its Higher Oxidation States

The structure of chromium trioxide has been determined,[1] and may be described as a linear polymer of chromium and oxygen atoms with two oxygens

---

[1] A. Byström and K. A. Wilhelmi, *Acta Chem. Scand.* **4**, 1131 (1950); F. Hanic and D. Stempelova, *Chem. Zvesti* **14**, 165 (1960); *Chem. Abstr.* **54**, 20402 (1960).

attached to the sides of each chromium. The CrO_4 units form distorted tetrahedra with a Cr—O distance of 1.79–1.81 Å. It is not appreciably soluble in acetic acid,[2] or in most common nonhydroxylic solvents. It does, however, dissolve in reagents such as water, acetic anhydride,[3] *tert*-butyl alcohol,[4] and pyridine[5] via reactions which lead to depolymerization:

$$(CrO_3)_n + H_2O \longrightarrow HO\!-\!\overset{\overset{\displaystyle O}{\|}}{\underset{\underset{\displaystyle O}{\|}}{Cr}}\!-\!OH$$

$$+\ CH_3\overset{\overset{\displaystyle O}{\|}}{C}O\overset{\overset{\displaystyle O}{\|}}{C}CH_3 \longrightarrow CH_3\overset{\overset{\displaystyle O}{\|}}{C}\!-\!O\!-\!\overset{\overset{\displaystyle O}{\|}}{\underset{\underset{\displaystyle O}{\|}}{Cr}}\!-\!O\!-\!\overset{\overset{\displaystyle O}{\|}}{C}CH_3$$

$$+\ (CH_3)_3COH \longrightarrow (CH_3)_3CO\!-\!\overset{\overset{\displaystyle O}{\|}}{\underset{\underset{\displaystyle O}{\|}}{Cr}}\!-\!OH \xrightarrow{\textit{tert-BuOH}} (CH_3)_3CO\!-\!\overset{\overset{\displaystyle O}{\|}}{\underset{\underset{\displaystyle O}{\|}}{Cr}}\!-\!OC(CH_3)_3$$

$$+\ \text{pyridine} \longrightarrow \overset{+}{N}\!-\!\overset{\overset{\displaystyle O}{\|}}{\underset{\underset{\displaystyle O}{\|}}{Cr}}\!-\!O^-$$

$$+\ HCl \longrightarrow Cl\!-\!\overset{\overset{\displaystyle O}{\|}}{\underset{\underset{\displaystyle O}{\|}}{Cr}}\!-\!Cl$$

The details of the oxidation by chromium(VI) will in some cases vary with the nature of the chromium(VI) species used, and one may expect the solvent used to have a marked effect on the rate and type of reaction which will occur.

[2] J. Roček and F. Šorm, *Collection Czech. Chem. Commun.* **20**, 1009 (1955); J. Roček, *Collection Czech. Chem. Commun.* **20**, 1249 (1955).

[3] A. Pictet and P. Genequand, *Chem. Ber.* **36**, 2215 (1903); H. S. Fry, *J. Am. Chem. Soc.* **33**, 697 (1911); H. L. Krauss, *Angew. Chem.* **70**, 502 (1958).

[4] H. Wienhaus, *Ber.* **47**, 322 (1914); W. Hückel and M. Blohm, *Ann.* **502**, 114 (1933).

[5] H. H. Sisler, J. D. Bush, and O. E. Accountius, *J. Am. Chem. Soc.* **70**, 3827 (1948); H. H. Sisler, W. C. L. Ming, E. Metter, and F. R. Hurley, *J. Am. Chem. Soc.* **75**, 446 (1953); O. E. Accountius, J. D. Bush, and H. H. Sisler, *Inorg. Syn.* **4**, 94 (1953); H. H. Sisler, N. El-Jadir, and D. H. Busch, *J. Inorg. Nucl. Chem.* **16**, 257 (1961).

In aqueous solution, and in the absence of other ions, the following equilibria obtain[6] (the constants refer to $25° C$):

$$H_2CrO_4 \rightleftharpoons H^+ + HCrO_4^- \qquad K_1 = 1.21 \text{ moles/liter}$$

$$HCrO_4^- \rightleftharpoons H^+ + CrO_4^- \qquad K_2 = 3.0 \times 10^{-7} \text{ mole/liter}$$

$$2\, HCrO_4 \rightleftharpoons Cr_2O_7^{2-} + H_2O \qquad K_d = 35.5$$

$$HCr_2O_7 \rightleftharpoons H^+ + Cr_2O_7 \qquad K_2' = 0.85 \text{ mole/liter}$$

$$H_2Cr_2O_7 \rightleftharpoons H^+ + HCr_2O_7^- \qquad K_1' = \text{large}$$

The monomer–dimer equilibrium constant may be determined by using the difference in absorption spectrum between the acid chromate and dichromate ions; the acid dissociation constants were obtained in conventional fashion. The dimerization equilibrium is of considerable importance. In water, at concentrations greater than about $0.05\,M$, the dichromate ion (and its protonated forms) is the predominant species; at lower concentrations, the monomer predominates. There is evidence that at higher concentrations polychromates are formed.[7] The thermodynamic functions for the above chromium species are given in Table 2-1.[8–10]

TABLE 2-1

THERMODYNAMIC FUNCTIONS FOR CHROMIUM(VI) DERIVATIVES

Species	$\Delta F_f°$	$\Delta H_f°$	$\Delta S_f°$	Reference
$CrO_4^{2-}{}_{(aq)}$	-171.1	-208.6	9.2	8
$HCrO_4^-{}_{(aq)}$	-180.0	-207.9	41.3	8
$Cr_2O_7^{2-}{}_{(aq)}$	-305.9	-352.2	57.2	8
$CrO_{3(s)}$		-142.1	17.5	9, 10

[6] J. D. Neuss and W. Rieman, *J. Am. Chem. Soc.* **56**, 2238 (1934); J. Y. P. Tong and E. L. King, *J. Am. Chem. Soc.* **75**, 6180 (1953); W. G. Davies and J. E. Prue, *Trans. Faraday Soc.* **51**, 1045 (1955); J. R. Howard, V. S. K. Nair, and G. H. Nancollas, *Trans. Faraday Soc.* **54**, 1034 (1958); G. Schwarzenbach and J. Meier, *J. Inorg. Nuc. Chem.* **8**, 302 (1958); N. Bailey, A. Carrington, K. A. K. Lott, and M. C. R. Symons, *J. Chem. Soc.* p. 290 (1960); Y. Sasaki, *Acta Chem. Scand.* **16**, 719 (1962).
[7] M. L. Freedman, *J. Am. Chem. Soc.* **80**, 2072 (1958); Á. Kiss and K. Bíró, *Acta Univ. Szeged. Sect. Sci. Nat., Acta Chem. et Phys.* **2**, 90 (1948); *Chem. Abstr.* **44**, 5706 (1950).
[8] C. N. Muldrow, Jr. and L. G. Hepler, *J. Am. Chem. Soc.* **79**, 4045 (1957); L. G. Hepler, *J. Am. Chem. Soc.* **80**, 6181 (1958).
[9] C. A. Neugebauer and J. L. Margrave, *J. Phys. Chem.* **61**, 1429 (1957).
[10] V. I. Spitsyn, N. S. Afonskii, and V. I. Tsviel'nikov, *Zh. Neorgan. Khim.* **5**, 1505 (1960).

If anions such as the chloride, sulfate, or phosphate ions are added to an aqueous solution of chromium(VI), one observes a change in visible spectrum which can be correlated with the formation of a new species[11]; for example, with the chloride ion:

$$H^+ + HO-\overset{\overset{O}{\|}}{\underset{\underset{O}{\|}}{Cr}}-O^- + Cl^- \;\rightleftharpoons\; Cl-\overset{\overset{O}{\|}}{\underset{\underset{O}{\|}}{Cr}}-O^- + H_2O$$

This reaction is analogous to the monomer–dimer equilibrium of chromic acid. The reactivity of the ion produced in this manner will be a function of the anion which is attached.

Complex formation between chromic acid and an anion results in a change in the dissociation constant.[12] In general, the more electron withdrawing anions lead to larger dissociation constants. Thus, the order of increasing effect on the constant is $H_3PO_4 < HCl < H_2SO_4 < HClO_4 < HNO_3$. The position of nitric acid is anomalous.

Organic compounds are often not soluble in water, and therefore a mixed solvent is commonly used in effecting chromic acid oxidations. Relatively few compounds are resistant to oxidation by chromic acid and the choice is fairly limited. The majority of work has employed acetic acid as the cosolvent. The monomer–dimer equilibrium constant in 91 % acetic acid has been deter-mined,[13] although it is still not clear whether monomeric chromium(VI) exists in this medium as the acid chromate ion or as the acetochromate ion $(CH_3COCrO_2O^-)$.[14]

The infrared and Raman spectra of the chromate ion and other related ions have been studied, and the force constants have been determined.[15] The ultraviolet spectrum of chromium(VI) has been discussed in connection with the nature of bonding in tetrahedral oxy-anions, and it has been interpreted

[11] F. Holloway, *J. Am. Chem. Soc.* **74**, 224 (1952); M. Cohen and F. H. Westheimer. *J. Am. Chem. Soc.* **74**, 4387 (1952); A. A. Woolf, *Chem. & Ind.* (*London*) p. 1320 (1954); K. B. Yatsimirskii and Vn. N. Vasil'eva, *Zh. Neorgan. Khim.* **1**, 984 (1956); *Chem. Abstr.* **51**, 3265 (1957); O. Lukkari, *Suomen Kemistilehti* **35B**, 91 (1962).

[12] D. G. Lee and R. Stewart, *J. Am. Chem. Soc.* **86**, 3051 (1964).

[13] K. B. Wiberg and T. Mill, *J. Am. Chem. Soc.* **80**, 3022 (1958).

[14] J. Roček, *Collection Czech. Chem. Commun.* **22**, 1509 (1957); M. C. R. Symons, *J. Chem. Soc.* p. 4331 (1963).

[15] H. Stammreich, D. Bassi, and O. Sala, *Spectrochim. Acta* **12**, 403 (1958); T. Dupuis, *Compt. Rend. Acad. Sci.* **246**, 3332 (1958); C. W. F. T. Pistorius, *J. Chem. Phys.* **28**, 514 (1958); C. G. Barraclough, J. Lewis, and R. S. Nyholm, *J. Chem. Soc.* p. 3552 (1959); Ya. S. Bobovich, *Opt. i Spektroskopiya* **11**, 161 (1961); F. Vratney, M. Dilling, F. Gugliotta, and C. N. R. Rao, *J. Sci. Ind. Res.* (*India*) **20B**, 590 (1961); K. Venkates-warlu and R. Thanalakshmi, *J. Sci. Ind. Res.* (*India*) **21B**, 461 (1962).

using a molecular orbital scheme[16] and using ligand field theory.[17] The electron spin resonance (e.s.r.) spectrum of the chromate ion has been obtained and interpreted[18] using the scheme of Wolfsberg and Helmholz.[16]

Besides chromic acid, the two most commonly used chromium(VI) derivatives are chromyl chloride and chromyl acetate. The first is prepared by the reaction of chromium trioxide with hydrogen chloride, or of potassium dichromate with sodium chloride and sulfuric acid.[19] It is a deep red liquid, b.p. 115.7° C, which decomposes on treatment with water and which is readily soluble in unreactive organic solvents such as carbon tetrachloride and carbon disulfide. The second is prepared by the addition of chromium trioxide to acetic anhydride.[20] Other chromyl compounds such as chromyl bromide,[21] chromyl fluoride,[22, 23] chromyl azide,[23] chromyl borate,[24] chromyl nitrate,[25] chromyl sulfate,[26] chromyl benzoate,[27] and chromyl trichloroacetate[27] have been prepared by similar methods. The physical properties of these compounds have been examined in some detail.[28]

[16] M. Wolfsberg and L. Helmholz, *J. Chem. Phys.* **20**, 837 (1952); A. Carrington, D. S. Schonland, and M. C. R. Symons, *J. Chem. Soc.* p. 659 (1957); cf. L. Helmholz, H. Brennan, and M. Wolfsberg, *J. Chem. Phys.* **23**, 853 (1955); N. Bailey, A. Carrington, K. A. K. Lott, and M. C. R. Symons, *J. Chem. Soc.* p. 290 (1960); U. Kläning and M. C. R. Symons, *J. Chem. Soc.* p. 3204 (1961); H. C. Mishra and M. C. R. Symons, *J. Chem. Soc.* p. 4411 (1962); cf. A. Carrington and M. C. R. Symons, *Chem. Rev.* **63**, 443 (1963).

[17] C. J. Ballhausen and A. D. Liehr, *J. Mol. Spectroscopy* **2**, 342 (1958); A. Carrington and D. S. Schonland, *Mol. Phys.* **3**, 331 (1960).

[18] A. Carrington, D. J. E. Ingram, D. S. Schonland, and M. C. R. Symons, *J. Chem. Soc.* p. 4710 (1956).

[19] H. H. Sisler, *Inorg. Syn.* **2**, 205 (1946); A. A. Vakhrushev, *Uch. Zap. Udmurtsk. Gos. Ped. Inst.* **11**, 143 (1957); *Chem. Abstr.* **54**, 6379 (1960): cf. W. H. Hartford and M. Darrin, *Chem. Rev.* **58**, 1 (1958).

[20] H. L. Krauss, *Angew. Chem.* **70**, 502 (1958).

[21] H. Zellner, *Oesterr. Akad. Wiss. Math-Naturw. Kl. Sitzber. Abt. IIb,* **158**, 317 (1949); H. L. Krauss and K. Stark, *Z. Naturforsch.* **17b**, 1 (1962).

[22] H. v. Wartenberg, *Z. Anorg. Allgem. Chem.* **247**, 135 (1941); G. D. Flesch and H. J. Svec, *J. Am. Chem. Soc.* **80**, 3189 (1958); N. Bartlett and P. L. Robinson, *J. Chem. Soc.* p. 3549 (1961).

[23] H. L. Krauss and F. Schwarzbach, *Chem. Ber.* **94**, 1205 (1961).

[24] S. Z. Haider, M. H. Khundkar, and K. De, *J. Inorg. Nucl. Chem.* **24**, 847 (1963).

[25] M. Schmiesser and D. Lützow, *Angew. Chem.* **66**, 230 (1954).

[26] A. Rokowsky and D. Tavassenkov, *Z. Anorg. Allgem. Chem.* **174**, 91 (1928); A. A. Woolf, *Chem. & Ind. (London)* p. 1320 (1954); K. B. Yatsimirskii and Vn. N. Vasil'eva, *Zh. Neorgan. Chem.* **1**, 1983 (1956).

[27] H. Schildknecht and W. Föttinger, *Ann.* **659**, 20 (1962).

[28] C. P. Smyth, A. J. Grossman, and S. R. Ginsburg, *J. Am. Chem. Soc.* **62**, 192 (1940); K. H. Hellwege, *Z. Physik* **117**, 596 (1941); M. Kantzer, *Compt. Rend. Acad. Sci.* **214**, 998 (1942); H. G. Dehmelt, *J. Chem. Phys.* **21**, 380 (1953); G. M. Schwab and S. Prakash, *Z. Physik. Chem. (Frankfurt)* **6**, 387 (1956); W. E. Hobbs, *J. Chem. Phys.* **28**, 1220 (1958); F. A. Miller, G. L. Carlson, and W. B. White, *Spectrochim. Acta* **15**, 709 (1959).

The most common lower oxidation state is chromium(III) and oxidations generally lead to this state. However, few if any reactions involve a three-electron transfer in one step, and therefore most reactions lead either to chromium(V) or chromium(IV) as an intermediate. These compounds may effect further oxidations and may lead to products different than those formed in the initial chromium(VI) oxidation.[29]

A derivative of chromium(V), barium hypochromate [$Ba_3(CrO_4)_2$], has been prepared by heating barium chromate with barium carbonate to 1000° C in a nitrogen atmosphere.[30] Aqueous solutions of potassium chromate containing a high concentration of potassium hydroxide are slowly converted at high temperature and in the absence of oxygen to green solutions which were shown to contain chromium(V) by titration[31] and by e.s.r. spectroscopy.[32] The spectrum of a solution showed a broad peak at 625 mμ. When the solution was shaken with oxygen, the chromate ion was regenerated, and when the solution was diluted with water, fairly rapid disproportionation to Cr^{III} and Cr^{VI} occurred.

Potassium chromium oxypentachloride, $CrOCl_3 \cdot 2\,KCl$, has been reported as the product of the reaction of chromic acid with potassium chloride and hydrogen chloride in glacial acetic acid.[33] It was obtained as garnet red rhombic prisms. Other quinquevalent chromium compounds which have been reported are chromium pentafluoride, a by-product in the reaction of fluorine with chromium metal,[34] and Cr_2O_5, obtained by heating chromium trioxide.[35]

A derivative of chromium(IV), chromium dioxide, has been prepared by the thermal decomposition of chromyl chloride[36] by heating chromic oxide (Cr_2O_3) with air,[37] by heating hydrated chromic oxide with chromium trioxide,[37] by the reduction of chromates with various reducing agents,[37] and by the thermal decomposition of aqueous chromic acid at 300–325° C in a sealed tube.[38] Chromium dioxide is a black, hygroscopic powder which is

[29] J. Hampton, A. Leo, and F. H. Westheimer, *J. Am. Chem. Soc.* **78**, 306 (1956).

[30] R. Scholder and W. Klemm, *Angew. Chem.* **66**, 461 (1954); K. Wieczffinski and M. Andrelowicz, *Roczniki Chem.* **36**, 1937 (1962); *Chem. Abstr.* **58**, 10953 (1963).

[31] N. Bailey and M. C. R. Symons, *J. Chem. Soc.* p. 203 (1957).

[32] A. Carrington, D. J. E. Ingram, D. S. Schonland, and M. C. R. Symons, *J. Chem. Soc.* p. 4710 (1956); cf. H. Kon, *Bull. Chem. Soc. Japan* **35**, 2054 (1962).

[33] H. von Wartenberg, *Z. Anorg. Allgem. Chem.* **250**, 122 (1942).

[34] H. von Wartenberg, *Z. Anorg. Allgem. Chem.* **247**, 135 (1941); **249**, 100 (1942); O. Glemser, R. Roesky, and K. H. Hellberg, *Angew. Chem. Intern. Ed. (Engl.)* **2**, 266 (1963).

[35] P. Pascal, "Nouveau Traité de Chimie Minerale," Vol. XIV, pp. 33ff. Masson, Paris, 1959; B. Takekazu and E. Hirota, *Natl. Tech. Rept.* **7**, 372 (1961); *Chem. Abstr.* **56**, 15113 (1962).

[36] A. Michael and J. Benard, *Bull. Soc. Chim. France* **10**, 315 (1943).

[37] M. J. Udy, "Chromium," Vol. I, pp. 128ff. Reinhold, New York, 1956.

[38] B. J. Thamer, R. M. Douglass, and E. Staritzky, *J. Am. Chem. Soc.* **79**, 547 (1957).

insoluble in water, but is decomposed by water to give chromic oxide and chromic acid.

Barium chromate(IV), Ba_2CrO_4, has been prepared by the thermal decomposition of $Ba_3(Cr(OH)_6)_2 \cdot H_2O$,[39] by the reaction of the same compound with barium hydroxide, by the reaction of barium chromate with chromic oxide and barium hydroxide, and by the hydrogenation of a mixture of barium chromate(VI) and barium hydroxide. Strontium chromate(IV), Sr_2CrO_4, was also prepared by the latter method. Barium orthochromate(IV), Ba_3CrO_5, was prepared by the reaction of barium chromate(VI) with chromic oxide and a large excess of barium hydroxide. Barium chromate(IV) dissolves in glacial acetic acid to give a stable green solution which turns brownish-yellow on the addition of water.

Chromium tetrafluoride has been prepared by the reaction of fluorine with chromium metal, chromic chloride, or chromic fluoride in the absence of oxygen.[34] (In the presence of oxygen, chromyl fluoride, CrO_2F_2, was obtained.) The visible absorption spectrum of chromium tetrafluoride contains two sharp, strong bands, at 556 and 580 mμ, with a broad weak band at 630–640 mμ. Chromium tetrachloride, prepared by heating chromic chloride with chlorine, is stable only in the gaseous state.[33] It does not have the characteristic absorption spectrum of chromium tetrafluoride, but shows continuous absorption at wavelengths below 487 mμ.

Chromium tetra-*tert*-butoxide, $((CH_3)_3CO)_4Cr$, has been prepared by the reaction of bisbenzenechromium, $(C_6H_6)_2Cr$, with di-*tert*-butyl peroxide at 90° C.[40] The compound was found as blue crystals, m.p. 37–38° C, which were sensitive to moisture and oxygen. It was paramagnetic, with a magnetic susceptibility of 2.88 Bohr magnetons, indicating two unpaired electrons.

Compounds derived from chromium(IV) are also obtained as a result of chromium(VI) oxidation in strong sulfuric acid[41] or acetic anhydride.[42]

III. Oxidation of Inorganic Species

Not only are chromium(IV) and (V) known as isolable species which are unstable on treatment with water, but good evidence is also available to show that they are reaction intermediates. This should not be surprising since the conversion of chromium(VI) to chromium(III) is a three-electron reduction, whereas few oxidations involve more than a net two-electron process. The best evidence for transient chromium intermediates comes from the phenomenon

[39] R. Scholder and G. Sperka, *Z. Anorg. Allgem. Chem.* **285**, 49 (1956); K. Wieczffinski and M. Andrelowicz, *Roczniki Chem.* **36**, 1397 (1962); *Chem. Abstr.* **58**, 10953 (1963).

[40] N. Hagihara and H. Yamazaki, *J. Am. Chem. Soc.* **81**, 3160 (1959).

[41] E. Pungor and J. Trompler, *J. Inorg. Nucl. Chem.* **5**, 123 (1957).

[42] K. B. Wiberg and P. A. Lepse, *J. Am. Chem. Soc.* **86**, 2612 (1964).

of induced oxidation,[1] and many examples of such oxidation are found in the reaction of chromium(VI) with other inorganic ions.

One of the first examples of an induced oxidation was found in the reaction of iodide ion with chromic acid.[2] In dilute acid ($0.001 N$) and at low concentrations, the rate of reaction is extremely slow. However, if ferrous iron is added, a rapid reaction occurs, leading to the formation of iodine. The reaction of iodide ion with ferric iron is slow under these conditions, indicating that the iodide ion was oxidized by some species other than chromium(VI) or iron(III). It is clear that the ferrous iron has in some way induced the oxidation of iodide.

The stoichiometry of the reaction in the presence of ferrous ion has been examined,[3] and when the concentration of iodide ion is large compared with that of Fe^{II}, it is found that two equivalents of the former are oxidized for each of the latter. The over-all stoichiometry under these conditions is

$$Cr^{VI} + 2 I^- + Fe^{II} \rightarrow Cr^{III} + I_2 + Fe^{III}$$

Another well-studied example is the oxidation of arsenious acid with chromic acid. This oxidation induces the oxidation of bromide, iodide, and manganous ions. When manganous ion is present in considerable excess, two equivalents of arsenious ion are oxidized for each equivalent of Mn^{II}. The stoichiometry is then

$$Cr^{VI} + AsO_3^{3-} + Mn^{II} \rightarrow Cr^{III} + AsO_4^{3-} + Mn^{III}$$

The ratio of the number of equivalents of substrate oxidized to the number of equivalents of inductor (H_3AsO_3 or Fe^{II} in the above examples) used is called the induction factor. This has the value 2 for the first example and 0.5 for the second. These two values are commonly found, and typical examples are summarized in Table 3-1. The induction factors which are given are the limiting values, i.e., those obtained using a relatively high concentration of acceptor. When lower concentrations of acceptor are used, the induction factor will be closer to unity.[4]

Induced oxidation has some of the characteristics of catalysis, the main difference being that a true catalyst is unchanged as a result of a reaction, whereas in induced oxidation the inductor is consumed. Further, as we saw above, the amount of inductor consumed usually bears a stoichiometric relation to the amount of product formed. It is interesting to note that the reaction

$$3 Mn^{II} + 2 Cr^{VI} \rightarrow 3 MnO_2 + 2 Cr^{III}$$

[1] F. Kessler, *Pogg. Ann.* [2] **119**, 218 (1863); cf. F. H. Westheimer, *Chem. Rev.* **45**, 419 (1949) for a review of induced oxidations involving chromium(VI).

[2] C. F. Schönbein, *J. Prakt. Chem.* **75**, 108 (1858).

[3] C. Benson, *J. Phys. Chem.* **7**, 1, 356 (1903).

[4] R. Luther and T. F. Rutter, *Z. Anorg. Allgem. Chem.* **54**, 1 (1907); R. Lang and J. Zwerina, *ibid.* **170**, 389 (1928).

is thermodynamically disfavored at pH > O; in the absence of arsenite the reverse reaction proceeds slowly. Nevertheless, the process including arsenite given above is thermodynamically favored because the inductor (arsenite) is consumed during the reaction.

TABLE 3-1

INDUCED OXIDATIONS IN WHICH CHROMIUM(VI)
IS THE OXIDIZING AGENT[a]

Inductor	Acceptor	Induction factor
Fe^{II}	I^-	2
H_3AsO_3	I^-	2
$VOSO_4$	I^-	2
$(VO)_2SO_4$	I^-	2
VSO_4	I^-	2
Ti^{III}	I^-	2
$UOSO_4$	I^-	0.5–0.7
H_3AsO_3	Mn^{II}	0.5
Fe^{II}	Br^-	[b]
$VOSO_4$	Br^-	[b]
Ti^{III}	Br^-	[b]

[a] This table was taken from F. H. Westheimer,
Chem. Rev. **45**, 419 (1949).
[b] The value was not determined.

With this introduction to the general phenomenon of induced oxidation, let us consider in more detail the oxidation of typical inorganic species.

1. ARSENIOUS ION

The oxidation of arsenious ion with chromic acid proceeds readily in aqueous solution. The kinetics of the reaction were first studied by DeLury,[5] and his data have been interpreted by Westheimer as favoring the rate law[6,7]:

$$v = k_a[As^{III}] [HCrO_4^-] [H^+] + k_b[As^{III}] [HCrO_4^-] [H^+]^2$$

It is interesting to note that the rate dependence is on the concentration of the acid chromate ion rather than on total chromium(VI). The two concentrations differ because of the dimerization of the acid chromate ion:

$$2 HCrO_4^- \rightleftharpoons Cr_2O_7^{2-} + H_2O$$

[5] R. E. DeLury, *J. Phys. Chem.* **7**, 239 (1903); **11**, 54 (1907).
[6] F. H. Westheimer, *Chem. Rev.* **45**, 419 (1949); cf. J. O. Edwards, *Chem. Rev.* **50**, 455 (1952).
[7] There is also a pH independent term involving the chromate ion. I. M. Kolthoff and M. A. Fineman, *J. Phys. Chem.* **60**, 1383 (1956).

Thus, as the concentration of chromium(VI) is increased, a progressively smaller portion of the total amount is in the form of the acid chromate ion and, experimentally, one observes that the rate constants decrease with increasing chromium(VI) concentration.

A recent kinetic study has indicated a more complex kinetic pattern.[8] The reaction was studied in two sets of experiments. In the first, high As^{III} and low chromic acid concentrations were used, and in the second, low As^{III} and high chromic acid concentrations were employed. In both cases, pseudo first order behavior was found, following the disappearance of Cr^{VI} in the first case and of As^{III} in the second.

The rate of reaction in the first set of experiments was found to have a nonlinear dependence on As^{III}. At a constant acid concentration, the rate behavior fit the equation:

$$\frac{d[Cr^{VI}]}{dt} = \frac{2kK[As^{III}][HCrO_4^-]}{1 + K[As^{III}]}$$

In a solution $0.2\,M$ in acetic acid, $0.2\,M$ in acetate ion with an ionic strength of 1.5 (potassium nitrate) at $25°\,C$, $k = 3.8 \times 10^{-4}\,sec^{-1}$ and $K = 22.4$ liters $mole^{-1}$. Evidence was found for general acid catalysis, but this was not explored in any detail.

The rate law suggests the formation of a complex between As^{III} and the acid chromate ion:

$$As^{III} + HCrO_4^- \rightleftharpoons As^{III} \cdot HCrO_4^-$$

$$As^{III} \cdot HCrO_4^- \rightarrow products$$

The complex is completely formed at high As^{III} concentrations, and since the concentrations of complex cannot then increase, the rate of reaction becomes independent of the As^{III} concentration.

If the constants given above are assumed to apply to the second series of experiments, the rate law becomes

$$\frac{d[As^{III}]}{dt} = \frac{3Kk[HCrO_4^-]}{1 + K[HCrO_4^-]}[As^{III}] + 3k_2[Cr_2O_7^{2-}][As^{III}]$$

with $k_2 = 1.16 \times 10^{-2}$ liters $mole^{-1}\,sec^{-1}$. Although the numerical value may be uncertain since it is derived from four experimentally measured quantities, it seems clear that both the acid chromate and dichromate ions may effect the oxidation.

The oxidation of arsenious acid induces the oxidation of manganous ion to an equilibrium mixture of manganic ion and manganese dioxide, and it induces the oxidation of iodide ion to iodine. The first of these induced oxidations has an induction factor of 0.5, and the second has a factor of 2.0.

[8] J. G. Mason and A. D. Kowalak, *Inorg. Chem.* 3, 1248 (1964).

Westheimer[6] has explored the various possibilities for explaining the results, but only one appears to be consistent with all the other data on this and related oxidations. Here one assumes that Cr^{IV} effects the oxidation of manganous ion and that Cr^V effects the oxidation of iodide ion. The formation of Cr^{IV} involves a two-electron oxidation of the inductor and leads to a one-electron oxidation of the acceptor, whereas the formation of Cr^V involves an effective one-electron oxidation of the inductor, and a two-electron oxidation of the acceptor. Since the inductor is the same in both of the induced oxidations, there must be some additional reaction which effects the Cr^{IV}–Cr^V inter-conversion. This is believed to be the reaction of Cr^{IV} with Cr^{VI} to give two Cr^V. Then, the series of reactions for the two cases may be written as[9]

(A) $\quad H_3AsO_3 + Cr^{VI} \rightarrow H_3AsO_4 + Cr^{IV}$
$\qquad\quad Cr^{IV} + Mn^{II} \rightarrow Cr^{III} + Mn^{III}$
$\qquad\qquad 2\ Mn^{III} \rightleftharpoons Mn^{II} + MnO_2$

(B) $\quad H_3AsO_3 + Cr^{VI} \rightarrow H_3AsO_4 + Cr^{IV}$
$\qquad\quad Cr^{IV} + Cr^{VI} \rightarrow 2\ Cr^V$
$\qquad\qquad Cr^V + I^- \rightarrow Cr^{III} + IO^-$
$\qquad\quad IO^- + I^- + 2H^+ \rightarrow I_2 + H_2O$

It is assumed that manganous ion will react rapidly with Cr^{IV}, but that the reaction between the latter and iodide is relatively slow, permitting the Cr^{IV} to be oxidized to Cr^V before reacting with I^-. The oxidation of iodide by Cr^V cannot occur by way of Cr^{IV} and iodine atoms because this would require that Cr^{IV} also react with I^- rapidly. But if this were the case, the Cr^{IV}–I^- reaction would compete with the Cr^{VI}–Cr^{IV} reaction and an induction factor of two would not be obtained.

The observation of complex formation between As^{III} and the acid chromate ion suggests that a mixed anhydride is formed, as is the case with many anions and Cr^{VI}. This may decompose in the rate-determining step to give As^V and Cr^{IV}:

$$H_3AsO_3 + HCrO_4^- + H^+ \rightleftharpoons HO\!-\!\underset{\underset{OH}{|}}{As}\!-\!O\!-\!\overset{\overset{O}{\|}}{\underset{\underset{O}{\|}}{Cr}}\!-\!OH + H_2O$$

$$HO\!-\!\underset{\underset{OH}{|}}{\overset{..}{As}}\!-\!O\!-\!\overset{\overset{O}{\|}}{\underset{\underset{O}{\|}}{Cr}}\!-\!OH \longrightarrow HO\!-\!\underset{\underset{OH}{|}}{\overset{+}{As}}\!=\!O + Cr^{IV}$$

$$H_2AsO_3^+ + H_2O \longrightarrow H_3AsO_4 + H^+$$

[9] It is unlikely that As^{IV} would be an intermediate in this reaction since it is apparently a rather unstable species.[6]

The oxidation by the dichromate ion may involve a similar intermediate, in analogy with the formation of polychromates.

2. FERROUS ION

The kinetics of the reaction of chromic acid with ferrous ion has been examined and leads to the rate law[10]:

$$v = k \frac{[HCrO_4^-][Fe^{II}]^2[H^+]^3}{[Fe^{III}]}$$

The most important feature of the rate law is the second order dependence on ferrous ion and inverse first order dependence on ferric ion. The latter is supported by the observation that fluoride ion, which forms a strong complex with ferric but not ferrous ion, greatly accelerates the oxidation.[11]

The effect of ferric ion has been interpreted as follows.[12] The first step is a reversible one in which ferric ion is produced:

$$Cr^{VI} + Fe^{II} \rightleftharpoons Cr^{V} + Fe^{III}$$

Subsequently, chromium(V) reacts with ferrous ion in a rate-determining step by one of the following schemes:

$$
\begin{array}{lll}
\text{(A)} & Cr^{V} + Fe^{II} \rightarrow Cr^{IV} + Fe^{III} & \text{slow} \\
& Cr^{IV} + Fe^{II} \rightarrow Cr^{III} + Fe^{III} & \text{rapid} \\
\text{(B)} & Cr^{V} + Fe^{II} \rightarrow Cr^{III} + Fe^{IV} & \text{slow} \\
& Fe^{IV} + Fe^{II} \rightarrow 2\,Fe^{III} & \text{rapid}
\end{array}
$$

The first of these appears the more reasonable, and the assumption that the chromium(V)–chromium(IV) transformation was the slow step would be in accord with the conclusions reached by Tong and King[13] on the mechanism of the oxidation of chromium(III) with cerium(IV). It has been suggested[13] that chromium(V) has coordination number four and that chromium(IV) has coordination number six. The slow step of conversion from one to the other might then result from the change in coordination number.

3. VANADOUS ION

The oxidation of vanadous ion at a constant acid concentration has been shown to give the rate law[14]:

$$v = \frac{k[VO^{2+}]^2[HCrO_4^-]}{[VO_2^+]}$$

[10] C. Benson, *J. Phys. Chem.* 7, 1, 356 (1903); J. H. Espenson and E. L. King, *J. Am. Chem. Soc.* **85**, 3328 (1963).
[11] R. A. Gortner, *J. Phys. Chem.* **12**, 632 (1908).
[12] C. Wagner and W. Preiss, *Z. Anorg. Allgem. Chem.* **168**, 265 (1928).
[13] J. Y. P. Tong and E. L. King, *J. Am. Chem. Soc.* **82**, 3805 (1960).
[14] J. H. Espenson, *J. Am. Chem. Soc.* **86**, 1883 (1964).

This is similar to the oxidation of ferrous ion, and suggests a similar mechanism:

$$V^{IV} + Cr^{VI} \rightleftharpoons V^V + Cr^V$$

$$V^{IV} + Cr^V \rightarrow V^V + Cr^{IV}$$

$$V^{IV} + Cr^{IV} \rightarrow V^V + Cr^{III}$$

Here again, the second step which may involve a change in coordination number for chromium is rate determining.

4. CHROMIC ION

The reaction between chromium(III) and chromium(VI) has been studied,[15] and the rate law for the slow exchange reaction (using isotopically labeled chromium) was found to be

$$v = [Cr^{III}]^{4/3}[H_2CrO_4]^{2/3}\{k[H^+]^{-2} + k'\}$$

A mechanism which is in accord with the rate law is:

$$\overset{*}{Cr}^{III} + Cr^{VI} \rightleftharpoons \overset{*}{Cr}^{IV} + Cr^V$$

$$\overset{*}{Cr}^{III} + Cr^V \rightleftharpoons Cr^{IV} + \overset{*}{Cr}^{IV} \qquad \text{slow}$$

$$\overset{*}{Cr}^V + Cr^{VI} \rightleftharpoons \overset{*}{Cr}^{VI} + Cr^V$$

Here, the reaction between chromium(III) and chromium(V) is the slow step. An alternate mechanism is the same as above except that the rate-determining step is

$$\overset{*}{Cr}^{III} + Cr^V \rightleftharpoons \overset{*}{Cr}^V + Cr^{III} \qquad \text{slow}$$

One might expect that the first and last steps would be rapid since they do not involve a change in coordination number for any species [assuming again that chromium(IV) has coordination number six as has chromium(III), and that chromium(V) has coordination number four as has chromium(VI)]. The slow step is the one in which the coordination number must change, regardless of which of the two possibilities is chosen.

5. OTHER INORGANIC COMPOUNDS

The chromic acid oxidation of other inorganic species has not received detailed study. In the oxidation of phosphorous acid,[16] manganous ion effects

[15] E. L. King and J. A. Neptune, *J. Am. Chem. Soc.* **77**, 3186 (1955); H. L. Krauss and G. Gnatz, *Chem. Ber.* **92**, 2110 (1959); C. Altman and E. L. King, *J. Am. Chem. Soc.* **83**, 2825 (1961).

[16] N. R. Dhar, *Ann. Chim.* (*Paris*) [9] **11**, 130 (1919); *J. Chem. Soc.* **111**, 707 (1917).

a rate reduction by a factor of two-thirds. Since, under the conditions used, manganese dioxide does not accumulate in the reaction mixture but rather effects disproportionation of chromium(IV) and/or chromium(V) to chromium(III) and chromium(VI), it is reasonable to propose the following series of reactions[6]:

$$HCrO_4^- + H_3PO_3 \rightarrow H_3PO_4 + Cr^{IV}$$

$$Cr^{IV} + Cr^{VI} \rightarrow 2\ Cr^V$$

$$2(Cr^V + H_3PO_3 \rightarrow H_3PO_4 + Cr^{III})$$

or

$$HCrO_4^- + H_3PO_3 \rightarrow H_3PO_4 + Cr^{IV}$$

$$3\ Cr^{IV}(+Mn^{II}) \rightarrow 2\ Cr^{III} + HCrO_4^-(+Mn^{II})$$

The oxidations of bromide[17] and iodide[18] ions have been studied. Both reactions are acid catalyzed, and the former proceeds only in fairly acidic solution. The oxidation of bromide ion is catalyzed by manganous ion. Here, it appears that chromic acid oxidizes manganous ion to Mn^{III}, which effects the oxidation of bromide ion.

The induction factor for iodide ion in the chromic acid oxidation of uranyl ion has been found to be approximately 1 rather than 2 as usually found.[19] Westheimer[6] has suggested the steps:

$$UO^{2+} + Cr^{VI} \rightarrow UO_2^{2+} + Cr^{IV}$$

$$UO^{2+} + Cr^{IV} \rightarrow U^V + Cr^{III}$$

$$U^V + Cr^{VI} \rightarrow U^{VI} + Cr^V$$

$$UO^{2+} + Cr^V \rightarrow UO_2^{2+} + Cr^{III}$$

or

$$Cr^V + 2\ I^- \rightarrow Cr^{III} + I_2$$

IV. Oxidations at Saturated Carbon–Hydrogen Bonds

The chromium(VI) oxidation at saturated carbon–hydrogen bonds may be conveniently divided into three classes: those in which the oxidation occurs α to an aromatic ring; those in which oxidation occurs α to a double bond; and those which involve oxidation of purely aliphatic groupings. The first class has found considerable use in the preparation of aryl carboxylic acids and aromatic aldehydes, as well as for the determination of the orientation of alkyl groups

[17] M. Bobtelsky and A. Glasner, *J. Chem. Soc.* p. 1376 (1948); M. Bobtelsky and A. Rosenberg, *Z. Anorg. Allgem. Chem.* **177**, 137 (1928); **182**, 93 (1929).

[18] R. E. DeLury, *J. Phys. Chem.* **7**, 239 (1903); R. F. Beard and N. W. Taylor, *J. Am. Chem. Soc.* **51**, 1973 (1929).

[19] W. Manchot, *Ber.* **39**, 1352 (1906).

attached to the aromatic nucleus. The other two classes of oxidation have been of less interest in synthetic work because they generally lead to mixtures of compounds which are formed in low yield.

Five different reagents have been frequently used to effect oxidation of carbon–hydrogen bonds by chromium(VI): chromic acid in water, in acetic acid, or in aqueous acetic acid; dichromate ion in aqueous solution at an elevated temperature; chromyl acetate in acetic anhydride or a mixture of acetic acid and acetic anhydride; *tert*-butyl chromate in a variety of solvents; and chromyl chloride in an inert solvent such as carbon disulfide or carbon tetrachloride. In the following discussion, the oxidation of the aryl alkanes will be considered first, followed by allylic oxidation, and the oxidation of alkanes. Each of the applicable species of chromium(VI) will be considered in turn.

A. OXIDATION OF ARYL ALKANES

1. CHROMIC ACID

Benzene itself is relatively resistant to oxidation by chromic acid. The oxidation proceeds very slowly in aqueous sulfuric acid, and leads only to carbon dioxide.[1] In contrast, the polycyclic aromatic hydrocarbons are readily oxidized by chromic acid. As examples, naphthalene is oxidized to 1,4-naphthoquinone and phthalic acid,[2] anthracene is oxidized to anthraquinone,[3] and phenanthrene is oxidized to phenanthraquinone.[4] As a result, in contrast to the successful oxidation of many alkyl substituted benzene derivatives, the chromic acid oxidation of alkyl side chains on polycyclic aromatic hydrocarbons is rarely satisfactory. Thus, 2,3-dimethylnaphthalene on oxidation gives 2,3-dimethyl-1,4-naphthoquinone.[5] The oxidation of these aromatic rings will be considered along with the alkenes.

With acidic chromic acid solutions, the alkyl group of an alkyl benzene, regardless of its length, is finally oxidized to a carboxyl group with the formation of an aromatic carboxylic acid. This provides a general method for the determination of the orientation of alkyl groups in substituted benzenes. Thus, toluene gives benzoic acid,[6] *m*- and *p*-xylene give the corresponding dicarboxylic acids,[7] 1,2,4-trimethylbenzene gives trimellitic acid,[8] and the *m*- and

[1] J. Guyot and L. J. Simon, *Compt. Rend. Acad. Sci.* **170**, 736 (1920).

[2] C. E. Groves, *Ann.* **167**, 357 (1873); F. Beilstein and A. Kurbatow, *Ann.* **202**, 215 (1880).

[3] J. Fritzsche, *J. Prakt. Chem.* [1] **106**, 287 (1869).

[4] R. Wendland and J. LaLonde, *Org. Syn. Coll. Vol.* **IV**, 757 (1963); R. P. Linstead and W. v. E. Doering, *J. Am. Chem. Soc.* **64**, 1998 (1942).

[5] L. I. Smith and I. M. Webster, *J. Am. Chem. Soc.* **59**, 662 (1937).

[6] R. D. Abell, *J. Chem. Soc.* p. 1379 (1951).

[7] R. Fittig, W. Ahrens, and L. Mattheides, *Ann.* **147**, 15 (1868).

[8] G. Schultz, *Ber.* **42**, 3604 (1909).

p-halo- and nitrotoluenes give the corresponding benzoic acids.[9] The older literature gives little information on the yield of product; typical yields appear to be on the order of 40–50%, with much of the remainder of the reaction involving ring oxidation.[10]

The oxidation of toluene has been examined in some detail. Abell[6] determined the composition of the residues from large-scale oxidations of toluene with aqueous acidic dichromate solution and was able to identify o-, m-, and p-tolyldiphenylmethanes, o-, m-, and p-tolyl phenyl ketones, and smaller amounts of benzyl alcohol, dibenzyl, anthraquinone, and diphenylmethane. All of these were formed in quite small amounts compared with benzoic acid.

With longer chains, the position of initial attack appears to be at the α position to the aromatic ring. Thus, ethylbenzene gives benzoic acid along with some acetophenone using chromic acid in acetic acid.[11] tert-Butylbenzene, having no α hydrogens, is very resistant to oxidation. With 1,4-di-tert-butyl-benzene, the aromatic ring is oxidized giving 2,5-di-tert-butylbenzoquinone.[12] The oxidation of n-propylbenzene[13] and n-octylbenzene,[14] under the conditions used, gave only benzoic acid.

The other products of the oxidation of aryl alkanes with aqueous acidic chromic acid have been investigated.[15] Besides benzoic acid, n-propylbenzene gave acetic acid; n-butylbenzene gave propionic and acetic acids; n-amyl-benzene gave butyric, propionic, and acetic acids; and n-hexylbenzene gave valeric, butyric, propionic, and acetic acids. With n-heptylbenzene, the quantity of caproic acid formed was too small to be detected by paper chromatography. The oxidation appears to provide a method for determining the nature of the alkyl group attached to the ring up to C-6. It will also distinguish between n-alkyl and sec-alkyl groups since isopropylbenzene, for example, gives only benzoic acid.

The oxidation of secondary alkyl groups such as in 2-butylbenzene also occurs at the carbon–hydrogen bond adjacent to the aromatic ring. The products of the reaction, usually a ketone and the carboxylic acid, may be considered to be formed via initial formation of a tertiary alcohol followed by dehydration and oxidation of the alkene which is formed.

[9] E. Wroblewsky, Ann. **168**, 147 (1873); F. Beilstein and P. Geitner, Ann. **139**, 331 (1866); F. Beilstein and A. Kuhlberg, Ann. **156**, 66 (1870).

[10] S. G. Brandenberger, L. W. Maas, and I. Dvoretzky, J. Am. Chem. Soc. **83**, 2146 (1961).

[11] C. Friedel and M. Balsohn, Bull. Soc. Chim. France [2] **32**, 615 (1879).

[12] E. Boedtker, Bull. Soc. Chim. France [3] **31**, 965 (1904).

[13] R. Fittig, C. Schaeffer, and J. König, Ann. **149**, 321 (1869).

[14] E. A. von Schweinitz, Ber. **19**, 640 (1886).

[15] M. Jurecek, M. Soucek, J. Churacek, and F. Renger, Z. Anal. Chem. **165**, 109 (1959).

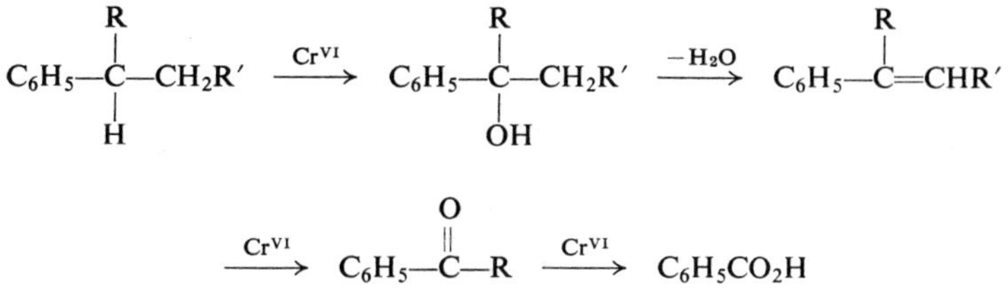

$$C_6H_5-\overset{\overset{\displaystyle R}{|}}{\underset{\underset{\displaystyle H}{|}}{C}}-CH_2R' \xrightarrow{Cr^{VI}} C_6H_5-\overset{\overset{\displaystyle R}{|}}{\underset{\underset{\displaystyle OH}{|}}{C}}-CH_2R' \xrightarrow{-H_2O} C_6H_5-\overset{\overset{\displaystyle R}{|}}{C}=CHR'$$

$$\xrightarrow{Cr^{VI}} C_6H_5-\overset{\overset{\displaystyle O}{||}}{C}-R \xrightarrow{Cr^{VI}} C_6H_5CO_2H$$

As examples, isopropylbenzene gives some 2-phenyl-2-propanol along with acetophenone on oxidation with chromium trioxide in acetic acid[16, 17]; 2-butylbenzene with the same reagent gives benzoic acid and acetophenone[18]; and 2-phenylheptane gives the last two products on oxidation with dichromate in aqueous sulfuric acid.[19] It is sometimes possible to oxidize a tertiary carbon–hydrogen bond in the presence of a methyl group, as with 1-methyl-4-isopropylbenzene which gives *p*-methylacetophenone and, on further oxidation, gives *p*-acetobenzaldehyde, *p*-toluic acid, and terephthalic acid.[17]

1,5-Diethyl-2-isopropylbenzene with dichromate in aqueous sulfuric acid gave the lactone A derived from the oxidation of the ethyl group to carboxyl and the isopropyl group to the corresponding tertiary alcohol.[20] Phenyl-cyclohexane with chromium trioxide in acetic acid gave 3-phenylcyclo-hexenone (B) which is almost certainly derived from the oxidation of the corresponding olefin.[21] Benzoylbutyric acid was also formed as a product.

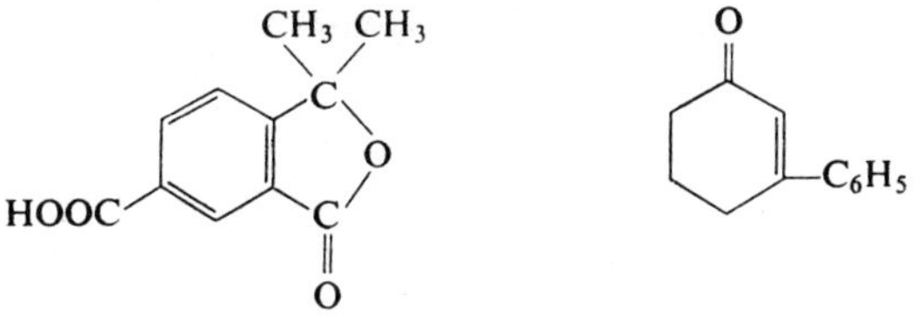

(A)   (B)

As other examples, tetralin is oxidized to α-tetralone,[22] and the following oxidation products were observed with partially hydrogenated anthracene[23] and phenanthrene[24] rings:

[16] E. Boedtker, *Bull. Soc. Chim. France* [3] **25**, 843 (1901).

[17] H. Meyer and K. Bernhauer, *Monatsh.* **53/54**, 721 (1929).

[18] J. Schramm, *Monatsh.* **9**, 613 (1888).

[19] A. Dobrjanski and A. Aliew, *Neft. Khoz.* **9**, 229 (1925); *Chem. Zentr.* p. 676 (1926).

[20] L. Francesconi and L. Venditti, *Gazz. Chim. Ital.* **32**, 309 (1902).

[21] L. F. Fieser and J. Szmuszkovicz, *J. Am. Chem. Soc.* **70**, 3352 (1948).

[22] W. A. Waters, *Nature* **158**, 380 (1946).

[23] M. Godchot, *Compt. Rend. Acad. Sci.* **140**, 250 (1905); *Ann. Chim. (Paris)* [8] **12**, 494 (1907).

[24] G. Schroeter, *Ber.* **57**, 2025 (1924).

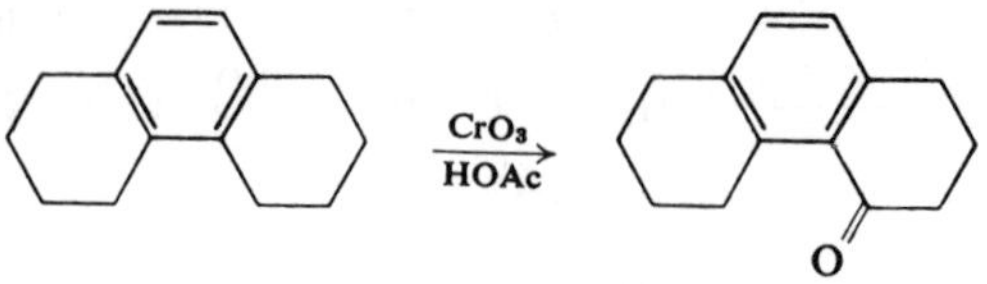

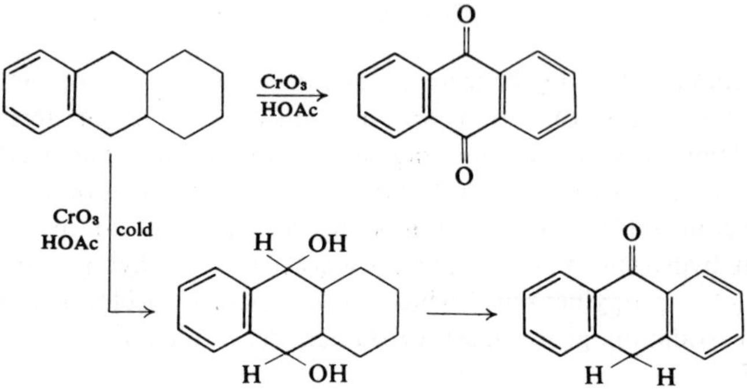

The oxidation of hydrocarbons with two or more aromatic rings follows the same general pattern outlined above. As examples, the phenyltoluenes give the phenylbenzoic acids,[25] and 2,4'-dimethyldiphenyl gives 2-p-tolylbenzoic acid.[26] Further oxidation of the diphenylcarboxylic acids leads to phthalic acids.[26]

In the diphenylmethanes, the methylene group is readily oxidized to a carbonyl group. Thus, diphenylmethane gives benzophenone in good yield,[27] and fluorene gives fluorenone.[28] Similarly, the dibenzylbenzenes are oxidized to the dibenzoylbenzenes[29] and 4-benzyl-n-propylbenzene is oxidized to p-benzoylbenzoic acid.[30] The methylene group is oxidized in preference to reaction at alkyl side chains. Thus, 4,4'-dimethyldiphenylmethane gives 4,4'-dimethylbenzophenone which may be further oxidized to benzophenone-4,4'-dicarboxylic acid.[31]

Whereas the oxidation of 1,1-diphenylethane gives benzophenone, the 1,1-diarylethanes with electron withdrawing group give some rearranged

[25] P. Jacobson, Ber. 28, 2551 (1895); G. Perrier, Bull. Soc. Chim. France [3] 7, 181 (1892); T. Carnelley, J. Chem. Soc. 29, 13 (1876).

[26] T. Carnelley, J. Chem. Soc. 37, 701 (1880).

[27] R. Slack and W. A. Waters, J. Chem. Soc. p. 1666 (1948); N. T. Farinacci, U.S. Patent 2, 794, 813 (1957).

[28] Y. Ogata and H. Akimoto, J. Org. Chem. 27, 294 (1962).

[29] T. Zincke, Ber. 9, 31 (1876); J. Rabzewitsch-Subkowski, J. Russ. Phys.-Chem. Soc. 46, 698 (1914).

[30] R. C. Fuson, J. Am. Chem. Soc. 48, 2937 (1926).

[31] H. Stephen, W. F. Short, and G. Gladding, J. Chem. Soc. p. 520 (1920); J. Weiler, Ber. 7, 1181 (1874).

product.[32] Thus, 1,1-di-(*p*-iodophenyl)ethane gives *p,p'*-diiodobenzophenone and *p*-iodobenzoic acid; and 1,1-di-(*p*-nitrophenyl)ethane gives 30% *p*-nitrobenzoic acid along with the ketone. It was also observed that rearrangement was favored by using higher concentrations of chromium(VI).

When the 1,2-diaryl alkanes are oxidized by chromic acid, the initial point of attack is still at the benzylic carbon, and generally fission of the carbon chain between the two aryl substituted carbons occurs. Rearrangement may also occur. As examples, 1,2-diphenylethane gives benzoic acid and benzophenone[33]; 1,2-diphenylpropane gives benzoic acid, benzophenone, and acetophenone[33]; 3,4-diphenylhexane gives propiophenone[34]; and 1,2-diphenylcyclopentane is oxidized to 1,3-dibenzoylpropane with chromic acid in acetic acid.[35]

The oxidation of triaryl substituted methanes gives the corresponding tertiary alcohol initially, and more vigorous oxidation leads to the breakdown of one aryl group with the formation of a diaryl ketone. Thus, triphenylmethane is oxidized to triphenylcarbinol and benzophenone.[36] Diphenyl-*m*-tolylmethane is oxidized to the tertiary alcohol and *m*-tolyl phenyl ketone by chromium trioxide in acetic acid,[37] and is oxidized to triphenylcarbinol-3-carboxylic acid by boiling aqueous chromic acid.[37] Diphenyl-(2,4-dimethylphenyl)methane (C) is oxidized with chromic acid mixture to 5-methyl-3,3-diphenylphthalide (D) and 3,3-diphenylphthalide-5-carboxylic acid (E).[38]

(C)   (D)   (E)

A typical procedure for the chromic acid oxidation of aryl alkanes follows.

Oxidation of p-Nitrotoluene by Aqueous Acidic Chromic Acid.[39] To a stirred mixture of 680 gm (2.3 moles) of sodium dichromate, 1500 ml of water and

[32] H. H. Szmant and J. F. Deffner, *J. Am. Chem. Soc.* **81**, 958 (1959).

[33] I. Necsoiu and C. D. Nenitzescu, *Acad. Rep. Populare Romine, Studii Cercetari Chim.* **9**, 225 (1961).

[34] A. Lepin and W. Reich, *J. Russ. Phys.-Chem. Soc.* **47**, 149 (1915).

[35] F. R. Japp and C. I. Burton, *J. Chem. Soc.* **51**, 423 (1887).

[36] W. Hemilain, *Ber.* **7**, 1206 (1874); M. Hanroit and O. Saint-Pierre, *Bull. Soc. Chim. France* [3] **1**, 773 (1889).

[37] A. Bistrzycki and J. Gyr, *Ber.* **37**, 1252, 3698 (1904).

[38] W. Hemilain, *Ber.* **16**, 2360 (1883).

[39] O. Kamm and A. O. Matthews, *Org. Syn. Coll. Vol.* **I**, 392 (1941).

TABLE 4-1

OXIDATION OF SUBSTITUTED BENZENES WITH AQUEOUS SODIUM DICHROMATE[a]

Compound	Sodium dichromate (% excess)	Sodium dichromate (gm) Water	Temperature (°C)	Time (hours)	Product	Yield (%)
A. Methyl groups[45]						
m,tert-Butyltoluene	66	0.60	250	18	m,tert-Butylbenzoic acid	71
o,tert-Butyltoluene	45	0.22	250	18	o,tert-Butylbenzoic acid	70
o-Fluorotoluene	100	0.38	250	18	—	—[b]
m-Fluorotoluene	50	0.50	250	18	m-Fluorobenzoic acid	35
p-Fluorotoluene	50	0.33	250	18	p-Fluorobenzoic acid	1[b]
p-Fluorotoluene	50[c]	0.19	250	18	p-Fluorobenzoic acid	55
o-Chlorotoluene	100	0.23	250	18	o-Chlorobenzoic acid	98
m-Chlorotoluene	50	0.33	250	18	m-Chlorobenzoic acid	73
p-Chlorotoluene	50	0.33	250	18	p-Chlorobenzoic acid	88
o-Bromotoluene	50	0.30	250	18	o-Bromobenzoic acid	92
o-Nitrotoluene	—	—	250	18	—	—[b]
m-Nitrotoluene	200[c]	0.17	250	18	m-Nitrobenzoic acid	82
p-Nitrotoluene	200[c]	0.17	250	18	p-Nitrobenzoic acid	94
2-Chloro-p-xylene	50	0.50	250	18	Chloroterephthalic acid	82
2-Bromo-p-xylene	22	0.40	250	18	Bromoterephthalic acid	68
2-Iodo-p-xylene	20	0.25	250	18	Iodoterephthalic acid	83
m-Methoxytoluene	150[c]	0.17	250	18	m-Methoxybenzoic acid	70
2-Methoxy-p-xylene	25[c]	0.25	250	18	Methoxyterephthalic acid	48
Phenyl p-tolyl ether	50	—	250	18	p-Phenoxybenzoic acid	
Di-p-tolyl ether	50	—	250	18	Diphenyl ether 4,4'-dicarboxylic acid	

B. Other alkyl groups[48]

Hydrocarbon		Temp.			Products	Yield (%)
p-Cymene	50	250	0.70	18	Terephthalic acid	92
Ethylbenzene	[a]	275	0.15	1	Phenylacetic acid	96
Ethylbenzene	[a]	300	0.15	1	Benzoic acid; Phenylacetic acid	55 / 12
n-Propylbenzene	[a]	275	0.23	1	Benzoic acid	54[e]
n-Propylbenzene		200	0.23	1	3-Phenylpropionic acid	76
Isopropylbenzene	[a]	275	0.23	1	Benzoic acid; 2-Phenylpropionic acid	24 / 70[e,f]
Isopropylbenzene		275	0.15	1	2-Phenylpropionic acid	84
n-Butylbenzene	[a]	275	0.30	1	Benzoic acid; 4-Phenylbutyric acid	14
n-Butylbenzene		275	0.08	1	4-Phenylbutyric acid	70[e,f]
tert-Butylbenzene	[a]	275	0.30	1	None	

[a] The reactions were carried out in a rocking autoclave.
[b] This compound was degraded by the oxidant.
[c] A phosphate buffer was used in this case.
[d] One mole of sodium dichromate was used per side chain carbon.
[e] The yield was based on the amount of hydrocarbon not recovered.
[f] Less sodium dichromate was used in this case.

230 gm (1.7 moles) of p-nitrotoluene is added 1700 gm of concentrated sulfuric acid over 30 minutes. The heat of dilution of sulfuric acid will cause the nitrotoluene to melt, and rapid oxidation will occur. The last half of the sulfuric acid must be added slowly in order to prevent too violent a reaction.

The mixture is heated to a gentle boil for one-half hour. When the reaction mixture has cooled, 2 liters of water is added, the cooled solution is filtered through a filter cloth, and the product washed with about 1 liter water. The acid is stirred with 1 liter of warm 5 % sulfuric acid, filtered, and dissolved in 5 % sodium hydroxide solution. After filtering, the solution is acidified, filtered, and the acid is washed with water and dried, giving 230–240 gm (82–86 %) of p-nitrobenzoic acid.

A smaller quantity of sulfuric acid must be used for the oxidation of aryl alkanes which are not substituted with electron withdrawing groups.[10]

2. AQUEOUS SODIUM DICHROMATE

The observation that the amount of ring degradation which occurs in the oxidation of xylene and related compounds increases with increasing acid concentration[10] suggests that the use of essentially neutral solutions would effectively suppress attack at the aromatic ring. This has been found to be the case. The oxidation of toluene,[40] the chlorotoluenes,[41] the xylenes,[42] the methylbenzo[c]phenanthrenes,[43] and acenaphthene[44] to their corresponding carboxylic acid, has been effected in good yield using aqueous sodium dichromate at elevated temperatures (200–300° C).

The oxidation has been examined in considerable detail by Friedman and co-workers.[45] The oxidation of methyl side chains (Table 4-1) proceeded very satisfactorily except for o-fluorotoluene, p-fluorotoluene, and o-nitrotoluene. The yield of product was generally superior to that obtained using chromic acid, and the isolation procedure was more simple. In all cases, the reactions were carried out in rocking autoclaves at 250° C for 18 hours.

The main virtue of this procedure is seen in the oxidation of side chains on polynuclear aromatic systems. Here, with chromic acid, ring oxidation occurs in preference to side chain oxidation. With aqueous sodium dichromate, the ring oxidation is made negligible under conditions which permit side chain oxidation. Thus, the methyl naphthalenes are oxidized to the corresponding

[40] Bozel-Maletra Soc. Ind. de Prod. Chim., Paris, German Patent 537, 982 (1930); *Frdl.* **18** (1), 518 (1933).

[41] BIOS Rept. No. 1786.

[42] J. Ogelvie and R. S. Wilder, U.S. Patent 2,379,032 (1945).

[43] M. S. Newman and H. Boden, *J. Org. Chem.* **26**, 1759 (1961).

[44] S. Kato, H. Hashimoto, and H. Sugiyama, *J. Soc. Org. Syn. Japan* **14**, 123 (1956).

[45] L. Friedman, D. L. Fishel, and H. Schechter, *J. Org. Chem.* **30**, 1453 (1965).

naphthoic acids in about 95% yield (Table 4-2), whereas with chromic acid 2-methylnaphthalene gives 2-methyl-1,4-naphthaquinone.[46, 47]

TABLE 4-2

OXIDATION OF SUBSTITUTED POLYCYCLIC AROMATIC HYDROCARBONS
WITH AQUEOUS SODIUM DICHROMATE[45]

Hydrocarbon	Sodium dichromate (% excess)	Product[a]	Yield (%)
1-Methylnaphthalene	42	1-Naphthoic acid	95
2-Methylnaphthalene	55	2-Naphthoic acid	93
1,2-Dimethylnaphthalene	47	1,2-Naphthalic anhydride	75
2,3-Dimethylnaphthalene	23	2,3-Naphthalene dicarboxylic acid	93
1,6-Dimethylnaphthalene	43	1,6-Naphthalene dicarboxylic acid	97
2,6-Dimethylnaphthalene	43	2,6-Naphthalene dicarboxylic acid	99
4-Methylbiphenyl	20	4-Biphenylcarboxylic acid	95
3-Methylfluorenone	34	Fluorenone-3-carboxylic acid	88
1-Methylphenanthrene	40	1-Phenanthroic acid	91
4-Methylphenanthrene	40	4-Phenanthroic acid	91
9-Methylphenanthrene	40	9-Phenanthroic acid	89
1-Methyl-7-isopropylphenanthrene	40	1,7-Phenanthrenedicarboxylic acid	89
9,10-Dimethylphenanthrene	40	9,10-Phenanthrenedicarboxylic anhydride	92
2-Methylanthracene	42	2-Anthroic acid	98
2-Methylanthracene	55	Anthraquinone-2-carboxylic acid	95
2-Methylanthraquinone	40	Anthraquinone-2-carboxylic acid	96
2-Methyltriphenylene	50	2-Triphenylenecarboxylic acid	92
6-Methylchrysene	40	6-Chrysene carboxylic acid	88
5-Methylbenzo[c]phenanthrene	40	5-Benzo[c]phenanthrene carboxylic acid	90
3-Methylfluoranthene	50	3-Fluoranthene carboxylic acid	90
Fluorene	70	Fluorenone	99
4H-Cyclopenta[def]phenanthrene	50	4H-Cyclopenta[def]phenanthrene-4-one	95

[a] All reactions were carried out in a rocking autoclave at 250° C for 18 hours.

It is possible to oxidize some aromatic rings under suitable conditions. Anthracene was oxidized by sodium dichromate at 250° C to anthraquinone (99%), 1,2-benzanthracene was oxidized to 1,2-benzanthraquinone (96%),

[46] L. F. Fieser, W. P. Campbell, E. M. Fry, and M. D. Gates, *J. Am. Chem. Soc.* **61**, 3216 (1939); P. P. T. Sah, *Rec. Trav. Chim.* **59**, 1021 (1940).

[47] It is interesting to contrast this oxidation with that of alkaline permanganate which gives phthalic and phthalonic acids. J. J. Ward, W. R. Kirner, and H. C. Howard, *J. Am. Chem. Soc.* **67**, 246 (1945).

and 4H-cyclopenta[def]phenanthrene was oxidized to 4H-cyclopenta[def]-phenanthren-4-one (94%). At a lower temperature (200° C) anthracene and 1,2-benzanthracene were not attacked; however, pyrene and dihydropyrene were extensively degraded.

The oxidation of alkyl groups other than methyl is particularly noteworthy.[48] The oxidation of ethylbenzene for 1 hour at 275° C gave phenylacetic acid in 96% yield (Table 4-1). More vigorous conditions led to the degradation of the acid to benzoic acid. Similarly, n-propylbenzene gave 3-phenylpropionic acid, isopropylbenzene gave 2-phenylpropionic acid, and n-butylbenzene gave 4-phenylbutyric acid.

Since tert-butylbenzene is not attacked by the oxidant, it appears that the initial attack is probably at the α-carbon to the aromatic ring. However, styrene, α-phenethyl alcohol, and acetophenone could be shown not to be intermediates in the oxidation of ethylbenzene since each gave benzoic acid and no phenylacetic acid under the oxidation conditions used with ethylbenzene.

Typical procedures for the sodium dichromate oxidation of the aryl alkanes follow.

2-Naphthoic Acid.[45] 2-Methylnaphthalene (320 gm, 2.25 moles), sodium dichromate (1050 gm, 3.50 moles, 50% excess), and water (1.8 liters) are shaken in a 3.25 liter autoclave for 18 hours at 250° C. The reactor is emptied at 60° C and the contents filtered to remove chromic oxide. The precipitate is washed with warm water (7 liters) until all of the sodium 2-naphthoate is removed. The aqueous solution is acidified with hydrochloric acid (1:1). After the mixture has cooled overnight, the precipitate is filtered, washed well with water, and air dried, giving 360 gm (2.09 moles, 93%) of 2-naphthoic acid.

Phenylacetic Acid.[46] A mixture of 0.025 mole of ethylbenzene, 0.050 mole of sodium dichromate dihydrate, and 100 ml of water is heated rapidly in a 300 ml autoclave to 275° C and shaken at this temperature for 1 hour. The autoclave is cooled rapidly and the contents filtered. The filtrate is extracted with ether to remove unchanged hydrocarbon, and then acidified with 6 N sulfuric acid. The acid is extracted with ether and isolated, giving 89% phenylacetic acid. From the first ether washing there is isolated 8% ethylbenzene giving a net 96% yield of phenylacetic acid.

3. CHROMYL ACETATE

The use of chromyl acetate for the oxidation of hydrocarbons appears first to have been reported by Thiele and Winter.[49] They found that the oxidation of

[48] R. H. Reitsema and N. L. Allphin, J. Org. Chem. 27, 27 (1962).
[49] J. Thiele and E. Winter, Ann. 311, 356 (1900).

several substituted toluenes with chromium trioxide in acetic anhydride in the presence of a strong acid such as sulfuric acid gave fair to good yields of the corresponding benzal diacetates (Table 4-3).

The reaction of aromatic aldehydes with acetic anhydride in the presence of a strong acid occurs much more rapidly than the oxidation of the aldehyde. The aldehyde diacetate is quite resistant to oxidation and this provides a route for the protection of aldehyde as it is formed. In the absence of the strong acid, the aldehyde is oxidized to the benzoic acid derivative and very little aldehyde may be isolated.[50]

The reaction is generally quite satisfactory for converting a toluene derivative to the corresponding aldehyde diacetate. In most reactions, the major by-product is the corresponding benzoic acid. Electron withdrawing substituents retard the reaction, and in one case, 2-methyl-5-chlorobenzenesulfonyl chloride,[51] the addition of boron trifluoride along with sulfuric acid markedly increased the yield.

Relatively little has been done using alkyl groups other than methyl. In one such case studied, the products were those expected for a chromic acid oxidation, except that complete degradation to benzoic acid did not occur.[52] In the oxidation of 1,2-diphenylethane and 1,2-diphenylpropane, the products were deoxybenzoin, benzaldehyde, and benzoic acid with the former and methyl-deoxybenzoin, acetophenone, and benzoic acid with the latter.[33] These results are in contrast to the oxidation with chromic acid in acetic acid which leads to a rearrangement product, benzophenone, with each of the compounds.

A typical procedure for the chromyl acetate oxidation of a substituted toluene follows.

p-Nitrobenzaldehyde Diacetate.[53] To a stirred solution of 50 gm (0.36 mole) of *p*-nitrotoluene in 400 ml of acetic anhydride which is cooled in an ice-salt bath is slowly added 80 ml of concentrated sulfuric acid. When the mixture has cooled to 0° C, a solution of 100 gm (1.0 mole) of chromium trioxide in 450 ml of acetic anhydride is added slowly, with stirring so that the temperature does not exceed 10° C, and stirring is continued for 2 hours at 5–10° C after the addition is completed. The reaction mixture is poured into two 3-liter beakers one-third filled with chipped ice, and water is added to make the total volume 5–6 liters. The solid is separated by filtration and washed with water until the washings are colorless. The product is suspended in 300 ml of 2% aqueous sodium carbonate solution and stirred. After thorough mixing, the solid is filtered, washed with water, and finally with 20 ml of ethanol. After

[50] P. A. Lepse, Ph. D. Thesis, University of Washington, Seattle, Washington, 1961.
[51] J. M. van der Zanden and G. de Vries, *Rec. Trav. Chim.* **74**, 1429 (1955).
[52] D. P. Archer and W. J. Hickinbottom, *J. Chem. Soc.* p. 4197 (1954).
[53] T. Nishimura, *Org. Syn. Coll. Vol.* **IV**, 713 (1963).

drying in a vacuum desiccator, there is obtained 60–61 gm (65–66%) of
p-nitrobenzaldehyde diacetate.

In preparing the solution of chromyl acetate, it is essential to add the chromium trioxide to the acetic anhydride slowly with cooling and stirring. The addition of acetic anhydride to chromium trioxide usually leads to a fire and often leads to an explosion. The solution of chromyl acetate in acetic anhydride

TABLE 4-3

REACTION OF CHROMYL ACETATE WITH ARYL ALKANES

Compound	Product	Per cent conversion	Reference
p-Xylene	Terephthalaldehyde tetraacetate	52	49
m-Xylene	Isophthalaldehyde tetraacetate	40–50	49
o-Xylene	Phthalaldehyde tetraacetate	14	49
Mesitylene	Mesitylenetrialdehyde hexacetate		54
2-Butylbenzene[a]	Acetophenone	1	52
	Propiophenone	0.5	
	2-Phenylbutan-2-ol acetate	0.5	
p-Nitrotoluene	p-Nitrobenzaldehyde diacetate	65–66	53
o-Nitrotoluene	o-Nitrobenzaldehyde diacetate	36–37	53
p-Bromotoluene	p-Bromobenzaldehyde diacetate	48–60	55
p-Cyanotoluene	p-Cyanobenzaldehyde diacetate	50–55	55
p-Cresyl acetate	p-Hydroxybenzaldehyde triacetate	17–23	49
2,4,6-Triacetoxytoluene	2,4,6-Triacetoxybenzaldehyde diacetate	6	49
Methyl p-tolyl sulfone	p-(Methylsulfonyl)benzaldehyde diacetate	52	56
2-Methyl-5-chloro-benzenesulfonyl chloride	4-Chloro-2-chlorosulfonylbenzaldehyde diacetate	34	51

[a] Based on the amount of hydrocarbon not recovered, the yields were 2, 1, and 1%, respectively.

loses its oxidizing power only slowly, and does not appear to be dangerous, unless heated to a temperature over about 50° C (Table 4-3).[49, 51–56]

4. CHROMYL CHLORIDE

In 1870, Carstanjen[57] reported that the reaction of toluene with chromyl chloride in acetic acid solution led to benzoic acid. Shortly thereafter, Étard[58] found that if an inert solvent such as carbon disulfide or carbon tetrachloride

[54] J. Bielecki, Chem. Zentr. 79, 1623 (1908).
[55] S. V. Lieberman and R. Connor, Org. Syn. Coll. Vol. II, 441 (1943).
[56] M. N. Shchukina and T. P. Sycheva, Zh. Obshchei Khim. 22, 1663 (1952).
[57] E. Carstanjen, J. Prakt. Chem. 110, 51 (1870).
[58] A. Étard, Compt. Rend. Acad. Sci. 84, 127 (1877).

was used in the reaction, a complex was formed with the composition $C_6H_5CH_3 \cdot 2CrO_2Cl_2$. The complex, on treatment with water, gave benzaldehyde in good yield ($\sim 90\%$). This important observation was extended by Étard to a study of the reaction of a large number of organic compounds with chromyl chloride.[59]

The reaction is generally carried out by adding a solution of chromyl chloride in carbon tetrachloride or carbon disulfide to a solution of the hydrocarbon in the same solvent. The reactions with the aryl alkanes are usually exothermic, and external cooling is employed. The Étard complex, which normally has the composition 1 hydrocarbon/$2CrO_2Cl_2$, precipitates from the reaction solution. The brown amorphous material is separated by filtration and added to water or sodium bisulfite solution to give the carbonyl products.

The filtrate, after removal of the Étard complex, usually contains chlorinated hydrocarbons. This is a normal by-product of the reaction, and it appears that chlorine substitution retards further reaction. Thus, benzyl chloride is less reactive than toluene toward chromyl chloride.[58] Halogen substitution in the *ortho* position of toluene appears to favor chlorination. In going from *o*-chloro to *o*-bromo and *o*-iodotoluene, the product changes from aldehyde and some of the benzal chloride to little aldehyde and mainly benzal chloride.[60] Whether this change in product is due to an electronic effect of the halogen atom, or whether it is a steric effect is not clear from the available data.

The reaction of *o*-nitrotoluene is of particular interest. Here, an Étard complex with an apparently normal composition is formed, but on treatment with water, it gives only a trace of *o*-nitrobenzaldehyde and mainly unchanged *o*-nitrotoluene.[61, 62] In this case, it appears as if an insoluble complex were formed between the nitrotoluene and chromyl chloride without oxidation having occurred. There is a suggestion that complex formation precedes the oxidation step in other cases.[63]

The Étard oxidation of triphenylmethane raises some interesting questions. The complex was first reported to have the composition $(C_6H_5)_3CH \cdot CrO_2Cl_2$.[64] More recently, Necsoiu *et al.*[65] have reported that the complex has the composition $(C_6H_5)_3CH \cdot 2CrO_2Cl_2$. To add to the confusion, triphenylmethane

[59] A. Étard, *Bull. Soc. Chim. France* [2] **27**, 249, 275 (1877); *Compt. Rend. Acad. Sci.* **84**, 391, 614, 951 (1877); **87**, 989 (1878); **90**, 534 (1880); **97**, 909 (1883); **116**, 434 (1893); **120**, 1058 (1891); *Ann. Chim. Phys.* [5] **22**, 218 (1881).

[60] C. M. Stuart and W. J. Elliott, *J. Chem. Soc.* **53**, 803 (1888).

[61] V. von Richter, *Ber.* **19**, 1060 (1886); H. D. Law and F. M. Perkin, *J. Chem. Soc.* **93**, 1633 (1908).

[62] L. V. Sulima and I. P. Gragerov, *J. Gen. Chem. USSR* (*Engl. Transl.*) **29**, 3787 (1959).

[63] O. H. Wheeler, *Can. J. Chem.* **38**, 2137 (1960).

[64] W. H. Hartford and M. Darrin, *Chem. Rev.* **58**, 39 (1958).

[65] I. Necsoiu, A. T. Balaban, I. Pascaru, E. Sliam, M. Elian, and C. D. Nenitzescu, *Tetrahedron* **19**, 1133 (1963).

has been oxidized using one and one-half equivalents of chromyl chloride giving 90 % of triphenylcarbinol.[62] It would appear that only one equivalent is necessary, and that the initial product formed a complex with a second chromyl chloride if an excess of the latter were used.

The complex from triphenylmethane, on treatment with ether, regenerated triphenylmethane.[62] On treatment with water–O^{18}, the complex gave triphenylcarbinol with an oxygen-18 content indicating that 80 % of the oxygen came from water and that only 20 % came from the oxidizing agent.[62] It appears that the triarylmethyl cation was formed during the decomposition reaction and that it reacted with water to give the labeled triphenylcarbinol and with ether to give triphenylmethane via a hydride abstraction. This latter type of process may also explain the formation of benzhydrol in the decomposition of the Étard complex from diphenylmethane with a solution of sulfur dioxide in acetic acid.[65] The normal decomposition of the Étard complex gives benzophenone.

We have seen previously that the oxidation of aryl alkanes with chromic acid gives largely oxidation at the carbon attached to the aromatic ring, and that the oxidation using aqueous sodium dichromate gives oxidation principally at the end of the aliphatic chain rather than at the α-position. The data of Table 4-4 show that the Étard reaction occurs preferentially at the carbon-one-removed from the aromatic ring. Thus ethylbenzene gives phenylacetaldehyde as the major oxidation product.[58, 66] Similar results have been obtained with cumene, cymene, and n-propylbenzene (Table 4-4).[67–74]

A typical procedure for the oxidation of an aryl alkane with chromyl chloride follows.

p-Iodobenzaldehyde.[67] To a solution of 43.6 gm (0.2 mole) of *p*-iodotoluene in 150 ml of carbon tetrachloride is added dropwise, with stirring and ice-water cooling, a solution of 65.2 gm (0.42 mole) of chromyl chloride in 150 ml of carbon tetrachloride. The addition requires 1 hour, the solution is stirred at room temperature for an hour, and is heated to reflux for 20 hours. The cooled solution is slowly poured into a stirred mixture of 60 gm of sodium sulfite, 300 gm water, and 300 gm ice. Diluted (1:1) hydrochloric acid is added to

[66] W. v. Miller and G. Rohde, *Ber.* **23**, 1070 (1890); **24**, 1356 (1891).

[67] O. H. Wheeler, *Can. J. Chem.* **36**, 667 (1958).

[68] H. D. Law and F. M. Perkin, *J. Chem. Soc.* **91**, 258 (1907); **93**, 1633 (1908).

[69] V. von Richter, *Ber.* **19**, 1060 (1886).

[70] W. v. Miller and G. Rohde, *Ber.* **23**, 1070 (1890); **24**, 1356 (1891).

[71] W. Dollfus, *Ber.* **26**, 1970 (1893).

[72] K. B. Wiberg, B. M. Marshall and G. Foster, *Tetrahedron Letters* p. 345 (1962).

[73] M. Weiler, *Ber.* **32**, 1050 (1899).

[74] O. H. Wheeler, *Can. J. Chem.* **36**, 949 (1958).

TABLE 4-4

REACTION OF CHROMYL CHLORIDE WITH ARYL ALKANES

Compound	Product	Per cent conversion[a]	Reference
Toluene	Benzaldehyde	90	64
Benzyl chloride	Benzaldehyde		59
Benzal chloride	No reaction		64
o-Xylene	o-Tolualdehyde	65	67, 68
m-Xylene	m-Tolualdehyde	60	67, 68
p-Xylene	p-Tolualdehyde	70–80	67, 68
p-Fluorotoluene	p-Fluorobenzaldehyde	35	67
o-Chlorotoluene	o-Chlorobenzaldehyde	52	60, 67, 68
m-Chlorotoluene	m-Chlorobenzaldehyde	45	67
p-Chlorotoluene	p-Chlorobenzaldehyde	75	67, 68
o-Bromotoluene	o-Bromobenzaldehyde	57	60, 67
	o-Bromobenzal chloride		
p-Bromotoluene	p-Bromobenzaldehyde	78	67
o-Iodotoluene	o-Iodobenzaldehyde	14	60, 67
	o-Iodobenzal chloride		
o-Nitrotoluene	o-Nitrobenzaldehyde	7	67
m-Nitrotoluene	m-Nitrobenzaldehyde	41	68
p-Nitrotoluene	p-Nitrobenzaldehyde	60–70	68, 69
p-Methoxytoluene	p-Methoxybenzaldehyde	0	67
p-Hydroxytoluene	p-Hydroxybenzaldehyde	0	67
p-Mercaptotoluene	p-Mercaptobenzaldehyde	0	67
p-Chloromethyltoluene	p-Chloromethylbenzaldehyde	3	67
p-Cyanotoluene	p-Cyanobenzaldehyde	1	67
Mesitylene	3,5-Dimethylbenzaldehyde	6	68
Ethylbenzene	Phenylacetaldehyde	Mainly	70
	Acetophenone	Little	
	Benzaldehyde	Little	
n-Propylbenzene	Benzyl methyl ketone	26	70–72
	Propiophenone	6	
	α-Chloropropylbenzene	26	
Cumene	Hydratropaldehyde	Mainly	70
	Acetophenone	Little	
Cymene	p-Methylhydratropaldehyde	Mainly	70
	p-Tolyl methyl ketone	Little	
p-Benzyltoluene	Phenyl p-tolyl ketone	55	73
p,p'-Bitolyl	p-(p'-Tolyl)benzaldehyde		73
Bibenzyl	Benzaldehyde	12	73
	Deoxybenzoin		
	Benzil	6	
	Benzoin	4	

[a] In many cases, considerable hydrocarbon is recovered and the actual yield is higher than the per cent conversion.

TABLE 4-4—*continued*

REACTION OF CHROMYL CHLORIDE WITH ARYL ALKANES

Compound	Product	Per cent conversion[a]	Reference
Diphenylmethane	Benzophenone	"Quant"	65, 68
Triphenylmethane	Triphenylcarbinol	93	62, 65
9-Methylanthracene	Anthraquinone	70	74
2-Methylanthracene	2-Methylanthraquinone	42	74
9-Methylphenanthrene	9-Phenanthraldehyde	30	74
	Phenanthraquinone	18	74
Fluorene	Fluorenone	35	74
2-Picoline	Unchanged reactant		74
2-Picoline-N-oxide	Unchanged reactant		74
3-Methylthiophene	Unchanged reactant		74

[a] In many cases, considerable hydrocarbon is recovered and the actual yield is higher than the per cent conversion.

dissolve chromium salts, the organic layer is separated, and the aqueous layer is extracted with carbon tetrachloride. The combined organic solution is washed with water, dried, and distilled, giving 27–30 gm (58–64%) of *p*-iodobenzaldehyde, b.p. 145–150° C at 25 mm Hg, m.p. 55–65° C.

5. MECHANISM OF THE CHROMIUM(VI) OXIDATION OF ARYL ALKANES

The first detailed study of the oxidation of aryl alkanes with chromic acid was reported by Slack and Waters.[75] They studied the oxidations of diphenyl-methane and triphenylmethane using glacial acetic acid as the solvent. The oxidation of diphenylmethane gave benzophenone along with *sym*-tetra-phenylethane (2%) and traces of benzoic acid, phenol, and succinic acid. Triphenylmethane gave triphenylcarbinol and a small amount of benzo-phenone. In both cases, an initial rapid reaction occurred, followed by slowing, and finally cessation of the reaction with about 17% of the oxidizing power remaining.

The decrease in rate of reaction with increasing time appears to be due to the production of acetate ion during the reaction. In the presence of excess strong acid such as sulfuric acid, the rate of reaction was essentially constant throughout the reaction. The addition of acetate ion retarded the reaction, whereas chromic ion had no effect.[76]

The oxidation of toluene to benzoic acid was studied under similar conditions

[75] R. Slack and W. A. Waters, *J. Chem. Soc.* p. 1666 (1948); p. 599 (1949).
[76] J. Roček and F. Šorm, *Collection Czech. Chem. Commun.* **20**, 1009 (1955); J. Roček, *ibid.* **20**, 1249 (1955).

by Ogata and co-workers.[77] The kinetic behavior was of the same type as that observed with diphenylmethane. However, the form of the rate expression differed with change of substituents, apparently due to a change in stoichiometry. The major difficulties in interpreting the data obtained in these two investigations lie in the facts that glacial acetic acid was used as the solvent, and that the hydrogen ion concentration was not maintained constant. The form of chromium(VI) in acetic acid is not known; it may well be in the form of dimers, trimers, and larger units. Actually, the solubility of chromium trioxide in acetic acid is very low (0.1 % or less),[76] suggesting that the solution used in the above investigations contained some impurity which facilitated the solution of the chromium trioxide.

TABLE 4-5

RELATIVE RATES OF OXIDATION BY CHROMIC
ACID IN 95% ACETIC ACID[a],[78]

Compound	Relative rate
Benzhydrol	30,000
Benzaldehyde	100
Fluorene	30
Anisole	3.4
Triphenylmethane	1.3
Diphenylmethane	1.00
Ethylbenzene	0.50
Toluene	0.16
Methylcyclohexane	0.08
Neopentylbenzene	0.03
Cyclohexane	0.01

[a] In 99% acetic acid, the relative rates of oxidation of toluene, ethylbenzene, isopropylbenzene and *tert*-butylbenzene were found to be 1:7.2:71.1:0.019 [F. Mareš and J. Roček, *Collection Czech. Chem. Commun.* **26**, 2370 (1961)].

In order to minimize these difficulties, Wiberg and Evans[78] studied the oxidation of diphenylmethane and several other compounds in 95% aqueous acetic acid using an acid catalyst in large concentration compared with that of the chromium(VI). These conditions are similar to those commonly used in synthetic experiments, but may lead to a different reaction than that studied by

[77] Y. Ogata, A. Fukui, and S. Yuguchi, *J. Am. Chem. Soc.* **74**, 2707 (1952); cf. Y. Ogata and H. Akimoto, *J. Org. Chem.* **27**, 294 (1962).
[78] K. B. Wiberg and R. J. Evans, *Tetrahedron* **8**, 313 (1960).

Slack and Waters, and Ogata *et al.* The relative rates of oxidation of a number of hydrocarbons and related compounds are summarized in Table 4-5.

The oxidation of diphenylmethane was studied in detail.[78] The reaction followed the rate law

$$v = k[CrO_3] [\text{diphenylmethane}]h_0$$

where h_0 is the Hammett acidity function.[79] When the reacting hydrogen was replaced by deuterium, the rate of reaction was decreased by a factor of 6.4 at 30° C. The introduction of a *p*-methyl group caused a small rate increase, whereas a *p*-nitro group caused a small rate decrease. The effect of substituents could be correlated with a reaction constant, ρ^+, of -1.40. This is similar to the effect of substituents observed by Ogata *et al.*[77] in the oxidation of toluene.

The observation of a kinetic isotope effect demonstrates that the cleavage of the carbon–hydrogen bond occurs in the rate-determining step. The possible mechanisms for this step include

(A) $R_3CH + Cr^{VI} \longrightarrow R_3C^+ + Cr^{IV}$

(B) $R_3C\overset{\cdot}{H} + Cr^{VI} \longrightarrow R_3C^{\cdot} + Cr^V$

(C) R_3C——$H \longrightarrow R_3C$—O—Cr^{IV}

Any one of these mechanisms will account for the preferential oxidation at the α-position to the aromatic ring. The small difference in rate of reaction between toluene, diphenylmethane and triphenylmethane, and the small value of ρ^+ observed in the oxidation demonstrate that process (A) cannot be correct. Considerably larger structural effects and effects of substituents would be expected for this mechanism.[78, 80] On the other hand, either mechanism (B) or mechanism (C) will account for the available data.

It is not possible to distinguish between mechanisms (B) and (C) based on the data presently available. There is evidence favoring (B) in the oxidation of the alkanes, and therefore (B) will be assumed in the following discussion. It should however be noted that the radical, if formed, is probably oxidized by one of the chromium species, possibly forming an ester similar to that formed in process (C).

The steps leading from the radical to benzophenone, in the case of diphenylmethane, cannot readily be studied since they follow the rate-determining step.

[79] Cf. M. A. Paul and F. A. Long, *Chem. Rev.* **57**, 1 (1957).
[80] K. B. Wiberg and R. Eisenthal, *Tetrahedron* **20**, 1151 (1964).

If the alcohol, benzhydrol, is formed as a reaction intermediate, the data of Table 4-5 indicate that it would rapidly be oxidized to benzophenone. However, there is no evidence showing that it is formed as an intermediate.

Some information on the steps following the slow step may be obtained from nonkinetic data. The chromic acid oxidation of (+)-o-2-butylbenzoic acid gives the lactone A with inversion of configuration [81]:

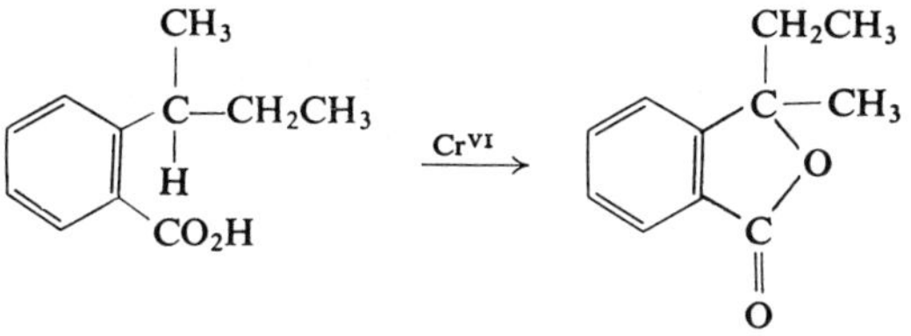

(A)

A simple explanation of this result would be that the radical first formed reacts with the adjacent chromium(V) to give a chromium(IV) ester with retention of configuration. Solvolysis of the ester with carbon–oxygen bond cleavage may then occur with participation of the carboxyl group leading to the lactone with net inversion of configuration.

A similar hypothesis will account for the partial rearrangement of 1,1-diaryl and 1,2-diarylethanes. The formation of a chromium(IV) ester might be followed by an elimination reaction giving the alkene. The rearranged products are those expected from the oxidation of the alkene [33]:

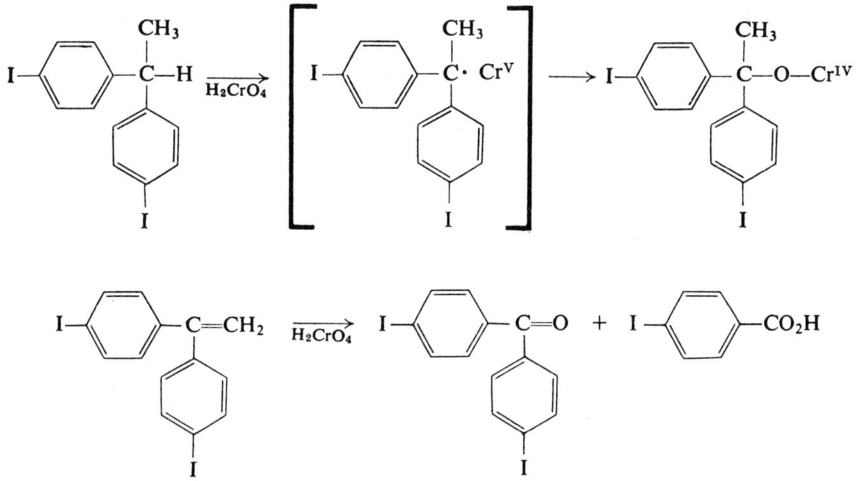

[81] E. C. Kramer, Jr., Ph. D. Thesis, Rutgers University, New Brunswick, New Jersey, 1959; *Dissertation Abstr.* **20**, 1584 (1959).

No study of the mechanism of the aqueous sodium dichromate oxidation of aryl alkanes has as yet been reported. The reaction appears to be initiated at the position α to the aromatic ring since *tert*-butylbenzene is unreactive.[48] The further reaction must involve the migration of the site of oxidation down the chain to the end, perhaps in a fashion resembling that of the Willgerodt reaction.

The mechanism of the oxidation of aryl alkanes with chromyl acetate in acetic anhydride has received little study. Some preliminary data show that the reaction proceeds in two steps with chromium(V) being a probable intermediate.[50] The behavior is similar to that observed in the oxidation of aromatic aldehydes, which will be discussed in detail in a later section.

Considerably more data are available concerning the oxidation of aryl alkanes with chromyl chloride. The reaction of chromyl chloride with toluene is first order in both reactants.[82] The complex, with a composition $C_6H_5CH_3 \cdot 2CrO_2Cl_2$, is converted on heating to a new complex, $C_6H_5CH_2 \cdot Cr_2O_4Cl_2$, by loss of hydrogen chloride.[58] The reactions with toluene and with triphenylmethane show a kinetic hydrogen isotope effect, and thus it may be presumed that the rate-determining step involves carbon–hydrogen bond cleavage.[83] Finally, the relative rates of oxidation of toluene, diphenylmethane, and triphenylmethane are $1:100:1000$.[82]

The relative rates of reaction appear to be too small to be attributed to a carbonium ion mechanism. For example, the solvolyses of benzyl chloride, benzhydryl chloride, and triphenylmethyl chloride in aqueous ethanol have the relative rates of $1:10^5:10^7$.[84] Thus, the initial step probably involves either a hydrogen atom abstraction or a cyclic process. If the former is correct, the radical formed may react with either chromyl chloride or the $HCrO_2Cl_2$ formed as a result of the hydrogen atom abstraction process. The possibilities are then:

(A) $\quad R_3CH + CrO_2Cl_2 \longrightarrow [R_3C^{\cdot} HCrO_2Cl_2]$

$\quad\quad [R_3C^{\cdot} HCrO_2Cl_2] \longrightarrow R_3C—O—Cr(OH)Cl_2$

(B) $\quad R_3CH + CrO_2Cl_2 \longrightarrow R_3C^{\cdot} + HCrO_2Cl_2$

$\quad\quad R_3C^{\cdot} + CrO_2Cl_2 \longrightarrow R_3C—O—CrOCl_2$

$\quad\quad R_3C—O—CrOCl_2 + R_3CH \longrightarrow R_3C—O—Cr(OH)Cl_2 + R_3C^{\cdot}$

[82] R. A. Stairs and J. W. Burns, *Can. J. Chem.* **39**, 960 (1961); cf. R. A. Stairs, *Can. J. Chem.* **40**, 1656 (1962).

[83] I. P. Gragerev and M. P. Ponomarchuk, *J. Gen. Chem. USSR (Engl. Transl.)* **32**, 3501 (1962); O. H. Wheeler, *Can. J. Chem.* **42**, 706 (1964).

[84] A. Streitwieser, Jr., *Chem. Rev.* **56**, 571 (1956).

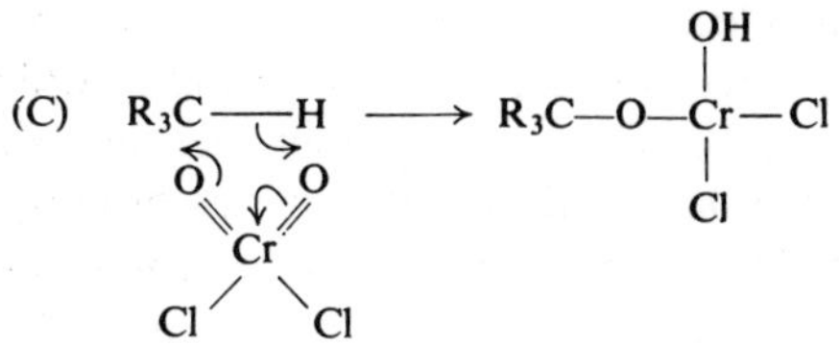

(C) R_3C——H $\longrightarrow$ R_3C—O—$\overset{\overset{\displaystyle OH}{|}}{\underset{\underset{\displaystyle Cl}{|}}{Cr}}$—Cl

The first involves cage recombination of the species formed in the primary step, whereas in the second, the carbon radical first formed reacts with chromyl chloride in a chain process. Any of the three will account for the data on the oxidation. Mechanisms (A) and (B) are preferred by this writer because they permit a ready explanation of the formation of chlorinated products as by-products of the reaction. The carbon radical need only attack the chromium derivative at chlorine rather than at oxygen. The rate of reaction of carbon radicals with oxidants such as chromium(VI) would be expected to be large, and one would not generally expect to find products derived from the coupling of these radicals. Thus the observation that these compounds are not formed is not opposed to this type of mechanism. It is possible for the chlorinated products to arise from a mechanism similar to (C), although this makes the two processes independent.

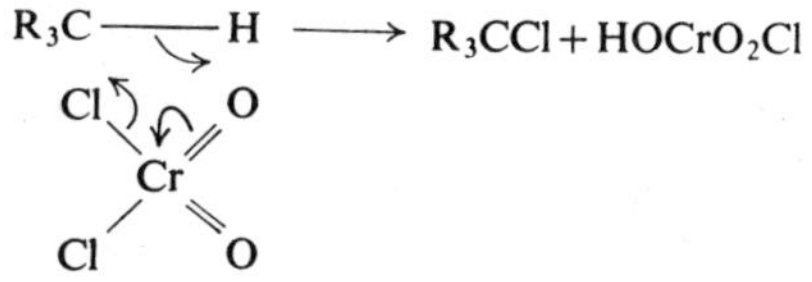

R_3C——H $\longrightarrow$ $R_3CCl + HOCrO_2Cl$

In any event, the first stable intermediate formed is probably the chromium-(IV) ester. In the case of toluene and substituted toluenes, the intermediate probably reacts with another equivalent of chromyl chloride to give the Étard complex having the structure A:

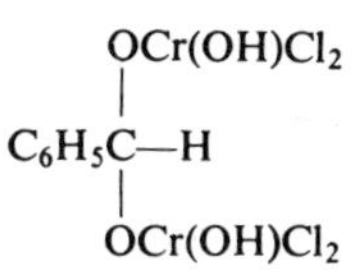

$\underset{\underset{\displaystyle OCr(OH)Cl_2}{|}}{\overset{\overset{\displaystyle OCr(OH)Cl_2}{|}}{C_6H_5C}}$—H

(A)

C_6H_5—CH $\begin{array}{c} O—Cr \overset{Cl}{\underset{Cl}{<}} \\ \diagup \qquad \diagdown \\ O—Cr—OH \\ | \\ Cl \end{array}$

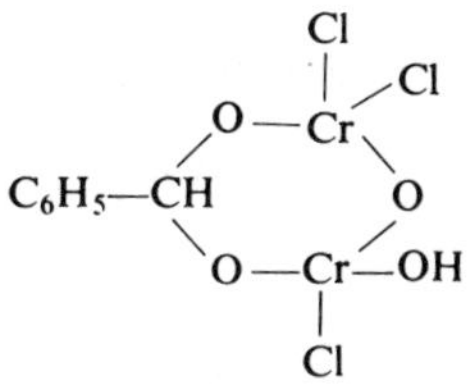

(B)

On heating, loss of hydrogen chloride may occur to give the structure B. Either of these would give benzaldehyde on treatment with water.

The magnetic susceptibility of the Étard complex derived from toluene has been determined, and the value corresponds with that expected for a compound

containing chromium(IV).[63] The electron spin resonance absorption of the
Étard complex was at first interpreted to indicate a compound in which one
chromium was in oxidation state 4, whereas the other was in oxidation
state 6.[65] A reinterpretation of the data indicated that it was fit more satisfactorily by assuming that both chromium atoms were in oxidation state 4.[80]

The oxidation of longer side chains probably occurs via the same initial step.
Thus, for example, *tert*-butylbenzene reacts only very slowly with chromyl
chloride and does not give the type of Étard complex formed by the other aryl
alkanes,[63] indicating the importance of the position α to the aromatic ring.
The products of the reaction are a function of the relative concentrations of
the two reactants in the oxidation mixture. Thus, for example, the oxidation
of *n*-propylbenzene gives largely benzyl methyl ketone when a low concentration of chromyl chloride is maintained, whereas the major product is
propiophenone if a relatively large concentration of chromyl chloride is used.[72]

These data indicate that the formation of products of oxidation at the α-
and β-positions to the aromatic ring involve two independent reactions
following the initial reaction. It is reasonable to conclude that the reaction of
the initial intermediate which gives β-oxidation products is independent of the
chromyl chloride concentration, and that the reaction which leads to α-
oxidation is dependent on the latter. A possible scheme is shown here. Evidence

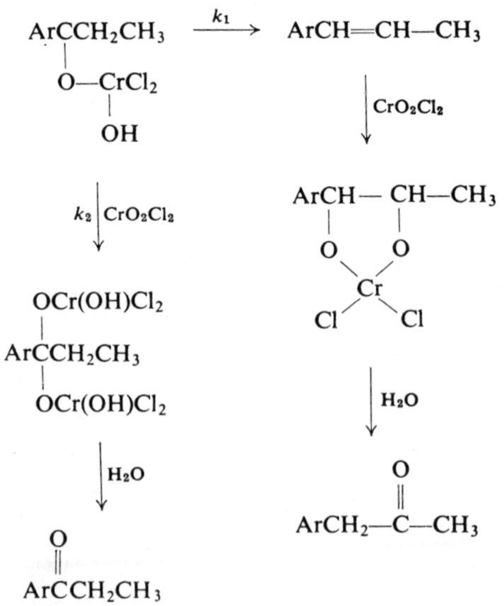

$$ArCCH_2CH_3 \xrightarrow{k_1} ArCH{=}CH{-}CH_3$$

$$\underset{OH}{\overset{O-CrCl_2}{|}}$$

$$\downarrow CrO_2Cl_2$$

$$k_2 \downarrow CrO_2Cl_2 \qquad ArCH{-}CH{-}CH_3$$

$$\underset{\underset{Cl}{\overset{Cr}{/}}\overset{}{\underset{Cl}{\backslash}}}{\overset{O\quad O}{|\quad|}}$$

$$\underset{OCr(OH)Cl_2}{\overset{OCr(OH)Cl_2}{|}}ArCCH_2CH_3$$

$$\downarrow H_2O$$

$$\downarrow H_2O \qquad \overset{O}{\overset{\|}{ArCH_2{-}C{-}CH_3}}$$

$$\overset{O}{\overset{\|}{ArCCH_2CH_3}}$$

supporting this scheme includes the following. The oxidation of 1-phenyl-
propene with chromyl chloride gave only benzyl methyl ketone, formed via
pinacol rearrangement of the addition compound, or rearrangement of the

latter during hydrolysis. The oxidation of *n*-propyl-β,β-d₂-benzene with chromyl chloride gave benzyl methyl ketone containing deuterium in the α-position, showing that the pinacol rearrangement had occurred.[72]

B. ALLYLIC OXIDATION

1. CHROMYL ACETATE

Some of the first examples of allylic oxidation by chromium(VI) were reported by Treibs and Schmidt.[85] Using a solution of chromium trioxide in a mixture of acetic anhydride and carbon tetrachloride, they were able to effect the oxidation of α-pinene to verbenone and verbenol; of dipentene to carvone and carveol; and of cyclohexene to cyclohexanol and cyclohexenone. In no case were the yields very satisfactory, and this procedure does not appear to have significant synthetic use. In a study of the oxidation of a variety of alkenes with chromyl acetate, Hickinbottom and his co-workers have found allylic oxidation to be a relatively minor reaction except in the case of cyclohexene.[86]

2. CHROMIC ACID

In an investigation of the oxidation of alkenes by chromic acid, Whitmore and Pedlow[87] observed that, in some cases, allylic oxidation occurred. Thus, cyclohexene could be converted to cyclohexenone (37%) along with adipic acid (25%), and 1-methylcyclohexene could be converted to 1-methylcyclohex-1-en-3-one (20%) and 2-methylcyclohex-1-en-3-one (2%). This appears to be one of the more satisfactory methods for obtaining cyclohexenone, but it does not appear to have found wide use:

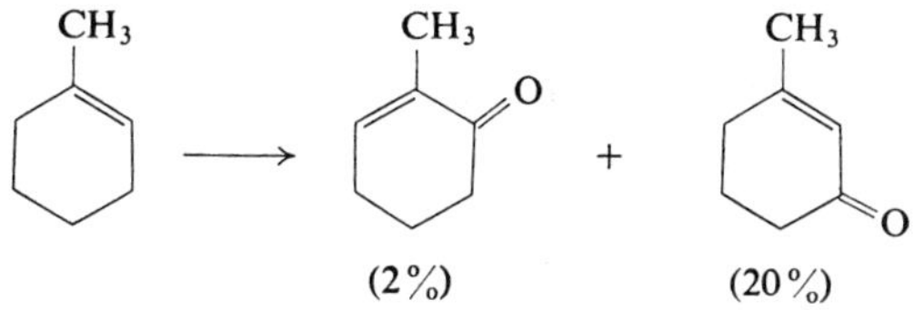

Allylic oxidation by chromic acid appears to be a relatively minor reaction with straight chain alkenes (see the discussion of oxidation of the double bond).

[85] W. Treibs and H. Schmidt, *Ber.* **61**, 459 (1928).
[86] See the discussion in Section V.
[87] F. C. Whitmore and G. W. Pedlow, *J. Am. Chem. Soc.* **63**, 758 (1941).

However, the cycloalkyl groups of a number of steroidal alkenes do undergo allylic oxidation. A typical reaction is shown here.[88]

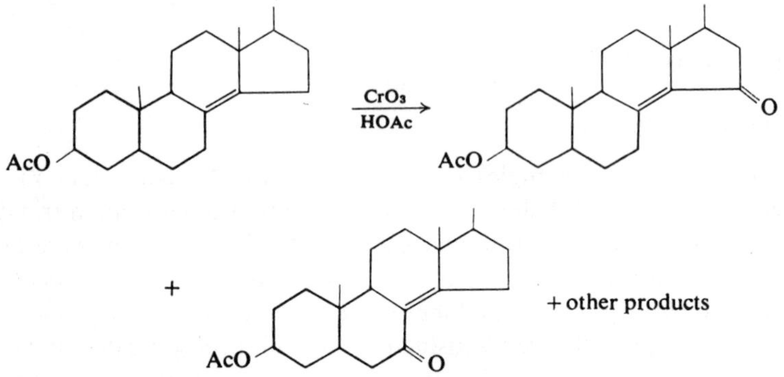

Oxidation of the double bond to an epoxide usually accompanies this reaction. The reactions of these compounds are considered in more detail in connection with oxidation of alkenes.

3. DI-*tert*-BUTYL CHROMATE

Allylic oxidation using di-*tert*-butyl chromate was first reported by Oppenauer and Oberrauch.[89] Using a solution of the reagent in a nonpolar organic compound (such as benzene) with added acetic anhydride, they were able to convert cyclohexene into cyclohexenone (40%) and *p*-quinone (24%); *β*-ionone to 4-ketoionone (38%):

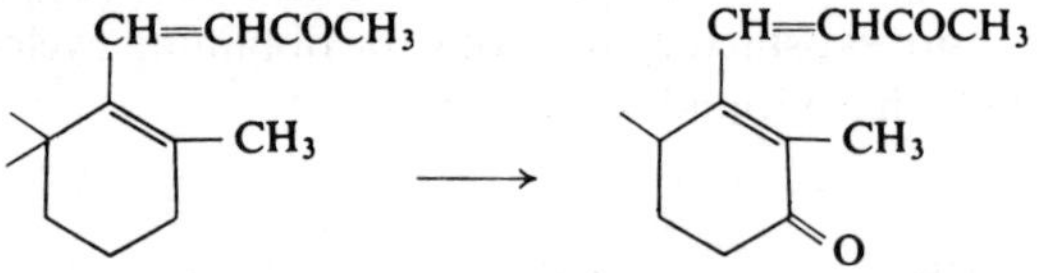

and cholesteryl acetate to 7-ketocholesteryl acetate (90%):

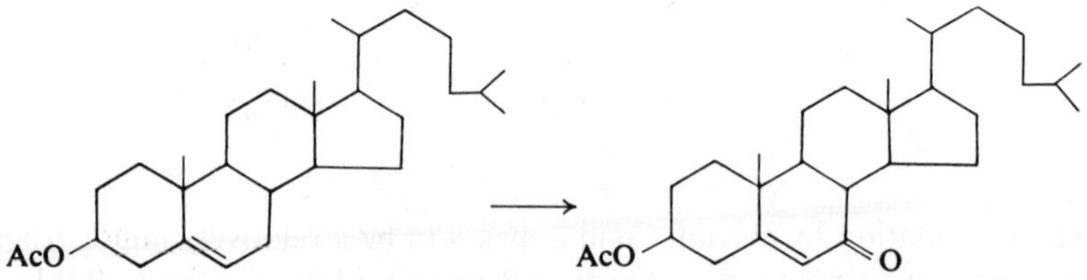

The nature of the reagent used is not clear. It may actually be diacetyl chromate

[88] H. E. Stavely and G. N. Bollenback, *J. Am. Chem. Soc.* **65**, 1285 (1943).
[89] R. V. Oppenauer and H. Oberrauch, *Anales Asoc. Quim. Arg.* **37**, 246 (1949).

formed by a reaction of the *tert*-butyl chromate with the acetic anhydride which is added to the solvent.

A number of other examples of this type of oxidation have been reported. The oxidation of α-pinene gives verbenone (38%) and a small amount of verbenol[90, 91]:

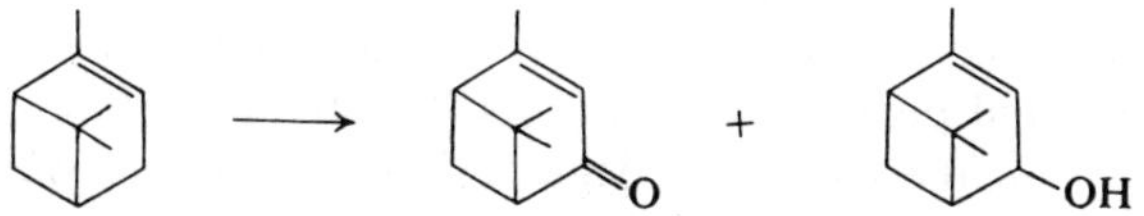

Carvomenthene gives carvotanacetone and piperitone[91, 92]

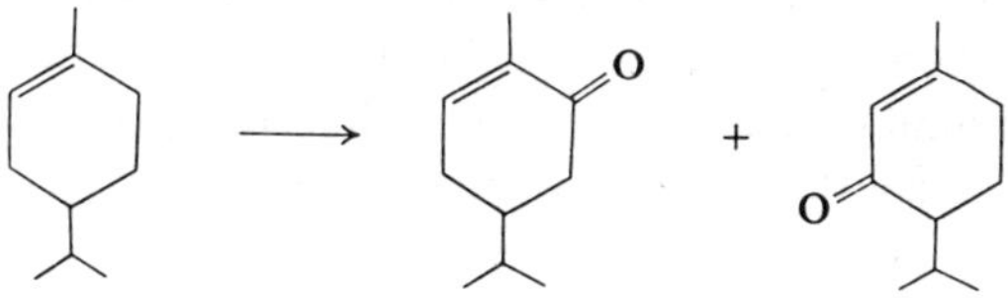

Limonene gives carbone (21%), isopiperitenone (13%), and piperitenone (3%)[93]:

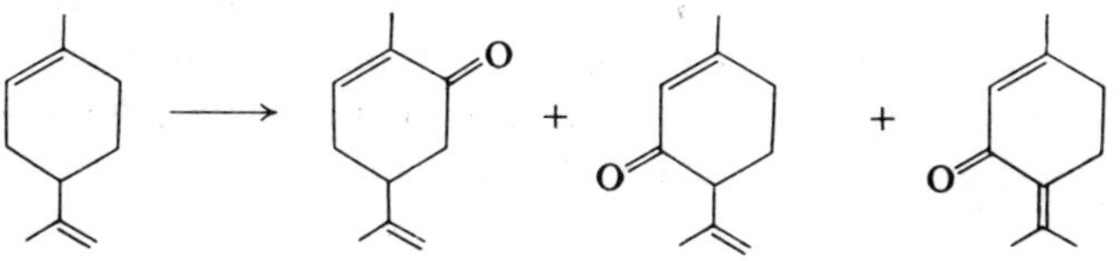

And α-terpineol gives 8-hydroxycarvotanacetone (15%), 8-hydroxypiperitone (7%), and homomethylterpinyl ketone (20%)[94]:

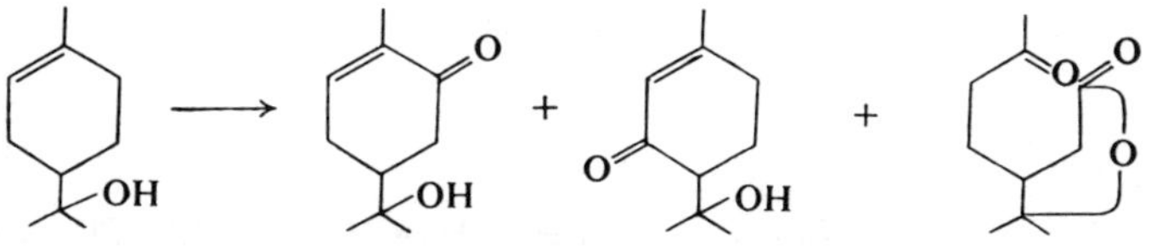

The latter compound is one of the major products of the chromic acid oxidation of α-terpineol,[95] and represents one of the few cases of attack at a double bond

[90] T. Matsuura and K. Fujita, *J. Sci. Hiroshima Univ. Ser.* **A16**, 173 (1952).
[91] G. Dupont, R. Dulou, and O. Mondou, *Bull. Soc. Chim. France* p. 433 (1952).
[92] K. Fujita and T. Matsuura, *J. Sci. Hiroshima Univ. Ser.* **A18**, 455 (1955) claim that no piperitone is formed in this oxidation. However, this is in variance with the observation of ref. 91, and with the results of the oxidations of similar compounds (see below).
[93] K. Fujita, *Nippon Kagaku Zasshi* **81**, 676 (1960); *ibid.* **78**, 1112 (1957).
[94] T. Matsuura and T. Suga, *Nippon Kagaku Zasshi* **78**, 1117 (1957); T. Matsuura, T. Suga, and K. Suga, *ibid.* 1122 (1957); T. Suga, *Bull. Chem. Soc. Japan* **31**, 569 (1958).
[95] O. Wallach, *Ber.* **28**, 1773 (1895).

by di-*tert*-butyl chromate. The oxidation of an α-terpinyl acetate proceeds in the same fashion except that it is possible to obtain 45 % of 8-acetoxycarvotanacetone.[94]

In other examples, terpinolene has been converted to piperitenone, 8-hydroxy-*p*-cymene, *p*-cymene, and α,*p*-dimethylstyrene[96]; *d*-3-*p*-menthene has been converted to *d*-carvone (50%) and *dl*-3-*p*-menthen-5-one (16%)[97]; and safrole has been converted to 3,4-methylenedioxycinnamaldehyde (4%), piperonal (7%), and piperonilic acid (8%).[98] In the oxidation of long chain unsaturated fatty acid esters, chain degradation is commonly observed.[99]

The above examples indicate this to be a potentially useful method, particularly since carbon–carbon double bonds are rarely attacked. There are, however, a number of types of side reaction which may occur. It should be noted that oxidation usually occurs at both sides of the double bond. This makes the chromium(VI) oxidation different than allylic oxidation by mercuric acetate,[100] lead tetraacetate,[101] or selenium dioxide.[102]

4. MECHANISM OF ALLYLIC OXIDATION BY CHROMIUM(VI)

Two types of mechanisms are possible for allylic oxidation. In the first, a hydrogen atom (or hydride ion) is removed from the alkene giving an allylic free radical (or carbonium ion), which is ultimately converted to the unsaturated ketone. In the second, oxidation at the double bond leads to a derivative of a ketol. Elimination of water then leads to the unsaturated ketone:

$$(A) \quad -CH_2-CH=CH-CH_2- \xrightarrow{-H\cdot} \left[\begin{array}{c} -\overset{\cdot}{C}H-CH=CH-CH_2- \\ \updownarrow \\ -CH=CH-\overset{\cdot}{C}H-CH_2- \end{array} \right]$$

$$\longrightarrow \quad -\overset{\overset{\displaystyle O}{\|}}{C}-CH=CH-CH_2- + -CH=CH-\overset{\overset{\displaystyle O}{\|}}{C}-CH_2-$$

[96] T. Matsuura, K. Saito, and Y. Shimakawa, *Bull. Chem. Soc. Japan* **33**, 1151 (1960).

[97] K. Fujita, *Bull. Chem. Soc. Japan* **34**, 968 (1961).

[98] T. Kuraoka, *Nippon Kagaku Zasshi* **82**, 50 (1961).

[99] Y. Watanabe, *Nippon Kagaku Zasshi* **80**, 310 (1959); **80**, 1187 (1959); *J. Sci. Hiroshima Univ. Ser.* **A24**, 453 (1960).

[100] W. Treibs and H. Bast, *Ann.* **561**, 165 (1949); W. Treibs, G. Lucius, H. Kögler, and H. Breslauer, *ibid.* **581**, 59 (1953).

[101] G. H. Whitham, *J. Chem. Soc.* p. 2232 (1961).

[102] A. Guillemonat, *Compt. Rend. Acad. Sci.* **200**, 1416 (1935); **201**, 904 (1935); **205**, 67 (1937); **206**, 1126 (1938); *Ann. Chim. (Paris)* **11**, 143 (1939).

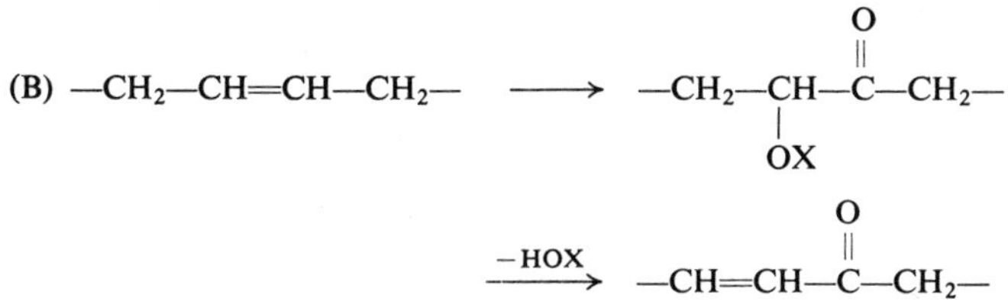

(B) $-CH_2-CH=CH-CH_2-$ $\longrightarrow$ $-CH_2-\underset{\underset{OX}{|}}{CH}-\overset{\overset{O}{||}}{C}-CH_2-$

$\xrightarrow{-HOX}$ $-CH=CH-\overset{\overset{O}{||}}{C}-CH_2-$

It can be seen that the first mechanism predicts that the products should contain a mixture of double bond isomers, and that the second predicts a double bond migration as a result of the reaction. The experimental data, particularly with regard to the steroidal alkenes, supports the first mechanism. Definitive evidence for this mechanism comes from the chromic acid oxidation of cyclohexene labeled with carbon-13 at the double bond. Mechanism (B) predicts that one-half of the original total label will be at the carbonyl carbon, whereas mechanism (A) predicts that only one-quarter of the label will be found at that position. The results are in accord with mechanism (A).[103]

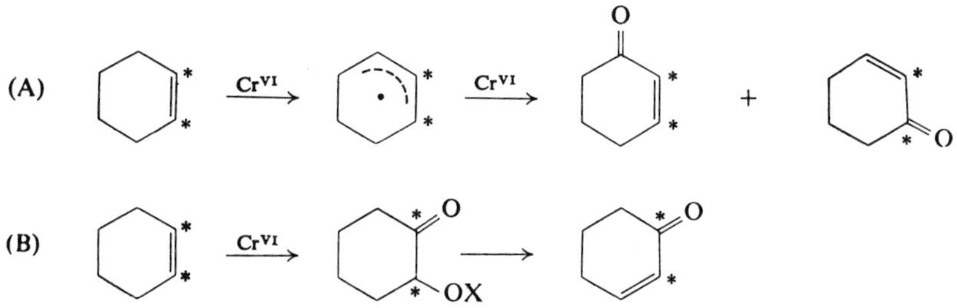

(A)

(B)

Although the mechanism of the chromic acid oxidation appears to be established by the above data, there are no data concerning allylic oxidation by chromyl acetate and di-*tert*-butyl chromate. It is not unreasonable to assume that the mechanisms may be similar.

C. OXIDATION OF ALKANES

1. CHROMIC ACID

The chromic acid oxidation of alkanes has not received wide use as a synthetic method. This results largely from the variety of reactions which may follow the initial oxidation step. The oxidation of a methyl group is rarely encountered since the relative rates of oxidation of primary, secondary, and tertiary carbon–hydrogen bonds are $1:110:7000$.[104] The lower reactivity of

[103] K. B. Wiberg and S. D. Nielsen, *J. Org. Chem.* **29**, 3353 (1964).
[104] F. Mareš and J. Roček, *Collection Czech. Chem. Commun.* **26**, 2370 (1961); J. Roček and F. Mareš, *ibid.* **24**, 2741 (1959); J. Roček, *ibid.* **22**, 1509 (1957).

Reactant	Product	Reference
$(CH_3CH_2)_3CH \longrightarrow$	$(CH_3CH_2)_3COH + CH_3CH_2\overset{O}{\overset{\Vert}{C}}CH_2CH_3 + CH_3CH_2CO_2H$	109
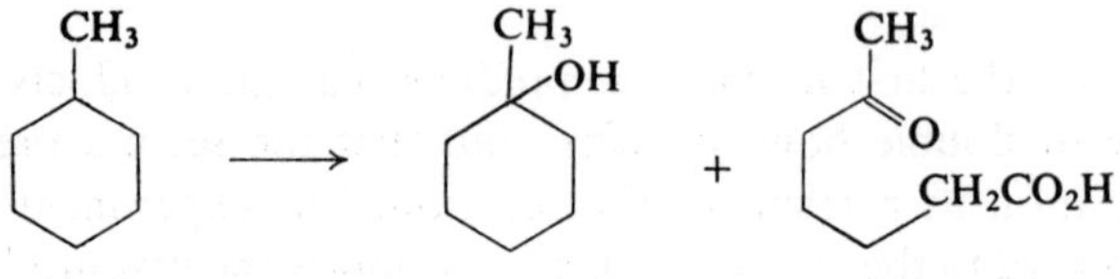		110, 111
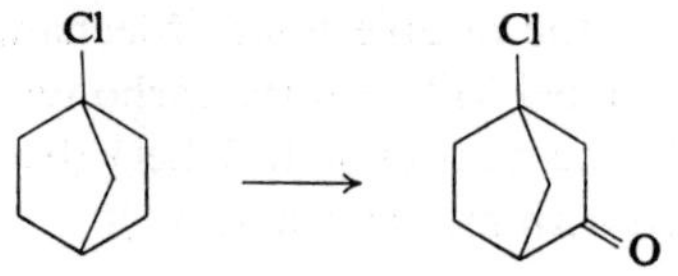		107
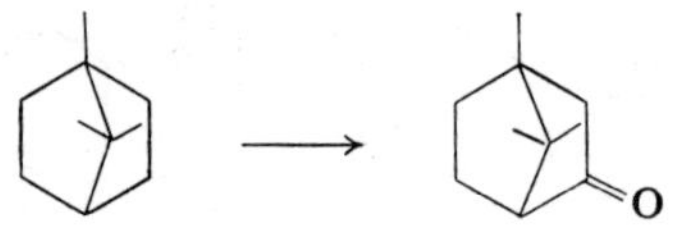		109
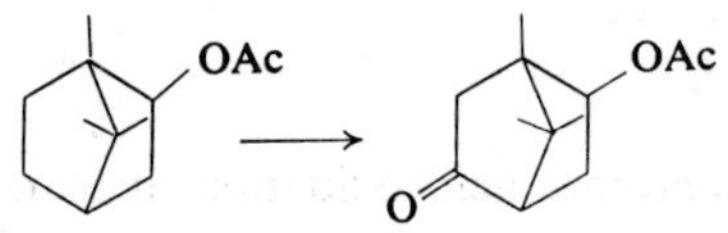		108
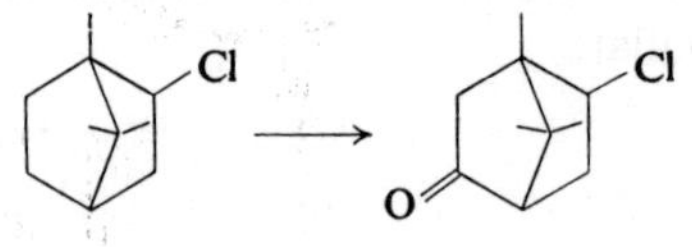		115
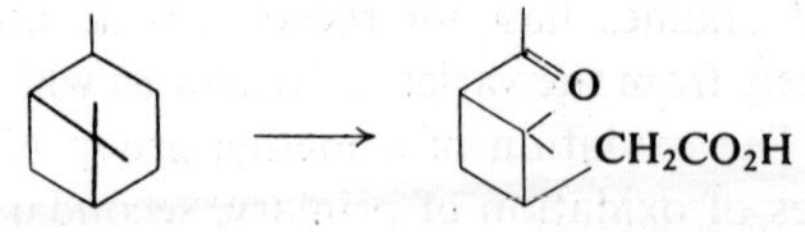		116

FIG. 4.1. (Continued next page.)

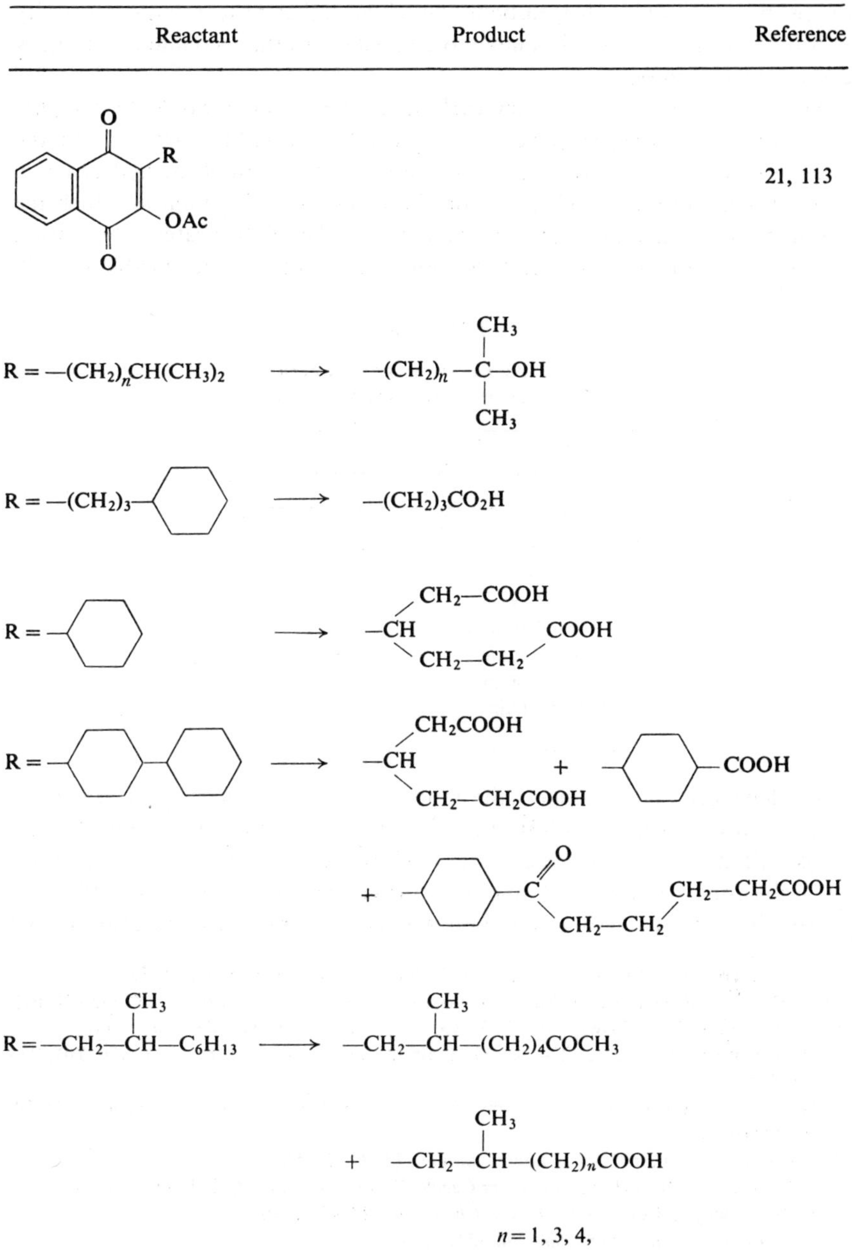

Reactant	Product	Reference

21, 113

$R = -(CH_2)_nCH(CH_3)_2$ $\longrightarrow$ $-(CH_2)_n-\overset{\overset{\displaystyle CH_3}{|}}{\underset{\underset{\displaystyle CH_3}{|}}{C}}-OH$

$R = -(CH_2)_3-\bigcirc$ $\longrightarrow$ $-(CH_2)_3CO_2H$

$R = \bigcirc$ $\longrightarrow$ $-CH\overset{\displaystyle CH_2-COOH}{\underset{\displaystyle CH_2-CH_2}{}}COOH$

$R = \bigcirc-\bigcirc$ $\longrightarrow$ $-CH\overset{\displaystyle CH_2COOH}{\underset{\displaystyle CH_2-CH_2COOH}{}}$ + $\bigcirc-COOH$

+ $\bigcirc-C\overset{\displaystyle O}{\underset{\displaystyle CH_2-CH_2}{}}CH_2-CH_2COOH$

$R = -CH_2-\overset{\overset{\displaystyle CH_3}{|}}{CH}-C_6H_{13}$ $\longrightarrow$ $-CH_2-\overset{\overset{\displaystyle CH_3}{|}}{CH}-(CH_2)_4COCH_3$

+ $-CH_2-\overset{\overset{\displaystyle CH_3}{|}}{CH}-(CH_2)_nCOOH$

$n = 1, 3, 4,$

FIG. 4-1. Oxidation of alkanes with chromic acid.

the primary carbon–hydrogen bond, which is similar to its relative reactivity in bromination,[105] makes it unable to compete with the secondary or tertiary carbon–hydrogen bonds.

The oxidation of a secondary carbon–hydrogen bond would lead to the formation of a ketone. Since ketones are readily oxidized by chromic acid, the yield of ketone depends on the relative rates of oxidation of the hydrocarbon and ketone, and one's ability to stop the reaction at the point at which the ketone yield is maximal. Data are available for the relative rates of oxidation of some cycloalkanes and the corresponding cycloalkanones (Table 4-6).[106]

TABLE 4-6

RELATIVE RATES OF OXIDATION OF
CYCLOALKANES AND CYCLOALKANONES

Ring	$k_{ketone}/k_{hydrocarbon}$
Cyclobutane	11.5
Cyclopentane	12.0
Cyclohexane	340
Cycloheptane	4.0
Cyclooctane	2.0
Cyclononane	0.96
Open-chain	

It can be seen that, in general, this is not a useful synthetic method. However, in some cases in which enolization of the ketone is rendered difficult, the rate of oxidation of the ketone is correspondingly reduced. Thus, in the oxidation of 1-chloronorcamphane[107] and of bornyl acetate[108] (Fig. 4-1),[109–116] a reasonable yield of ketone may be obtained. The rate of enolization of the

[105] P. C. Anson, P. S. Fredricks, and J. M. Tedder, *J. Chem. Soc.* p. 918 (1959).

[106] F. Mareš, J. Roček, and J. Sicher, *Collection Czech. Chem. Commun.* **26**, 2355 (1961).

[107] K. B. Wiberg, B. R. Lowry, and T. H. Colby, *J. Am. Chem. Soc.* **83**, 3998 (1961).

[108] H. Schrötter, *Monatsh.* **2**, 224 (1881); J. Bredt and A. Goeb, *J. Prakt. Chem.* **101**, 273 (1921).

[109] W. F. Sager and A. Bradley, *J. Am. Chem. Soc.* **78**, 1187 (1956); W. F. Sager, *ibid.* **78**, 4970 (1956).

[110] J. Roček, *Collection Czech. Chem. Commun.* **23**, 833 (1958).

[111] P. Kourim and R. Tykva, *Collection Czech. Chem. Commun.* **26**, 2511 (1961).

[112] K. B. Wiberg and G. Foster, *J. Am. Chem. Soc.* **83**, 423 (1961).

[113] L. F. Fieser, *J. Am. Chem. Soc.* **70**, 3237 (1948).

[114] F. Mareš and J. Roček, *Collection Czech. Chem. Commun.* **26**, 2389 (1961).

[115] J. Bredt and P. Pinten, *J. Prakt. Chem.* **115**, 45 (1927).

[116] A. Lipp, *Ber.* **56**, 2098 (1923).

ketone is reduced because of the strain involved in introducing a double bond into the ring system.

A major reaction in the oxidation of tertiary carbon–hydrogen bonds is oxidation to the corresponding tertiary alcohol. Sager and Bradley[109] found that the oxidation of 3-ethylpentane led to the formation of 3-ethyl-3-pentanol, which then underwent dehydration and further oxidation to diethyl ketone. The concentrations of these compounds as a function of time are indicated in

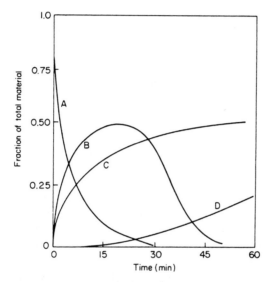

FIG. 4-2. Composition-time curves for the chromic acid oxidation of triethylmethane. The curves are: A, triethylmethane; B, triethylcarbinol; C, diethyl ketone; and D, propionic acid.

Fig. 4-2. It can be seen that up to 50% of the tertiary alcohol may be isolated. In a similar investigation, Roček[110] has shown that 1-methylcyclohexanol is a major intermediate in the oxidation of methylcyclohexane. It is interesting that essentially none of the corresponding acetate was found, whereas it is stable under the reaction conditions.

The monocarboxylic acids formed in the oxidation of alkylcyclohexanes have been studied.[15] Methylcyclohexane gives acetic acid, ethylcyclohexane gives acetic and propionic acids, n-propylcyclohexane gives acetic, propionic, and butyric acids, and n-butylcyclohexane gives the last three acids plus a trace of valeric acid. Longer chain alkyl groups do not give longer chain acids because the rate of oxidation of the acid formed becomes comparable to the rate of oxidation of the alkane.

The products arising from the chromic acid oxidation of methylcyclohexane have been studied in detail, using isotope dilution analyses.[111] The results were:

Adipic acid	7.4%
Glutaric acid	8.2%
Succinic acid	3.4%
6-Ketoheptanoic acid	53.1%
Cyclohexanone	2.2%
2-Methylcyclohexanone	0.3%
3-Methyl-2-cyclohexenone	0.6%
1-Acetoxy-1-methylcyclohexane	0.7%
1-Methylcyclohexane	11.2%
	87.1%

Under the conditions of the experiment, 1-methylcyclohexanol would have been further oxidized. The main product was the keto acid which would be expected as the product of the oxidation of 1-methylcyclohexene.

The stereochemistry of the oxidation of a tertiary carbon–hydrogen bond has been studied. Oxidation of (+)-3-methylheptane proceeded with 72–85% retention of configuration, and the degree of retention was unaffected by the addition of cerous ion.[112] Here again, none of the corresponding acetate was found.

The effect of structure on the reactivity of alkanes in chromic acid oxidation has been studied in detail by Roček and his co-workers.[104, 106] An increase in the length of alkyl groups attached to the reaction site causes a small increase in rate of oxidation. The addition of bulky groups such as *tert*-butyl causes only a slight decrease in rate, indicating that steric effects are not very important. Hydrogens in the equatorial position of a cyclohexane ring are 4–10 times as reactive as the axial hydrogens. Phenyl substitution at the reaction site causes a significant, but not very large, increase in rate (Table 4-6). The only type of carbon–hydrogen bond which has markedly reduced reactivity is found at the bridgehead of a strained bicyclic system such as camphane.

In some oxidations, rearrangement may occur. The oxidation of neohexane, for example, leads to pinacolone and acetone in about equal amounts.[104] The acetone could be formed via the initial formation of neohexyl alcohol, a cleavage reaction initiated by chromium(V) (cf. alcohol oxidation) giving acetaldehyde and *tert*-butyl alcohol, and finally oxidation of the latter to acetone. Or, it could be formed via the neohexyl carbonium ion, rearrangement and elimination to 2,3-dimethyl-2-butene, and oxidation to acetone:

$$\text{(A)} \quad CH_3-\underset{\overset{|}{CH_3}}{\overset{\overset{CH_3}{|}}{C}}-CH_2CH_3 \xrightarrow{Cr^{VI}} CH_3-\underset{\overset{|}{CH_3OH}}{\overset{\overset{CH_3}{|}}{C}}-CH-CH_3 \xrightarrow{Cr^V} CH_3-\underset{\overset{|}{CH_3}}{\overset{\overset{CH_3}{|}}{C}}-OH + CH_3CHO$$

$$\xrightarrow{Cr^{VI}} CH_3-\overset{\overset{O}{\|}}{C}-CH_3 + CH_3\overset{\overset{O}{\|}}{C}OH + CO_2$$

$$\text{(B)} \quad CH_3-\underset{\overset{|}{CH_3}}{\overset{\overset{CH_3}{|}}{C}}-CH_2CH_3 \xrightarrow{Cr^{VI}} CH_3-\underset{\overset{|}{CH_3}}{\overset{\overset{CH_3}{|}}{C}}-CHCH_3 \longrightarrow CH_3-\underset{\overset{|}{CH_3}}{\overset{\overset{CH_3}{|}}{C}}=C-CH_3$$

$$\xrightarrow{Cr^{VI}} CH_3\overset{\overset{O}{\|}}{C}CH_3$$

The latter was shown to be the correct path by labeling the methyl of the ethyl group with carbon-14 and examining the activity of the product acetone. The pinacolone was found to be formed with essentially no rearrangement.[80]

The oxidation of 2-alkylnaphthoquinones is of interest because of the unusual oxidation pattern.[21, 113] Unlike other alkyl substituted aromatic rings, oxidation does not occur at the carbon adjacent to the ring, but rather at a carbon removed from the ring by several carbons (Fig. 4-1). It has been suggested that the position of attack is determined by the initial formation of a complex between chromic acid and the ring.[113] It is also possible that the quinone ring is acting as an electron withdrawing group, reducing reactivity at the α-carbon in the same fashion as found with carboxylic acids.[114]

2. CHROMYL ACETATE

The oxidation of a number of hydrocarbons has been investigated by Archer and Hickinbottom[117] and Foster and Hickinbottom.[118] Typical results are shown in Fig. 4-3. With 2,3-dimethylbutane, as well as with many of the other compounds, the apparent site of attack is a carbon adjacent to a tertiary carbon–hydrogen bond. Attack at the tertiary carbon–hydrogen bond is, however, considerably more rapid than attack at a secondary or primary bond. Thus the reaction must involve a hydrogen migration.

The products of the reaction are quite similar to those found in the oxidation of the alkenes which would be formed by initial attack at the tertiary carbon–hydrogen bond and loss of an adjacent hydrogen. It is believed that the

[117] D. P. Archer and W. J. Hickinbottom, *J. Chem. Soc.* p. 4197 (1954).
[118] G. Foster and W. J. Hickinbottom, *J. Chem. Soc.* p. 215 (1960).

Reactant	Product	Reference

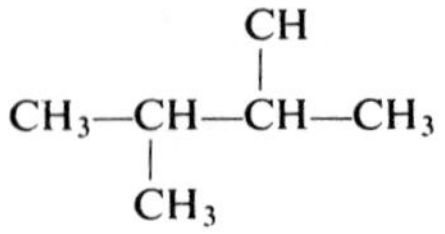

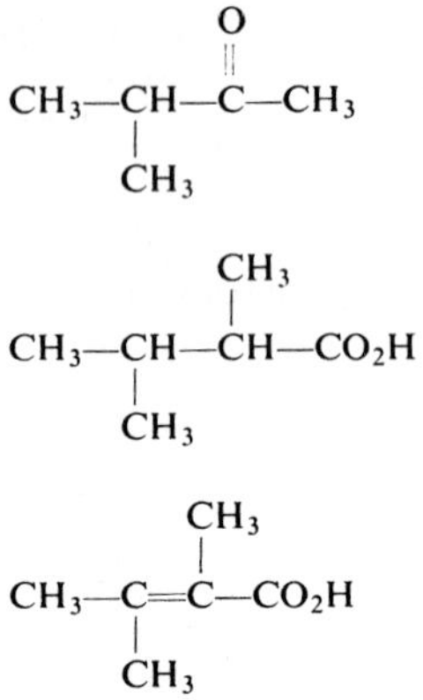

$$\underset{\underset{CH_3}{|}}{CH_3-CH-CH-CH_3} \overset{CH}{\underset{}{|}} \longrightarrow \underset{\underset{CH_3}{|}}{CH_3-CH-\overset{\overset{O}{||}}{C}-CH_3} \qquad 118$$

$$\underset{\underset{CH_3}{|}}{CH_3-CH-CH-CO_2H} \overset{CH_3}{\underset{}{|}}$$

$$\underset{\underset{CH_3}{|}}{CH_3-C=C-CO_2H} \overset{CH_3}{\underset{}{|}}$$

$$\underset{\underset{CH_3}{|}}{CH_3-\overset{\overset{CH_3}{|}}{C}-CH_2CH_3} \longrightarrow \underset{\underset{CH_3}{|}}{CH_3-\overset{\overset{CH_3}{|}}{C}-\overset{\overset{O}{||}}{C}-CH_3} \qquad 118$$

$$\underset{\underset{CH_3}{|}}{CH_3-\overset{\overset{CH_3}{|}}{C}-CH_2-\overset{\overset{CH_3}{|}}{CH}-CH_3} \longrightarrow \underset{\underset{CH_3}{|}}{CH_3-\overset{\overset{CH_3}{|}}{C}-CH_2-\overset{\overset{O}{||}}{C}-CH_3} \qquad 117$$

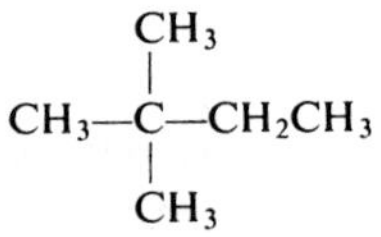

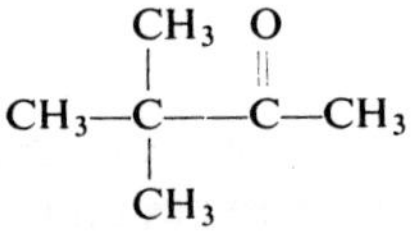

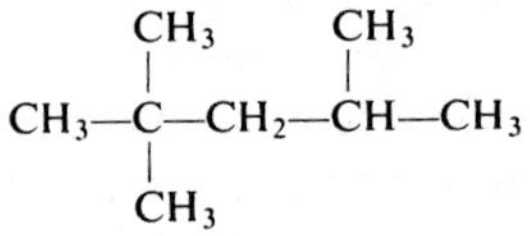

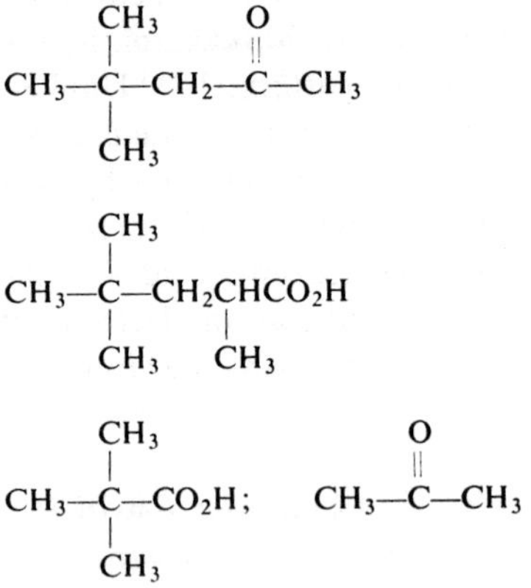

$$\underset{\underset{CH_3}{|} \quad \underset{CH_3}{|}}{CH_3-\overset{\overset{CH_3}{|}}{C}-CH_2CHCO_2H}$$

$$\underset{\underset{CH_3}{|}}{CH_3-\overset{\overset{CH_3}{|}}{C}-CO_2H}; \quad CH_3-\overset{\overset{O}{||}}{C}-CH_3$$

$$\underset{\underset{CH_3}{|} \quad \underset{CH_3}{|} \quad \underset{CH_3}{|}}{CH_3-\overset{\overset{CH_3}{|}}{C}-CH_2-CH-CH_2-\overset{\overset{CH_3}{|}}{C}-CH_3} \longrightarrow \underset{\underset{CH_3}{|} \quad \underset{CO_2H}{|} \quad \underset{CH_3}{|}}{CH_3-\overset{\overset{CH_3}{|}}{C}-CH_2-CH-CH_2-\overset{\overset{CH_3}{|}}{C}-CH_3} \qquad 117$$

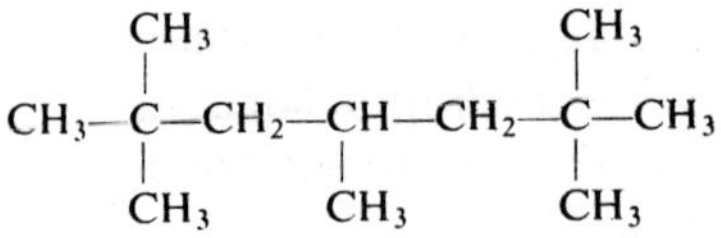

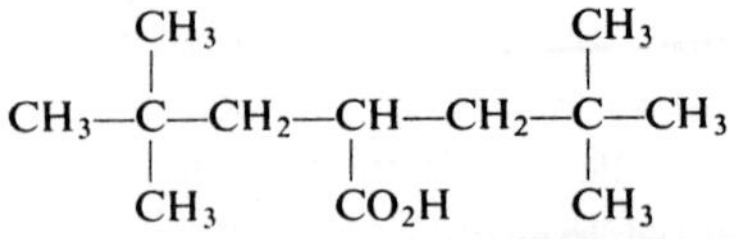

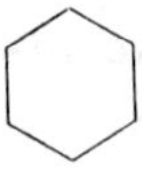

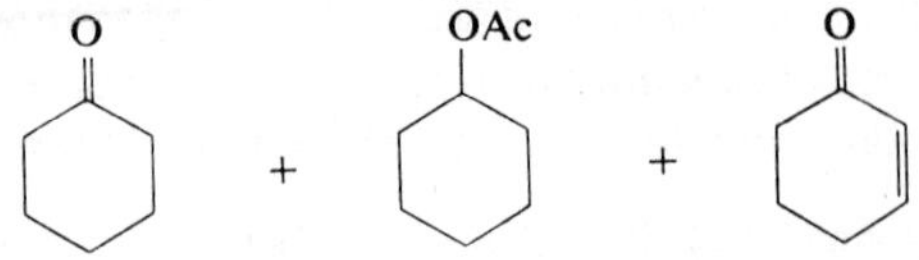

117

FIG. 4-3. (Continued next page.)

Reactant	Product			Reference

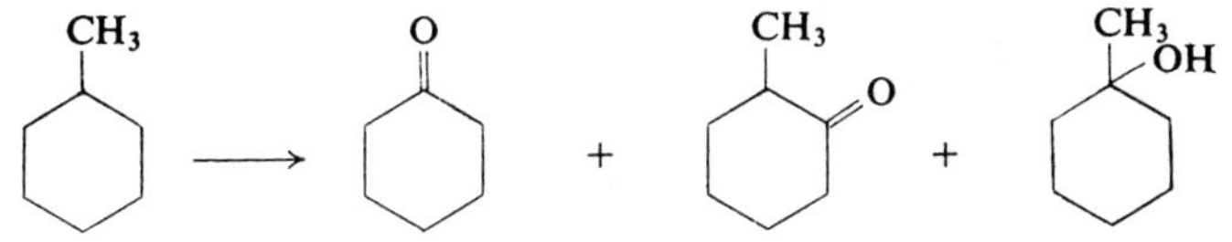

118

$$+ CH_3\overset{O}{\overset{\|}{C}}(CH_2)_3CO_2H + HO_2C(CH_2)_4CO_2H$$

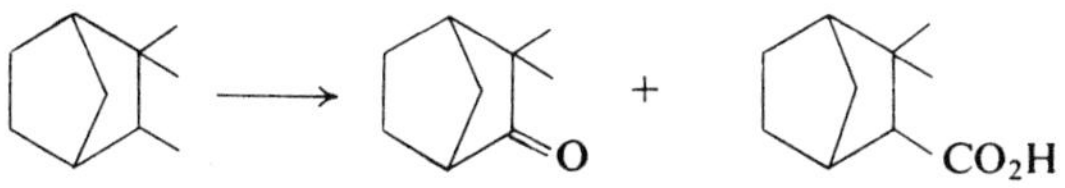

117

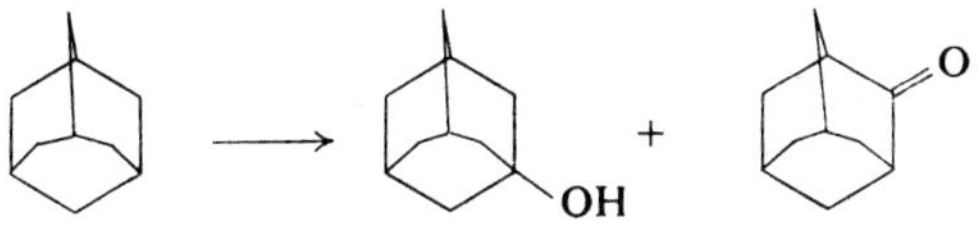

(71%)   (9%)

119

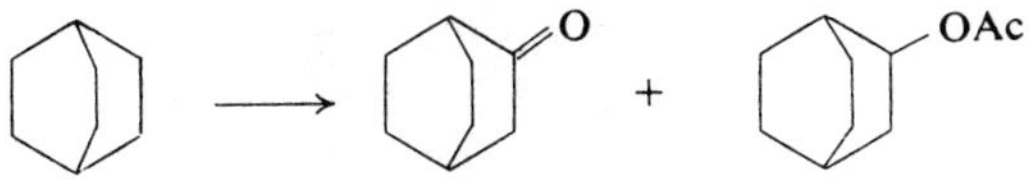

(40%)   (4%)

119

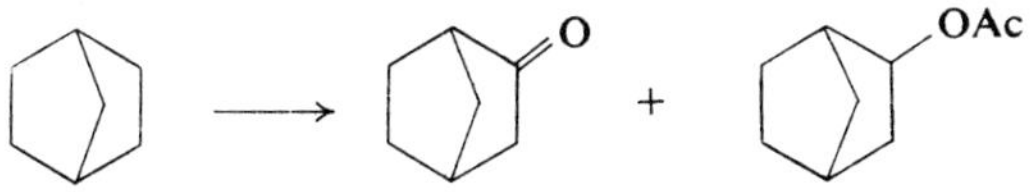

(23%)   (6%)

119

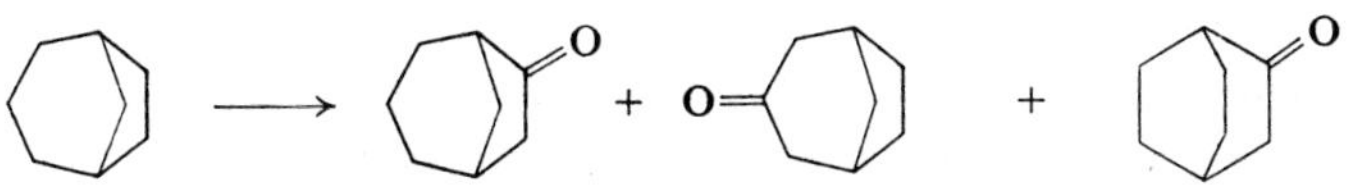

(16%)   (7%)   (10%)

119

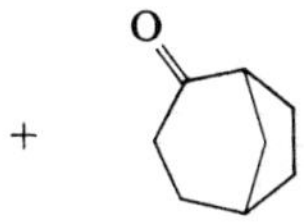

(3%)

FIG. 4-3. (Continued next page.)

Reactant	Product	Reference

FIG. 4-3. Oxidation of alkanes with chromyl acetate.

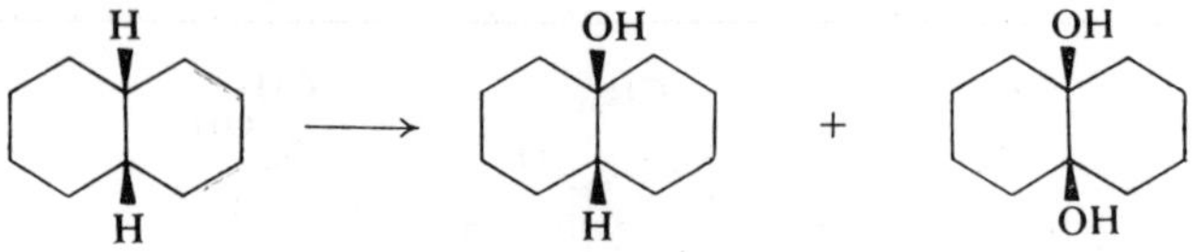

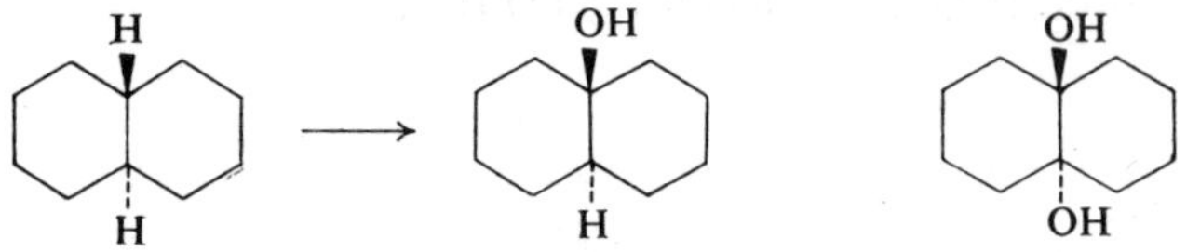

alkene is the intermediate in the reaction. The only difficulty with this interpretation is that the oxidation of alkenes leads to epoxides along with the other products. Hickinbottom argues that the chromium-containing intermediates formed in the oxidation of the alkane may lead to ring opening of the epoxide. Cleavage of the epoxide would also lead to the observed products.

Interesting results have been obtained in the oxidation of some cyclic compounds with chromyl acetate.[119] The relatively strain-free compound, adamantane, reacts preferentially at the tertiary carbon–hydrogen bond to give 1-adamantol. This is obtained in good yield since elimination to an alkene is not possible. With norbornane, bicyclo[2.2.2]octane, and bicyclo-[3.2.1]octane, reaction at the tertiary carbon–hydrogen bond is suppressed because of the increase in strain associated with a change in hybridization at that position. Thus, oxidation occurs at one of the methylene positions. A one-carbon methylene bridge is not attacked, again presumably because of the increase in strain resulting from a change in hybridization.

The results of the oxidation of cis- and trans-decalins indicate that the chromyl acetate oxidation is stereospecific,[119] just as the chromic acid oxidation.

An interesting difference between chromic acid and chromyl acetate is found in the oxidation of neohexane. Whereas cleavage to acetone is a major reaction with the former reagent, it is negligible with the latter.[104] Neither reagent led to a significant amount of carbon atom scrambling in the reaction forming pinacolone.[80]

[119] P. v. R. Schleyer and R. D. Nicholas, Abstr. Am. Chem. Soc. Meeting, Chicago, Illinois, September, 1961 p. 75Q.

3. Chromyl Chloride

The chromyl chloride oxidation of several alkanes has been studied by Tillotson and Houston[120] and by Hobbs and Houston.[121] They found that the oxidation proceeded more rapidly at a tertiary carbon–hydrogen bond than at a secondary bond, and that a trace of alkene was needed in order to initiate the reaction. Thus, pure methylcyclohexane gave essentially no reaction with chromyl chloride at 35° C. The addition of 1 % of methylcyclohexene led to a rapid reaction, and the Étard complex was formed in good yield.

In general, the products are similar to those obtained in the chromyl acetate oxidation, and it is reasonable to assume that the products derived from attack at a tertiary carbon–hydrogen bond arise by way of an alkene as the intermediate (cf. Fig. 4-4 on pp. 120 and 121).[121–124]

4. Mechanism of Oxidation of Alkanes

As a result of a number of investigations, there is a considerable body of data concerning the mechanism of the oxidation of alkanes with chromic acid in aqueous acetic acid. The data may be summarized as follows:

a. The kinetic rate law is[104]:

$$v = k[\text{alkane}][\text{CrO}_3]h_0$$

b. The relative rates of oxidation of primary, secondary, and tertiary hydrogens are 1:110:7000.[104]

c. The oxidations of 3-ethylpentane and of 3-methylheptane show a kinetic hydrogen isotope effect. In the latter case $k_H/k_D = 2.5$.[109, 112]

d. The rates of oxidation of cycloalkanes from C-5 to C-12 parallel the rates of solvolysis of the corresponding tosylates. An even better correlation is found with the heat of combustion of the hydrocarbons. The rate of oxidation of cyclobutane is much slower than might be expected based on the rate of solvolysis of cyclobutyl tosylate.[106]

e. The oxidation of 3-ethylpentane occurs 2.9 times as rapidly as that of isobutane and, in general, increasing bulk around the tertiary carbon increases the rate of oxidation.[104] Steric acceleration is fairly generally observed, whereas steric hindrance is found only in extreme cases.

f. No anchimeric assistance is found in the oxidations of isocamphane, camphane, and cyclobutane.[106]

[120] A. Tillotson and B. Houston, *J. Am. Chem. Soc.* **73**, 221 (1951).

[121] C. C. Hobbs, Jr. and B. Houston, *J. Am. Chem. Soc.* **76**, 1254 (1954).

[122] J. R. Celeste, M.S. Thesis, University of Delaware, Newark, Delaware, 1956.

[123] S. J. Cristol and K. R. Eilar, *J. Am. Chem. Soc.* **72**, 4353 (1950).

[124] The product was originally reported to be hexahydrobenzaldehyde,[121] but this was subsequently shown to be incorrect.[72]

g. The oxidation of a hydrocarbon with asymmetry at the tertiary position leads to a tertiary alcohol with retention of configuration. Cerous ion does not affect the degree of retention of configuration.[112]

h. In the oxidation of 3-ethylpentane in glacial acetic acid with added azide ion, 10% of 3-ethyl-3-pentyl azide is formed.[125]

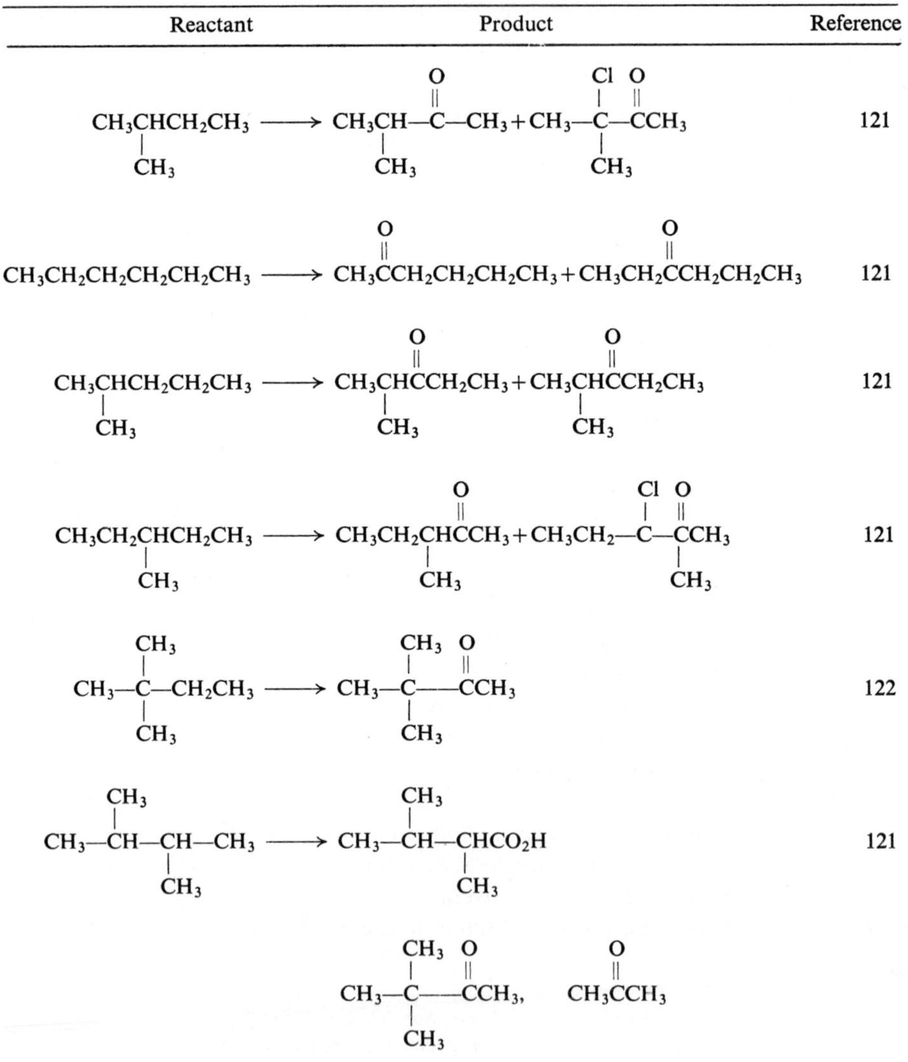

Reactant	Product	Reference
		121
$CH_3CH_2CH_2CH_2CH_2CH_3$		121
		121
		121
		122
		121

Fig. 4-4. (Continued next page.)

[125] I. Necsoiu and C. D. Nenitzescu, *Chem. & Ind.* (*London*) p. 377 (1960).

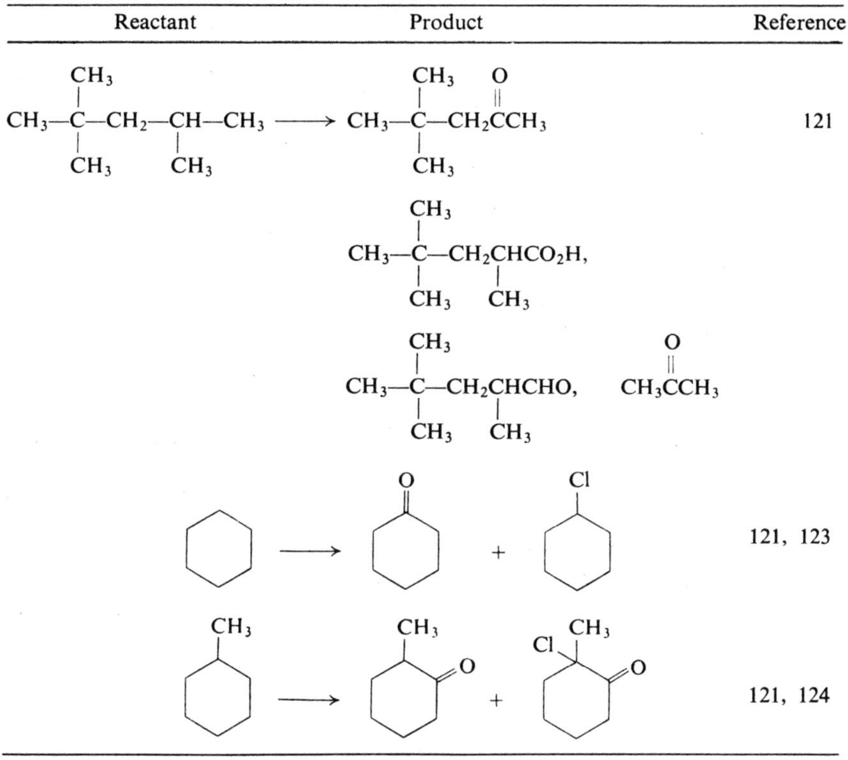

Reactant	Product	Reference
CH₃—C(CH₃)(CH₃)—CH₂—CH(CH₃)—CH₃	CH₃—C(CH₃)(CH₃)—CH₂CCH₃ (with =O)	121

The reactant is:

$$CH_3-\underset{\underset{CH_3}{|}}{\overset{\overset{CH_3}{|}}{C}}-CH_2-\underset{\underset{CH_3}{|}}{CH}-CH_3 \longrightarrow$$

Products:

$$CH_3-\underset{\underset{CH_3}{|}}{\overset{\overset{CH_3}{|}}{C}}-CH_2\overset{\overset{O}{\parallel}}{C}CH_3$$

$$CH_3-\underset{\underset{CH_3}{|}}{\overset{\overset{CH_3}{|}}{C}}-CH_2\underset{\underset{CH_3}{|}}{CH}CO_2H,$$

$$CH_3-\underset{\underset{CH_3}{|}}{\overset{\overset{CH_3}{|}}{C}}-CH_2\underset{\underset{CH_3}{|}}{CH}CHO, \qquad CH_3\overset{\overset{O}{\parallel}}{C}CH_3$$

121, 123

121, 124

Fig. 4-4. Oxidation of alkanes with chromyl chloride.

i. The product of the oxidation at a tertiary C—H bond is normally the tertiary alcohol and very little acetate is found.[106, 110]

j. In the oxidation of neohexane, a major product is acetone, which is produced via a rearrangement presumably involving 2,3-dimethyl-2-butene as an intermediate.[80, 104]

The observation of a reasonably large kinetic isotope effect indicates that the rate-determining step is the cleavage of the carbon–hydrogen bond. As in the oxidation of the aryl alkanes, there are three basic mechanisms by which the reaction may occur:

(A) $R_3CH + Cr^{VI} \longrightarrow R_3C^+ + Cr^{IV}$

(B) $R_3CH + Cr^{VI} \longrightarrow R_3C^{\bullet} + Cr^{V}$

(C) $R_3C{-\!-}H \longrightarrow R_3C{-}O{-}CrO_3H$

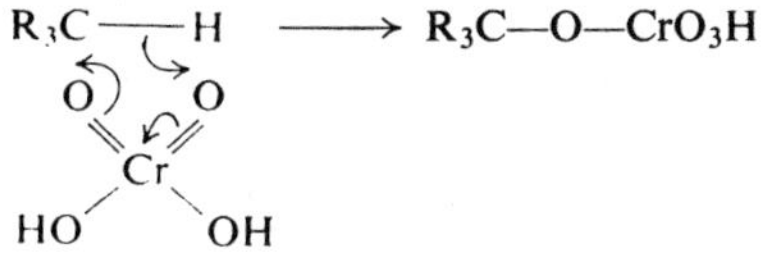

The small differences in rates of oxidation of primary, secondary, and tertiary hydrogens compared with the relative rates of solvolysis of primary, secondary, and tertiary halides ($\sim 1:10^5:10^7$) makes the first possibility unlikely. The relative rates of oxidation are similar to the relative rates of hydrogen abstraction by bromine atoms ($\sim 1:100:3000$), and these data are permissive for mechanism (B). Similarly, the absence of anchimeric assistance in the oxidation of cyclobutane, camphane, and isocamphane makes mechanism (A) unlikely, but is in accord with mechanism (B).

The insertion of mechanism (C) may also be in accord with the experimental observations. However, if the pentacoordinate carbon in the activated complex were to assume the trigonal bipyramid configuration,

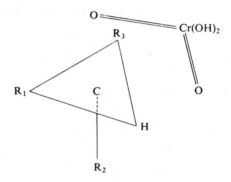

there would appear to be increased crowding of the alkyl groups in the activated complex and one would expect a rate decrease on going from isobutane to 3-ethylpentane rather than the observed rate increase. Similarly, on the basis of mechanism (C), one would not expect a linear free energy relationship between rates of oxidation of cycloalkanes, and rates of solvolysis of cycloalkyl tosylates.

Perhaps the strongest argument against mechanism (C) comes from the observation that the bridgehead position of norbornyl derivatives is reactive in a process leading to a pentacovalent activated complex.[126] The low reactivity of the bridgehead position of norbornane in chromic acid oxidation suggests that the oxidation involves a tricovalent carbon in the activated complex.[104, 119] In the absence of bond angle deformation, as in adamantane, a bridgehead position is reactive in the oxidation.[119] The above considerations make it reasonable to assume that mechanism (B) correctly represents the course of the reaction.

If mechanism (B) is correct, the nature of the next step is demonstrated by the observation of retention of configuration during oxidation.[112, 119] It is

[126] H. Minato, J. C. Ware, and T. G. Traylor, *J. Am. Chem. Soc.* **85**, 3024 (1963).

clear that the radical formed is not free, but rather reacts further before asymmetry is lost. The most reasonable proposal appears to be that the radical reacts in the solvent cage with the chromium(V) ion which was simultaneously formed. The chromium(IV) ester thus formed may be hydrolyzed to the observed product. The stereochemical result suggests that the chromium(IV) ester was hydrolyzed with chromium–oxygen bond cleavage. In accord with this conclusion, it was observed that the hydrolysis of tetra-*tert*-butoxy-chromium proceeded with chromium–oxygen bond cleavage.[127]

$$R_3CH + H_2CrO_4 \longrightarrow [R_3C^{\cdot} H_3CrO_4] \longrightarrow R_3C\text{—}O\text{—}\underset{\overset{|}{OH}}{\overset{\overset{OH}{|}}{Cr}}\text{—}OH \xrightarrow{H_2O} R_3COH$$

There remains the questions of why rearrangement is observed in the oxidation of neohexane and some other compounds, why azides are formed in the presence of azide ion, and why tertiary hydrogens are about 7000 times as reactive as primary hydrogens. Roček[128] has tried to explain all of these by suggesting that the solvent cage trapped radical formed in the initial step should be written as a resonance hybrid of the structures

$$[R_3C^{\cdot} \; Cr^V] \leftrightarrow [R_3C^+ \; Cr^{IV}]$$

The resonance hybrid could either decompose to the carbonium ion or undergo combination to give the chromium(IV) ester which is now generally regarded as the reaction intermediate which leads to the alcohol formed.[112, 128]

The kinetic data can only give information on the nature of the activated complex for the reaction. In terms similar to those used for explaining the "polar" effects found in free radical reactions, we may write

$$[R_3C\text{—}H \; OCrO_3H_2] \leftrightarrow [R_3C^{\cdot} \; H\text{—}OCrO_3H_2] \leftrightarrow [R_3C^+ \; H \; \bar{O}CrO_3H_2]$$

where there is a small contribution from the third structure because of the electron withdrawing character of the chromic acid, and the possibility of stabilization of the tertiary carbonium ion by the attached alkyl groups. The contribution of this cannonical structure to the hybrid cannot be significantly greater than in the case of hydrogen abstraction by bromine atoms.

The species formed following the activated complex may react further by combination of the two parts to form the chromium(IV) ester, by diffusion of the two parts away from each other followed by oxidation of the carbon radical by chromic acid, or by an electron transfer leading to the alkyl carbonium ion and chromium(IV).

[127] K. B. Wiberg and G. Foster, *Chem. & Ind.* (*London*) p. 108 (1961).
[128] J. Roček, *Tetrahedron Letters* p. 135 (1962).

The stereochemical observation demonstrates that a major portion of the reaction leading to alcohol proceeds via combination to the Cr^{IV} ester followed by hydrolysis with chromium–oxygen bond cleavage.[112, 117] This will give the alcohol with retention of configuration. Only 72–85 % retention was observed, and therefore a small part of the reaction proceeded by a different path, possibly via oxidation of the radical by chromium(VI). Little of the alcohol was formed via the carbonium ion, for the other expected product from such a reaction, the corresponding acetate, has not been found in significant quantity.

The carbonium ion, which is certainly involved in some cases, may be formed by the electron transfer process, or by a reaction of the chromium(IV) ester with carbon–oxygen bond cleavage. It is difficult to decide between these two possibilities. In any event, the formation of a small amount of azide and of the rearrangement of neohexane may be explained in either way.

The oxidation of the hydrocarbons by the chromium species of intermediate valence which are almost certainly involved (cf. the discussion of the mechanism of alcohol oxidation) appears to be similar to the chromium(VI) oxidation since nearly identical stereochemical results were obtained in the absence and presense of cerous ion which removes these intermediates.

In view of the similarity in the relative rates of oxidation of primary, secondary, and tertiary carbon–hydrogen bonds by chromyl acetate[118] and by chromic acid,[104] it is reasonable to suppose that the rate-controlling step is the same in both cases. In the oxidation at a tertiary carbon–hydrogen bond, the product generally has the oxygen function at an adjacent methylene group. This suggests[117, 118] that the initial oxidation leads to an alkene [perhaps via a chromium(IV) ester followed by elimination]. The alkene may then be converted to the observed products via an epoxide or related intermediate followed by a pinacol-type rearrangement. The mechanism of the oxidation of alkenes will be discussed in the following section.

The chromyl chloride oxidation of alkanes appears to proceed in a similar fashion. The observation that an alkene catalyzes the reaction suggests that the initial step may be the generation of a free radical followed by propagation steps such as

$$R \cdot + CrO_2Cl_2 \; \rightarrow \; ROCrOCl_2$$

$$ROCrOCl_2 + RH \; \rightarrow \; ROCr(OH)Cl_2 + R \cdot$$

However, more work will be necessary before this or any other scheme may be established.

After the initial stage, an alkene is probably formed, and this is further oxidized to the observed products. It will be noted that the products of the chromyl acetate and chromyl chloride oxidations are essentially the same. Thus, the product forming stages are probably similar.

V. Oxidation at Carbon–Carbon Double Bonds

The oxidation of alkenes may lead to several different products. Allylic oxidation has already been discussed. The oxidation may also lead to an epoxide, a ketol, acids or ketones derived by cleavage of the double bonds, or acids or ketones having the same number of carbon atoms as the alkane via a rearrangement. As a consequence of the variety of reactions, chromic acid oxidation of alkenes is not a generally useful synthetic reaction, but is useful in some special cases such as the tetraphenylethylenes, and in the Barbier-Wieland degradation. The reactions are of interest with regard to the mode of reaction of chromic acid. Unfortunately, there are no data bearing on the difference in reaction between chromium(VI) and the intermediate chromium species, and this must be kept in mind in reading the following discussion.

1. CHROMIC ACID

In considering the chromic acid oxidation of carbon–carbon double bonds, it is necessary to distinguish between the use of acetic acid as the solvent, and the use of aqueous sulfuric acid. Although the initial reaction may be the same in the two cases, the ultimate products are sometimes different. The oxidation in acetic acid will be considered first.

The simplest cases which may be considered are the tetraphenylethylenes, for here reaction at a position other than the double bond is relatively unlikely. A number of these compounds have been investigated, and with a deficiency of chromic acid the product is primarily the corresponding epoxide.[1] The use of a larger amount of oxidant leads to the benzophenone in good yield:

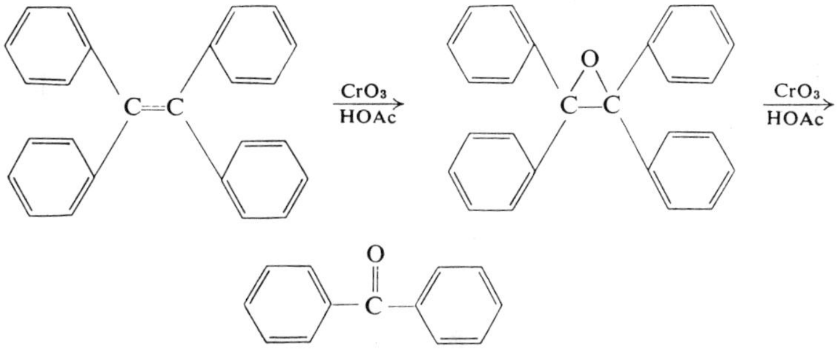

Although the reactions are not as simple in the aliphatic cases, epoxides are often found as products. Thus, the oxidation of α-ergosteryl acetate leads to a

---

[1] A. Behr, *Ber.* **5**, 277 (1872); H. Blitz, *Ann.* **296**, 219 (1897); W. Bockemuller and R. Janssen, *ibid.* **542**, 166 (1939).

mixture of ketones formed by allylic oxidation and to the epoxides derived from the ketones[2]:

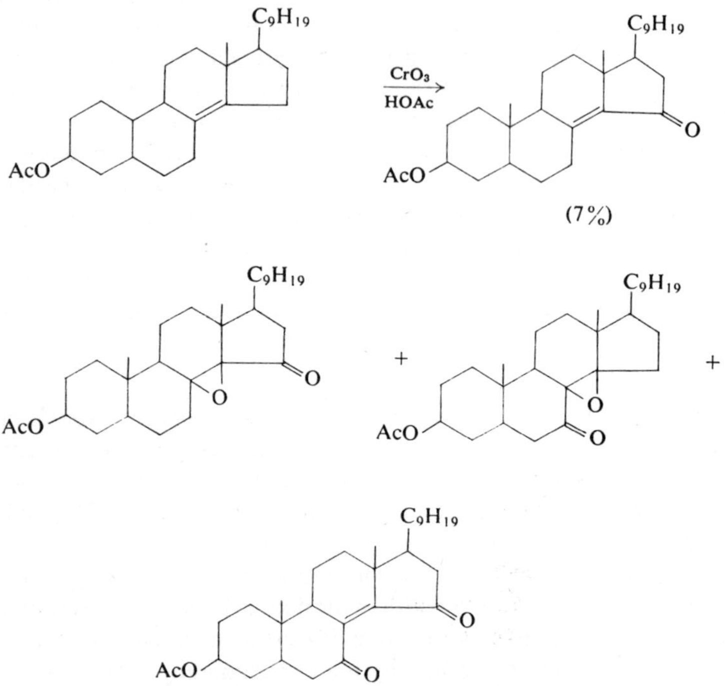

Similar results have been obtained with α-cholesteryl acetate,[3] 5-methyl-$\Delta^{8,9}$-norcholestene-3,6-diol diacetate,[4] and cis-3-acetoxy-Δ^5-cholesten-4-ol.[5] In the cases of α-dihydroergosterol,[6] α-spinosterol,[6] and Δ^7-cholestenyl acetate,[7] double bond migration occurs in part prior to epoxide formation leading to two epoxyketones:

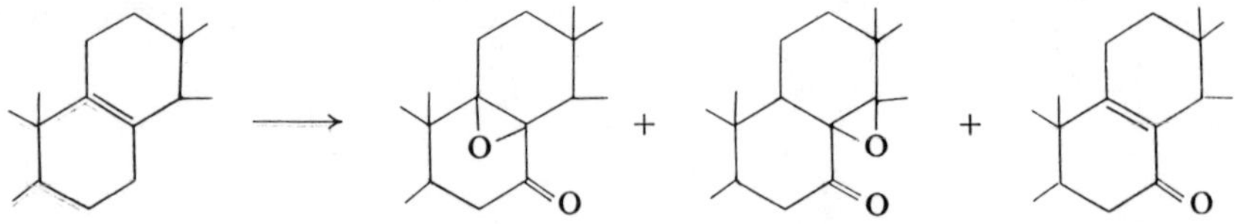

[2] H. E. Stavely and G. N. Bollenback, *J. Am. Chem. Soc.* **65**, 1285 (1943).

[3] O. Wintersteiner and M. Moore, *J. Am. Chem. Soc.* **65**, 1513 (1943).

[4] V. A. Petrov, *J. Chem. Soc.* p. 999 (1939).

[5] V. A. Petrov and W. W. Starling, *J. Chem. Soc.* p. 60 (1940).

[6] H. E. Stavely and G. N. Bollenback, *J. Am. Chem. Soc.* **65**, 1290, 1600 (1943).

[7] L. F. Fieser, K. Nakanishi, and W.-Y. Huang, *J. Am. Chem. Soc.* **75**, 4719 (1953).

The oxidation of other steroidal double bonds commonly leads to ketols or to allylic oxidation in which a double bond migration occurred. Both reactions may be rationalized in terms of the initial formation of an epoxide followed by ring opening and oxidation.[8] Dehydration of the ketol might give the allylic oxidation product. In favor of this formulation, it may be noted that cholesterol α-oxide on mild chromic acid oxidation gave cholestane-3,6-dione-5a-ol,[9] and this is a major product of the oxidation of cholesterol.[10]

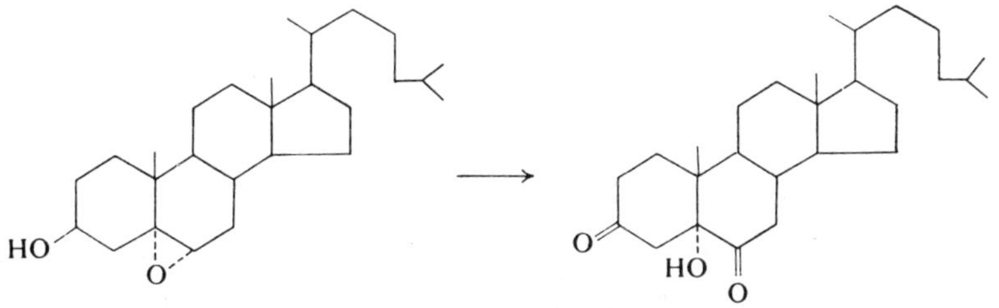

On the other hand, the reaction leading to the ketol may not involve the diol, but rather it may proceed via direct oxidation of the oxide. In the oxidation of a double bond, it is also possible that the initial compound formed on reaction with chromic acid, whatever its structure, decomposes to give the epoxide and the ketol in two separate reactions, and that at least part of the ketol is formed directly and not via the epoxide. Evidence has previously been given showing that allylic oxidation normally does not involve attack at the double bond, but rather proceeds via an allyl radical or carbonium ion.[11] This will lead to the double bond isomerization which is observed.

The Barbier-Wieland degradation[12] has proved to be of value in the degradation and modification of steroids. It involves the reaction of an ester with the phenyl Grignard reagent followed by dehydration and chromic acid oxidation:

$$RCH_2CO_2CH_3 + C_6H_5MgBr \longrightarrow RCH_2\overset{\overset{\textstyle OH}{|}}{C}(C_6H_5)_2 \longrightarrow$$

$$RCH{=}C(C_6H_5)_2 \xrightarrow[\text{HOAc}]{\text{CrO}_3} RCO_2H$$

[8] L. F. Fieser and M. Fieser, "Natural Products Related to Phenanthrene," 3rd ed. pp. 227ff. Reinhold, New York, 1949.

[9] L. Ruzicka and W. Bosshard, *Helv. Chim. Acta* **20**, 244 (1937).

[10] W. C. J. Ross, *J. Chem. Soc.* p. 737 (1946).

[11] K. B. Wiberg and S. Nielsen, *J. Org. Chem.* **29**, 3353 (1964).

[12] P. Barbier and R. Locquin, *Compt. Rend. Acad. Sci.* **156**, 1443 (1913); H. Wieland, O. Schlichting, and R. Jacobi, *Z. Physiol. Chem.* **161**, 80 (1926); cf. ref. 8.

Here, the oxidation step often proceeds quite well, with up to 60–65% of the chain shortened acid being produced.[13] As an example, by the use of two Barbier-Wieland steps and an ozonization, methyl deoxycholate (a readily obtainable steroid) was converted to pregnane-3α,12α-diol-20-one in an 8% over-all yield[13]:

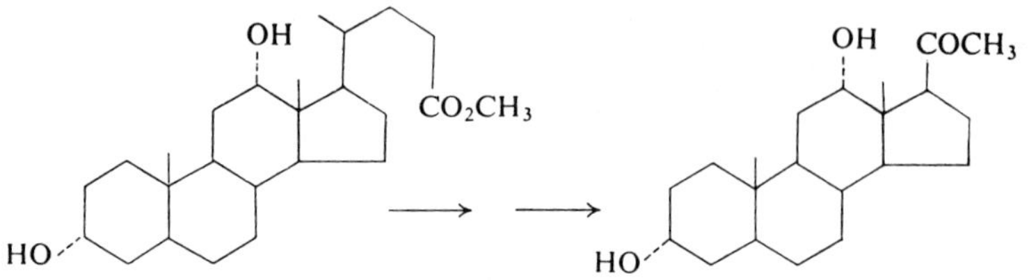

The oxidation of steroidal dienes is of particular interest. Windaus[14] observed that the chromic acid oxidation of $\Delta^{3,5}$-cholestadiene gave some Δ^4-cholestene-3,6-dione. Fieser and his co-workers have oxidized $\Delta^{7,9(11)}$-dienes to the corresponding enediones in 10–15% yield using sodium dichromate in acetic acid[15]:

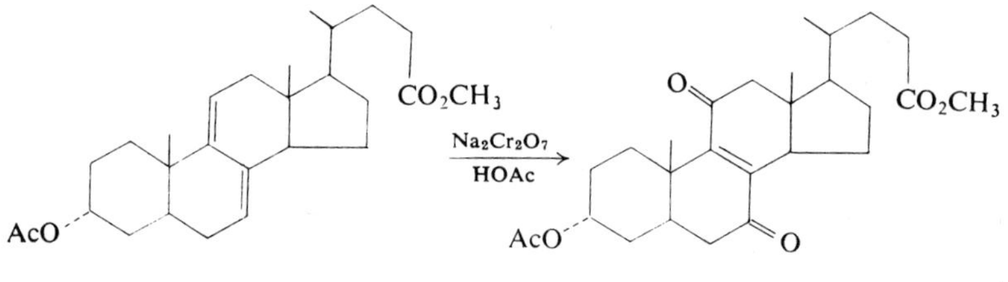

(15%)

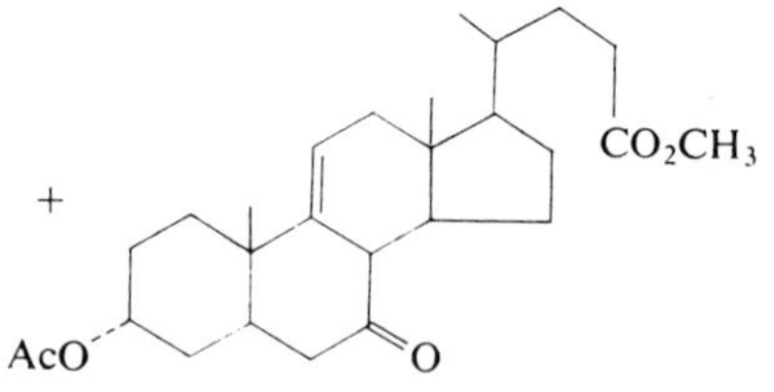

(41%)

A number of similar observations have been made.[16]

[13] W. M. Hoehn and H. L. Mason, *J. Am. Chem. Soc.* **60**, 1493 (1938).

[14] A. Windaus, *Ber.* **39**, 2249 (1906).

[15] L. F. Fieser, J. E. Herz, and W. Y. Huang, *J. Am. Chem. Soc.* **73**, 2397 (1951); L. F. Fieser, W.-Y. Huang, and J. C. Babcock, *ibid.* **75**, 116 (1953); L. F. Fieser and J. E. Herz, *ibid.* **75**, 121 (1953).

[16] J. Elks, R. M. Evans, A. G. Long, and G. H. Thomas, *J. Chem. Soc.* p. 451 (1954); D. H. R. Barton and G. F. Laws, *J. Chem. Soc.* p. 52 (1954).

In contrast to the relative simplicity of the reactions carried out in acetic acid, the oxidation in aqueous acidic medium commonly leads to rearrangement (Fig. 5-1). In the case of camphene, the rearrangement product, camphor, may be obtained in 88% yield with the aid of an emulsifier.[17] Hickinbottom and Wood[18] have suggested that an epoxide may be the intermediate in many reactions[19] and indeed most of the rearrangement products which have been observed may be accounted for by assuming an acid catalyzed pinacol-type rearrangement of an intermediate epoxide. Thus, 4,4-dimethyl-2-neopentyl-1,2-epoxypentane on treatment with aqueous acid is readily converted to 4,4-dimethyl-2-neopentylbutyraldehyde.[21] The acid corresponding to the latter is the principal product of the chromic acid oxidation of 4,4-dimethyl-2-neopentyl-1-pentene[22]:

$$
\begin{array}{c}
\underset{\substack{|\\ CH_3}}{\overset{\substack{CH_3\\|}}{CH_3\!-\!C}}\!-\!CH_2\!-\!\underset{\substack{\|\\ CH_2}}{C}\!-\!CH_2\!-\!\underset{\substack{|\\ CH_3}}{\overset{\substack{CH_3\\|}}{C}}\!-\!CH_3 \xrightarrow{CrO_3} CH_3\!-\!\underset{\substack{|\\ CH_3}}{\overset{\substack{CH_3\\|}}{C}}\!-\!CH_2\!-\!CH\!-\!\underset{\substack{|\\ CO_2H}}{C}\!-\!CH_2\!-\!\underset{\substack{|\\ CH_3}}{\overset{\substack{CH_3\\|}}{C}}\!-\!CH_3
\end{array}
$$

$$
CH_3\!-\!\underset{\substack{|\\ CH_3}}{\overset{\substack{CH_3\\|}}{C}}\!-\!CH_2\!-\!\underset{\substack{\diagdown O\\ CH_2}}{C}\!-\!CH_2\!-\!\underset{\substack{|\\ CH_3}}{\overset{\substack{CH_3\\|}}{C}}\!-\!CH_3 \xrightarrow[H_2O]{H_3O^+} CH_3\!-\!\underset{\substack{|\\ CH_3}}{\overset{\substack{CH_3\\|}}{C}}\!-\!CH_2\!-\!CH\!-\!CH_2\!-\!\underset{\substack{|\\ CH_3}}{\overset{\substack{CH_3\\|}}{C}}\!-\!CH_3
$$

It is interesting to note that in the oxidation of 2,3-dimethyl-2-butene, the ratio of normal oxidation to acetone, and oxidative rearrangement to pinacolone are acid dependent.[20] The former is the major product when the sulfuric acid concentration is less than 50%, and the latter predominates in more acidic solution.

The principal discordant observation is that camphene oxide on treatment with aqueous acid gives camphenilanaldehyde,[23] whereas the oxidation of

[17] A. A. Berlin, A. B. Davenkov, and L. E. Kalliopin, *J. Appl. Chem. USSR (Engl. Transl.)* **18**, 217 (1945); *Chem. Abstr.* **40**, 3741 (1946).

[18] W. J. Hickinbottom and D. G. M. Wood, *Nature* **168**, 33 (1951).

[19] The possibility that a glycol may be the intermediate has also been considered, but Hickinbottom[20] has pointed out that the glycol is oxidized and/or cleaved at a rate which is faster than that of rearrangement. Thus, it cannot be an intermediate.

[20] W. J. Hickinbottom, D. R. Hogg, D. Peters, and D. G. M. Wood, *J. Chem. Soc.* p. 4400 (1954).

[21] P. D. Bartlett, G. L. Frazer, and R. B. Woodward, *J. Am. Chem. Soc.* **63**, 495 (1941).

[22] A. Butleroff, *Ber.* **12**, 1482 (1879); *J. Russ. Phys.-Chem. Soc.* **11**, 203 (1879); J. B. Conant and G. W. Wheland, *J. Am. Chem. Soc.* **55**, 2499 (1933); F. C. Whitmore and K. C. Laughlin, *ibid.* **56**, 1128 (1934); F. C. Whitmore and C. D. Wilson, *ibid.* **56**, 1397 (1934); F. C. Whitmore and J. D. Surmatis, *ibid.* **63**, 2200 (1941).

[23] W. J. Hickinbottom and D. G. M. Wood, *J. Chem. Soc.* p. 1906 (1953).

camphene with chromic acid in aqueous acid gives camphor, not camphenilanic acid. However, it is difficult to see how the oxidation of camphene could lead to camphor since the methylene of the former presumably becomes the methyl of the latter. A reasonable assumption is that the acid catalyzed rearrangement and hydration of camphene to isoborneol is more rapid under the reaction conditions than is the oxidation of camphene. Oxidation of isoborneol would be expected to give camphor:

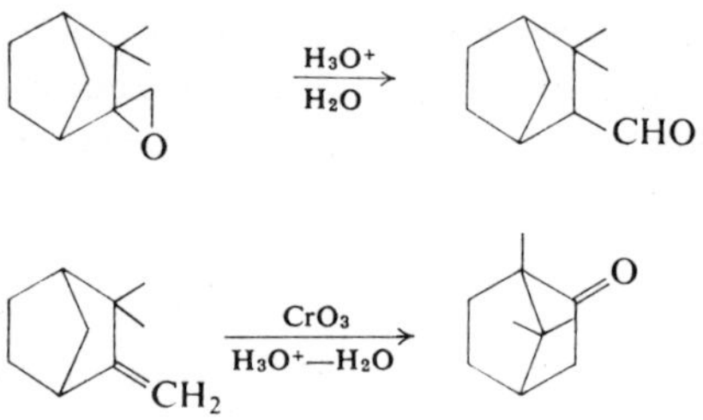

In view of the observation that chromic acid in acidic solution effects an electrophilic attack at an aromatic ring,[24] and the suggestion that the addition of chromyl chloride to an alkene involves an electrophilic addition,[25] the alternate suggestion by Hickinbottom et al.[26] that the initial step might be the electrophilic addition of H_2CrO_4 (or similar species) to the double bond is of interest. The intermediate might decompose to the epoxide by loss of chromium(IV), or might lead directly to rearrangement products without involving the epoxide.

In this connection, it is interesting to note that the chromic acid oxidation of a group of 1,1-diarylethylenes gave only cleavage products and no epoxides.[27] The epoxides were found to be unreactive under the conditions used for the oxidation, and thus it was assumed that the epoxides were not intermediates in the chromic acid oxidation.

Zeiss and Zwanzig[28] studied the oxidation of 1-methylfenchene with chromic acid and found the products to be mainly camphor with a small amount (6%) of fenchone, the rearrangement product. In view of the small amount of rearranged product, they concluded that the electrophilic addition of H_2CrO_4 was not the initial step, arguing that the resultant cation should

[24] S. G. Brandenberger, L. W. Maas, and I. Dvoretzky, J. Am. Chem. Soc. 83, 2146 (1961).
[25] S. J. Cristol and K. R. Eilar, J. Am. Chem. Soc. 72, 4353 (1950).
[26] W. J. Hickinbottom, D. Peters, and D. G. M. Wood, J. Chem. Soc. p. 1360 (1955).
[27] W. J. Hickinbottom and G. E. M. Moussa, J. Chem. Soc. p. 4195 (1957); G. E. M. Moussa, J. Appl. Chem. (London) 12, 385 (1962).
[28] H. H. Zeiss and F. R. Zwanzig, Chem. & Ind. (London) p. 545 (1956); J. Am. Chem. Soc. 79, 1733 (1957).

give a larger amount of rearrangement. This conclusion, however, is open to question:

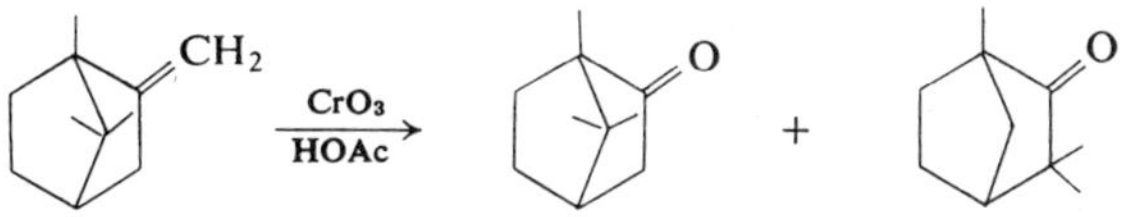

See Fig. 5-1.[29-35]

2. CHROMYL ACETATE

The oxidation of alkenes with chromyl acetate has been examined in some detail by Hickinbottom and his co-workers.[18, 20, 23, 26, 27, 31, 32] The major product in many cases was an epoxide (Table 5-1). With 4,4-dimethyl-2-

TABLE 5-1

OXIDATION OF ALKENES WITH CHROMYL ACETATE IN ACETIC ANHYDRIDE

Alkene	Products	Per cent conversion[a]	Reference
2-Pentene	3-Penten-2-one	6	26
2-Methyl-2-butene	2-Methyl-2,3-epoxybutane	4	26
	3-Methyl-2-butanone ⎫		
	3-Methyl-2-butenal ⎬	2	
	3-Methyl-3-buten-2-one ⎭		
2,3-Dimethyl-1-butene	2,3-Dimethyl-1,2-epoxybutane	9	20, 26
	3-Methyl-2-butanone ⎫	3	
	2,3-Dimethyl-2-butenal ⎬		
2,4-Dimethyl-2-pentene	2,4-Dimethyl-2,3-epoxypentane	20	26
1-Octene	Hexanoic acid ⎫	5	26
	Heptanoic acid ⎭		
	1-Octen-3-one	3	
2,4,4-Trimethyl-1-pentene	2,4,4-Trimethyl-1,2-epoxy-pentane	7 (21)	32
4,4-Dimethyl-2-neopentyl-1-pentene	4,4-Dimethyl-2-neopentyl-1,2-epoxypentane	25	31
	3,3-Dimethyl-2-neopentylbutyric acid		
Cyclohexene	1,2-Epoxycyclohexane	0.5 (5)	26
	Cyclohexen-3-one	1 (10)	
	Cyclohexane-1,2-dione	0.2 (2)	
Camphene	Camphene oxide	7 (12)	23
1,1-Diphenylethylene	1,1-Diphenylethylene oxide	88	27

[a] The per cent conversion is based on the amount of hydrocarbon taken. When the amount actually consumed was available, the yield was calculated and these figures are given in parentheses.

Reaction	Reference

$$CH_2{=}CH_2 \longrightarrow HCO_2H + CO_2 + CH_3\overset{O}{\overset{\|}{C}}OH + CH_3\overset{O}{\overset{\|}{C}}H$$

29

$$CH_3CH{=}CH_2 \longrightarrow CH_3CO_2H + HCO_2H + CO_2 + CH_3\overset{O}{\overset{\|}{C}}CH_3 + HO_2CCO_2H$$

29

$$\underset{CH_3}{\overset{CH_3}{>}}C{=}CH_2 \longrightarrow \underset{CH_3}{\overset{CH_3}{>}}C{=}O + CH_3\overset{O}{\overset{\|}{C}}OH + \underset{CH_3}{\overset{CH_3}{>}}CHCO_2H$$

30

$$\underset{CH_3}{\overset{CH_3}{>}}C{=}C\underset{CH_3}{\overset{CH_3}{<}} \longrightarrow CH_3-\underset{CH_3}{\overset{CH_3O}{\underset{\|}{C}}}-CCH_3 + CH_3-\underset{CH_3}{\overset{CH_3}{C}}-CO_2H + CH_3\overset{O}{\overset{\|}{C}}CH_3$$

22, 31

$$CH_4-\underset{CH_3}{\overset{CH_3}{C}}-CH_2-\underset{CH_3}{\overset{}{C}}{=}CH_2 \longrightarrow CH_3-\underset{CH_3}{\overset{CH_3}{C}}-CH_2CH-CO_2H + CH_3-\underset{CH_3}{\overset{CH_3}{C}}-CH_2\overset{O}{\overset{\|}{C}}CH_3$$

31, 32

$$CH_3-\underset{CH_3}{\overset{CH_3}{C}}-CH{=}\underset{CH_3}{\overset{}{C}}-CH_3 \longrightarrow CH_3-\underset{CH_3}{\overset{CH_3}{C}}-CO_2H + CH_3\overset{O}{\overset{\|}{C}}CH_3 + CH_3-\underset{CH_3}{\overset{CH_3}{C}}-\underset{CH_3}{\overset{CH_3}{C}}-CO_2H$$

31

$$CH_3-\underset{CH_3}{\overset{CH_3}{C}}-CH_2-\underset{CH_3}{\overset{CH_3}{C}}-CH_2-\underset{CH_3}{\overset{CH_3}{C}}-CH_3 \longrightarrow CH_3-\underset{CH_3}{\overset{CH_3}{C}}-CH_2\overset{O}{\overset{\|}{C}}CH_2\underset{CH_3}{\overset{CH_3}{C}}-CH_3 +$$

$$CH_3-\underset{CH_2}{\overset{CH_3}{C}}-CH_2-\underset{CO_2H}{\overset{CH_3}{CH}}-\underset{CH_3}{\overset{CH_3}{C}}-CH_3 + CH_3-\underset{CH_3}{\overset{CH_3}{C}}-CO_2H + CH_3-\underset{CH_3}{\overset{CH_3}{C}}-CH_2CO_2H$$

22

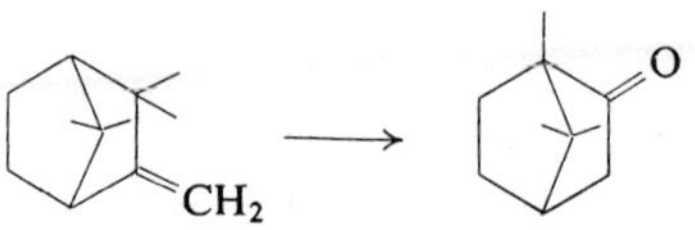

12

FIG. 5-1. (Continued next page.)

Reaction	Reference

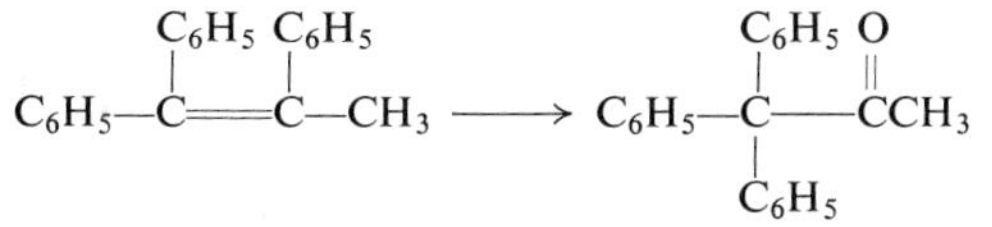

$$\underset{\underset{}{C_6H_5}}{C_6H_5-C}\!\!=\!\!\underset{}{\overset{C_6H_5}{C}}-CH_3 \longrightarrow C_6H_5-\underset{\underset{C_6H_5}{|}}{\overset{\overset{C_6H_5}{|}}{C}}-\overset{O}{\overset{||}{C}}CH_3 \qquad\qquad 33$$

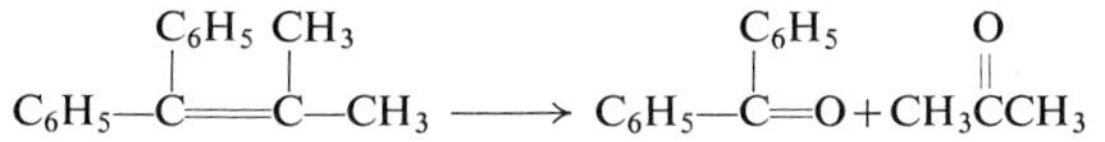

$$\underset{}{\overset{C_6H_5}{C_6H_5-C}}\!\!=\!\!\overset{CH_3}{C}-CH_3 \longrightarrow \overset{C_6H_5}{C_6H_5-C}\!\!=\!\!O + CH_3\overset{O}{\overset{||}{C}}CH_3 \qquad 27$$

$$\underset{\underset{CH_3}{|}}{C_6H_5-CH}-\overset{C_6H_5}{C}\!\!=\!\!C-C_6H_5 \longrightarrow C_6H_5-CH-\underset{\underset{C_6H_5}{|}}{\overset{\overset{C_6H_5}{|}}{C}}-\overset{O}{\overset{||}{C}}CH_3 \qquad 34$$

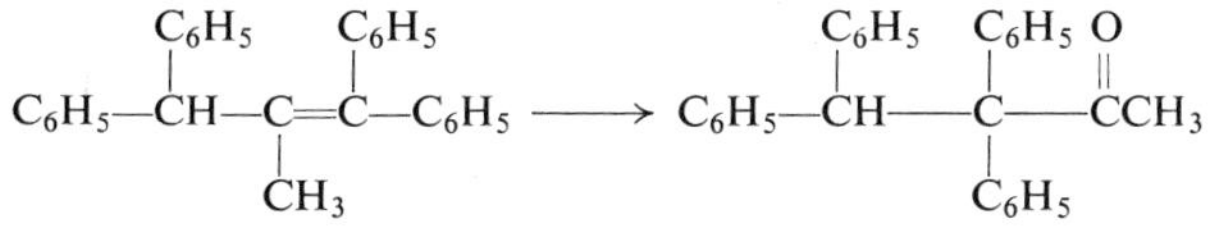

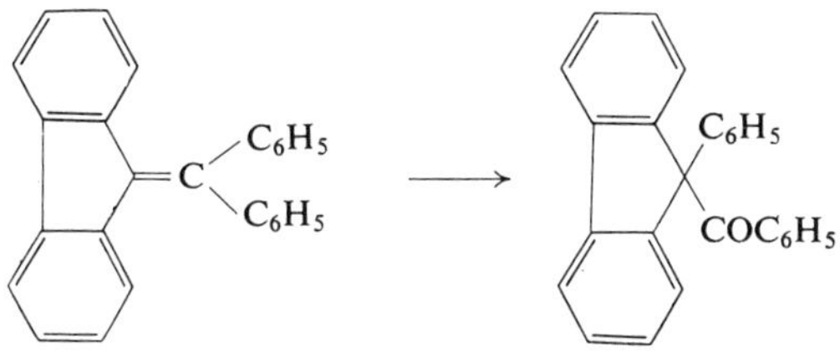

35

FIG. 5-1. Oxidation of alkenes with chromic acid in aqueous acidic medium.

neopentyl-1-pentene, a 25 % yield (based on hydrocarbon used) of the epoxide may be isolated, and 1,1-diphenylethylene gave 88 % of the epoxide.[27]

The yield of epoxide appears to be greatest when one side of the double bond is disubstituted. Cyclohexene gives a relatively low yield of epoxide, whereas none could be isolated from the oxidation of 2-pentene or 1-octene. The other products which are formed might reasonably arise via a pinacol rearrangement of the epoxide, or via allylic oxidation. Thus 3-methyl-2-butanone is the expected rearrangement product derived from 2-methyl-2,3-epoxybutane, and 3-methyl-2-butenal is formed via an allylic oxidation of 2-methyl-2-butene.

Although it is tempting to speculate that the majority of the reaction proceeds via the epoxide as an intermediate, it is difficult to support such a hypothesis. First, the yield of products isolated is low, and in most cases, the

[29] M. Berthelot, *Ann.* **150**, 373 (1869); O. Zeidler and F. Zeidler, *ibid.* **197**, 243 (1879).
[30] A. Butleroff, *Z. Chem.* [2] **7**, 485 (1871); *J. Chem. Soc.* **25**, 295 (1872).
[31] W. J. Hickinbottom and D. G. M. Wood, *J. Chem. Soc.* p. 1600 (1951).
[32] A. Beyers and W. J. Hickinbottom, *J. Chem. Soc.* p. 1334 (1948).
[33] W. Schlenk and E. Bergmann, *Ann.* **479**, 42 (1930).
[34] C. F. Koelsch and R. V. White, *J. Am. Chem. Soc.* **65**, 1639 (1943).
[35] H. Klinger and C. Lonnes, *Ber.* **29**, 2152 (1896).

yield of epoxide is quite low. There are few data on the rate of decomposition of the expected epoxides in the reaction media, and thus it is not known whether the lability of the epoxide is yield controlling. It is clear that much additional data on the stoichiometry of the reaction and on the relative rates of reaction of possible intermediates is needed.

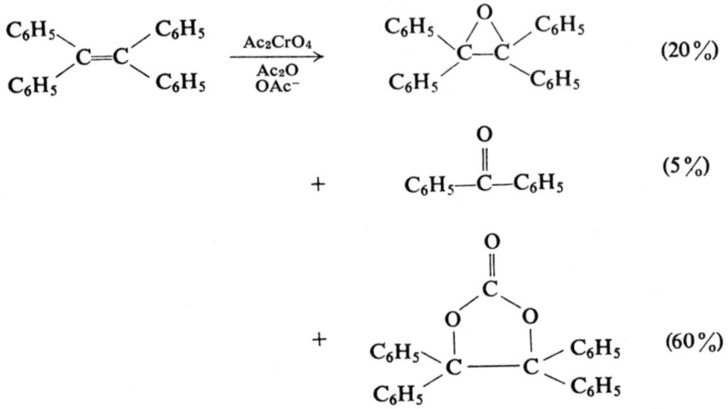

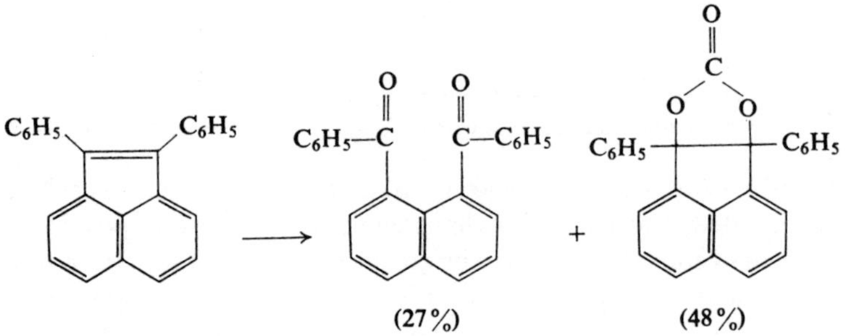

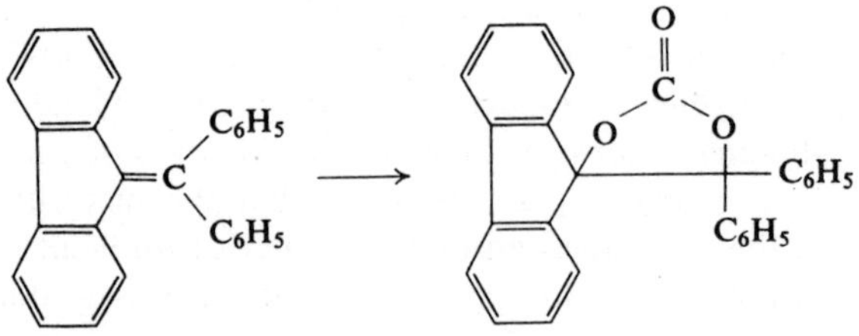

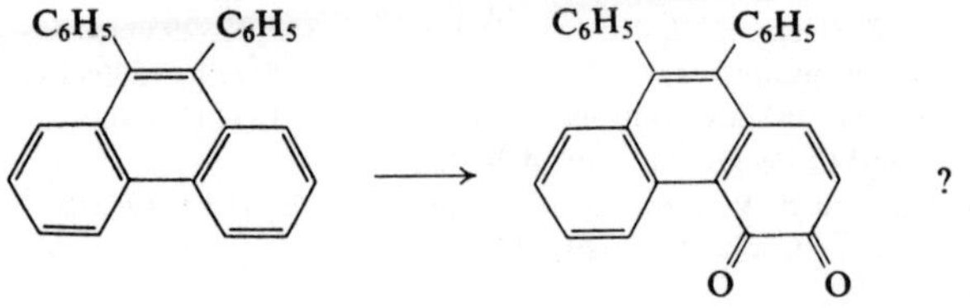

The oxidation of cyclic alkenes with chromyl trichloroacetate in acetone–carbon tetrachloride solution has been found to give the cleavage product, the dialdehyde, in fairly good yield. Thus, cyclooctene gave 61 % of the dialdehyde, cycloheptene gave 59%, and cyclohexene gave 46%.[36] A comparison of oxidations by chromyl acetate, chromyl benzoate, and chromyl trifluoroacetate in carbon tetrachloride solution was given.

The oxidation of tetraphenylethylene with chromic acid in acetic acid gives largely tetraphenylethylene oxide.[1] However, with chromyl acetate in acetic anhydride, benzopinacol carbonate is also formed.[37] The yield of the carbonate was increased by the addition of acetate ion, and the carbonate was not formed unless an acid anhydride (acetic and propionic were used) was present. Using substituted tetraphenylethylenes, it was shown that the reaction was not stereospecific. A summary of the conversions which were effected is given in the accompanying scheme (p. 134). It appears that only tetraphenylethylenes will give a significant amount of the carbonate as product.

3. Chromyl Chloride

Although there had been a few earlier studies of the reaction of chromyl chloride with alkenes,[38] the first study which helped to elucidate the nature and products of the reaction was that of Cristol and Eilar.[39] They found that the major product of the reaction with cyclohexene was *trans*-2-chlorocyclohexanol, and that 1-alkenes gave about 50% yields of chlorhydrins with the hydroxyl group in the 1-position.

A more detailed study of the reaction with cyclohexene has been made by Stairs, Diaper and Gatzke.[40] They found the products to be:

trans-2-Chlorocyclohexanol	21%
cis-2-Chlorocyclohexanol	14%
Cyclohexanone	6%
2-Cyclohexenone	17%
Cyclohexene (recovered)	21%
Higher boiling materials	22%

[36] H. Schildknecht and W. Föttinger, *Ann.* **659**, 20 (1962).

[37] W. A. Mosher, F. W. Steffgen, and P. T. Lansbury, *J. Org. Chem.* **26**, 670 (1961).

[38] A. Étard, *Compt. Rend. Acad. Sci.* **116**, 434 (1893); G. G. Henderson and R. W. Smith, *J. Chem. Soc.* **55**, 45 (1889); G. G. Henderson and T. Gray, *ibid.* **83**, 1299 (1903); G. G. Henderson and I. M. Heilbron, *ibid.* **93**, 288 (1908); **99**, 1887 (1911); G. G. Henderson, J. M. Robertson, and D. C. Brown, *ibid.* **121**, 2717 (1922); J. Bredt and W. Jagelki, *Ann.* **310**, 112 (1900); J. Sword, *Chem. News* **133**, 1 (1926); G. G. Henderson and D. Chisholm, *J. Chem. Soc.* **125**, 107 (1924).

[39] S. J. Cristol and K. R. Eilar, *J. Am. Chem. Soc.* **72**, 4353 (1950).

[40] R. A. Stairs, D. G. M. Diaper, and A. L. Gatzke, *Can. J. Chem.* **41**, 1059 (1963).

In the case of cyclopentene, the *trans-* and *cis-*chlorhydrins were formed in 6 and 18% yield, respectively. The addition to 1-alkenes was also studied, and with 1-hexene, the products were:

2-Chloro-1-hexanol	33%
1-Chloro-2-hexanol	9%
2-Chlorohexanal	2%
1-Chloro-2-hexanone	5%
2-Hexenal or 1-hexen-3-one	2%

The reaction of chromyl chloride with 1,1-disubstituted ethylenes is of particular interest. The oxidation of 2-methyl-1-pentene gives largely 2-methylpentanal, and the oxidation of camphene appears to give largely camphenilanaldehyde.[41]

$$\underset{\displaystyle CH_3}{CH_3CH_2CH_2\overset{\textstyle CH_3}{C}=CH_2} \xrightarrow{CrO_2Cl_2} \xrightarrow{H_2O} CH_3CH_2CH_2\overset{\textstyle CH_3}{CH}CHO$$

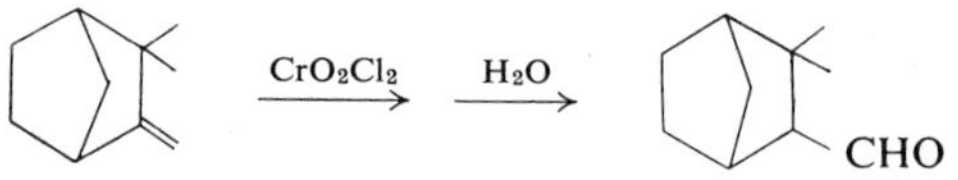

The same type of reaction occurs with styrene derivatives. The oxidation of β-methylstyrene gives benzyl methyl ketone,[42] and although other substituted styrenes have not been studied as such, they are believed to be intermediates in the Étard oxidation of the aryl alkanes, and rearranged compounds of the above types are the major products of the latter reaction.[42]

$$C_6H_5CH{=}CHCH_3 \xrightarrow{CrO_2Cl_2} \xrightarrow{H_2O} C_6H_5CH_2\overset{\textstyle O}{\overset{\|}{C}}CH_3$$

$$C_6H_5\overset{\textstyle CH_3}{\underset{\textstyle CH_3}{CH}} \xrightarrow{CrO_2Cl_2} \left[C_6H_5\overset{\textstyle }{\underset{\textstyle CH_3}{C}}{=}CH_2 \right] \xrightarrow{CrO_2Cl_2} \xrightarrow{H_2O} C_6H_5\overset{\textstyle }{\underset{\textstyle CH_3}{CH}}CHO$$

4. Oxidation of Aromatic Rings

The chromic acid oxidation of polynuclear aromatic compounds generally leads to nuclear oxidation rather than to side chain oxidation. Thus 1-methylnaphthalene gives 5-methyl-1,4-naphthoquinone[43] rather than 1-naphthoic acid. Typical examples are given in Table 5-2.[44-63]

[41] J. Bredt and W. Jagelki, *Ann.* **310**, 112 (1900).
[42] K. B. Wiberg, B. Marshall, and G. Foster, *Tetrahedron Letters* p. 345 (1962).
[43] J. Herzenberg and S. Ruhemann, *Ber.* **60**, 893 (1927).

TABLE 5-2

OXIDATION OF AROMATIC RINGS WITH CHROMIC ACID

Reactant	Products	Reference
Naphthalene	1,4-Naphthoquinone	48
	Phthalic acid	
1-Methylnaphthalene	5-Methyl-1,4-naphthoquinone	43
2-Methylnaphthalene	2-Methyl-1,4-naphthoquinone	49
2,3-Dimethylnaphthalene	2,3-Dimethyl-1,4-naphthoquinone	50
2,6-Dimethylnaphthalene	2,6-Dimethyl-1,4-naphthoquinone	51
1,2,5-Trimethylnaphthalene	1,2,5-Trimethyl-3,4-naphthoquinone	45
	2,5-Dimethyl-1,4-naphthoquinone	
	2,5-Dimethyl-1,4-diacetoxynaphthalene	
	3-Methylacetophenone-2-carboxylic acid	
2-*tert*-Butylnaphthalene	2-*tert*-Butyl-1,4-naphthoquinone	52
1,6-Dimethyl-4-isopropyl-naphthalene	6-Methyl-4-isopropyl-1-naphthoic acid	53
	2,5-Dimethyl-8-isopropyl-1,4-naphthoquinone	
Anthracene	Anthraquinone	54
1-Methylanthracene	1-Methyl-9,10-anthraquinone	55
2-Methylanthracene	Anthraquinone-2-carboxylic acid	56
2,6-Dimethylanthracene	2,6-Dimethyl-9,10-anthraquinone	57
1,3,6-Trimethylanthracene	1,3,6-Trimethyl-9,10-anthraquinone	58
1,3,5,7-Tetramethylanthracene	1,3,5,7-Tetramethyl-9,10-anthraquinone	59
1,2,3,4-Tetrahydroanthracene	1,2,3,4-Tetrahydro-9,10-anthraquinone	60
Phenanthrene	Phenanthraquinone	61
1-Methylphenanthrene	1-Methyl-9,10-phenanthraquinone	62
9-Ethylphenanthrene	Phenanthraquinone	44
1,2,3,4-Tetrahydrophenanthrene	1-Keto-1,2,3,4-tetrahydrophenanthrene	63

[44] R. Pschorr, *Ber.* **39**, 3128 (1906).

[45] I. M. Heilbron and D. G. Wilkinson, *J. Chem. Soc.* p. 2546 (1930); p. 2809 (1932).

[46] L. Friedman, D. L. Fishel, and H. Schechter, *J. Org. Chem.* **30**, 1453 (1965).

[47] S. G. Brandenberger, L. W. Maas, and I. Dvoretzky, *J. Am. Chem. Soc.* **83**, 2146 (1961).

[48] C. E. Groves, *Ann.* **167**, 357 (1873); F. Beilstein and A. Kurbatow, *Ann.* **202**, 213 (1880).

[49] N. A. Orlow, *Ber.* **62**, 715 (1929); P. P. T. Sah, *Rec. Trav. Chim.* **59**, 1021 (1940).

[50] L. I. Smith and I. M. Webster, *J. Am. Chem. Soc.* **59**, 662 (1937).

[51] R. Weissgerber and O. Kruber, *Ber.* **52**, 346 (1919).

[52] N. G. Bromby, A. T. Peters, and F. M. Rowe, *J. Chem. Soc.* p. 144 (1943).

[53] L. Ruzicka, J. Meyer, and M. Mingazzini, *Helv. Chim. Acta* **5**, 365 (1922).

[54] J. Fritzsche, *J. Prakt. Chem.* [1] **106**, 287 (1869).

[55] O. Fischer and A. Sapper, *J. Prakt. Chem.* [2] **83**, 203 (1911).

[56] J. Weiler, *Ber.* **7**, 1186 (1874); H. Meyer and K. Bernhauer, *Monatsh.* **53/54**, 721 (1929).

[57] R. Anschutz, *Ann.* **235**, 319 (1886).

[58] K. Elbs, *J. Prakt. Chem.* [2] **41**, 142 (1890).

[59] J. Dewar and H. O. Jones, *J. Chem. Soc.* **85**, 218 (1904).

[60] G. Schroeter, *Ber.* **57**, 2014 (1924).

[61] R. Wendland and J. LaLonde, *Org. Syn. Coll. Vol.* **IV**, 757 (1963); R. P. Linstead and W. v. E. Doering, *J. Am. Chem. Soc.* **64**, 1998 (1942).

[62] R. Pschorr, *Ber.* **39**, 3106 (1906).

[63] G. Schroeter, H. Müller, and J. Y. S. Huang, *Ber.* **62**, 645 (1929).

In a few cases, alkyl groups are removed in the process of forming quinones. As examples, 9-ethylphenanthrene gives phenanthraquinone,[44] and 1,2,5-trimethylnaphthalene gives 2,5-dimethyl-1,4-naphthoquinone[45] along with other products. All of these oxidations depend on the use of an acidic medium, for when a neutral solution of chromium(VI) is used, ring oxidation does not occur under conditions which lead to oxidation of side chains.[46]

Although the benzene ring is considerably more resistant to oxidation than are the polynuclear aromatic compounds, it does suffer degradation during oxidation when electron releasing groups are present. This has been examined in some detail for a series of alkyl substituted benzenes.[47] It was found that the amount of ring degradation increased with increasing acid concentration, and with increasing degree of alkyl substitution.

5. MECHANISM OF THE OXIDATION OF ALKENES

It is difficult to formulate a detailed mechanism for the chromium(VI) oxidation because of the diversity of reactions and the lack of certain basic information. Thus, there are no data on the role of chromium(IV) and (V) in determining the products of the reaction. It is not known whether epoxide formation from aliphatic alkenes is stereospecific. The relative rates of oxidation of mono-, di-, tri-, and tetrasubstituted alkenes have not been determined.

The general course of the reaction may, however, be deduced, and this has been discussed by Hickinbottom and Moussa[27] and by Hickinbottom and Davis.[64] The observation that 1,1-diphenylethylene gives only benzophenone and acetone on oxidation with aqueous chromic acid, whereas 1,1-diphenylethylene oxide is stable under the reaction conditions suggests that the epoxide may not be an intermediate in the reaction. The principal product using chromyl acetate as the oxidant is the epoxide. It is likely that the initial attack is of the same type with both forms of chromium(VI), suggesting the formation of an intermediate which may lead either to the epoxide, or to the other products which are observed.

It is, however, strange that 1,1-diphenylethylene oxide should be so inert to aqueous sulfuric acid. It is possible that the lack of reactivity may result from its low solubility in water. In this case, the epoxide could be an intermediate in the oxidation in aqueous sulfuric acid since it would be formed in a highly dispersed state which should be much more reactive than the bulk epoxide. The reactivity of this epoxide toward water and acid in a homogeneous medium should be determined.

The reaction may involve an electrophilic attack of chromium(VI)[27, 64] at the double bond in a fashion similar to the addition of bromine to an alkene in a polar medium (A),[65] or it may involve simultaneous addition to both sides

[64] M. A. Davis and W. J. Hickinbottom, *J. Chem. Soc.* p. 2205 (1958).
[65] Cf. P. B. D. de la Mare, *Quart. Rev. (London)* 3, 126 (1949).

(A)

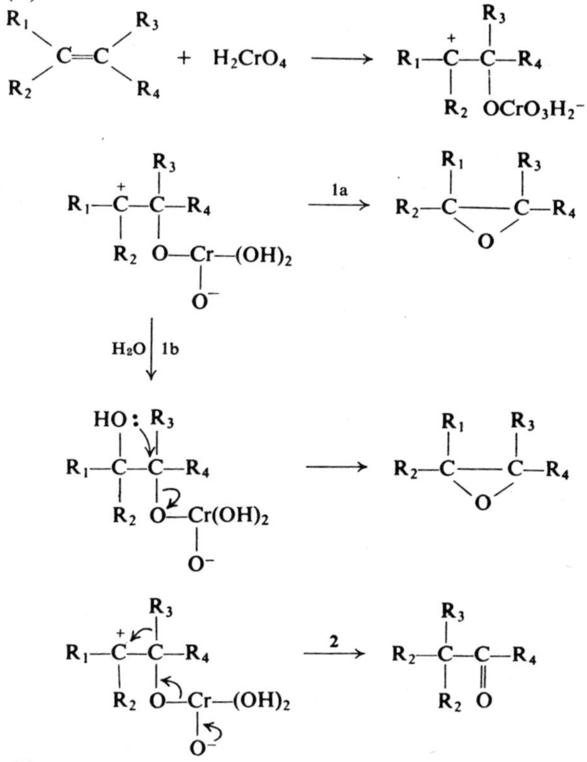

$$R_1R_2C=CR_3R_4 + H_2CrO_4 \longrightarrow R_1\overset{+}{\underset{R_2}{C}}\text{--}\underset{OCrO_3H_2^-}{\overset{R_3}{C}}\text{--}R_4$$

$$R_1\overset{+}{\underset{R_2}{C}}\text{--}\underset{O\text{--}Cr\text{--}(OH)_2}{\overset{R_3}{\underset{\overset{|}{O^-}}{C}}}\text{--}R_4 \xrightarrow{\text{1a}} \underset{R_2\text{--}C\overset{R_1}{\underset{O}{\diagdown}}C\text{--}R_4}{\overset{R_3}{}}$$

$$\text{H}_2\text{O} \downarrow \text{1b}$$

$$\underset{R_2\ O\text{--}Cr(OH)_2}{\overset{HO\!:\ R_3}{R_1\text{--}C\text{--}C\text{--}R_4}}\underset{\overset{|}{O^-}}{} \longrightarrow R_2\text{--}C\overset{R_1\quad R_3}{\underset{O}{\diagup\!\diagdown}}C\text{--}R_4$$

$$R_1\overset{+}{\underset{R_2}{C}}\text{--}\underset{O\text{--}Cr\text{--}(OH)_2}{\overset{R_3}{C}}\text{--}R_4 \xrightarrow{2} R_2\text{--}C\overset{R_3}{\underset{R_2\ O}{\|}}C\text{--}R_4$$

(B)

$$R_1R_2C=CR_3R_4 + H_2CrO_4 \longrightarrow \underset{\underset{HO\diagup Cr \diagdown OH}{O\qquad O}}{R_2\text{--}\overset{R_1}{C}\text{--}\overset{R_3}{C}\text{--}R_4}$$

$$\underset{\underset{HO\diagup Cr \diagdown OH}{O\qquad O}}{R_2\text{--}\overset{R_1}{C}\text{--}\overset{R_3}{C}\text{--}R_4} \xrightarrow{1} R_2\text{--}C\overset{R_1\quad R_3}{\underset{O}{\diagup\!\diagdown}}C\text{--}R_4$$

$$\underset{\underset{HO\diagup Cr \diagdown OH}{O\qquad O}}{R_2\text{--}\overset{R_1}{C}\text{--}\overset{R_3}{C}\text{--}R_4} \xrightarrow{2} R_1\text{--}C\overset{R_3}{\underset{R_2\ O}{\|}}C\text{--}R_4$$

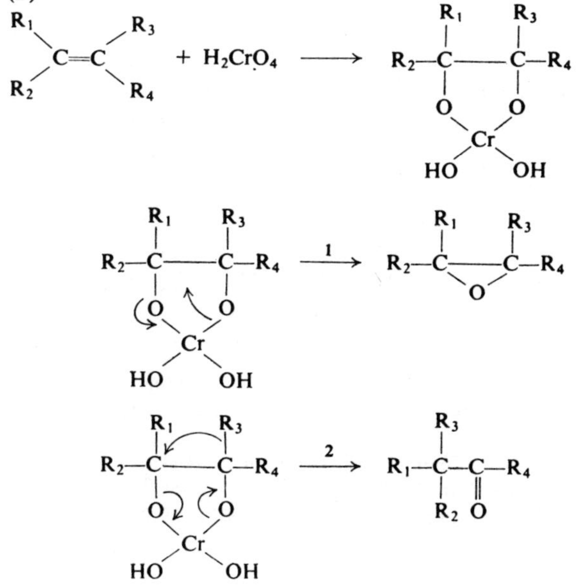

of the double bond [28] in a fashion similar to permanganate ion (B).[66] Either of the mechanisms shown here could account for the formation of epoxides and for the other products which are observed.

The observation that conjugated dienes are oxidized to enediones,[14, 15] suggests an initial electrophilic attack in analogy with the 1,4- addition of bromine to dienes. However, the major product still involves the oxidation of only one double bond, and the cyclic intermediate shown in (B) might lead to the enedione via an S_N2' attack of water at the double bond:

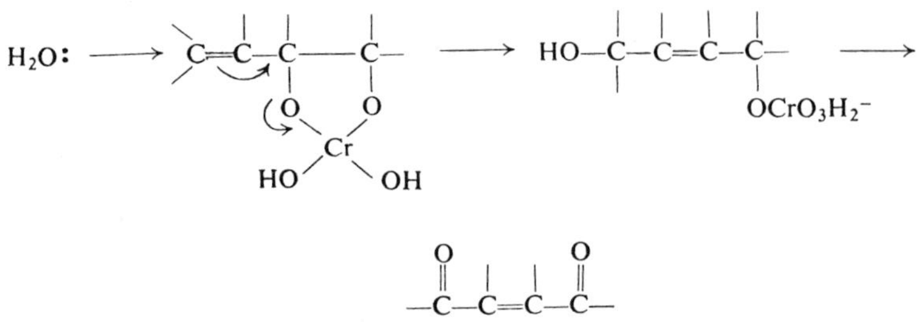

The observation that 1-methyl-α-fenchene is oxidized with very little rearrangement might be interpreted as favoring the mechanism in which the cyclic ester is formed.[28] However, in view of the facts that camphene adds hydrogen chloride to give camphene hydrochloride and that the latter undergoes a rapid solvolysis to camphene hydrate,[67] one cannot assume that rearrangements in these systems will be facile. It would appear that the presently available data are not adequate to permit a decision between the two mechanisms.

The occurrence of rearrangement in both the chromic acid and chromyl acetate oxidations of alkenes indicates that a carbonium ion may be formed at some point in the reaction. This may occur in the ring opening of the epoxide which is formed, or from a chromium-containing intermediate which precedes epoxide formation. Again, the available data do not permit a decision between the two possibilities.

Much information is available on the oxidation of tetraarylethylenes. Here, the oxidation with chromic acid leads almost exclusively to the epoxide, which is formed in a nonstereospecific fashion. Thus, the oxidation of each of the 1,2-diphenyl-1,2-(p-chlorophenyl) ethylenes gave mixtures of the two stereo-isomeric epoxides. If the initial reaction of chromic acid with the alkenes proceeded in a fashion analogous to the permanganate oxidation of alkenes,[66] we might expect the epoxide formation to be stereospecific (reaction B-1

[66] J. Boeseken, *Rec. Trav. Chim.* **40**, 553 (1921); **47**, 683 (1928); K. B. Wiberg and K. A. Saegebarth, *J. Am. Chem. Soc.* **79**, 2822 (1957).
[67] H. Meerwein and K. van Emster, *Ber.* **53**, 1815 (1920); **55**, 2500 (1922).

above). On the other hand, if electrophilic attack occurred, rotation about the double bond should occur before the ring closure step (reaction A-1 above) leading to a mixture of the two possible isomers.

In the reaction of the tetraarylethylenes with chromyl acetate, a similar path will lead to the observed cyclic carbonates:

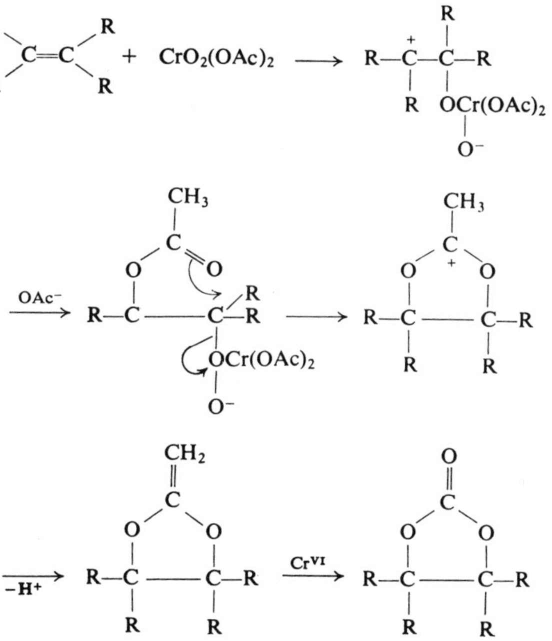

Again, the reaction of the carbonium ion intermediate with acetate ion would have low stereospecificity, and would lead to an over-all lack of stereospecificity. The reaction path given above appears to be unique for the tetraphenylethylenes. Corresponding products are not obtained in other cases.

In the oxidation of alkenes with chromyl chloride, evidence has been obtained for electrophilic addition.[68] First, the reaction with cyclohexene leading to the chlorhydrins is not stereospecific. A reaction proceeding via a cyclic intermediate might be expected to give only the *trans*-chlorhydrin. Second, the rate of reaction between the alkene and chromyl chloride appears to be increased markedly by increased alkyl substitution at the double bond. This might not be expected for a cyclic intermediate. However, the data are not sufficient to establish any one mechanism.

In the oxidation of alkyl substituted benzenes with chromic acid, it has been observed that the ratio of ring oxidation to side chain oxidation increases

[68] A. L. Gatzke, Ph. D. Thesis, Queen's University, Kingston, Ontario, Canada, 1964.

with increasing acid concentration, and with increasing alkyl substitution on the ring. This suggests that the reaction with the ring involves an electrophilic attack, and that the reagent involved is protonated chromic acid:

$$
\text{C}_6\text{H}_6 + \left[\begin{array}{c} \text{OH} \\ | \\ \text{HO—C}=\text{O} \\ | \\ \text{OH} \end{array} \right]^+ \longrightarrow \begin{array}{c} \text{OH} \\ | \\ \text{—O—Cr—OH} \\ | \\ \text{OH} \end{array} \longrightarrow \text{products}
$$

Presumably, the protonated chromic acid would be a more reactive electrophilic species than chromic acid itself, and is sufficiently reactive to attack an activated aromatic ring. The subsequent steps in the reaction have not been studied, but it is reasonable to suppose that they involve the loss of a proton, hydrolysis to a phenol, and further oxidation of the latter.

VI. Oxidation of Alcohols

The major use of chromic acid in synthetic chemistry is in the oxidation of primary and secondary alcohols to aldehydes and ketones, respectively. As a result, alcohol oxidation by this reagent has received extensive investigation. Many forms of chromium(VI) have been used: chromic acid in water or aqueous acetic acid catalyzed by mineral acid; chromic acid in water–acetone catalyzed by mineral acid; sodium dichromate in acetic acid; chromium trioxide–pyridine complex; and *tert*-butyl chromate. Each of these has some advantages, and each will be considered in turn.

1. CHROMIC ACID IN WATER OR AQUEOUS ACETIC ACID

The oxidation of a secondary alcohol such as isopropyl alcohol[1] occurs in essentially quantitative yield if no complicating structural features are present. Some typical results are summarized in Table 6-1. It is obvious that the reaction will be less satisfactory if an easily oxidizable functional group such as a carbon–carbon double bond, a sulfide linkage, or a phenolic or amine group is present, or if the compound is sensitive to acid. A less obvious difficulty is the possibility of a cleavage reaction as is found with phenyl *tert*-butyl carbinol:

$$
\begin{array}{c} \text{OH} \\ | \\ \text{C}_6\text{H}_5\text{—C—C(CH}_3)_3 \\ | \\ \text{H} \end{array} \xrightarrow{\text{Cr}^{\text{VI}}} \begin{array}{c} \text{O} \\ || \\ \text{C}_6\text{H}_5\text{CC(CH}_3)_3 \end{array} + \text{C}_6\text{H}_5\text{CHO} + (\text{CH}_3)_3\text{COH}
$$

Here, a major portion of the reaction gives cleavage to benzaldehyde and *tert*-butyl alcohol, and a smaller quantity of the expected ketone is obtained. This type of cleavage occurs with many alcohols. The oxidation of 2-heptanol

[1] F. H. Westheimer and A. Novick, *J. Chem. Phys.* **11**, 506 (1943).

gives a trace of amyl acetate; 4-methyl-3-hexanol gives a small amount of 2-butanol and 2-butanone; 2,2-dimethyl-3-hexanol gives some *tert*-butyl alcohol and *n*-butyraldehyde,[2, 3] and cyclobutanol gives 4-hydroxybutyraldehyde and cyclobutanone in comparable amounts.[4]

Phenyl alkyl carbinols generally give larger amounts of cleavage. Thus, phenylisopropyl carbinol gives 6% cleavage and phenyl-*tert*-butyl carbinol gives up to 60% cleavage.[5, 6] Other examples are known.

One of the most interesting features of chromic acid oxidation is the virtual elimination of the cleavage reaction of phenyl alkyl carbinols by the addition of manganous ion.[5, 6] The manganous ion in aqueous acetic acid is known to catalyze the disproportionation of chromium(IV) and/or (V). Thus, we may presume that the cleavage reaction occurs via the chromium species of intermediate valence, and that the ketone is formed via a normal oxidation of chromium(VI). The use of manganous ion may be useful in many cases of alcohol oxidation.

The oxidation of primary alcohols leads to extra problems. The aldehydes which result are fairly easily oxidized, and will be converted to the corresponding carboxylic acids (cf. Table 6-2). However, this does not account for the low yields often obtained. The major side reaction involves the equilibrium between the aldehyde and unreacted alcohol to give the hemiacetal which may be further oxidized to the ester[7]:

$$RCH_2OH \longrightarrow RCHO$$

$$RCH_2OH + RCHO \rightleftharpoons R-\underset{\underset{OH}{|}}{\overset{\overset{H}{|}}{C}}-OCH_2R$$

$$R-\underset{\underset{OH}{|}}{\overset{\overset{H}{|}}{C}}-OCH_2R + Cr^{VI} \longrightarrow R-\underset{\underset{O}{\|}}{C}-OCH_2R$$

This direct oxidation to an ester has found some synthetic application, as in the oxidation of *n*-butyl alcohol to *n*-butyl butyrate.[8]

[2] W. A. Mosher and E. O. Langerak, *J. Am. Chem. Soc.* **71**, 286 (1949).

[3] H. A. Neidig, D. L. Funck, R. Uhrich, R. Baker, and W. Kreiser, *J. Am. Chem. Soc.* **72**, 4617 (1950).

[4] J. Roček and A. Radkowsky, private communication.

[5] J. Hampton, A. Leo, and F. H. Westheimer, *J. Am. Chem. Soc.* **78**, 306 (1956).

[6] J. J. Cawley and F. H. Westheimer, *J. Am. Chem. Soc.* **85**, 1771 (1963).

[7] W. A. Mosher and D. M. Preiss, *J. Am. Chem. Soc.* **75**, 5605 (1953).

[8] Cf. G. R. Robertson, *Org. Syn. Coll. Vol.* **I**, 138 (1941).

The formation of esters may be minimized if the aldehyde is removed as it is formed. This is often possible because of the lower boiling point of the aldehyde compared with the alcohol, and in many cases a stream of carbon dioxide or nitrogen will serve to sweep the aldehyde out of the reaction mixture. Some typical synthetic results of primary alcohol oxidation are summarized in Table 6-2.

Typical procedures for the chromic acid oxidation of alcohols follow.

2-Octanone.[9] 2-Octanol (120 gm, 147 ml) is added dropwise during 1.5 hours to a vigorously stirred solution of sodium dichromate dihydrate (90 gm) and concentrated sulfuric acid (120 gm, 66 ml) in water (600 ml). The mixture is heated under reflux on a boiling water bath for 2 hours, and the ketone is then isolated by steam distillation. Distillation at atmospheric pressure gives 110–115 gm 2-octanone (92–96%), b.p. 172–173° C.

3-Hexanone.[2] A solution of 80 gm (0.8 mole) of chromium trioxide in 50 ml water and 125 ml of glacial acetic acid is added dropwise to a stirred solution of 168 gm (1.4 moles) of 3-hexanol in 100 ml of glacial acetic acid over a period of 5.8 hours. The temperature is kept below 30° C at all times. The oil layer formed on dilution of the reaction mixture with water is separated, and washed with bicarbonate solution and with water. The aqueous layer is steam distilled and the oil layer, after washing as before, is combined with the main portion. After drying, distillation through a column gives 100 gm (63%) of 3-hexanone. Some 3-hexanol (11 gm, 7%) is recovered.

Propionaldehyde.[10] One hundred grams (125 ml, 1.7 moles) of *n*-propyl alcohol is placed in a three-necked flask equipped with a stirrer, a dropping funnel, and a condenser maintained at 60° C. A condenser set for downward distillation is connected to the top of the first condenser. The alcohol in the flask is heated to boiling, stirred, and a mixture of 164 gm (0.56 mole) of potassium dichromate, 120 ml of concentrated sulfuric acid (2.2 moles), and 1 liter of water is added over a period of 30 minutes. The solution is kept vigorously boiling during the addition and for 15 minutes thereafter. The propionaldehyde which distills is dried over sodium sulfate and distilled, giving 44–47 gm (45–49%), having b.p. 48–55° C.

n-Butyl n-Butyrate.[8] To a stirred mixture of 240 ml (4.3 moles) of concentrated sulfuric acid, 240 ml of water and 240 gm (296 ml, 3.24 moles) of *n*-butyl alcohol which was cooled in an ice-salt bath is added a solution of 320 gm (1.07 moles) of sodium dichromate in 200 ml of water. The addition is made as rapidly as

[9] F. G. Mann and J. W. G. Porter, *J. Chem. Soc.* p. 456 (1944).
[10] C. D. Hurd and R. N. Meinert, *Org. Syn. Coll. Vol.* **II**, 541 (1943).

possible, maintaining the reaction mixture under 20° C. The emulsion is diluted with an equal volume of water. The oil which separates is washed three times with water, dried over a few grams of sodium sulfate, and distilled through a column collecting the material having b.p. 150–170° C (170–175 ml). It is washed with five 15-ml portions of 60% sulfuric acid, with dilute sodium hydroxide solution, and with water. After drying, distillation gives 96–110 gm (41–47%) of *n*-butyl *n*-butyrate, b.p. 162–166° C.

2. CHROMIC ACID AND ACETONE

In an investigation of the chromic acid oxidation of acetylenic carbinols, Bowden *et al.*[41] found that acetone had decided advantages as the solvent. In their procedure, a solution of chromic acid in dilute sulfuric acid is added to an acetone solution of the alcohol. In some cases, a sharp end point is noted on adding the theoretical amount of oxidant. One of the advantages of acetone as the solvent is that the reaction proceeds more rapidly in acetone than in acetic acid. In the oxidation of secondary alcohols, the ketone formed is effectively protected against further oxidation because of the large excess of acetone.

The reagent concentration can usually be adjusted so that an upper layer consisting of an acetone solution of the organic compound separates from the lower (usually saturated) solution of chromium salts. The separation of the layers appears to be of considerable importance in protecting the product from further oxidation. The color of the layer gives a useful indication of the presence of excess chromic acid. When the ketone produced is itself easily oxidized, it is advantageous to introduce the chromic acid solution well below the surface of the liquid so as to avoid undue contact with the upper layer. Rapidly oxidized alcohols require the theoretical amount of chromic acid; the more slowly oxidized compounds require an excess of oxidant. The reactions are usually carried out at 0–20° C, and normally proceed in good yield (cf. Tables 6-1, 6-2, method C).

Some primary alcohols have been oxidized to acids using this reagent. The yields are not as good as with secondary alcohol oxidation, but appear to be as good or better than those obtained using other oxidants or other conditions.

A typical procedure for utilizing the reagent follows.[41]

Oct-3-yn-2-one. A solution of 10.3 gm of chromium trioxide in 30 ml of water and 8.7 ml of sulfuric acid is added over 2 hours to a stirred solution of oct-3-yn-2-ol (15 gm) in 30 ml of acetone at 5–10° C. After stirring for an additional 30 minutes, the mixture is diluted to 250 ml with water, and the product is isolated by ether extraction. Distillation gives 11.5 gm (80%) of oct-3-yn-2-one, b.p. 70.5–71.5°C at 14 mm.

TABLE 6-1

OXIDATION OF SECONDARY ALCOHOLS TO KETONES

Product	Yield (%)	Method[a]	Reference
2-Pentanone	74	A	11
3-Pentanone	57	A	11
2-Hexanone	80	A	12
3-Methyl-2-pentanone	81	A	13
3-Hexanone	85	A	14
2-Heptanone	70	A	15
	83	B	2
3,3-Dimethyl-2-pentanone	36	B	16
3-Heptanone	70	A	15
4-Methyl-3-hexanone	63	B	2
4-Heptanone	70	A	15
2,4-Dimethyl-3-pentanone	74	A	17
2-Octanone	96	A	9
3-Methyl-2-heptanone	68	A	18
2,2-Dimethyl-3-hexanone	41	B	2
2,4-Dimethyl-3-hexanone	68	A	19
Methyl cyclopentyl ketone	54	A	20
Methyl cyclohexyl ketone	85	A	11
Cyclohexanone	85	A	21
2-Methylcyclohexanone	85	A	22
3-Methylcyclohexanone	90	A	23, 24
4-Methylcyclohexanone	74	A	25

[a] The methods used are: A, dichromate ion in aqueous sulfuric acid; B, chromium trioxide in acetic acid or aqueous acetic acid; C, dichromate ion in aqueous sulfuric acid added to the alcohol in acetone solution.

11 C. R. Yohe, H. U. Louder, and G. A. Smith, *J. Chem. Educ.* **10**, 374 (1933).

12 V. Grignard and M. Fluchaire, *Ann. Chim.* (*Paris*) [10] **9**, 5 (1928); G. W. Bennett and F. Elder, *J. Chem. Educ.* **13**, 273 (1936).

13 R. B. Wagner and J. A. Moore, *J. Am. Chem. Soc.* **72**, 974 (1950).

14 L. I. Smith, H. E. Ungnade, W. M. Lauer, and R. M. Leekley, *J. Am. Chem. Soc.* **61**, 3079 (1939).

15 M. L. Sherrill, *J. Am. Chem. Soc.* **52**, 1982 (1930).

16 F. C. Whitmore and C. E. Lewis, *J. Am. Chem. Soc.* **64**, 2964 (1942).

17 F. C. Whitmore and E. E. Stahley, *J. Am. Chem. Soc.* **55**, 4153 (1933).

18 S. G. Powell, *J. Am. Chem. Soc.* **46**, 2514 (1924).

19 W. G. Young and J. D. Roberts, *J. Am. Chem. Soc.* **67**, 319 (1945).

20 B. Gredy, *Ann. Chim.* (*Paris*) [11] **4**, 22 (1935).

21 A. E. Osterberg and E. C. Kendall, *J. Am. Chem. Soc.* **42**, 2616 (1920).

22 F. K. Signaigo and P. L. Cramer, *J. Am. Chem. Soc.* **55**, 3326 (1933); E. W. Warnhoff, D. G. Martin, and W. S. Johnson, *Org. Syn.* **37**, 8 (1957).

23 A. K. Macbeth and J. A. Mills, *J. Chem. Soc.* p. 709 (1945).

24 J. E. Nickels and W. Heintzelman, *J. Org. Chem.* **15**, 1142 (1950).

25 H. E. Ungnade and A. D. McLaren, *J. Org. Chem.* **10**, 29 (1945).

TABLE 6-1—*continued*

OXIDATION OF SECONDARY ALCOHOLS TO KETONES

Product	Yield (%)	Method[a]	Reference
2-Ethylcyclohexanone	86	A	24
3-Ethylcyclohexanone	84	A	25
2,4-Dimethylcyclohexanone	79	A	26
2,6-Dimethylcyclohexanone	93	A	24
3,4-Dimethylcyclohexanone	93	A	24
3,5-Dimethylcyclohexanone	92	A	24
4-*n*-Propylcyclohexanone	82	A	27
4-Isopropylcyclohexanone	82	A	28
2,4-Diethylcyclohexanone	90	A	24
5-Methyl-2-isopropylcyclohexanone	94	A	29
4-Cyclohexylcyclohexanone	87	B	30
2-Decalone	94	A	31
1-Methyl-2-decalone	80	A	31
o-Methylacetophenone	60	B	32
p-Methylacetophenone	50	B	32
Phenyl isopropyl ketone	75	B	33
Phenyl *n*-butyl ketone	93	B	33
Phenyl *tert*-butyl ketone	64	B	33
Phenyl *tert*-amyl ketone	74	B	33
2-Phenylcyclohexanone	80	B	34
4-Phenylcyclohexanone	40	A	35
7-Acenaphthenone	65	B	36
3-Acetylbiphenyl	81	A	37
Dipivaloyl	50	B	38
Cyclopentene-3,5-dione	79	A	39

[26] E. C. Kornfeld, R. G. Jones, and T. V. Parke, *J. Am. Chem. Soc.* **71**, 150 (1949).

[27] H. E. Ungnade and A. Ludutsky, *J. Org. Chem.* **10**, 520 (1945).

[28] R. B. Frank, R. E. Berry, and O. L. Shotwell, *J. Am. Chem. Soc.* **71**, 3889 (1949).

[29] A. S. Hussey and R. H. Baker, *J. Org. Chem.* **25**, 1434 (1960).

[30] C. H. Shunk and A. L. Wilds, *J. Am. Chem. Soc.* **71**, 3946 (1949).

[31] H. Adkins and G. F. Hager, *J. Am. Chem. Soc.* **71**, 2965 (1949).

[32] G. Lock and R. Schreckeneder, *Ber.* **72**, 516 (1939).

[33] H. A. Neidig, D. L. Funck, R. Uhrich, R. Baker, and W. Kreiser, *J. Am. Chem. Soc.* **72**, 4617 (1950).

[34] C. C. Price and J. V. Karabinos, *J. Am. Chem. Soc.* **62**, 1159 (1940).

[35] H. E. Ungnade, *J. Org. Chem.* **13**, 361 (1948).

[36] L. F. Fieser and J. Cason, *J. Am. Chem. Soc.* **62**, 432 (1940).

[37] W. F. Huber, M. Renoll, A. G. Rossow, and D. T. Mowry, *J. Am. Chem. Soc.* **68**, 1109 (1946).

[38] N. J. Leonard and P. M. Mader, *J. Am. Chem. Soc.* **72**, 5388 (1950).

[39] G. H. Rasmusson, H. O. House, E. F. Zaweski, and C. H. DePuy, *Org. Syn.* **42**, 36 (1962).

TABLE 6-1—*continued*

OXIDATION OF SECONDARY ALCOHOLS TO KETONES

Product	Yield (%)	Method[a]	Reference
2-Methyl-2-cyclopentenone	67	B	40
Methyl ethynyl ketone	40	C	41
3-Pentyn-2-one	67	C	42
n-Propyl ethynyl ketone	70	C	41
3-Octyn-2-one	80	C	41
Phenyl ethynyl ketone	80	C	41
α,γ-Dichloroacetone	75	A	43
Chloromethyl *n*-propyl ketone	83	A	44
Methoxymethyl methyl ketone	29	A	45
2-Methoxycyclohexanone	46	A	46
3-Methoxycyclohexanone	20	A	46
4-Methoxycyclohexanone	65	A	47
m-Methoxybenzophenone	25	A	48

Steroidal alcohols:

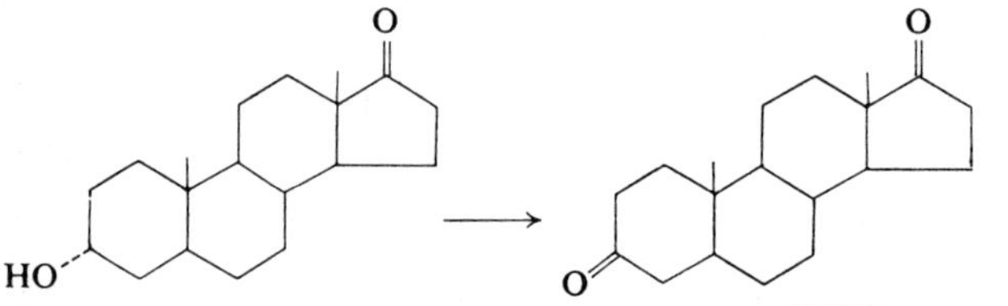

(96%)   C   49

[40] E. Dane, J. Schmitt, and C. Rautenstrauch, *Ann.* **532**, 29 (1937).
[41] K. Bowden, I. M. Heilbron, E. R. H. Jones, and B. C. L. Weedon, *J. Chem. Soc.* p. 39 (1946).
[42] E. A. Braude, E. R. H. Jones, F. Sondheimer, and J. B. Toogood, *J. Chem. Soc.* p. 607 (1949).
[43] J. B. Conant and O. R. Quayle, *Org. Syn. Coll. Vol.* **I**, 211 (1941).
[44] R. C. Elderfield and C. Ressler, *J. Am. Chem. Soc.* **72**, 4059 (1950).
[45] R. P. Mariella and J. L. Leech, *J. Am. Chem. Soc.* **71**, 3558 (1949).
[46] H. Adkins, R. M. Elofson, A. G. Rossow, and C. C. Robinson, *J. Am. Chem. Soc.* **71**, 3622 (1949).
[47] C. S. Marvel and W. L. Walton, *J. Org. Chem.* **7**, 88 (1942).
[48] T. R. Lea and R. Robinson, *J. Chem. Soc.* p. 2351 (1926).
[49] W. S. Johnson, W. A. Vredenburgh, and J. E. Pike, *J. Am. Chem. Soc.* **82**, 3409 (1960).

TABLE 6-1—*continued*

OXIDATION OF SECONDARY ALCOHOLS TO KETONES

Product	Yield	Method[a]	Reference
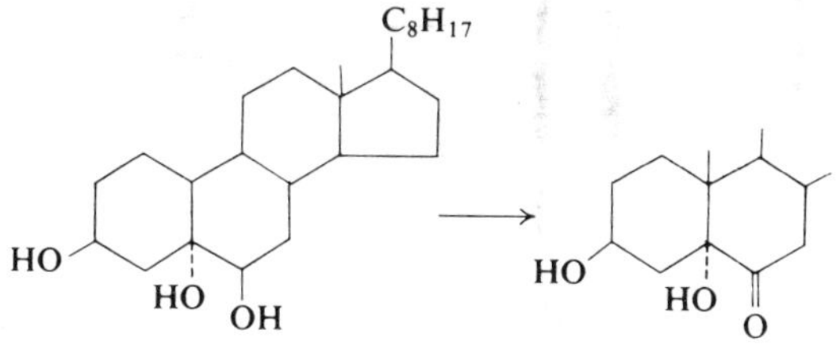 (65%)		B	50
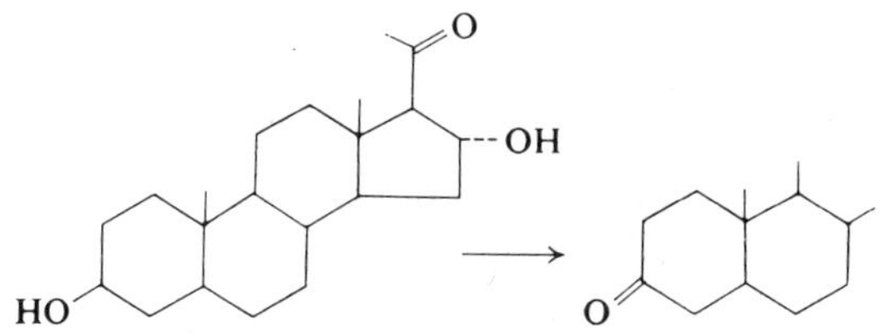 (31%)		B	51
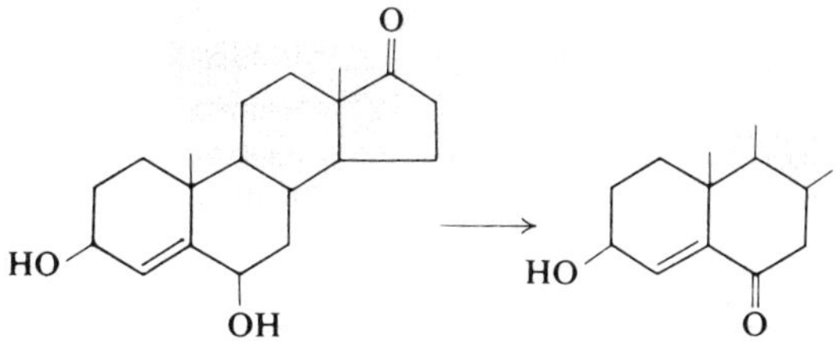 (36%)		B	52
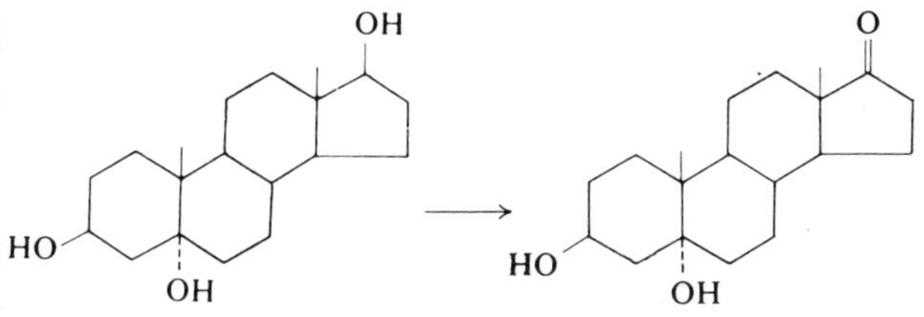 (30%)		B	53

[50] B. Ellis and V. Petrow, *J. Chem. Soc.* p. 1078 (1939).
[51] R. Neher, P. Desaulles, E. Vischer, P. Wieland, and A. Wettstein, *Helv. Chim. Acta* **41**, 1667 (1958).
[52] M. Davis and V. Petrow, *J. Chem. Soc.* p. 2536 (1949).
[53] J. Iriarte, J. N. Shoolery, and C. Djerassi, *J. Org. Chem.* **27**, 1139 (1962).

TABLE 6-1—*continued*

OXIDATION OF SECONDARY ALCOHOLS TO KETONES

Product	Yield	Method[a]	Reference

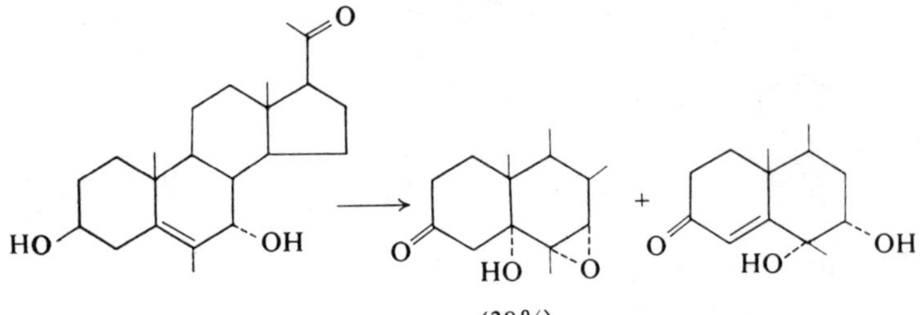

(38%)

C   53

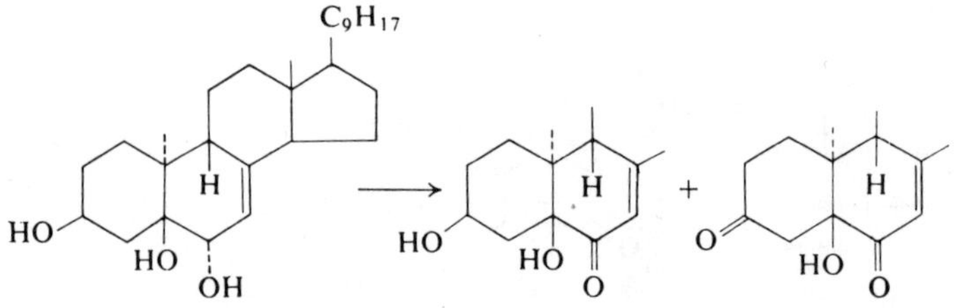

(20%)   (33%)

C   54

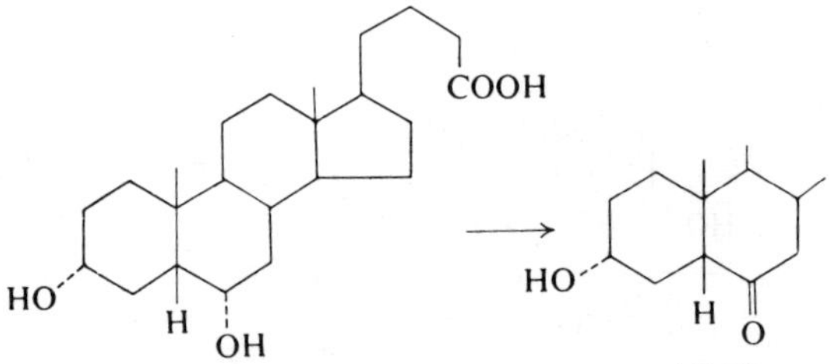

(40%)

B   55

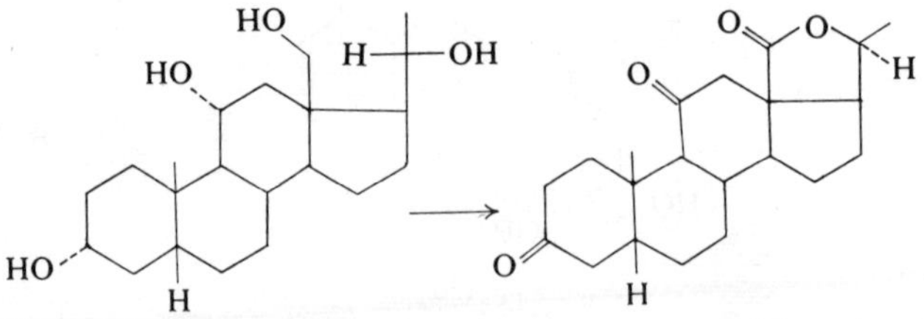

(32%)

B   56

[54] P. A. Mayor and G. D. Meakins, *J. Chem. Soc.* p. 2792 (1960).

[55] H. Wieland and E. Dane, *Z. Physiol. Chem.* **212**, 41 (1932).

[56] K. Heusler, J. Kalvoda, C. Meystre, P. Wieland, G. Anner, A. Wettstein, G. Cainelli, D. Arigoni, and O. Jeger, *Helv. Chim. Acta* **44**, 502 (1961).

TABLE 6-2

OXIDATION OF PRIMARY ALCOHOLS TO ALDEHYDES AND ACIDS

Product	Yield (%)	Reference
A. Aldehydes		
Acetaldehyde	72	57
Propionaldehyde	49	10
Isobutyraldehyde	64	58
n-Valeraldehyde	50	59
Isovaleraldehyde	60	60
2-Methylbutyraldehyde	52	61
Cyclopropanecarboxaldehyde	—	62
Cyclohexanecarboxaldehyde	35	63
1-Naphthaldehyde	42	64
4-Methyl-1-naphthaldehyde	84	65
2-Thiophenecarboxaldehyde	65	66
2-Pentenal	50	67
2-Hexenal	50	67
2-Heptenal	75	67
4-Octenal	35	68
2-Nonenal	50	67
Citral	42	69
Propargylaldehyde	46	70
3,3,3-Trifluoropropionaldehyde	57	71
Methoxyacetaldehyde	17	72
Ethoxyacetaldehyde	10	72
Phenoxyacetaldehyde	20	73
2-Chloro-6-nitrobenzaldehyde	87	74
2-Chlorocrotonaldehyde	—	75

[57] E. Wertheim, *J. Am. Chem. Soc.* **44**, 2658 (1922).

[58] W. Fossek, *Monatsh.* **2**, 614 (1881); **4**, 660 (1883).

[59] R. Kuhn and C. Grundmann, *Ber.* **70**, 1894 (1937).

[60] L. Bouveault and L. Rousset, *Bull. Soc. Chim. France* [3] **11**, 300 (1894); C. Weygand, "Organic Preparations," p. 143. Wiley (Interscience), New York, 1945.

[61] V. Neustädter, *Monatsh.* **27**, 879 (1906); E. J. Badin and E. Pacsu, *J. Am. Chem. Soc.* **67**, 1352 (1945).

[62] N. J. Demjanov and K. Fortunatov, *Ber.* **40**, 4397 (1907).

[63] N. Zelinsky and J. Gutt, *Ber.* **40**, 3050 (1907).

[64] B. L. West, *J. Am. Chem. Soc.* **42**, 1656 (1920).

[65] K. Ziegler and P. Tiemann, *Ber.* **55**, 3406 (1932).

[66] W. S. Emerson and T. M. Patrick, Jr., *J. Org. Chem.* **14**, 790 (1949).

[67] R. Delaby and S. Guillot-Allégrè, *Bull. Soc. Chim. France* **53**, 301 (1933); C. J. Martin, A. I. Schepartz, and B. F. Daubert, *J. Am. Chem. Soc.* **70**, 2601 (1948).

[68] M. Jacobson, *J. Am. Chem. Soc.* **72**, 1489 (1950).

[69] M. Stoll and A. Commarmont, *Helv. Chim. Acta* **32**, 1355 (1949).

[70] F. Wille and L. Saffer, *Ann.* **568**, 34 (1950); J. Sauer, *Org. Syn. Coll. Vol. IV*, 813 (1963).

[71] A. L. Henne, R. L. Pelley, and R. M. Alm, *J. Am. Chem. Soc.* **72**, 3370 (1950).

[72] C. D. Hurd and J. L. Abernethy, *J. Am. Chem. Soc.* **63**, 1966 (1941).

TABLE 6-2—*continued*

OXIDATION OF PRIMARY ALCOHOLS TO ALDEHYDES AND ACIDS

Product	Yield (%)	Reference
B. Acids		
2-Methylbutyric acid	52	76
Heptanoic acid	70	77
3-Fluoropropionic acid	80	78
4-Fluorobutyric acid	75	79
Pent-2-en-4-ynoic acid	60[a]	79
But-3-ynoic acid	28[a]	79
Non-2-en-4-ynoic acid	21[a]	79
6-Oxanon-2-en-4-ynoic acid	23[a]	79
Acetylenedicarboxylic acid	23[a]	79
1,6-Hex-2-en-4-yndioic acid	40[a]	79

[a] These oxidations were carried out using acetone as the solvent.

3. DICHROMATE ION IN ACETIC ACID

In an investigation of the oxidation of primary alcohols, Bowman *et al.*[80] found that potassium dichromate in glacial acetic acid was a useful reagent. Some typical results are shown in Table 6-3. It was found that dichromate–acetic acid and chromium trioxide–acetic acid gave comparable yields in the oxidation of allylic alcohols, but with the saturated alcohols the former reagent was the more satisfactory.

The oxidation of cholestanol to cholestanone also proceeds very satisfactorily using this procedure.[81] Thus it is probably a good method for the oxidation of secondary alcohols.

A typical procedure illustrating the use of this reagent follows.

Dichromate Oxidation.[80] A mixture of 10 gm (0.34 mole) of finely powdered potassium dichromate and 500 ml of glacial acetic acid is warmed to 95–100° C. A solution of 0.1 mole of the alcohol in 150 ml of acetic acid is added, with

[73] A. Halasz, *Bull. Soc. Chim. France* [5] **8**, 170 (1941).
[74] L. Gindraux, *Helv. Chim. Acta* **12**, 921 (1929).
[75] M. Julia, *Compt. Rend. Acad. Sci.* **234**, 2615 (1952).
[76] W. Marckwald, *Ber.* **37**, 1038 (1904).
[77] A. Darapsky and W. Engels, *J. Prakt. Chem.* **146**, 238 (1936).
[78] E. Gryszkiewicz-Trochimowski, *Rec. Trav. Chim.* **66**, 430 (1947).
[79] I. M. Heilbron, E. R. H. Jones, and F. Sondheimer, *J. Chem. Soc.* p. 1586 (1947); p. 604 (1949).
[80] M. I. Bowman, C. E. Moore, H. R. Deutsch, and J. L. Hartman, *Trans. Kentucky Acad. Sci.* **14**, 33 (1953).
[81] L. F. Fieser, *J. Am. Chem. Soc.* **75**, 4386 (1953).

TABLE 6-3

OXIDATION OF ALCOHOLS WITH DICHROMATE IN ACETIC ACID

Alcohol	Per cent yield (aldehyde or ketone)[a]	Reference
n-Amyl alcohol	65	80
Isoamyl alcohol	63	80
2-Ethyl-1-hexanol	68	80
Dodecanol	84 (55)	80
Tetradecanol	(42)	80
Hexadecanol	68 (61)	80
Octadecanol	(65)	80
Allyl alcohol	100	80
Benzyl alcohol	86	80
4-Chloro-1-butanol	62	80
Cholestanol	(86)	81

[a] The yield of isolated aldehyde or ketone is given in parentheses. The other value is the apparent amount as determined using 2,4-dinitrophenylhydrazine.

stirring at a rate sufficient to maintain the oxidizing temperature. The reaction mixture is maintained at the reaction temperature for 3–8 minutes, and cooled. The solution is diluted with a large volume of water and the aldehyde is filtered (if solid and insoluble) or extracted with ether.

In the oxidation of cholestanol, Fieser[81] used the more soluble sodium dichromate dihydrate. This probably leads to a lower rate of oxidation and may not be satisfactory with the less reactive primary alcohols.

4. CHROMIUM TRIOXIDE–PYRIDINE COMPLEX

The observations that chromic acid esters of primary or secondary alcohols are readily decomposed to the corresponding carbonyl compounds,[82] and that esters of chromic acid are rapidly formed by the reaction of alcohols with chromic acid,[83] led Sarett and his group at Merck[84] to explore the usefulness of the fairly stable pyridine–chromium trioxide complex[85] in alcohol oxidation. Their expectation that the complex might not oxidize other functional groups such as double bonds or thioether groups was realized. The application to the oxidation of a group of steroidal alcohols was very successful, giving yields of ketones on the order of 70–90%.

[82] F. Holloway, M. Cohen, and F. H. Westheimer, *J. Am. Chem. Soc.* **73**, 65 (1951).
[83] H. Wienhaus, *Ber.* **47**, 322 (1914).
[84] G. I. Poos, G. E. Arth, R. E. Beyler, and L. H. Sarett, *J. Am. Chem. Soc.* **75**, 422 (1953).
[85] H. H. Sisler, J. D. Bush, and O. E. Accountius, *J. Am. Chem. Soc.* **70**, 3827 (1948).

The usefulness in the oxidation of other alcohols has been examined by Holum,[86] and much of the available data are summarized in Table 6-4.[86-95]

TABLE 6-4

OXIDATION OF ALCOHOLS BY THE PYRIDINE–CHROMIUM TRIOXIDE COMPLEX

Alcohol	Product	Yield (%)	Reference
Saturated alcohols			
1-Heptanol	Heptanal	10	86
1-Dodecanol	Dodecanal	18	
Cyclopentanol	Cyclopentanone	21	
Cyclohexanol	Cyclohexanone	45	
Cycloheptanol	Cycloheptanone	63	
Cyclooctanol	Cyclooctanone	72	
2-Octanol	2-Octanone	18	
Allylic alcohols			
Geraniol	Geranial	66	86
Nerol	Neral	83	
Cinnamyl alcohol	Cinnamaldehyde	81	
Benzylic alcohols			
Benzyl alcohol	Benzaldehyde	63	86
p-Isopropylbenzyl alcohol	*p*-Isopropylbenzaldehyde	83	
o-Methoxybenzyl alcohol	*o*-Methoxybenzaldehyde	89	
m-Methoxybenzyl alcohol	*m*-Methoxybenzaldehyde	60	
p-Methoxybenzyl alcohol	*p*-Methoxybenzaldehyde	76	
o-Hydroxybenzyl alcohol	*o*-Hydroxybenzaldehyde	17	
m-Hydroxybenzyl alcohol	*m*-Hydroxybenzaldehyde	75	
p-Hydroxybenzyl alcohol	*p*-Hydroxybenzaldehyde	50	
o-Nitrobenzyl alcohol	*o*-Nitrobenzaldehyde	30	
m-Nitrobenzyl alcohol	*m*-Nitrobenzaldehyde	50	
p-Nitrobenzyl alcohol	*p*-Nitrobenzaldehyde	28	
3,4-Methylenedioxybenzyl alcohol	Piperonal	85	
Veratryl alcohol	Veratraldehyde	41	
Benzhydrol	Benzophenone	71	
Other nonsteroidal alcohols			
Furfuryl alcohol	Furfural	46	86
Cirtonellol	Citronellal	25	

[86] J. R. Holum, *J. Org. Chem.* **26**, 4814 (1961).

TABLE 6-4—*continued*

OXIDATION OF ALCOHOLS BY THE PYRIDINE–CHROMIUM TRIOXIDE COMPLEX

Alcohol	Product	Yield (%)	Reference

Steroidal alcohols and related compounds

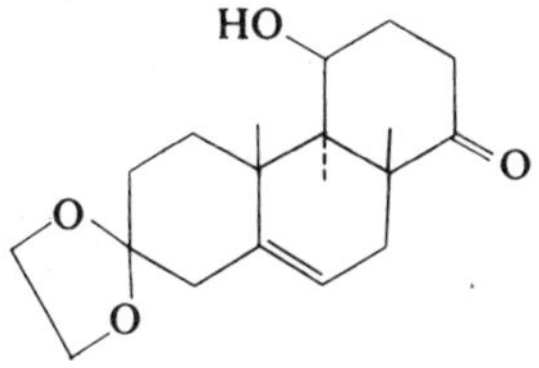	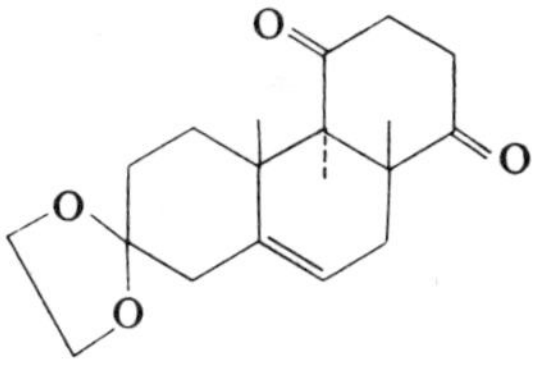	89	87
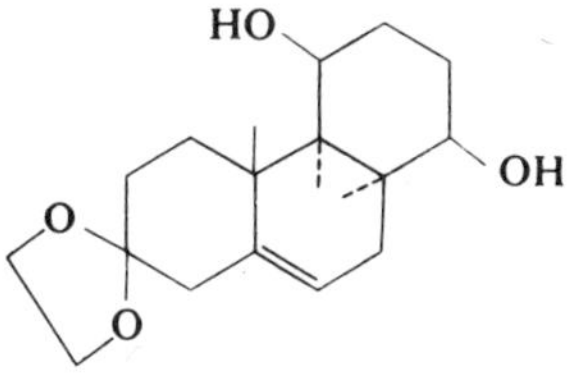	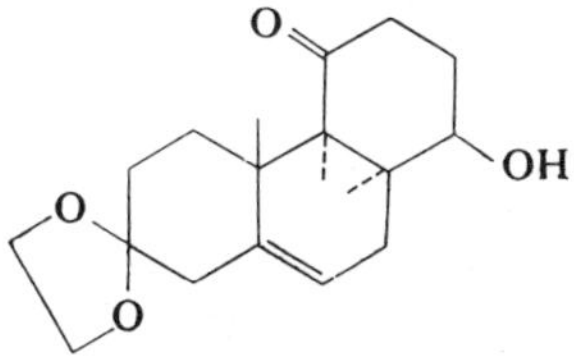	73	87
		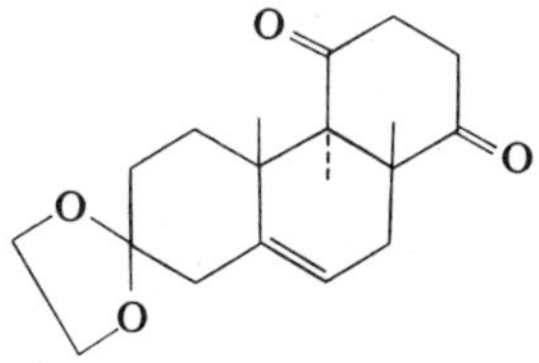 16	
		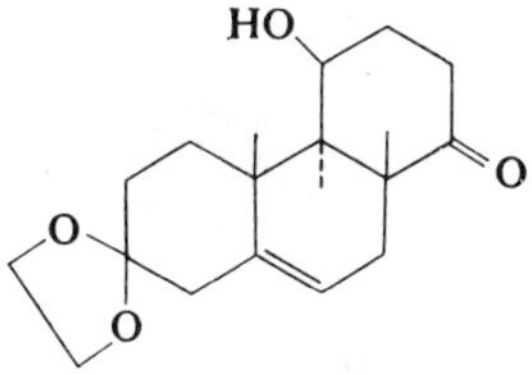 7	
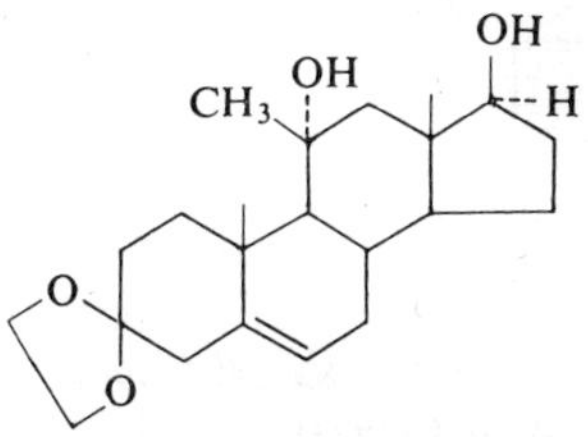	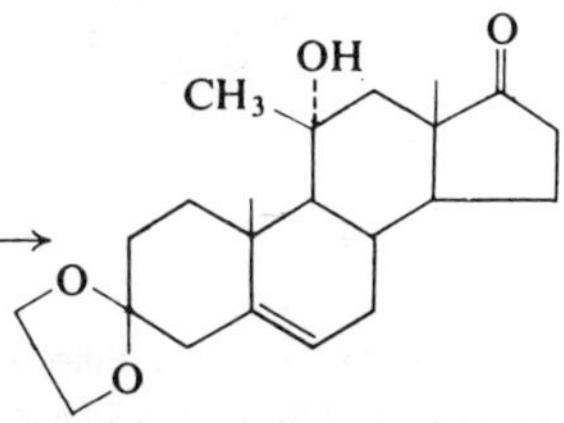	63	88

[87] G. I. Poos, G. E. Arth, R. E. Beyler, and L. H. Sarett, *J. Am. Chem. Soc.* **75**, 422 (1953).
[88] J. A. Zderic, E. Batres, D. C. Limón, H. Carpio, J. Lisci, G. Monroy, E. Necoechea, and H. J. Ringold, *J. Am. Chem. Soc.* **82**, 3404 (1960).

TABLE 6-4—*continued*

OXIDATION OF ALCOHOLS BY THE PYRIDINE–CHROMIUM TRIOXIDE COMPLEX

Alcohol	Product	Yield (%)	Reference
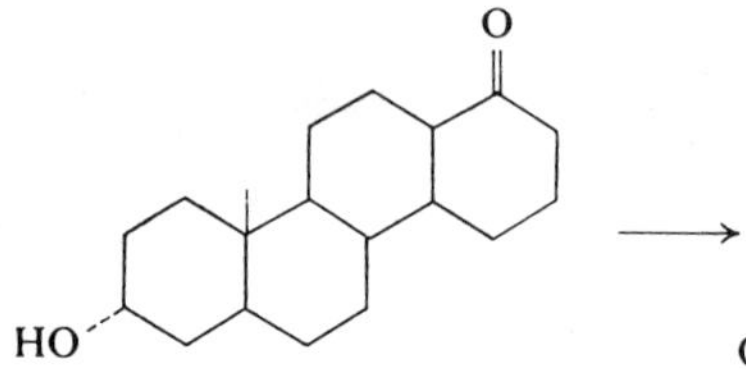	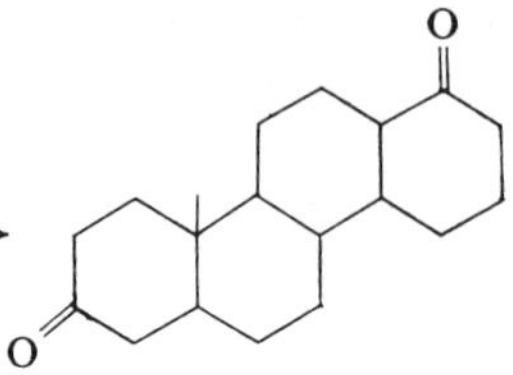	92	89
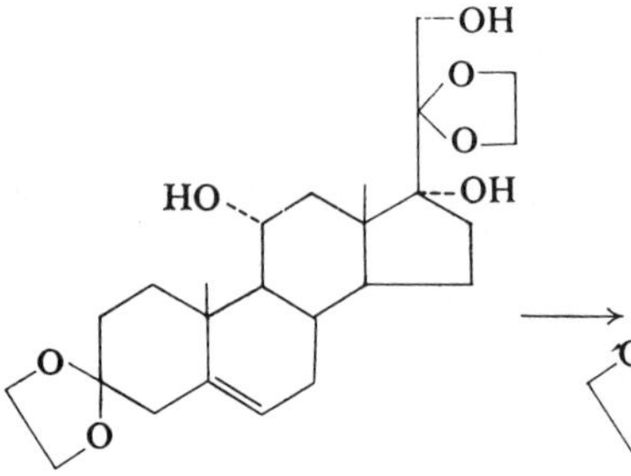	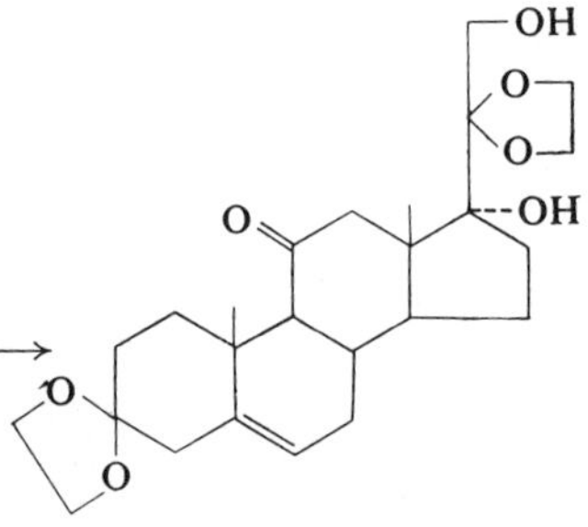	89	90
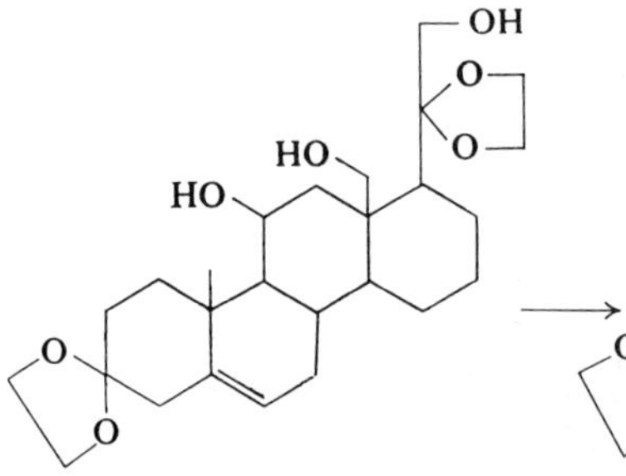	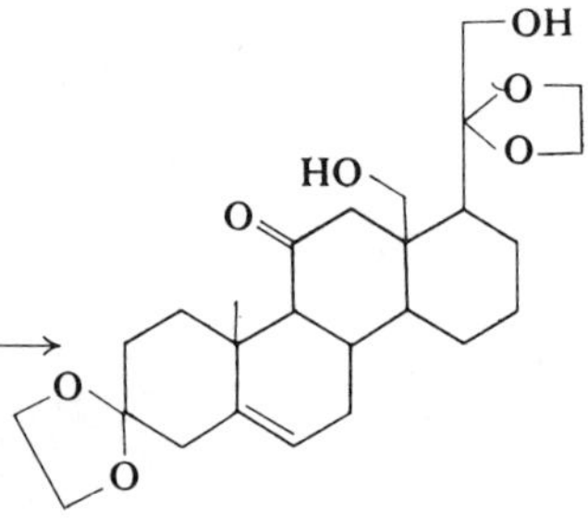	20	91
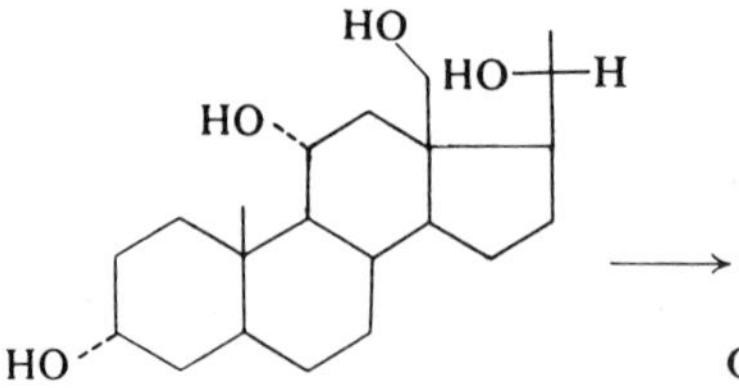	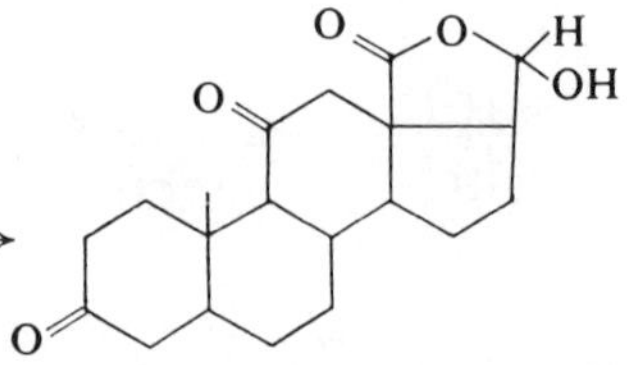	22	92

[89] W. S. Johnson, W. A. Vredenburgh, and J. E. Pike, *J. Am. Chem. Soc.* **82**, 3409 (1960).

[90] W. S. Allen, S. Bernstein, and R. Littell, *J. Am. Chem. Soc.* **76**, 6116 (1954).

[91] J. Schmidlin and A. Wettstein, *Helv. Chim. Acta* **43**, 973 (1960).

[92] K. Heusler, J. Kalvoda, C. Meystre, P. Wieland, G. Anner, A. Wettstein, G. Cainelli, D. Arigoni, and O. Jeger, *Helv. Chim. Acta* **44**, 502 (1961).

TABLE 6-4—*continued*

OXIDATION OF ALCOHOLS BY THE PYRIDINE–CHROMIUM TRIOXIDE COMPLEX

Alcohol	Product	Yield (%)	Reference
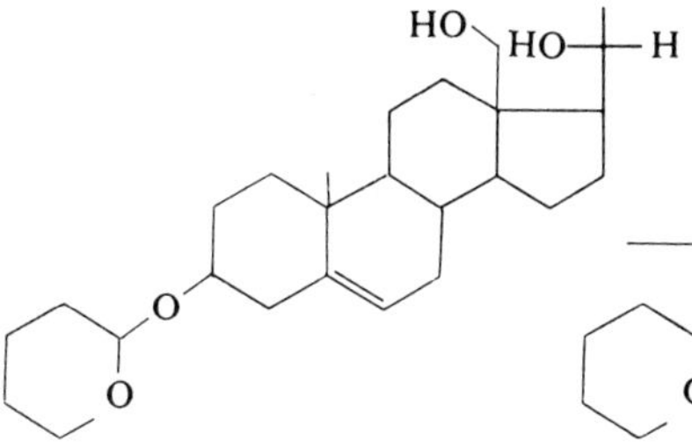	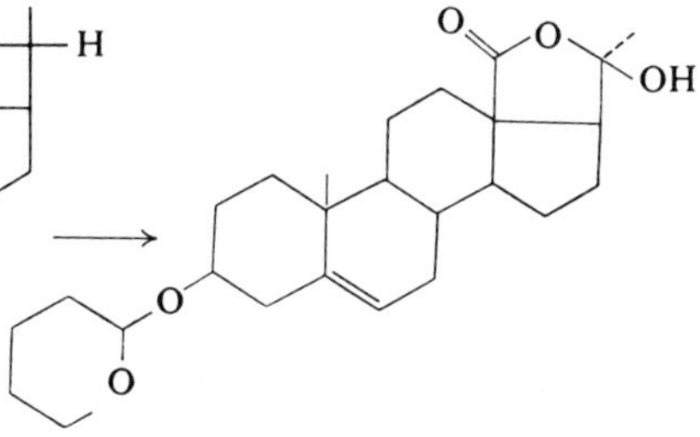	87	93
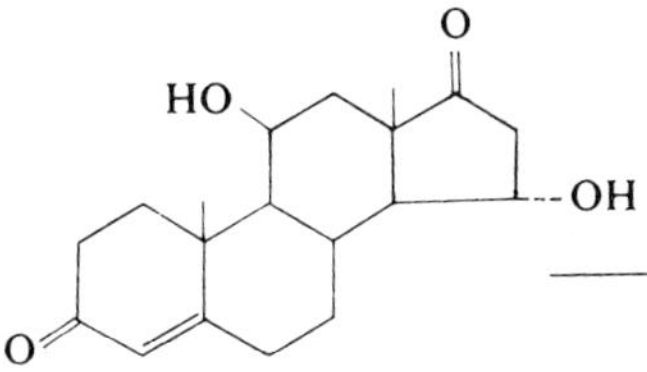	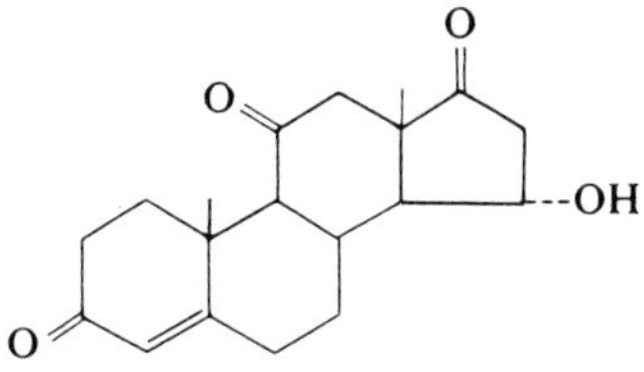	83	94
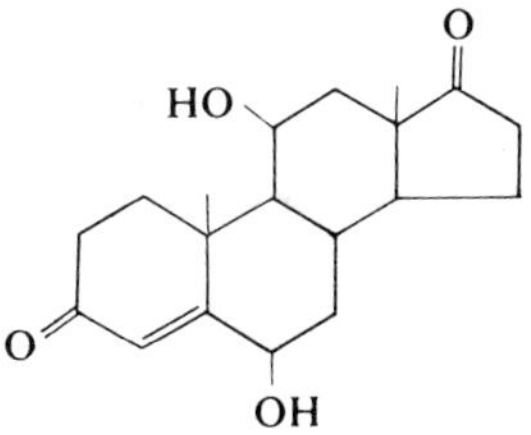	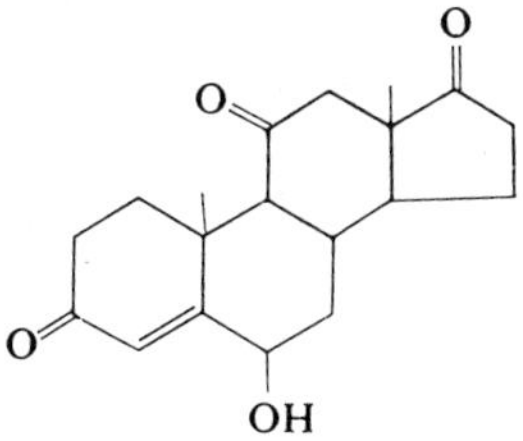	55	94
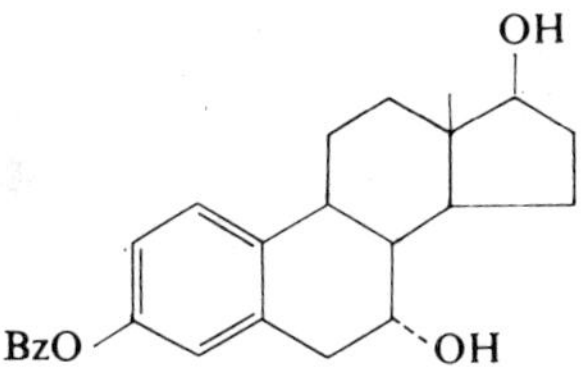	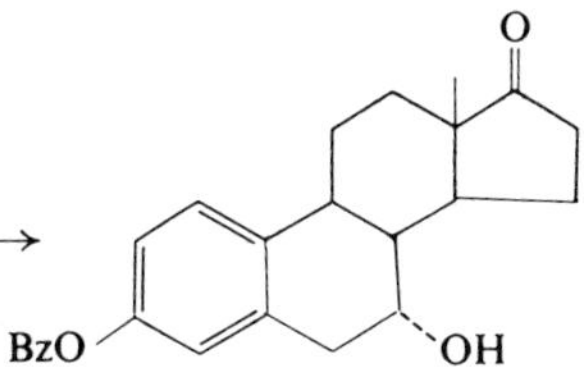	25	95

[93] L. Lábler and F. Sŏrm, *Collection Czech. Chem. Commun.* **25**, 2855 (1960).
[94] J. Urech, E. Vischer, and A. Wettstein, *Helv. Chim. Acta* **43**, 1077 (1960).
[95] J. Iriarte, H. J. Ringold, and C. Djerassi, *J. Am. Chem. Soc.* **80**, 6105 (1958).

The normal conditions involve the use of an excess (3:1) of the oxidant, and a period of 15–22 hours at room temperature. Holum notes that good yields of oxidation product were obtained when the reaction mixture darkened rapidly on addition of the alcohol. When this did not occur, relatively poor yields were obtained. This suggests that a major reason for the low yield found with some of the alcohols listed in Table 6-4 is the low rate of reaction, and the order of increasing yield fits well with the order of increasing reactivity discussed in Section VI,6. This is further supported by the observation that, whereas citronellol gives only 25% citronellal under the usual conditions, a shorter reaction time at a higher temperature (40° C) gives 47% citronellal.

This method does not appear to be as convenient as the preceding ones because of the increased difficulty in working up the reaction mixture, the relatively long reaction times, and the possible danger in dissolving chromium trioxide in pyridine (never add pyridine to chromium trioxide!). However, it is still one of the better methods available, and is particularly useful with acid-sensitive compounds, or with compounds having functional groups which are easily oxidized by chromic acid.

5. tert-BUTYL CHROMATE

The oxidation of alcohols using tert-butyl chromate was first reported by Oppenauer and Oberrauch.[96] They found that a solution of this oxidant in petroleum ether effected the oxidation of primary alcohols to aldehydes in excellent yield. For example, hexadecanol is converted to hexadecanal in 80–85% yield, geraniol is converted to geranial in 85% yield, and benzyl alcohol is converted to benzaldehyde in 94% yield.[96]

The oxidation of secondary alcohols also proceeds quite satisfactorily. Thus, cyclohexanol is converted to cyclohexanone in 89% yield (along with 8–10% adipic acid)[97] and methyl ricinoleate is converted to methyl 12-oxo-octadecenoate in 71% yield.[98] The one case in which a poor result was obtained was in the oxidation of 3,5-octadiene-2,7-diol to the corresponding dione.[99] The oxidation of primary and secondary alcohols by tert-butyl chromate has been reviewed.[100]

It appears that this procedure has little advantage over the ones previously given in the oxidation of secondary alcohols. It may, however, be a superior reagent for the oxidation of primary alcohols to aldehydes.

A typical procedure follows.

[96] R. V. Oppenauer and H. Oberrauch, *Anales Asoc. Quim. Arg.* **37**, 246 (1949).

[97] T. Suga, *Nippon Kagaki Zasshi* **80**, 918 (1959); *Chem. Abstr.* **55**, 3464 (1961).

[98] S. Maruta and Y. Suzuki, *Kogyo Kagaku Zasshi* **60**, 31 (1957); *Chem. Abstr.* **53**, 4126 (1959).

[99] H. H. Inhoffen, H. Pommer, K. Winkelmann, and H. J. Aldag, *Chem. Ber.* **84**, 87 (1951).

[100] T. Matsuura and T. Suga, *Koryo* **62**, 13 (1961).

Hexadecanal.[96] To 370 gm (5 moles) of *tert*-butyl alcohol is added 185 gm (1.85 moles) of chromium trioxide over a period of 10 minutes with external cooling. The temperature must be kept low because over 60° C a vigorous decomposition may occur, leading to an explosion. The red solution is diluted with 1.5 liters of petroleum ether (b.p. 30–70° C), and the water formed is removed using anhydrous sodium sulfate. The solution prepared in this fashion is designated as type A.

A solution of 182 gm (0.75 mole) of hexadecanol in 1 liter of petroleum ether is added to the *tert*-butyl chromate solution, and the mixture is allowed to stand for 14 days. Approximately 80–85 % of the reaction occurs in the first 24 hours, and then the reaction becomes very slow. The latter stage may be accelerated by warming the solution.

The mixture is treated with 1 liter of water in a 6-liter flask, and oxalic acid is added in portions with constant agitation in order to decompose the remaining chromium(VI). The petroleum ether solution is green due to hydrocarbon soluble chromium salts. These are removed by the addition of 250 ml of sulfuric acid and 500 ml of acetic acid followed by agitation for 4 hours. The organic layer is separated, and after standing overnight it is filtered through some sodium sulfate. The solution is washed with 2 *N* sodium carbonate solution to remove palmitic acid (2.4 gm), and with dilute hydrochloric acid and water. After drying over sodium sulfate, distillation of the solvent gives 174 gm of residue. This is dissolved in warm benzene and allowed to stand at 0° C for 2 days. The white precipitate (137 gm, m.p. 70.5–72° C) of the aldehyde trimer is filtered. Partial concentration of the filtrate followed by standing for 4 weeks gives an additional 34 gm of the trimer, m.p. 70–72° C, for a total of 171 gm (94 %).

6. MECHANISM OF THE OXIDATION OF ALCOHOLS

The first serious attempt to understand the mechanism of the chromic acid oxidation of alcohols was made by Westheimer and Novick,[101] who found the rate law for the oxidation of isopropyl alcohol to be:

$$v = k_a[HCrO_4^-][R_2CHOH][H^+] + k_b[HCrO_4^-][R_2CHOH][H^+]^2$$

This rate law has been found to apply to the oxidation of all other primary or secondary alcohols which have been studied.[102] It is important to note the

[101] F. H. Westheimer and A. Novick, *J. Chem. Phys.* **11**, 506 (1943).

[102] M. Cohen and F. H. Westheimer, *J. Am. Chem. Soc.* **74**, 4387 (1952); H. G. Kuivila and W. J. Becker, III, *ibid.* **74**, 5329 (1952); V. Antony and A. K. Chatterji, *Z. Anorg. Allgem. Chem.* **280**, 110 (1955); H. Kwart and P. S. Francis, *J. Am. Chem. Soc.* **77**, 4907 (1955); J. Schreiber and A. Eschenmoser, *Helv. Chim. Acta* **38**, 1529 (1955); J. Roček and J. Krupička, *Chem. & Ind.* (*London*) p. 1668 (1957); S. V. Anantakrishnan and N. Venkatasubramanian, *Current Sci.* (*India*) **27**, 438 (1958); J. Roček and J. Krupička, *Collection Czech. Chem. Commun.* **23**, 2068 (1958); S. V. Anantakrishnan

kinetic dependence on the concentration of the acid chromate ion rather than on total chromium(VI). This is one way in which alcohol oxidation differs from the oxidation of hydrocarbons.

The nature of the rate-controlling step was established by Westheimer and Nicolaides[103] who observed a kinetic isotope effect $k_H/k_D = 7$ for the oxidation of isopropyl-α-d alcohol. The isotope effect has been reinvestigated and has also been studied with ethanol with essentially the same result.[104] The slow step must then involve the cleavage of the alcohol carbon–hydrogen bond. The existence of prior equilibrium steps involving protonation was demonstrated by the observation that the reaction proceeded more rapidly in deuterium oxide than in water.[105]

The above observations may be accounted for by either a one-electron or a two-electron rate-determining step in which the C—H bond was cleaved. Watanabe and Westheimer[106] showed that it was possible to distinguish between the two possibilities using the phenomenon of induced oxidation discussed previously. When the oxidation of isopropyl alcohol was carried out in the presence of a large excess of manganous ion, it was found that one-half mole of manganese dioxide was formed for each mole of acetone produced.[106] Thus, the steps in oxidation in the presence of Mn^{II} must have been:

$$R_2CHOH + Cr^{VI} \rightarrow R_2C{=}O + Cr^{IV}$$

$$2\,Cr^{IV} + Mn^{II} \rightarrow MnO_2 + 2\,Cr^{III}$$

The nature of the reaction in the absence of manganous ion was indicated by the fact that when a high concentration of the alcohol was used, the rate of reaction in the presence of manganous ion was one-half that found in its absence.[107] The most probable reaction sequence, which excludes schemes

and N. Venkatasubramanian, *Current Sci. (India)* **28**, 325 (1959); A. C. Chatterji and V. Antony, *Z. Physik. Chem. (Leipzig)* **210**, 103 (1959); N. Venkatasubramanian, *Proc. Indian Acad. Sci. Sect.* **A50**, 156 (1959); S. V. Anantakrishnan and N. Venkatasubramanian, *Proc. Indian Acad. Sci. Sect.* **A51**, 310 (1960); N. Venkatasubramanian, *J. Sci. Ind. Res. (India)* **20B**, 385 (1961); *Proc. Indian Acad. Sci. Sect.* **A53** (2), 80 (1961).

[103] F. H. Westheimer and N. Nicolaides, *J. Am. Chem. Soc.* **71**, 25 (1949).

[104] M. Cohen and F. H. Westheimer, *J. Am. Chem. Soc.* **74**, 4387 (1952); L. Kaplan, *ibid.* **77**, 5469 (1955); J. W. Cornforth and G. Popják, *Nature* **164**, 1053 (1949).

[105] R. Brownell, A. Leo, Y. W. Chang, and F. H. Westheimer, *J. Am. Chem. Soc.* **82**, 406 (1960).

[106] W. Watanabe and F. H. Westheimer, *J. Chem. Phys.* **17**, 61 (1949).

[107] Although the conclusions drawn are probably correct, it should be noted that the rate of reaction in the absence of manganous ion is actually 1.2 order in isopropyl alcohol, whereas in the presence of the latter, it is 1.0 order in isopropyl alcohol. Thus the ratio of the two rates may be varied over a considerable range of varying the isopropyl alcohol concentration.

which should lead to autocatalytic reactions and those involving the formation of the good reducing agent Cr^{II}, was:

$$R_2CHOH + Cr^{VI} \rightarrow R_2C{=}O + Cr^{IV}$$

$$Cr^{IV} + Cr^{VI} \rightarrow 2\,Cr^{V}$$

$$2(Cr^{V} + R_2CHOH \rightarrow R_2C{=}O + Cr^{III})$$

Thus, only one-third of the total oxidation is effected by chromium(VI) and two-thirds is effected by chromium(V). The importance of this conclusion will be discussed below.

Having established the over-all nature of the reaction, it was necessary to determine the detailed nature of the rate-determining step. The observation that esters of chromic acid could be prepared, and that the ones derived from primary or secondary alcohols were decomposed by pyridine to give the corresponding carbonyl compounds, showed that the process:

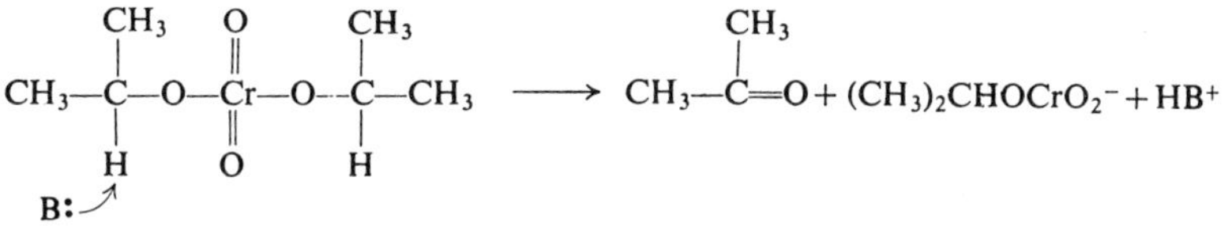

$$\underset{\underset{\text{B:}}{\overset{|}{H}}}{\overset{\overset{CH_3}{|}}{CH_3{-}C}}{-}O{-}\underset{\overset{||}{O}}{\overset{O}{Cr}}{-}O{-}\underset{\overset{|}{H}}{\overset{\overset{CH_3}{|}}{C}}{-}CH_3 \longrightarrow \underset{\overset{|}{H}}{\overset{\overset{CH_3}{|}}{CH_3{-}C}}{=}O + (CH_3)_2CHOCrO_2^- + HB^+$$

could occur.[81, 108] Westheimer then proposed that the oxidation of primary and secondary alcohols proceeded via the acid chromate esters as intermediates[109]:

$$R_2CHOH + HCrO_4^- + H^+ \rightarrow R_2CHOCrO_3H + H_2O$$

$$R_2CHOCrO_3H + H^+ \rightarrow R_2CHOCrO_3H_2^+$$

$$R_2CHOCrO_3H \xrightarrow{k_1} R_2C{=}O + Cr^{IV}$$

$$R_2CHOCrO_3H_2^+ \xrightarrow{k_2} R_2C{=}O + Cr^{IV}$$

This reaction sequence fits the available data on the kinetics and isotope effect for isopropyl alcohol oxidation, and evidence has appeared demonstrating that the acid chromate esters are formed in the reaction solutions.[110]

[108] H. L. Krauss, *Z. Naturforsch.* **136**, 199 (1958).

[109] D. G. Lee and R. Stewart, *J. Am. Chem. Soc.*, in press, have shown that the chromate esters in most cases probably include an anion derived from the solvent. Thus, using sulfuric acid as the acid catalyst, the structure is probably

$$R_2CHOCrOSO_3^-\ \left(\overset{O}{\underset{O}{\overset{||}{}\underset{||}{}}}\right)$$

[110] U. Kläning, *Acta Chem. Scand.* **11**, 1313 (1957); **12**, 576 (1958).

This proposal has stirred much controversy, with many papers appearing both supporting and arguing against it. In particular, the papers of Roček which presented important arguments favoring a hydride abstraction mechanism should be noted.[111]

The question of the intermediacy of the chromic acid ester has been settled by an investigation of the oxidation of the sterically hindered alcohol, 3β-28-diacetoxy-6β-hydroxy-18β-12-oleanen (A).[112] Here, conditions could be found under which the kinetic hydrogen isotope effect in the oxidation could be reduced to unity. Under these conditions, the cleavage of the alcohol carbon–hydrogen bond was no longer rate limiting, but rather a previous step had assumed this role. That previous step can only be the formation of the acid chromate ester.

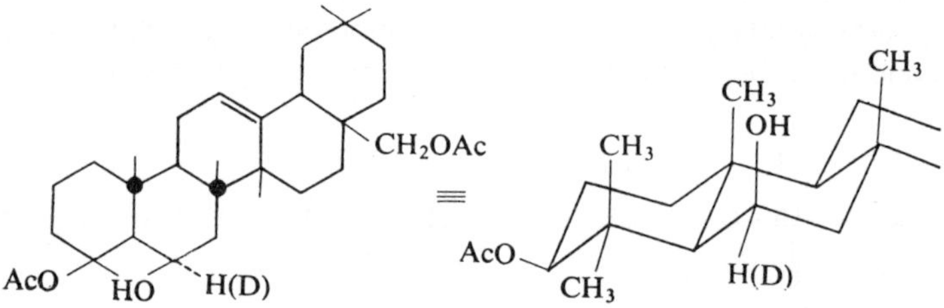

(A)

Even if we know that this ester is an intermediate, it is not clear just how the ester is converted to products. It was originally thought that the reaction showed general base catalysis by pyridine, but this was later shown to be incorrect.[111, 113] There is, at the present time, no evidence for the involvement of an external base in the rate-controlling step; nor is there good evidence against such a process. The possible mechanisms are:

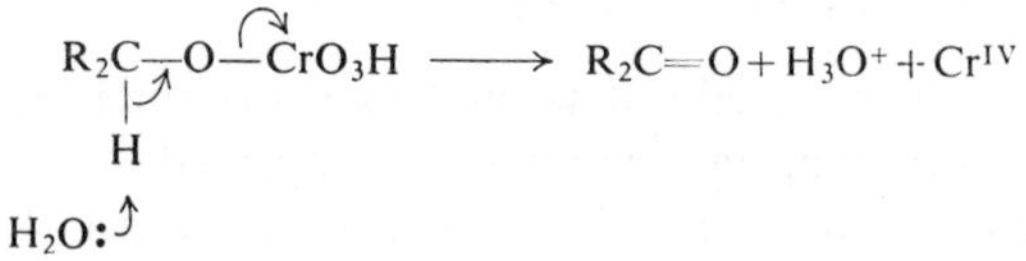

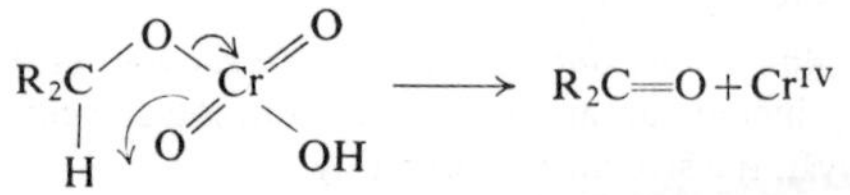

[111] J. Roček and J. Krupicka, *Chem. & Ind.* (*London*) p. 1668 (1957); *Chem. Listy* **52**, 1735 (1958); J. Roček, *Collection Czech. Chem. Commun.* **25**, 1052 (1960).

[112] J. Roček, F. H. Westheimer, A. Eschenmoser, L. Moldoványi, and J. Schreiber, *Helv. Chim. Acta* **45**, 2554 (1962).

[113] F. H. Westheimer and Y. W. Chang, *J. Phys. Chem.* **63**, 438 (1959).

(C) $\quad R_2C\overset{O}{\underset{\underset{H}{O}}{\diagdown}}\overset{O}{\underset{OH}{\diagup}}Cr\overset{O}{\diagup} \longrightarrow R_2\overset{\bullet}{C}\overset{O}{\underset{HO}{\diagdown}}\overset{O}{\underset{OH}{\diagup}}Cr \longrightarrow R_2C{=}O + Cr^{IV}$

Before discussing these possibilities, it is first necessary to review the other available information concerning the oxidation by chromium(VI).

The effect of substituents on the oxidation of α-phenethanols has been studied by Kwart and Francis[114] and was correlated with a reaction constant, ρ, of -0.37 to -1.01 under a variety of different reaction conditions. They attempted to determine the value of ρ for the equilibrium forming the acid chromate ester, but the value which they obtained seems too large in comparison with the values found for other esterification equilibria,[115] and for the effect of structure on chromate ester formation from aliphatic alcohols.[110, 111] In view of the uncertainty associated with the above determination of the effect of substituents on the chromate ester equilibrium reaction, possibly the more satisfactory assumption is that the effect of substituents is negligible and that the observed ρ is that for the rate-determining step.

The effect of substituents in the oxidation of aliphatic alcohols has been studied by Roček,[111] who obtained $\rho^* = -1.06$, and for a series of aryl trifluoromethylcarbinols ρ was -1.01.[116] The agreement between the two results is strongly indicative of a relatively electron poor reacting carbon in the activated complex for alcohol oxidation.

Other structural factors have been studied. Kuivila and Becker[117] determined the effect of ring size on the rate of oxidation, giving the data shown in Table 6-5. The constant k_1 refers to the reaction of the acid chromate ester,

TABLE 6-5

RATES OF CHROMIC ACID OXIDATION OF CYCLANOLS

Compound	k_1(mole^2 liters^{-2} minutes^{-1})	k_2(mole^3 liters^{-3} minutes^{-1})
2-Propanol	0.053	1.94
Cyclooctanol	0.47	13.5
Cycloheptanol	0.61	12.4
Cyclohexanol	0.16	3.24
Cyclopentanol	0.13	4.90
Cyclobutanol	0.20	5.07

[114] H. Kwart and P. S. Francis, *J. Am. Chem. Soc.* **77**, 4907 (1955).
[115] Cf. H. H. Jaffé, *Chem. Rev.* **53**, 191 (1953).
[116] R. Stewart and D. G. Lee, *Can. J. Chem.* **42**, 439 (1964).
[117] H. G. Kuivila and W. J. Becker, III, *J. Am. Chem. Soc.* **74**, 5329 (1952).

and k_2 refers to the reaction of its conjugate acid. The rate constant for cyclo-butanol was questioned by the above authors, but Roček[118] has shown that the reaction products are normal (cyclobutanone and cleavage products) and that cyclopropanecarboxaldehyde is not formed.

The observation that 5-, 7-, and 8-membered ring alcohols are more reactive than cyclohexanol is in accord with the normal expectation for a change from a tetrahedral to a trigonal arrangement about the reacting carbon.[119] How-ever, the variation in rate is considerably smaller than normally found.

The effect of conformation on the rate of oxidation has been studied by a number of investigators,[120-126] and it is found that in the cyclohexane series, the compounds with an *axial* hydroxy group are generally oxidized more rapidly than the corresponding *equatorial* isomers by a factor of about 3. This has been used in the determination of the configuration of steroidal alcohols.[127] The preference for the *axial* isomer in the oxidation is in accord with the general trend found in comparing the two isomers,[128] and may arise from the 1,3-diaxial interaction between the hydroxy group of the reactant alcohol and the nearby axial hydrogens.

Kwart and Francis[122] and Richer and co-workers[124] have investigated an interesting series of alcohols giving the data summarized in Table 6-6. The data for the *cis*- and *trans*-4-*tert*-butylcyclohexanols were first obtained and interpreted by Winstein and Holness[120] in terms of the effect of configuration about the alcohol carbon on the equilibrium constant for acid chromate ester formation and on the rate constant for the decomposition of the ester. Kwart and Francis continued this line of reasoning in interpreting the other data.[122, 125]

Although the separation into equilibrium and kinetic effects is sometimes useful, in the present case it is well to remember that the absolute rate theory reduces most kinetic problems to a question of the difference in enthalpy and entropy between the original reactants and the activated complex, and that

[118] J. Roček, private communication.
[119] H. C. Brown and M. Gerstein, *J. Am. Chem. Soc.* **72**, 2926 (1950); H. C. Brown, R. S. Fletcher, and R. B. Johannesen, *ibid.* **73**, 212 (1951).
[120] S. Winstein and N. J. Holness, *J. Am. Chem. Soc.* **77**, 5562 (1955).
[121] J. Schreiber and A. Eschenmoser, *Helv. Chim. Acta* **38**, 1529 (1955).
[122] H. Kwart and P. S. Francis, *J. Am. Chem. Soc.* **81**, 2116 (1959).
[123] H. Favre and J. C. Richer, *Can. J. Chem.* **37**, 411 (1959).
[124] J. C. Richer, L. A. Pilato, and E. L. Eliel, *Chem. & Ind. (London)* p. 2007 (1961).
[125] H. Kwart, *Chem. & Ind. (London)* p. 610 (1962).
[126] F. Šipoš, J. Krupička, M. Tichý, and J. Sicher, *Collection Czech. Chem. Commun.* **27**, 2079 (1962).
[127] G. Grimmer, *Ann.* **636**, 42 (1960).
[128] D. H. R. Barton, *Experientia* **6**, 316 (1950); *J. Chem. Soc.* p. 1027 (1953).

TABLE 6-6

STRUCTURAL EFFECTS ON RATES OF CHROMIC ACID
OXIDATION[122, 124, 125]

Alcohol	Relative rate
cis-2-tert-Butylcyclohexanol	50.6
trans-3,3,5-Trimethylcyclohexanol	50.2
Isoborneol	49.1
1-Indanol	26.0
Borneol	25.0
α-Tetralol	17.0
trans-2-tert-Butylcyclohexanol	10.7
endo-Norborneol	9.7
trans-3-tert-Butylcyclohexanol	6.0
cis-2-Methylcyclohexanol	4.6 (3.1)
exo-Norborneol	3.9
trans-3-Methylcyclohexanol	3.7
cis-4-tert-Butoxycyclohexanol	2.5
cis-4-Methylcyclohexanol	2.4
cis-3,3,5-Trimethylcyclohexanol	1.5
4,4-Dimethylcyclohexanol	1.4
Cyclopentanol	1.3
trans-2-Methylcyclohexanol	1.2 (1.9)
Cyclohexanol	1.0
cis-3-tert-Butylcyclohexanol	0.9
cis-3-Methylcyclohexanol	0.9
trans-4-Methylcyclohexanol	0.8
trans-4-tert-Butylcyclohexanol	0.8
2-Propanol	0.5
7-Hydroxynorbornane	0.2

the nature, energies, and conformation of species along the way have no bearing on the observed rate of reaction. If one assumes that the activated complex is one in which the reacting carbon goes from a tetrahedral state to one which approaches trigonal, then most of the observed data are easily accommodated.

The difference in rate between epimeric alcohols probably results from the difference in relief of nonbonded repulsive interactions. Thus for the borneol–isoborneol pair, isoborneol is the more reactive since the hydroxy group suffers nonbonded repulsion from the *gem*-dimethyl group, and in the *endo*- and *exo*-norboneol pair, the *endo* isomer is the more reactive because of the nonbonded repulsion from the neighboring hydrogens. In each case, the activated complex must have sufficiently approached the trigonal state so that the nonbonded interactions are decreased, even with the addition of the large chromium group.

Isoborneol
k(relative)=   1.96

Borneol
1.00

endo-Norborneol
k(relative)=   2.49

exo-Norborneol
1.00

Wilcox, Sexton, and Wilcox[129] have estimated the nonbonded repulsive interactions for a number of secondary alcohols, and have compared the free energy of activation changes in chromic acid oxidation with the calculated energy differences for the alcohols. A good linear free energy relationship was obtained, with a slope of 0.74. This suggests that about three-quarters of the repulsive interactions have been eliminated in going to the activated complex. This does not, however, mean that the activated complex lies three-quarters of the way from sp^3 to sp^2 hybridization, for the nonbonded repulsion drop off rapidly with an increase in distance.[129, 130]

To summarize the above data, the reacting carbon in the activated complex has suffered a small decrease in electron density, and the hybridization at that carbon is between sp^2 and sp^3. Stewart and Lee[116] have argued that a proton abstraction from the acid chromate ester should have a positive ρ value,[131] using the base catalyzed conversion of benzyl nitrate to benzaldehyde as a model. The ρ value for this reaction is $+3.4$.[132] They suggested that the cyclic

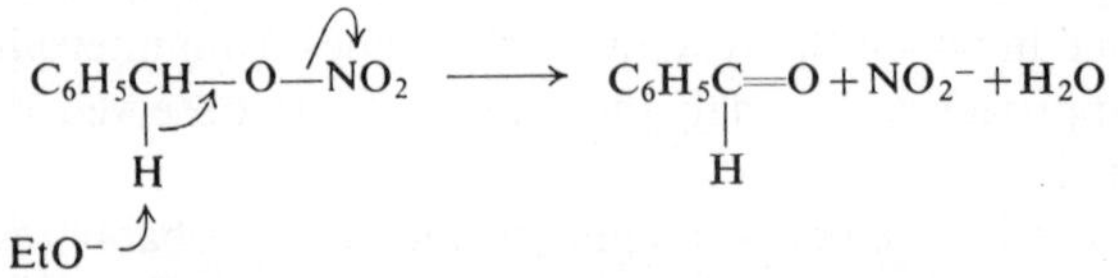

$$C_6H_5CH_2-O-NO_2 \longrightarrow C_6H_5C=O + NO_2^- + H_2O$$

mechanism could account for the negative ρ value; since in such a mechanism

[129] C. F. Wilcox, Jr., M. Sexton, and M. F. Wilcox, *J. Org. Chem.* **28**, 1079 (1963).

[130] H. Kwart, J. A. Ford, Jr., and G. C. Corey, *J. Am. Chem. Soc.* **84**, 1252 (1962).

[131] This suggestion was originally made by Roček[111] in arguing in favor of the hydride abstraction mechanism.

[132] E. Buncel and A. N. Bourns, *Can. J. Chem.* **38**, 2457 (1960).

charge separation is minimized, and stabilization of the incipient carbonyl group could be the important factor in determining the value of ρ. It is known that methoxy groups stabilize the carbonyl of phenyl alkyl ketones, and that nitro groups destabilize the carbonyl group.[133]

The above argument appears untenable since the reaction of benzyl nitrate requires a relatively high concentration of a strong base in order to attain a reasonable rate of reaction. Thus, the driving force for the reaction must be in large measure the neutralization of the base by the proton being abstracted. This would, of course, lead to a fairly negative ρ. The chromic acid oxidation proceeds rapidly with no bases other than water and the oxygen bonded to chromium being present, even though the acid chromate ester is present in relatively small concentration. Thus, the driving force in the transition from chromate ester to ketone must be the reduction of chromium(VI).[134]

It appears to this writer that the above data are in accord with either the proton abstraction mechanism or the cyclic mechanism. The assumption that the reaction has considerable E1 character would suggest that general base catalysis would not be observed, and that the solvent would be the only important base. Both mechanisms predict an activated complex having a hybridization between sp^2 and sp^3, and a negative value of ρ.

To be complete, mechanism (C), above, should be considered. Here, the role of the acid chromate ester is simply to bring the oxidant and reductant together, and the hydrogen abstraction step involves a hydrogen atom. The reaction would be completed by an electron transfer through the C—O—Cr bond. An immediate reaction to this mechanism might be that it is the same as the cyclic mechanism (B) since the transfer of the second electron should occur simultaneously with the hydrogen abstraction. However, if one remembers that in the inorganic oxidation-reduction reactions the slow process was the interconversion between chromium(V) and chromium(IV), presumably due to a change in coordination number, the proposal does not seem so unreasonable. The hydrogen atom transfer, which involves no change in coordination number by chromium, may occur first, to be followed by solvent reorganization about chromium which will permit the increase in coordination number in the transfer of the second electron. This mechanism will also account for the experimental observations. The hydrogen is transferred in the rate-determining step; a change in hybridization toward sp^2 will occur; and hydrogen atom abstraction reactions are generally characterized by a small negative ρ.[135]

[133] J. W. Baker and H. B. Hopkins, *J. Chem. Soc.* p. 1089 (1949).
[134] One might say that the benzyl nitrate reaction is an E2 elimination, whereas the chromate ester decomposition has more the character of an E1 elimination. Of course, it cannot be a pure E1 elimination since a kinetic hydrogen isotope effect is observed.
[135] G. A. Russell, *J. Org. Chem.* **23**, 1407 (1958).

Little more can be said about the mechanism of the oxidation by chromium(VI) at the present time. We must now consider the reaction of chromium-(V) which is presumably the important chromium species of intermediate valence in alcohol oxidation. The kinetic analysis of Westheimer and Watanabe[106] indicates that the oxidation by chromium(V) is a net two-electron process. The tritium kinetic isotope effect for the oxidation of isopropyl alcohol by chromium(V) has been determined using a competitive technique, giving $k_H/k_T = 5.9$ (0.3 M acid), 3.6 (1.0 M acid), and 2.8 (2.0 M acid).[136] In a similar fashion, the deuterium isotope effect has been determined for the chromium(V) oxidation of benzhydrol in 65% acetic acid, giving $k_H/k_D = 5.9$.[137] The corresponding isotope effects for oxidation by chromium(VI) were $k_H/k_T = 17$ for isopropyl alcohol, and $k_H/k_D = 9.5$ for benzhydrol. Although the isotope effect with chromium(V) is smaller than that found with chromium(VI), it is clear that C—H bond cleavage is still a rate-controlling step. The decrease in the tritium isotope effect for isopropyl alcohol with increasing acid concentration suggests that some other process may become important at higher acid concentrations.

The one case in which a difference between chromium(V) and chromium(IV) appears is in the oxidation of an alcohol having a *tert*-alkyl group such as phenyl-*tert*-butylcarbinol. As mentioned previously, the oxidation under certain conditions gives a maximum of about 67% of cleavage products (benzaldehyde and *tert*-butyl alcohol), the remainder being the expected ketone. The degree of cleavage was repressed by the addition of cerous or manganous ions, indicating that the cleavage was effected by chromium(IV) or (V) and not by chromium(VI).

The details of the cleavage reaction were studied by Westheimer and his co-workers.[4, 5] In the presence of sodium acetate and cerous ion, one ceric ion was produced for each chromium(VI) which had reacted. A kinetic isotope effect of $k_H/k_D = 12$ at 0° C, and 9 at 25° C, was observed in the oxidation of the deuterium-labeled alcohol. However, no isotopic fractionation occurred in the benzaldehyde–benzaldehyde-d formed in the competitive oxidation of phenyl-*tert*-butylcarbinol and its deuterium-labeled derivative. When phenyl-*tert*-butylcarbinol was labeled with oxygen-18, the *tert*-butyl alcohol formed by the cleavage reaction had no oxygen-18.

From these data, it was concluded that the reagent effecting cleavage was chromium(V), since this would account for the observed 67% maximum cleavage. The isotope effect was attributed to the rate-determining oxidation by chromium(VI) which leads only to ketone. The cleavage reaction does not involve the hydrogen attached to the reaction center, as indicated by the lack

136 L. Kaplan, *J. Am. Chem. Soc.* **77**, 5469 (1955).
137 K. B. Wiberg and W. P. Giddings, unpublished results.

of isotopic fractionation in the competitive oxidation of the labeled and unlabeled alcohols. The data suggest two possible mechanisms[138]:

(A) C_6H_5—CH—C(CH$_3$)$_3$ + Cr^V $\longrightarrow$ C_6H_5—CH—C(CH$_3$)$_3$
    | |
    OH   O—Cr^V

               H
               |
     $\longrightarrow$ C_6H_5—C=$\overset{+}{O}$C(CH$_3$)$_3$ + Cr^{III}

     $\xrightarrow{H_2O}$ C_6H_5CHO + (CH$_3$)$_3$COH

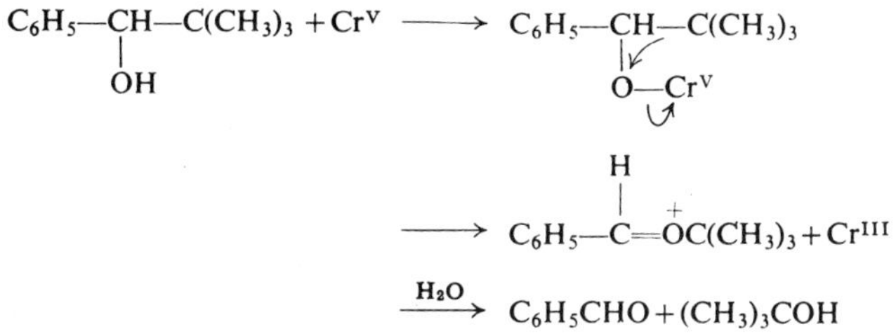

(B) C_6H_5—CH—C(CH$_3$)$_3$ + Cr^V $\longrightarrow$ C_6H_5—CH—C(CH$_3$)$_3$
    | |
    OH   O—Cr^V

     $\longrightarrow$ C_6H_5CHO + (CH$_3$)$_3$C$^+$

     $\xrightarrow{H_2O}$ C_6H_5CHO + (CH$_3$)$_3$COH

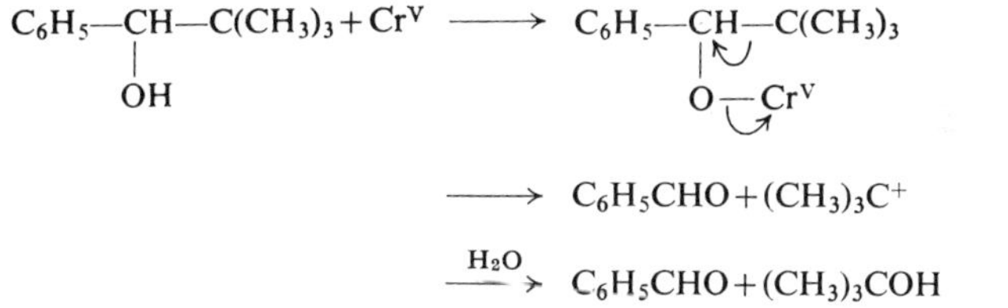

The lack of oxygen-18 in the *tert*-butyl alcohol formed in the cleavage of the labeled alcohol, coupled with the previous observation that the di-*tert*-butyl acetal of benzaldehyde is hydrolyzed in oxygen-18-labeled water to give unlabeled alcohol,[138] indicates that mechanism (A) is incorrect. Support for mechanism (B) is found in the observation that phenyl apocamphylcarbinol is oxidized without cleavage.[139] One would expect a process leading to a cation to be disfavored if the *tert*-group were apocamphyl. However, in the Baeyer-Villiger reaction, which involves an activated complex similar to that in (A), apocamphyl rearranges in preference to phenyl.[140]

Although the above data do much to define the nature of the reaction by chromium(V), it is clear that much is still to be learned about the details of the reactions which follow the rate-determining step.

Before concluding this section, the studies of Sager[141] and of Roček[142] on the mechanism of the oxidation of tertiary alcohols should be mentioned. It was found that the rates of reactions are independent of the concentration of oxidant, and that they correspond to the rates of the acid-catalyzed dehydration

[138] J. J. Cawley and F. H. Westheimer, *Chem. & Ind.* (*London*) p. 656 (1960).
[139] P. T. Lansbury, V. A. Pattison, and J. W. Diehl, *Chem. & Ind.* (*London*) p. 653 (1962).
[140] M. F. Hawthorne, W. D. Emmons, and K. S. McCallum, *J. Am. Chem. Soc.* **80**, 6393 (1958).
[141] W. F. Sager, *J. Am. Chem. Soc.* **78**, 4970 (1956).
[142] J. Roček, *Collection Czech. Chem. Commun.* **23**, 833 (1957); **25**, 375 (1960).

of the alcohols. Thus, the initial step is the formation of the alkene which is then oxidized by chromic acid.

VII. Oxidation of Diols

One of the first investigations of the chromic acid oxidation of diols was reported by Slack and Waters.[1] They found that the oxidation of ethylene glycol led to only a small amount of cleavage (1–2% formaldehyde being isolated), and that 2,3-butylene glycol gave somewhat more cleavage (20–30%)

A more detailed investigation was reported by Chatterji and Mukherjee.[2] The effect of methyl substitution on the degree of cleavage was confirmed and it was found that pinacol readily gave cleavage to acetone. The kinetic rate laws for several glycols were:

Ethylene glycol $v = k_a[\text{diol}]\,[\text{HCrO}_4{}^-]\,[\text{H}^+] + k_b[\text{diol}]\,[\text{HCrO}_4{}^-]\,[\text{H}^+]^2$

Propylene glycol and 2,3-butylene glycol $v = k[\text{diol}]\,[\text{HCrO}_4{}^-]\,[\text{H}^+]^2$

Pinacol $v = k[\text{diol}]\,[\text{HCrO}_4{}^-]\,[\text{H}^+]$

It is clear that two reactions are possible. In the first, normal oxidation occurs giving an α-hydroxycarbonyl compound, which may be further oxidized. In the case of ethylene glycol, both glyoxal and oxalic acid were isolated. In the second, which is favored by increasing methyl substitution, cleavage of the carbon–carbon bond occurs. The first reaction is characterized by an activation enthalpy of about 11 kcal/mole, and an activation entropy of about -39 e.u. and the second has $\Delta H^{\ddagger} \approx 16$ kcal/mole and $\Delta S^{\ddagger} \approx -18$ e.u.

The first reaction presumably occurs via the same mechanism as is operative with isopropyl alcohol[3]:

$$\text{HOCH}_2\text{CH}_2\text{OH} + \text{HCrO}_4{}^- + \text{H}^+ \rightleftharpoons \text{HOCH}_2\text{CH}_2\text{OCrO}_3\text{H} + \text{H}_2\text{O}$$
$$\text{HOCH}_2\text{CH}_2\text{OCrO}_3\text{H} \rightarrow \text{HOCH}_2\text{CH}{=}\text{O} + \text{Cr}^{\text{IV}}$$

One may wonder why the process

$$\text{HO}{-}\text{CH}_2{-}\text{CH}_2{-}\text{O}{-}\text{CrO}_3\text{H} \longrightarrow 2\text{CH}_2{=}\text{O} + \text{Cr}^{\text{IV}}$$

should be so unfavorable with ethylene glycol. Roček and Westheimer[4] have calculated the change in enthalpy associated with each of the two reactions

[1] R. Slack and W. A. Waters, *J. Chem. Soc.* p. 594 (1949).

[2] A. K. Chatterji and S. K. Mukherjee, *Z. Physik. Chem.* (*Leipzig*) **207**, 372 (1957); **208**, 281 (1958); **210**, 166 (1959).

[3] Further support for this view may be found in the facts that 2-methoxyethanol and ethylene glycol react at about the same rate, and that the rate of oxidation of ethylene glycol fits a Taft plot for the oxidation of primary alcohols. J. Roček, *Collection Czech. Chem. Commun.* **25**, 1052 (1960).

[4] J. Roček and F. H. Westheimer, *J. Am. Chem. Soc.* **84**, 2241 (1962).

and concluded that oxidation to a hydroxy aldehyde (or ketone) is energetically favored by 15 kcal/mole or more. It is interesting that the reagents commonly used for glycol cleavage (lead tetraacetate and periodic acid) do not satisfactorily effect secondary alcohol oxidation. Presumably, if a mechanistic pathway is available, oxidation of a primary or secondary alcohol group to a carbonyl should take preference over glycol cleavage.

The oxidation of pinacol has been studied in some detail by Chang and Westheimer.[5] They confirmed the kinetic results of Chatterji and Mukherjee, and found a solvent isotope effect, $k_{D_2O}/k_{H_2O} = 2.7$. Further, the monomethyl ether of pinacol was oxidized at a very low rate.

The solvent isotope effect suggests that oxygen–hydrogen bond cleavage does not occur in the rate-determining step. Since the monomethyl ether was not readily oxidized, it appears that a cyclic chromate ester is probably the intermediate. Decomposition in a fashion similar to that suggested for lead tetraacetate[6] and periodic acid[7] would give the observed products:

$$R_2C-OH \atop R_2C-OH \quad + HCrO_4^- + H^+ \quad \longrightarrow \quad {R_2C-O \atop R_2C-O}{>}Cr{<}{O \atop O} \quad \longrightarrow \quad {R_2C=O \atop R_2C=O} \quad + Cr^{IV}$$

Here, it appears that a direct reduction of Cr^{VI} to Cr^{IV} occurs, despite any possible difficulty with regard to change in coordination number.

Further evidence for cyclic chromate ester formation may be found in the observation that *cis*-1,2-dimethyl-1,2-cyclopentanediol is oxidized to 2,6-heptanedione at a rate 17,000 times faster than the *trans*-isomer.[4] The large difference in rate cannot be accommodated if one assumes that the preferred reaction involves a noncyclic mechanism. The effect of the methyl substitution on the rate of cleavage was studied, and for the series—ethylene glycol, propylene glycol, 2,3-butylene glycol and pinacol—the relative rates were 10^{-5}, 10^{-3}, 10^{-2}, and 1, respectively. It was assumed that alkyl substitution stabilized the activated complex for the decomposition of the cyclic chromate ester.

Although considerable information has been obtained about the mechanism of the oxidation of diols by chromic acid, it is clear that more work needs to be done. The reason for a change in mechanism with increasing methyl substitution is still not clear. (Note that pinacol is *more* reactive than ethylene glycol and that *trans*-1,2-dimethyl-1,2-cyclopentanediol, which can only undergo cleavage via a noncyclic mechanism, has about the same reactivity as *trans*-1,2-cyclopentanediol which can undergo normal oxidation to a ketol.) Further, it is not understood why chromic acid is able to effect both normal

[5] Y. W. Chang and F. H. Westheimer, *J. Am. Chem. Soc.* **82**, 1401 (1960).
[6] R. Criegee, L. Kraft, and B. Rank, *Ann.* **507**, 159 (1933).
[7] G. J. Buist and C. A. Bunton, *J. Chem. Soc.* p. 4580 (1957).

oxidation and cleavage, whereas most other oxidants can effect only one of these two reactions.

The oxidation of diols by chromyl chloride has been investigated by Slack and Waters.[1] Hydrobenzoin, benzpinacol, and pinacol all gave insoluble complexes which, on hydrolysis, gave cleavage products in good yield. The adduct from benzpinacol was found to contain two molecules of chromyl chloride. The simple diols were not studied.

VIII. Oxidation of Aldehydes

The chromic acid oxidation of aldehydes is not particularly useful as a synthetic method since aldehydes are generally more difficult to obtain than are the corresponding carboxylic acids. However, the oxidation does proceed in a satisfactory fashion. Heptanoic acid is obtained in 70% yield from the aldehyde,[1] and furfural is converted to furoic acid in 75% yield.[2] Further, the aldehyde is an intermediate in the more common oxidation of a primary alcohol to a carboxylic acid.

The first kinetic study of the chromic acid oxidation of aldehydes was reported by Lucchi.[3] He studied the oxidation of a series of aromatic aldehydes in acetic acid solution using sulfuric acid as the catalyst. The reaction was first order in the aldehyde and in chromium(VI). Electron withdrawing substituents were found to facilitate the reaction.

Further studies of benzaldehyde oxidation were reported by Graham and Westheimer,[4] and by Wiberg and Mill.[5] In aqueous solution, the reaction had the rate law:

$$v = k_a[\text{RCHO}][\text{HCrO}_4^-][\text{H}^+] + k_b[\text{RCHO}][\text{HCrO}_4^-][\text{H}^+]^2$$

whereas in aqueous acetic acid it was:

$$v = k[\text{RCHO}][\text{HCrO}_4^-]h_0$$

The results are analogous to those obtained for isopropyl alcohol. The reaction also shows a kinetic hydrogen isotope effect,[5,6] indicating that carbon–hydrogen bond cleavage occurs in the rate-determining step.

When the rates of reaction in different acetic acid–water mixtures were compared at a constant value of h_0, it was found that a relatively small change occurred.[5] This is in marked contrast to the oxidation of isopropyl alcohol for

[1] A. Darapsky and W. Engles, *J. Prakt. Chem.* **146**, 238 (1936).

[2] C. D. Hurd, J. W. Garrett, and E. N. Osborne, *J. Am. Chem. Soc.* **55**, 1082 (1933).

[3] E. Lucchi, *Boll. Sei. Fac. Chim. Ind. Bologna* **208**, 333 (1940); *Gazz. Chim. Ital.* **71**, 729, 752 (1941).

[4] G. T. E. Graham and F. H. Westheimer, *J. Am. Chem. Soc.* **80**, 3030 (1958).

[5] K. B. Wiberg and T. Mill, *J. Am. Chem. Soc.* **80**, 3022 (1958); K. B. Wiberg, *ibid.* **76**, 5371 (1954).

[6] E. M. Hodnett, *J. Chem. Phys.* **31**, 275 (1958).

which there is a considerable increase in rate of oxidation with decreasing water content, again at a constant h_0 value.

The effect of substituents in the oxidation of aromatic aldehydes was quite small, with *p*-nitro giving some rate acceleration. The value of ρ was $+1.02$.[5] A series of aliphatic aldehydes has also been studied and, on the basis of the hydrated form of the aldehyde as the reactant, ρ^* was found to be -1.2.[7] The difference between the reaction constants for the two types of aldehydes is approximately the reaction constant expected for the hydration equilibrium for the aromatic aldehydes. Thus, if the aromatic aldehydes were assumed to react in the hydrated form (or some equivalent structure), the ρ value for the reaction would be about -1, corresponding to the value obtained in the oxidation of aliphatic aldehydes and of alcohols. The assumption that the reaction involves the hydrate of the aldehyde (either actually or effectively) is in agreement with the results obtained in varying the water content of the acetic acid–water mixtures.

The data on the rates of oxidation of aliphatic aldehydes[7, 8] is quite similar to that obtained for the aromatic aldehydes. Formaldehyde, for example, gives the rate law[8, 9]:

$$v = k[\text{HCHO}]\,[\text{HCrO}_4^-]\,[\text{H}^+]^2/(1 + a[\text{H}^+])$$

where the term which is second order in acid is the principal one up to rather high acid concentrations. Both formaldehyde[9] and acetaldehyde[10] show a kinetic isotope effect. The values for formaldehyde at $25°$ C range from 5.5 to 6.8, with the higher value obtained at the lower acid concentration. Kemp and Waters suggested that the change in isotope effect was due to the effect of acid concentration on the reactions of chromium(IV) and/or (V). Although such effects are known from studies of competitive oxidation of labeled and unlabeled substrates,[11] it seems unlikely that they would be found in the present case where the isotope effects were obtained from two separate rate measurements. Possibly the change in isotope effect results from a difference in isotope effect for the terms in the rate expression which are first and second order in the acid concentration.

In studying the oxidation of formaldehyde in aqueous solution, Chatterji and Mukherjee[8] observed rate retardation by manganous and cerous ion and were able to show that the induction factor with the former was 0.5. This indicates that chromium(IV) is the product of the oxidation by chromium(VI).

[7] J. Roček, *Tetrahedron Letters* No. 5, 1 (1959).
[8] A. K. Chatterji and S. K. Mukherjee, *J. Am. Chem. Soc.* **80**, 3600 (1958); A. C. Chatterji and V. Antony, *Z. Physik Chem. (Leipzig)* **210**, 103 (1959).
[9] T. J. Kemp and W. A. Waters, *Proc. Roy. Soc.* **A274**, 480 (1962).
[10] J. W. Cornforth and G. Popják, *Nature* **164**, 1053 (1949).
[11] L. Kaplan, *J. Am. Chem. Soc.* **77**, 5469 (1955).

Similar but less clear-cut results were obtained with the aromatic aldehydes.[4, 5] Again, this result is the same as that obtained with isopropyl alcohol.

Some of the possible mechanisms for the reaction which meet the requirements of rate-determining carbon–hydrogen bond cleavage and the involvement of the hydrate of the aldehyde or its equivalent follow. They are written using a single proton, and the terms which are second order in acid require the conjugate acid of one of the species.

(A)

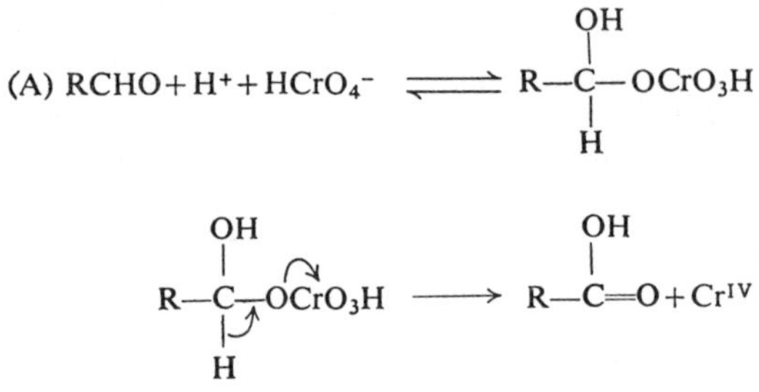

$$\text{(A) } RCHO + H^+ + HCrO_4^- \rightleftharpoons R-\underset{\underset{H}{|}}{\overset{\overset{OH}{|}}{C}}-OCrO_3H$$

$$R-\underset{\underset{H}{|}}{\overset{\overset{OH}{|}}{C}}-OCrO_3H \longrightarrow R-\overset{\overset{OH}{|}}{C}=O + Cr^{IV}$$

(B) First step same as in (A)

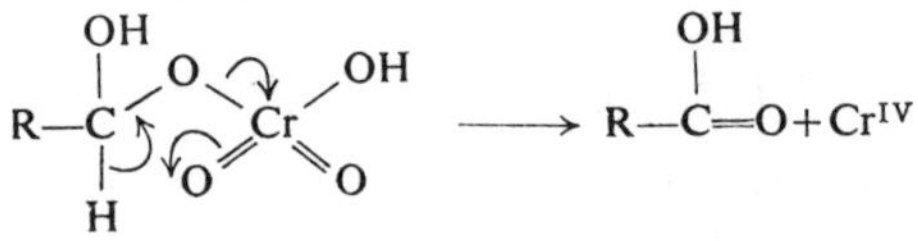

$$R-\underset{\underset{H}{|}}{\overset{\overset{OH}{|}}{C}}\cdots O\cdots Cr(\!=\!O)(=O)OH \longrightarrow R-\overset{\overset{OH}{|}}{C}=O + Cr^{IV}$$

(C)

$$\text{(C) } RCHO + H_2O \rightleftharpoons R-\underset{\underset{OH}{|}}{\overset{\overset{OH}{|}}{C}}-H$$

$$R-\underset{\underset{OH}{|}}{\overset{\overset{OH}{|}}{C}}-H \quad O{=}CrO_3H_2 \longrightarrow R-\overset{\overset{O}{\|}}{C}-OH + Cr^{IV}$$

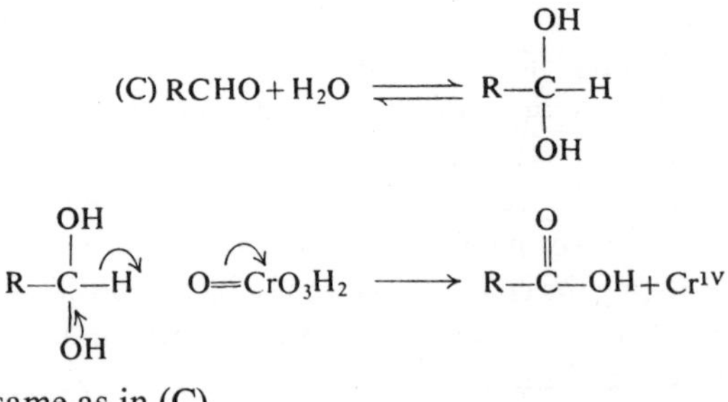

(D) First step same as in (C)

$$R-\underset{\underset{OH}{|}}{\overset{\overset{OH}{|}}{C}}-H + H_2CrO_4 \longrightarrow \left[R-\underset{\underset{OH}{|}}{\overset{\overset{OH}{|}}{C}}{}^{\bullet}\, Cr^V \right]$$

$$\left[R-\underset{\underset{OH}{|}}{\overset{\overset{OH}{|}}{C}}{}^{\bullet}\, Cr^V \right] \longrightarrow R-\overset{\overset{OH}{|}}{C}=O + Cr^{IV}$$

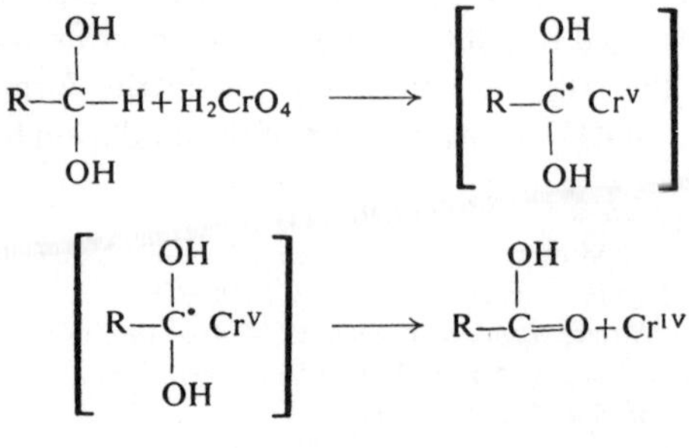

Using an acid concentration which leads to a second order dependence on acid in the oxidation of acetaldehyde, a solvent kinetic isotope effect, $k_{D_2O}/k_{H_2O} = 6.29$, was observed.[12] For formaldehyde, the solvent isotope effect was $k_{D_2O}/k_{H_2O} = 5.37$.[9] These results are essentially the same as that obtained in the oxidation of isopropyl alcohol ($k_{D_2O}/k_{H_2O} = 6.26$),[13] and arise because D_3O^+ in D_2O behaves as a stronger acid than H_3O^+ in H_2O. The value is as large as one could expect, and this indicates that oxygen–hydrogen bond cleavage does not occur in the rate-controlling step. Unless one wished to argue that the hydride transfer occurred without the loss of a proton, mechanism (C) could be discounted. Since it seems unlikely that the reaction would lead to the conjugate acid of the acid rather than to the acid itself, mechanism (C) will be assumed not to be operative.

If a hydrogen atom abstraction were to occur as in mechanism (D), the aldehyde hydrate would have to be the reactant. In view of the stability of the aldehyde diacetates and acetates toward air oxidation, which is in sharp contrast to the aromatic aldehydes themselves, it appears very unlikely that hydrogen atom abstraction from the hydrate of the aldehyde would take preference over hydrogen atom abstraction from the free aldehyde.

This leaves mechanisms (A) and (B) which are the exact counterparts of the two possible mechanisms for alcohol oxidation. At the present time, there are no data which permit one to distinguish between them. Both mechanisms lead to chromium(IV) which may react further as follows:

$$Cr^{IV} + Cr^{VI} \rightarrow 2\ Cr^V$$

$$2(Cr^V + RCHO \rightarrow RCO_2H + Cr^{III})$$

or

$$Cr^{IV} + RCHO \rightarrow RCO\cdot + Cr^{III}$$

$$RCO\cdot + Cr^{VI} \rightarrow RCO_2H + Cr^V$$

$$Cr^V + RCHO \rightarrow RCO_2H + Cr^{III}$$

It is not possible to study these steps using a direct kinetic approach. It is, however, possible to study them using a competitive technique.

Suppose the oxidation of a mixture of benzaldehyde and *p*-chlorobenzaldehyde were effected by chromic acid, and suppose the first possibility, involving chromium(V) as the only other oxidant, were correct. Then, one-third of the oxidation would be effected by chromium(VI) and two-thirds by chromium(V). Each species will react with the two aldehydes at the appropriate relative rates. The relative rates of reaction toward chromium(VI) may be

[12] K. B. Wiberg and W. H. Richardson, unpublished results.
[13] R. Brownell, A. Leo, Y. W. Chang, and F. H. Westheimer, *J. Am. Chem. Soc.* **82**, 406 (1960).

determined by a direct kinetic experiment using each of the two aldehydes in turn. The relative reactivity observed in the competitive oxidation may then be corrected for the effect of chromium(VI), giving the relative reactivity toward chromium(V).[14] The data are summarized in Table 8-1. The kinetic isotope effect for the oxidation of chromium(V) may be obtained in the same way, giving $k_H/k_D = 4.1$ as compared with $k_H/k_D = 4.3$ for chromium(VI).

TABLE 8-1

EFFECT OF SUBSTITUENTS ON THE RATE OF OXIDATION
OF AROMATIC ALDEHYDES BY CHROMIUM(VI) AND
THE INTERMEDIATE CHROMIUM SPECIES

Substituent	k/k_0 (Cr^{VI})	k/k_0 (Cr^V–Cr^{IV})
p-CH$_3$	0.69	0.81
p-Cl	1.38	1.20
m-Cl	1.91	1.42

If it is assumed that chromium(V) is the active species, the value of ρ for its reaction is 0.45 as compared with 0.77 for chromium(VI). On the other hand, if both chromium(V) and chromium(IV) are assumed to be involved, ρ for chromium(V) would be 1.6–2.2 if ρ for chromium(IV) were between -0.5 and -1.0.

The kinetic isotope effect shows that the cleavage of the carbon–hydrogen bond is still rate controlling in the second phase of the oxidation. Whether chromium(V) or chromium(IV) is the active intermediate cannot be readily determined from the data, and further information dealing with related systems such as alcohol oxidation is needed. One interesting nonkinetic observation is that triphenylacetaldehyde is oxidized by chromic acid to give approximately one-third triphenylacetic acid and two-thirds triphenylcarbinol and carbon monoxide.[12] The ester mechanism might be expected to give either triphenylacetic acid or triphenylcarbinol and formic acid (which would be oxidized to carbon *dioxide*):

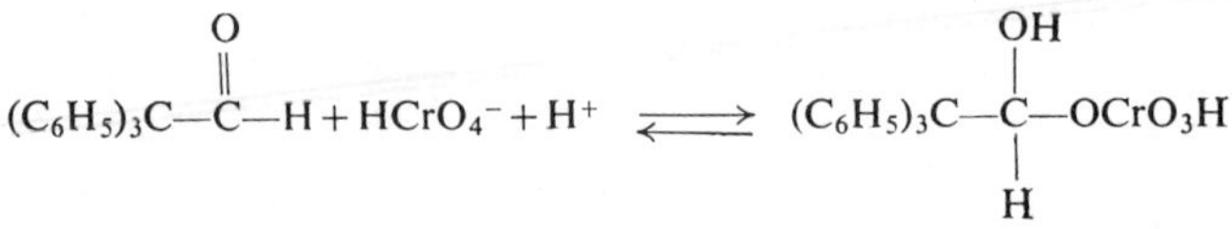

$$(C_6H_5)_3C\overset{O}{\overset{\|}{-}}C-H + HCrO_4^- + H^+ \rightleftharpoons (C_6H_5)_3C-\overset{OH}{\underset{H}{\overset{|}{C}}}-OCrO_3H$$

---

[14] K. B. Wiberg and W. H. Richardson, *J. Am. Chem. Soc.* **84**, 2800 (1962).

then

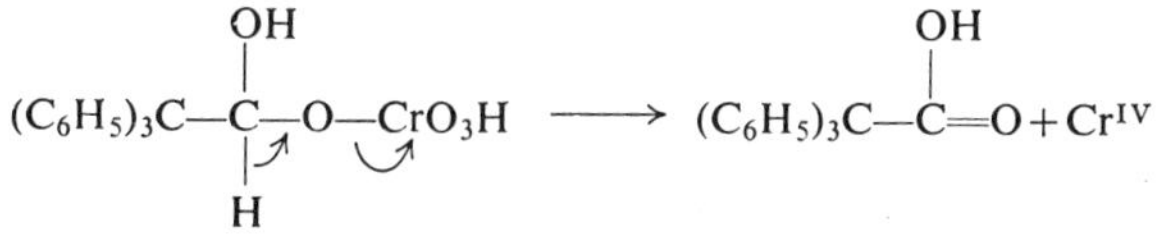

$$(C_6H_5)_3C-\underset{\underset{H}{|}}{\overset{\overset{OH}{|}}{C}}-O-CrO_3H \longrightarrow (C_6H_5)_3C-\overset{\overset{OH}{|}}{C}=O+Cr^{IV}$$

or

$$(C_6H_5)_3C-\underset{\underset{H}{|}}{\overset{\overset{OH}{|}}{C}}-O-CrO_3H \longrightarrow (C_6H_5)_3C^+ + H\overset{\overset{O}{||}}{C}OH + Cr^{IV}$$

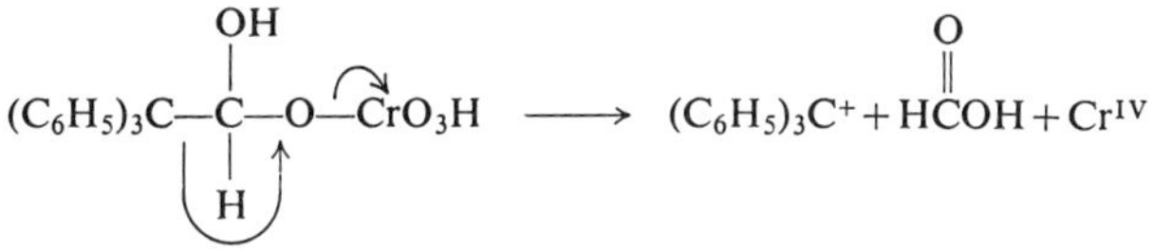

whereas either a hydride or hydrogen atom abstraction might lead to triphenylcarbinol and carbon *monoxide*:

$$(C_6H_5)_3C-\overset{\overset{O}{||}}{C}-H+Cr^V \longrightarrow (C_6H_5)_3C-\overset{\overset{O}{||}}{C^+}+Cr^{III}$$

$$(C_6H_5)_3C-\overset{\overset{O}{||}}{C^+} \longrightarrow (C_6H_5)_3C^+ + CO$$

$$(C_6H_5)_3C^+ + H_2O \longrightarrow (C_6H_5)_3COH + H^+$$

or

$$(C_6H_5)_3\overset{\overset{O}{||}}{C}CH+Cr^V \longrightarrow (C_6H_5)_3\overset{\overset{O}{||}}{C}C^\bullet + Cr^{IV}$$

$$(C_6H_5)_3\overset{\overset{O}{||}}{C}C^\bullet \longrightarrow (C_6H_5)_3C^\bullet + CO$$

$$(C_6H_5)_3C^\bullet + H_2CrO_4 \longrightarrow (C_6H_5)_3C-O-\underset{\underset{O}{||}}{\overset{\overset{OH}{|}}{Cr}}-OH$$

$$\longrightarrow (C_6H_5)_3COH + Cr^V$$

The observations concerning the products of the reaction suggest that one-third of the reaction proceeds via the ester mechanism and two-thirds proceeds via either of the mechanisms given above. On the other hand, triphenylacetaldehyde may well be an atypical aldehyde, and the above results may have little to do with the oxidation of benzaldehyde. It is interesting to note that the permanganate oxidation of triphenylacetaldehyde leads only to triphenyl-acetic acid, whereas the ceric ion oxidation leads to complete conversion to triphenylcarbinol and carbon monoxide.

The oxidation of benzaldehyde with chromyl acetate is quite different from the chromic acid oxidation.[15] First, chromium(V) is moderately stable in this medium and, when the course of the reaction is followed spectrophoto-metrically at 465 mμ, the absorbance first goes up and then down. Evidence has been presented indicating that the species causing the increasing absorbance is chromium(V). This reacts with the aldehyde leading to the acid and chromium(IV). In this medium, the latter is the normal form of chromium as a result of an oxidation—it very slowly is converted to chromium(III) on standing. A possible scheme for the reaction might be:

$$RCHO + Cr^{VI} \rightarrow RCO\cdot + Cr^{V}$$

$$RCO\cdot + Cr^{VI} \rightarrow RCO_2H + Cr^{V}$$

$$RCHO + Cr^{V} \rightarrow RCO\cdot + Cr^{IV}$$

$$RCO\cdot + Cr^{V} \rightarrow RCO_2H\cdot + Cr^{IV}$$

This set of reactions will account for the observed kinetic data, as will some other schemes.

Both steps of the reaction show a kinetic isotope effect ($k_H/k_D = 2.3$ and 3.3, respectively), and both are characterized by a small value of ρ (-0.1 and -0.9, respectively). When oxygen-labeled chromyl acetate was used as the oxidant in ordinary acetic anhydride solvent, oxygen was transferred from one of the Cr=O bonds of the oxidant to the aldehyde.

These data are in accord with the hypothesis that hydrogen atom abstraction occurs in the initial step, and that the acyl radical thus formed reacts with oxygen of the acetyl chromate to give the intermediate which ultimately leads to products via chromium–oxygen bond cleavage. The results of the oxidation of triphenylacetaldehyde, which leads to triphenylcarbinol and carbon monoxide, are also in accord with this hypothesis.

IX. Oxidation of Ketones

The chromic acid oxidation of ketones generally leads to carbon–carbon bond cleavage with the formation of two carboxylic acids. Thus, diethyl ketone gives propionic and acetic acids,[1] and cyclohexanone gives adipic acid along with some glutaric and succinic acids.[2] The relative rates of oxidation

[15] K. B. Wiberg and P. A. Lepse, *J. Am. Chem. Soc.* **86**, 2612 (1964).
[1] W. F. Sager and A. Bradley, *J. Am. Chem. Soc.* **78**, 1187 (1956).
[2] F. Mareš, J. Roček, and J. Sicher, *Collection Czech. Chem. Commun.* **26**, 2355 (1961).

of a series of cycloalkanones has been determined, and the order of decreasing reactivity was found to be C_6, C_9, C_8, C_5, C_7, C_4.[2] The rates of oxidation of a series of methyl alkyl ketones has also been studied, and the rates of reaction were found to increase with increasing chain length.[3]

The kinetics of the chromic acid oxidation of cyclohexanone has been studied.[4,5] The rate of reaction was found to be proportional to the concentrations of ketone, acid chromate ion, and acid. A kinetic isotope effect, $k_H/k_D = 5.5$, was observed in comparing the rates of oxidation of cyclohexanone and cyclohexanone-d_4, and a solvent isotope effect, $k_{D_2O}/k_{H_2O} = 4$–5, was also observed.[4]

It has been suggested that the enol is an intermediate in the reaction.[3-5] The formation of the enol cannot be rate determining since the rate of oxidation had a first order dependence on chromium(VI) concentration, and a measurement of the rate of enolization showed it to be more rapid than oxidation.[6] Under these circumstances, how can the reaction involve the enol as the intermediate and still give a kinetic isotope effect? Water's explanation is as follows.[4] The rate of formation of the enol will be reduced by the presence of the α-deuterium, whereas the conversion of the enol back to the ketone will proceed at a normal rate. The steady state concentration of enol will be reduced by a factor corresponding to the isotope effect for the enolization, and any subsequent reaction which depends on the concentration of enol will be reduced in rate accordingly. This will be the case until much of the deuterium has been "washed out" of the ketone via the exchange reaction.

In the present case, the rate of enolization is faster than that of oxidation by only a factor of about 10. Thus, using an excess of ketone, a normal isotope effect will be noted through a major portion of the reaction. If enolization were much faster than oxidation, the effect of deuterium substitution on the rate of oxidation would be negligible. A corollary of these considerations is the conclusion that the use of higher concentrations of chromic acid should make oxidation and enolization rates approximately equal. Thus, it should be possible to obtain a reaction which approaches zero order in chromic acid by using higher concentrations. This has not as yet been tested.

The solvent isotope effect is larger than normal for a reaction involving a single proton (i.e., about 2.6). It is possible to account for this on the basis of the above mechanism. The formation of the enol and its return to ketone are both acid catalyzed and so the change from H_3O^+ to D_3O^+ should have the same effect on both forward and reverse reactions. However, starting with

[3] G. Petit, *Bull. Soc. Chim. France* **12**, 568 (1945).
[4] P. A. Best, J. S. Littler, and W. A. Waters, *J. Chem. Soc.* p. 822 (1962).
[5] K. Umeda and K. Tarama, *Nippon Kagaku Zasshi* **83**, 1216 (1962); *Chem. Abstr.* **58**, 12378 (1963).
[6] J. S. Littler, *J. Chem. Soc.* p. 827 (1962).

unlabeled ketone, the forward reaction involves cleavage of a C—H bond, the reverse involves cleavage of an O—D bond. The isotope effect for the reverse reaction will cause a higher than normal steady state concentration of enol until isotopic equilibration has been effected. The increased concentration of enol coupled with the normal effect of D_2O as the solvent in increasing the concentration of H_2CrO_4 at a given acid concentration will result in a larger than normal solvent isotope effect.

Although the species involved in the rate-determining step have been identified by the above data, the nature of the reaction which occurs and the course of the following steps have not been determined. The rate-controlling step could, for example, involve the attack of chromic acid on the double bond of the enol, or it could involve the decomposition of the chromic acid ester of the enol.[4]

Two additional observations are worth recording. First, the oxidation of deoxybenzoin under conditions which maintain a low chromium(VI) concentration throughout the reaction leads to about 8% bidesyl along with the expected benzil.[7] This suggests that a free radical intermediate may be involved in the oxidation of this ketone. Second, in the oxidation of cyclohexanone, about 68% of the chromic acid used leads to adipic acid, and about 15% leads to glutaric acid.[8] The ratio of glutaric to adipic acid is concentration dependent. Further, adipic acid is stable toward further oxidation by chromium(VI) under the conditions used. Thus, some intermediate was formed which could be oxidized either to adipic or glutaric acid.

X. Oxidation of Carboxylic Acids

The oxidation of oxalic acid by chromium(VI) has been studied by several investigators.[1-4] Snethlage[3] studied the reaction in media containing 0–96% sulfuric acid. The rate of reaction was proportional to the concentrations of chromic acid and of oxalic acid. However, the order with respect to the former varied between 1–1.5, and with respect to the latter the order was 1–2. The rate of reaction reached a maximum at 70% sulfuric acid. The oxidation of oxalic acid is incomplete if the sulfuric acid concentration is lower than about 20%,[3,4] suggesting complex formation between oxalic acid and chromium(III).

[7] K. B. Wiberg and A. L. Gatzke, unpublished results.
[8] J. Roček and Sr. A. Riehl, private communication.
[1] A. N. Dey and N. R. Dhar, Z. Electrochem. **32**, 586 (1926).
[2] K. Jablczynski, Z. Anorg. Allgem. Chem. **60**, 38 (1908).
[3] H. C. S. Snethlage, Rec. Trav. Chim. **59**, 111 (1940).
[4] J. I. Aznáres and J. B. V. Raga, Anales Real Soc. Espan. Fis. Quim. (Madrid) Ser. **B50**, 545, 656 (1954); Chem. Abstr. **48**, 13510 (1954); **49**, 766 (1955).

The oxidation of formic acid[5-8] in aqueous sulfuric acid solution gave approximately first order dependence on formic acid and chromium(VI), followed the square of the acid concentration at low acidity, and followed h_0 at higher acid concentrations. The reaction of deuteroformic acid indicated an isotope effect, $k_H/k_D = 7.2$ at 25° C.[9] A solvent isotope effect, $k_{D_2O}/k_{H_2O} = 5.7$ was also found,[9] and this corresponds to that expected for a reaction involving two protons in the rate-determining step. Two mechanisms appear attractive for the reaction:

(A) $H^+ + H-\overset{\overset{O}{\|}}{C}-OH + H_2CrO_4 \rightleftharpoons H\overset{\overset{O}{\|}}{C}-O-\overset{\overset{O}{\|}}{\underset{\underset{OH}{|}}{\overset{+}{Cr}}}-OH + H_2O$

$H-\overset{\overset{O}{\|}}{C}-O-\overset{\overset{O}{\|}}{\underset{\underset{OH}{|}}{\overset{+}{Cr}}}-OH \longrightarrow H^+ + CO_2 + Cr^{IV}$

(B) $H-O-\overset{\overset{O}{\|}}{C}-H \quad O=CrO_3H_3^+ \longrightarrow H^+ + CO_2 + Cr^{IV}$

The available data do not permit a decision between these and other possible mechanisms.

The rate of oxidation of malonic acid[10] in aqueous sulfuric acid increases with acid concentration and reaches a maximum between 70 and 96% sulfuric acid. The temperature dependence of the rate of oxidation of this acid was determined and compared with that of formic, succinic, and adipic acids.

The oxidation of propionic acid in aqueous sulfuric acid has been studied.[11] Acetic acid and carbon dioxide were the principal products. The rate of reaction had a first order dependence on propionic acid and on chromium(VI), and a second order dependence on acid concentration.

Several longer chain acids have been studied.[12, 13] The effect of a carboxyl group on the rate of oxidation at the α, β, γ, and δ positions was determined. The rates of reaction (relative to a position on a paraffin chain) were 0.016,

---

[5] D. J. W. Kreulen and D. T. J. TerHorst, *Rec. Trav. Chim.* **59**, 1165 (1940).

[6] H. C. S. Snethlage, *Rec. Trav. Chim.* **60**, 877 (1941).

[7] A. V. Mahajani and A. K. Bhattacharya, *Proc. Natl. Acad. Sci. India Sect. A* **23** (2), 65 (1954); A. V. Mahajani, *ibid.* **26** (1), 49 (1957).

[8] E. Pungor and J. Trompler, *J. Inorg. Nucl. Chem.* **5**, 123 (1957).

[9] T. J. Kemp and W. A. Waters, *Proc. Roy. Soc.* **A274**, 480 (1963).

[10] H. C. S. Snethlage, *Rec. Trav. Chim.* **61**, 213 (1942).

[11] M. H. Tocher, *J. Chem. Educ.* **35**, 207 (1958).

[12] J. Sicher, M. Tichý, F. Šipoš, and M. Pankova, *Collection Czech. Chem. Commun.* **26**, 2418 (1961).

[13] O. Metz, *Fette, Seifen, Anstrichmittel* **61**, 995 (1959).

0.059, 0.26, and 0.78, respectively, indicating a large inductive effect of the carboxyl group.[12] The oxidation of a series of dicarboxylic acids was also studied; beginning with sebacic acid, the rate dependence on chain length was constant and gave the same value as observed with n-paraffins.[12] It is clear that these oxidations proceed via the same mechanism as the hydrocarbons. The mechanism of oxidation *alpha* to the carboxyl group remains to be determined.

The oxidation of α-hydroxy acids appears to lead to aldehydes. Lactic acid is converted to acetaldehyde in aqueous solution,[14] and p-methyl mandelic acid is converted to terephthalaldehyde tetraacetate by chromyl acetate in acetic anhydride.[15] It seems very unlikely that either reaction involves initial oxidation to a keto acid. Thus, decarboxylation probably occurs as part of the oxidation step, possibly via the path:

$$
\begin{array}{c}
\text{OH} \\
| \\
\text{CH}_3\text{CHCO}_2\text{H} + \text{HCrO}_4^- + \text{H}^+
\end{array}
\longrightarrow
\begin{array}{c}
\text{O}-\text{CrO}_3\text{H} \\
| \\
\text{CH}_3-\text{C}-\text{C}-\text{O}-\text{H} \\
| \quad \| \\
\text{H} \quad \text{O}
\end{array}
$$

$$
\longrightarrow
\begin{array}{c}
\text{O} \\
\| \\
\text{CH}_3-\text{C}-\text{H} + \text{CO}_2 + \text{Cr}^{IV}
\end{array}
$$

The reaction may also occur via mixed anhydride formation between the carboxyl group and chromic acid, followed by cleavage to the above products.

XI. Oxidation at Sulfur

The oxidation of sulfides with chromic acid leads to sulfones. Using this method, diphenyl sulfone (quantitative),[1] ethylene diphenyl disulfone,[2] dibenzyl sulfone (24%),[3] and methylene diphenyl disulfone (18%)[3] have been prepared. However, the oxidation is usually effected more satisfactorily using other oxidants such as potassium permanganate.

The one interesting feature of the oxidation of sulfides lies in the fact that the common mechanisms for chromic acid cannot apply. Using diacetyl chromate, the oxidation of diphenyl sulfide is very fast—considerably faster than the oxidation of aldehydes or hydrocarbons.[4] When the oxidant was labeled with oxygen-18 at the Cr=O group, complete oxygen transfer was observed. Although the data are not adequate to establish a mechanism, they suggest that an electron transfer from the sulfide to chromium(VI) may occur,

[14] E. T. Chapman and M. H. Smith, *J. Chem. Soc.* **20**, 173 (1867).

[15] L. Dyksterhuis and D. E. A. Rivett, *J. S. African Chem. Inst.* **15**, 20 (1962).

[1] J. Stenhouse, *Ann.* **140**, 290 (1866).

[2] F. Ewerlöf, *Ber.* **4**, 717 (1871).

[3] R. L. Shriner, H. C. Struck, and W. J. Jorison, *J. Am. Chem. Soc.* **52**, 2060 (1930).

[4] K. B. Wiberg and P. A. Lepse, *J. Am. Chem. Soc.* **86**, 2612 (1964).

followed by attack of the sulfur radical on the Cr=O bond of the oxidant. Presumably, the conversion of the sulfoxide thus formed to the product sulfone would proceed in the same fashion since complete oxygen transfer was involved in both steps.

XII. Miscellaneous Oxidation Reactions

Besides the cases mentioned above, there are a number of other types of compounds which have been subjected to chromic acid oxidation. Some of the more recent work will be described here.

The oxidation of *N*-alkylarylamines leads to aldehydes in yields up to 37%.[1] Quinones and other oxidation products are also found. Aliphatic amines were not oxidized under the reaction conditions used. The oxidation was developed into a degradative procedure for aliphatic amines by first allowing them to react with 2,4-dinitrochlorobenzene and then effecting the oxidation.[2]

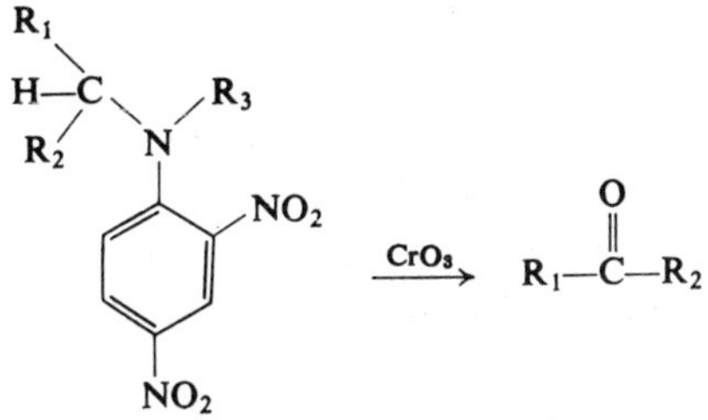

Another related case of oxidation *alpha* to a nitrogen is found in the reaction of 21-deoxyajmaline-17-epi-*O*-acetate with chromium trioxide in pyridine[3]:

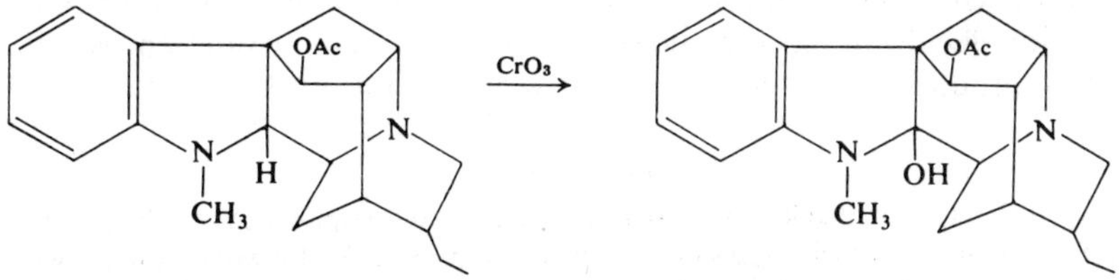

The oxidation of tetraphenylfuran has been found to give *cis*-dibenzoylstilbene which is further oxidized to the enol benzoate[4]:

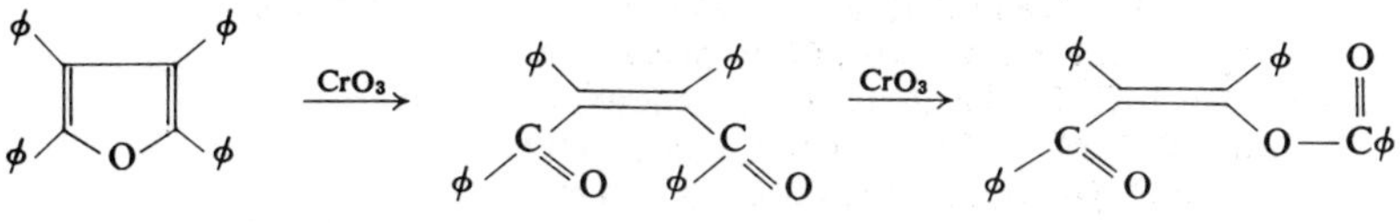

[1] F. W. Neumann and C. W. Gould, *Anal. Chem.* **25**, 751 (1953).
[2] A. T. Bottini and R. E. Olsen, *J. Org. Chem.* **27**, 452 (1962).
[3] M. F. Bartlett, B. F. Lambert, and W. I. Taylor, *J. Am. Chem. Soc.* **86**, 729 (1964).
[4] R. E. Lutz, W. J. Welstead, R. G. Bass, and J. I. Dale, *J. Org. Chem.* **27**, 1112 (1962).

The chromic acid oxidation of several pentoses has been studied,[5] and the rates of reaction have been compared with that of the hexoses. In some cases, isomerization at a position adjacent to the site of attack has been found.[6]

The oxidation of organoboranes has been found to be facile and leads to a convenient method for the conversion of olefins to ketones via hydroboration.[7] Boronic acids are also easily oxidized by chromic acid.[8] The rate of reaction is first order in the boronic acid and in chromium(VI). Between pH 2–6, the rate of reaction is independent of the acid concentration. Oxidation at pH 5 gives an alcohol as the product, whereas at higher acid concentrations, the alcohol is further oxidized to a ketone. The active oxidants may be identified from the pH rate profile to be $HCrO_4^-$ and $H_3CrO_4^+$. The reaction with $HCrO_4^-$ was suggested to proceed as follows:

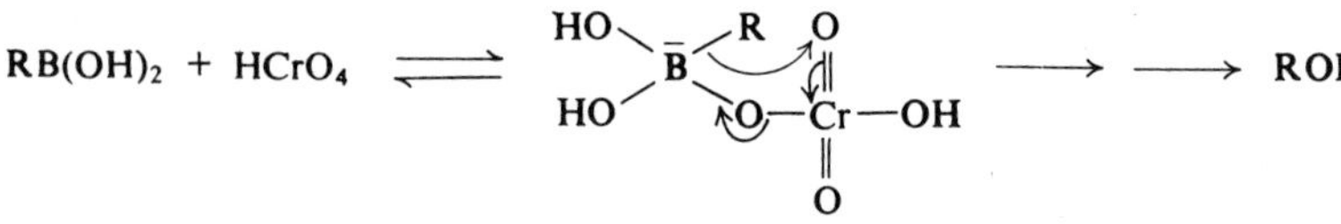

The reaction is remarkably sensitive to the structure of the alkyl group. At 30° in 0.114 M perchloric acid, the rate constants for oxidation with R = $tert$-butyl, ethyl, and methyl are 7.5×10^{-2}, 6.6×10^{-4} and 2.4×10^{-7}, respectively.

The oxidation of tri-n-butyl phosphate has been studied, and it was concluded that the first step involved transesterification, followed by decomposition of the chromium(VI) ester.[9]

Hexaphenyldisilane has been found to be quite resistant to chromic acid oxidation. Under relatively vigorous conditions, some oxidation occurred, but the products could not be separated and identified.[10]

ACKNOWLEDGMENTS

The writer wishes to thank those who have read this manuscript, and particularly J. Roček and W. A. Waters, for their suggestions and helpful criticism. He also wishes to acknowledge the assistance of a National Science Foundation grant in the preparation of the manuscript.

[5] M. N. Tul'chinskii, *Zh. Obshch. Khim.* **32**, 2699 (1962); *Chem. Abstr.* **58**, 9214 (1963).

[6] A. F. Krasso, E. Weiss, and T. Reichstein, *Helv. Chim. Acta* **46**, 2538 (1963).

[7] H. C. Brown and C. P. Garg, *J. Am. Chem. Soc.* **83**, 2951 (1961).

[8] J. C. Ware and T. G. Traylor, *J. Am. Chem. Soc.* **85**, 3026 (1963).

[9] T. G. Tuch and R. M. Walters, *J. Chem. Soc.* p. 4712 (1963).

[10] T. C. Wu and H. Gilman, *J. Org. Chem.* **23**, 913 (1958).

CHAPTER **III**

Oxidation by Vanadium(V), Cobalt(III), and Manganese(III)

W. A. Waters

and

J. S. Littler

I. Introduction 186
  A. Thermodynamic Evidence for One-Equivalent Processes 186
  B. Kinetic and Other Evidence for One-Equivalent Processes . . . 187
II. The Chemical Natures of the Oxidizing Species 188
  A. Vanadium(V) in Aqueous Solution 189
  B. Cobalt(III) in Aqueous Solution 190
  C. Manganese(III) in Aqueous Solution 192
  D. Nonaqueous Solution 194
  E. Analytical Methods 195
III. Reduction by Inorganic Species 195
  A. Reduction of Vanadium(V) 195
  B. Reduction of Cobalt(III) and Manganese(III) 196
  C. Some Reactions which Generate Free Radicals 198
IV. Oxidation of Alcohols and Related Compounds 198
V. The Oxidation of Glycols and Related Compounds 204
  A. Oxidation by Vanadium(V) 204
  B. Oxidation by Manganese(III) and Cobalt(III) 206
  C. Oxidation of α-Hydroxy Acids 207
  D. Oxidation of Hydroxy Ketones 210
VI. Aldehydes 211
  A. Aliphatic Aldehydes 211
  B. Formaldehyde 220
  C. Other Aldehydes 222
VII. Ketones 223
  A. The Mechanism of the Oxidation 223
  B. Product Studies 227
VIII. Carboxylic Acids 228
  A. Oxalic Acid 228
  B. Formic Acid 230
  C. Malonic Acid 231
  D. Other Acids 234

IX. Other Oxidations 235
    A. Hydrocarbons 235
    B. Phenols 237
    C. Compounds Containing Nitrogen 238
    D. Catalyzed Oxidations 238
X. Biochemical Significance 240

I. Introduction

Oxidations of organic compounds by pentavalent vanadium, trivalent cobalt, and trivalent manganese can conveniently be considered together because of certain similarities between these oxidants. It is generally observed that these are one-equivalent oxidants (i.e., $M^{n+} \rightarrow M^{(n-1)+} + e^-$); they have similar redox potentials; and the reactive ion in each case in aqueous solution is a cation which is stable in solutions of mineral acids, though unstable in neutral solution. They are all ions of transition metals [unlike cerium(IV) which is otherwise rather similar], but they might be expected to differ in behavior from oxidants such as permanganate or chromate which have reactive oxy-anions.

A. THERMODYNAMIC EVIDENCE FOR ONE-EQUIVALENT PROCESSES

The range of redox processes which can possibly occur is limited by thermo-dynamic considerations. The simple one-equivalent process is open to all these oxidants:

$$M^{n+} + S \rightarrow M^{(n-1)+} + R \cdot \tag{1}$$

$$M^{n+} + R \cdot \rightarrow M^{(n-1)+} + P$$

when

$$S = \text{substrate} \quad (\text{e.g., } RCH_2OH)$$

$$R = \text{radical} \quad (\text{e.g., } R\text{—}CHOH)$$

$$P = \text{product} \quad (\text{e.g., } RCHO)$$

but the alternative two-equivalent processes may also be available:

$$2\,M^{n+} \rightleftharpoons M^{(n+1)+} + M^{(n-1)+} \tag{2}$$

$$M^{(n+1)+} + S \rightarrow M^{(n-1)+} + P$$

or

$$M^{n+} + S \rightarrow M^{(n-2)+} + P \tag{3}$$

$$M^{n+} + M^{(n-2)+} \rightarrow 2\,M^{(n-1)+}$$

When oxidants of similar redox potential are compared [e.g., bromine and vanadium(V)], it is often observed that two-equivalent oxidations proceed faster than one-equivalent ones, since (a) no high energy free radicals are formed during two-equivalent processes, and (b) there is, over-all, twice the free energy change. If a two-equivalent path is available it is therefore likely to be the favored reaction course.

In the case of manganese, the manganese(IV)–manganese(III) potential in $15 N$ sulfuric acid is recorded as 1.64 volts, and the manganese(III)–manganese(II) potential as 1.50 volts.[1] This gives the manganese(IV)–manganese(II) couple a potential of 1.57 volts, which is rather higher than 1.24 volts as listed for solid manganese dioxide.[2] Thus, thermodynamically, manganese(IV) [arising by Scheme (2) above] could be both a very powerful two-equivalent oxidant and also a vigorous one-equivalent oxidant. The latter reaction has been suggested as part of schemes for the permanganate–oxalate and manganese dioxide–oxalate reactions[3, 4]

$$Mn^{IV} + \text{oxalic acid} \rightleftharpoons Mn^{IV}\text{–oxalate complex}$$

$$Mn^{IV} \text{ oxalate} \rightarrow Mn^{III} + C_2O_4^- \text{ (or } CO_2 + CO_2^-)$$

$$Mn^{IV} + C_2O_4^- \rightarrow Mn^{III} + 2 CO_2$$

Reactions of Mn^{IV} may be of importance in some other reactions, e.g., the oxidation of malonic acid by manganese(III) sulfate.

As vanadium(VI) and cobalt(IV) are unknown in aqueous solution, mechanisms like Scheme (2) above are most improbable; likewise the Co^{II}_{aq}–Co^{I}_{aq} and Mn^{II}_{aq}–Mn^{I}_{aq} couples are too low for Scheme (3) to be possible. However, the vanadium(IV)–vanadium(III) couple is not so low ($E_0 = 0.36$ volt),[5] so Scheme (3) must be considered for vanadium. The potential of the vanadium(V)–vanadium(III) couple is 0.68 volt. This is comparable with that of the weak two-equivalent oxidants iodine (0.536 volt) or arsenic acid (0.559 volt), and so it is unlikely to be involved in any organic oxidations, though it may be important in the oxidations of hydrazine,[6] sulfite,[7] or comparable inorganic reducing agents.

B. KINETIC AND OTHER EVIDENCE FOR ONE-EQUIVALENT PROCESSES

Scheme (1) above, unlike Schemes (2) and (3), requires the generation of a free radical $R\cdot$, and, although this is normally rapidly oxidized to P, it also

[1] G. Grube and K. Huberich, *Z. Elektrochem.* **29**, 8 (1923); G. Grube and M. Staesche, *ibid.* **31**, 362 (1925); K. J. Vetter and G. Manecke, *Z. Physik. Chem.* (*Leipzig*) **195**, 270, 337 (1950).

[2] A. K. Covington, T. Cressey, B. G. Lever, and H. R. Thirsk, *Trans. Faraday Soc.* **58**, 1975 (1962).

[3] A. W. Adamson, *J. Phys. Colloid Chem.* **55**, 293 (1951).

[4] S. J. Adler and R. M. Noyes, *J. Am. Chem. Soc.* **77**, 2036 (1955).

[5] W. M. Latimer, "Oxidation Potentials," 2nd ed. Prentice-Hall, Englewood Cliffs, New Jersey, 1952.

[6] W. C. E. Higginson, D. Sutton, and P. Wright, *J. Chem. Soc.* p. 1380 (1953); W. C. E. Higginson and D. Sutton, *J. Chem. Soc.* p. 1402 (1953).

[7] W. C. E. Higginson and J. W. Marshall, *J. Chem. Soc.* p. 447 (1957).

has a choice of other reactions,[8] some of which produce effects which cannot be observed if radicals are not present:

(1) Reaction with oxygen, $R \cdot + O_2 \rightarrow RO_2 \cdot$. This is very common, and it may result in considerable changes in both the observed reaction kinetics and the natures of the oxidation products.

(2) Reduction of inorganic ions, $R \cdot + M^{(n+1)+} \rightarrow R^+ + M^{n+}$. Mercuric chloride is easily reduced by many radicals to insoluble mercurous chloride, which is relatively inert toward reoxidation by the oxidant M^{n+}. Induced reductions such as this may alter the observed kinetics.

(3) Reaction with added organic materials, e.g.,

$$R \cdot + CH_3CH_2OH \rightarrow RH + CH_3\dot{C}HOH$$

This occurs when organic molecules, normally inert to the oxidant, are added to a reacting mixture of manganese(III) pyrophosphate and malonic acid.[8]

(4) Oxidation of inorganic ions, e.g., $R \cdot + M^{(n-1)+} \rightarrow R^+ + M^{n+}$. The effect of this is to alter the observed kinetics.

(5) Polymerization of an added olefinic monomer, such as acrylonitrile or acrylamide. The polymer is itself detectable, and the kinetics may be altered if the polymer radical is not itself eventually oxidized. The nature of the radical $R \cdot$ may be found by end-group investigations, and the yield of the normal products may be decreased.

(6) The radical may dimerize or disproportionate, giving characteristic products.

All of these phenomena have been observed when manganese(III) pyrophosphate is the oxidant, and some of them have been observed with all the oxidants under consideration. The most generally applicable are (1) and (5), which are usually sufficiently rapid to compete with the oxidation of $R \cdot$ by a second equivalent of oxidant.[9] For reaction (6) to compete, it must have a bimolecular rate constant of ca. 10^8 or greater, as must the dimerization reaction of two polymer radicals (5).[10]

II. The Chemical Natures of the Oxidizing Species

Although evidence of the type outlined in Section I shows that the oxidants V^V, Co^{III}, and Mn^{III} have much in common, there are many differences in their detailed behavior, and it is important to know in what forms they occur under the conditions which have been used for oxidations.

[8] A. Y. Drummond and W. A. Waters, *J. Chem. Soc.* p. 2836 (1953); p. 2456 (1954).
[9] E. Collinson, F. S. Dainton, B. Mile, S. Tazuke, and D. R. Smith, *Nature* **198**, 26 (1963).
[10] G. Mino, S. Kaizerman, and E. Rasmussen, *J. Am. Chem. Soc.* **81**, 1494 (1959).

A. VANADIUM(V) IN AQUEOUS SOLUTION

Vanadium(V) occurs in aqueous solution, in the acidity region where it is a useful oxidant (pH < 1) as a cation of simplest formula VO_2^+.[11] Considerable discussion has taken place as to whether or not this should be more correctly written $[V(OH)_4]^+$,[12] or even $[V(OH)_4OH_2]^+$.[13] It seems to be agreed, however, that a lower coordination number than six is probably correct for cations which are devoid of *d*-electrons. The redox potential of the vanadium(V)–vanadium(IV) couple increases with acidity in the region from pH 1.5 to $2N$ acid (as would be expected if the species concerned are $VO_2^+{}_{aq}$ and $VO^{2+}{}_{aq}$[14]), but rather more steeply than this at higher acidities; presumably the activity of water is reduced at higher acidities and so influences the redox equilibrium.

$$VO_2^+ + 2\,H^+ + e^- \; \rightleftharpoons \; VO^{2+} + H_2O$$

Although the free energy available for oxidation increases in this complex fashion, the kinetic behavior of vanadium(V) in general depends on the activity of the pentavalent species concerned, for the over-all reactions are seldom kinetically reversible. The oxidations can be acid catalyzed, exhibiting either $C_{H_3O^+}$ or h_0 (Hammett acidity function) dependence, though if the substrate is easily attacked, an uncatalyzed path may also be observable.

The prevalence of this type of kinetics can be rationalized by assuming the presence of a small proportion of a further vanadium species, $[V(OH)_3]^{2+}{}_{aq}$, as the oxidant in the acid-catalyzed reaction. Though the kinetics themselves tell us nothing about the extent of formation of this cation, there is spectrophotometric evidence for ternary complex formation from VO_2^+, H_3O^+, and alcohol molecules[15]; the shift of the charge-transfer spectrum of vanadium(V) in this complex, and general ideas of polarity, indicate that $[V(OH)_3]^{2+}$ must be a better oxidant than is VO_2^+ itself.

In aqueous perchloric acid the kinetics of alcohol oxidation by vanadium(V) accords with the following equations:

$$VO_2^+ + H_3O^+ \; \overset{K_1}{\rightleftharpoons} \; [V(OH)_3]^{2+}$$

$$[V(OH)_3]^{2+} + ROH \; \overset{K_2}{\rightleftharpoons} \; [V(OH)_3OHR]^{2+} \; \overset{k}{\underset{\text{(slow)}}{\longrightarrow}} \; \text{products}$$

[11] F. J. C. Rossotti and H. Rossotti, *Acta Chem. Scand.* **10**, 957 (1956); J. Meier and G. Schwarzenbach, *Chimia (Aarau)* **12**, 328 (1958); N. Ingri and F. Brito, *Acta Chem. Scand.* **13**, 1971 (1959).

[12] M. J. LaSalle and J. W. Cobble, *J. Phys. Chem.* **59**, 519 (1955).

[13] H. C. Mishra and M. C. R. Symons, *J. Chem. Soc.* p. 4411 (1962); G. Schwarzenbach and G. Geier, *Helv. Chim. Acta* **46**, 906 (1963).

[14] L. P. Ducret, *Ann. Chim. (Paris)* **6**, 705 (1951).

[15] J. S. Littler and W. A. Waters, *J. Chem. Soc.* p. 4046 (1959).

whence

$$\frac{-d}{dt}[V^V] = k[V(OH)_3OHR^{2+}]$$

$$= kK_1 K_2[VO_2^+][H_3O^+][ROH]$$

and the ternary reaction complex can rationally be given a tetrahedral structure

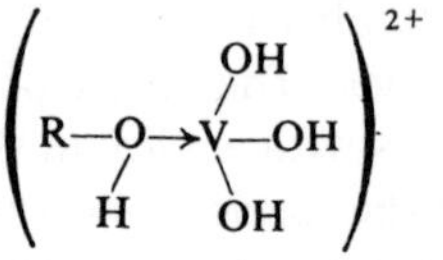

$$\left(\begin{array}{c} OH \\ | \\ R-O\rightarrow V-OH \\ / \quad \backslash \\ H \quad OH \end{array}\right)^{2+}$$

In this case there is no possibility of any cyclic complex formations of the vanadium with the substrate, and a dependence on hydrogen ion concentration, i.e., $C_{H_3O^+}$ is found. If, however, the place of a water molecule in the complex $V(OH)_3ROH^{2+}$ can be taken by an adjacent group in the organic substrate (as with pinacol, or α-hydroxy acids), a dependence on the Hammett acidity function, h_0, might be expected, and is in fact found:

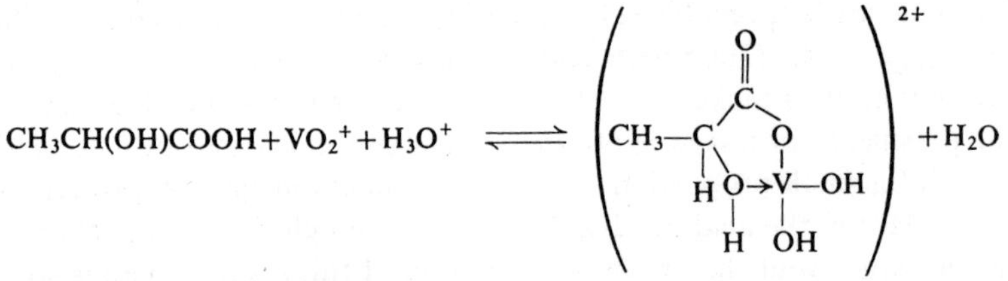

$$CH_3CH(OH)COOH + VO_2^+ + H_3O^+ \rightleftharpoons \left(\begin{array}{c} O \\ \| \\ C \\ CH_3-C \quad O \\ | \quad | \\ H O \rightarrow V-OH \\ | \quad | \\ H \quad OH \end{array}\right)^{2+} + H_2O$$

The cyclic complex is again tetrahedral.

As the distinction between $C_{H_3O^+}$ and h_0 dependence arises from the difference in degree of hydration not only of the transition state of the reaction but also of the reversibly formed complex, the appropriate functions have been found to fit more closely than in reactions where the water molecule is taking part merely as a nucleophile. Hence acidity functions can be used empirically, for vanadium(V), as a test for chelate complex formation.

In sulfuric acid, vanadium(V) cations are complexed by sulfate groups, so that the reaction kinetics become more complicated, though reaction rates do not change greatly from those in perchloric acid solution.

B. COBALT(III) IN AQUEOUS SOLUTION

Cobalt(III), unlike vanadium(V), but like manganese(III), invariably exists as an octahedrally coordinated ion, and has d electrons which can become involved both in electron transfer reactions and in ligand bonding (Co^{III} is d^6; Mn^{III} is d^4). In particular, the gain of an electron by an ion of cobalt(III) is much easier when it is in the high spin (paramagnetic) state (e.g., CoF_6^{3-}) than when it is in the low spin (diamagnetic) state [e.g., $Co(NH_3)_6^{3+}$], because the electron transfer can then occur without change of the electron spin state [both CoF_6^{4-} and $Co(NH_3)_6^{2+}$ ions are in the high spin state], i.e., without a change of multiplicity and also without extensive reorganization of the metal–ligand bonds.[16] This theory is supported by the relationship between the redox potentials of various cobalt(II)–cobalt(III) couples, and the natures of the attached ligand groups.[17]

Water is a particularly important ligand in that, although the Co^{3+}_{aq} ion is spin paired, it requires very little excitation energy to achieve the high spin state[18]; this energy may be further reduced if the ion is slightly hydrolyzed and one water molecule is replaced by OH^-, which has a smaller ligand field. Cobalt(III) when in the low spin state exchanges its ligands slowly,[19] and hence the rapid exchange of water [20] and probably of organic hydroxy compounds with cobalt(III) ions requires their excitation to the high spin state. This ligand exchange step (if $k_2 \gg k_{-1}$) might conceivably determine the rate of

$$CoOH(H_2O)_5^{2+} + ROH \underset{k_{-1}}{\overset{k_1}{\rightleftharpoons}} CoOR(H_2O)_5^{2+} + H_2O \xrightarrow{k_2} Co^{II} + radical$$

an oxidation. An alternative possibility, more probable with cobalt(III) than with other oxidants, is that oxidation might proceed by an outer-sphere mechanism, in which an electron is transferred more easily via an OH^- ligand than via a water molecule.[21]

The lowest empty orbitals (t_{2g}) of the high spin form of cobalt(III) have lobes between the ligands which are more accessible to overlap with the π or p-orbitals of a reducing agent than are the only empty orbitals (e_g) of the low spin form, which have lobes directed along the metal-ligand bond direction. Thus the mechanism on p. 202 for the oxidation of a tertiary alcohol can be written

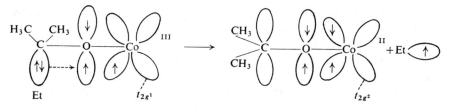

[16] B. R. James, J. R. Lyons, and R. J. P. Williams, *Biochemistry* **1**, 379 (1962).

[17] L. E. Orgel, "An Introduction to Transition Metal Chemistry; Ligand Field Theory." Methuen, London, 1960.

[18] H. L. Friedman, J. P. Hunt, R. A. Plane, and H. Taube, *J. Am. Chem. Soc.* **73**, 4028 (1951).

[19] H. Taube, *Chem. Rev.* **50**, 69 (1952); H. U. D. Wiesendanger, W. H. Jones, and C. S. Garner, *J. Chem. Phys.* **27**, 668 (1957).

[20] H. L. Friedman, H. Taube, and J. P. Hunt, *J. Chem. Phys.* **18**, 759 (1950).

[21] D. R. Stranks, *in* "Modern Coordination Chemistry" (J. Lewis and R. G. Wilkins, eds.), p. 78, Wiley (Interscience), New York, 1960; see also *Discussions Faraday Soc.* **29** (1960); N. S. Biradar, D. R. Stranks, and M. S. Vaidya, *Trans. Faraday Soc.* **58**, 2421 (1962).

where the p-orbital of the oxygen which eventually forms the ketone π-bond passes on the electron without a change of multiplicity to a half-empty t_{2g} orbital.

Similar diagrams can be drawn for other reactions of oxidants, which have empty or partly empty low lying d-orbitals. If the oxidant is vanadium(V), which has no d-electrons, a change of multiplicity must of course occur.

Hence a variety of considerations indicate that ligand field effects may overbalance the electrostatic effect of the higher charge on Co^{3+}_{aq}, and result in an important contribution to oxidation by paths involving $CoOH^{2+}_{aq}$. The pK_a for hydrolysis of Co^{3+}_{aq} is somewhat uncertain, as the hydrolyzed species tends to dimerize and also to oxidize water very rapidly, but it appears to be about 2.[22]

$$Co(H_2O)_6^{3+} \rightleftharpoons Co(H_2O)_5OH^{2+} + H^+$$

$$2\,Co(H_2O)_5OH^{2+} \rightleftharpoons Co(H_2O)_5-O-Co(H_2O)_5^{4+} + H_2O \qquad \text{etc.}$$

The hydrolyzed form may well be present in sufficiently high concentration even in $1-2\,M$ acid for its reactivity to be observable.

In sulfuric acid, sulfate formation introduces complications, but it is possible to account for the effect of sulfate ions on the basis of the partial removal of cobalt(III) as an inert ion, $CoSO_4^+_{aq}$,[23] since the kinetically determined stability constant of this material is closely comparable with that determined independently from equilibrium measurements.[24]

C. MANGANESE(III) IN AQUEOUS SOLUTION

Much less is known about manganese(III) than about cobalt(III). A solution of the cation $Mn(H_2O)_6^{3+}$ in perchloric acid has been obtained recently, but it is stable only in the presence of a large excess of Mn^{2+}. It was prepared by reduction of permanganate by manganous ions, and from the data given it can be calculated that the redox potential of the $Mn^{3+}_{aq}-Mn^{2+}_{aq}$ couple is not higher than 1.565 volts.[25] A value of 1.56 volts in $3\,M$ perchloric acid has been found by direct measurement, and data has also been obtained on the hydrolysis and disproportionation equilibria of Mn^{3+}_{aq}.[25a] Other studies in perchloric acid have been carried out with solutions of the chloride complex, $MnCl^{2+}$. This is relatively stable in the presence of excess chloride ions, and it

[22] L. H. Sutcliffe and J. R. Weber, *Trans. Faraday Soc.* **52**, 1225 (1956); **55**, 1892 (1959); *J. Inorg. Nucl. Chem.* **12**, 281 (1960); J. H. Baxendale and C. F. Wells, *Trans. Faraday Soc.* **53**, 800 (1957).

[23] D. G. Hoare and W. A. Waters, *J. Chem. Soc.* p. 971 (1962).

[24] K. G. Ashurst and W. C. E. Higginson, *J. Chem. Soc.* p. 343 (1956).

[25] D. R. Rosseinsky, *J. Chem. Soc.* p. 1181 (1963).

[25a] P. G. Desideri, *J. Electroanal. Chem.* **6**, 344 (1963); H. Diebler and N. Sutin, *J. Phys. Chem.* **68**, 174 (1964); J. P. Fackler and I. D. Chawla, *Inorg. Chem.* **3**, 1130 (1964)

is quite a weak complex.[26] From the stability constant of this complex, and the above potential, the potential of $MnCl^{2+}_{aq}-Mn^{2+}_{aq}$ is found to be 1.50 volts, and for this reason $MnCl^{2+}$ is unstable and tends to decompose to give manganese(II) and chlorine, though an equilibrium can be established in strong hydrochloric acid.[27]

The sulfate complex of manganese(III) in sulfuric acid is easy to prepare and is stable, provided that the acidity is not too low,[28] though from the observed redox potential (1.51 volts in 7.5 M acid, possibly a little higher in 4.5 M acid[1]) the stability constant of this complex should be comparable with, or less than, that of the chloride complex. The stabilizing effect of sulfate ions must be due to their effect either on the disproportionation

$$K = \frac{[Mn^{II}][Mn^{IV}]}{[Mn^{III}]^2}$$

equilibrium or on the rate of hydrolysis of manganese(IV). Since K is of the order of 10^{-3} in sulfuric acid $(4.5\,M)^1$ and the effect of the sulfate complexing is to reduce the activity of manganese(III) by a factor of about ten, the rate of precipitation of manganese dioxide, if proportional to $[Mn^{IV}]^2$, should be reduced ten-thousandfold.

Fluoride is often added to permanganate oxidations to suppress precipitation of manganese dioxide or oxidation by transient manganese(III) or (IV) species. From the known stability constant[26] of MnF^{2+}_{aq} the potential can be calculated to be below 1.41 volts, showing that even though MnF^{2+}_{aq} should still be quite powerful as an oxidant, the concentration of manganese(IV) in equilibrium with it must be greatly reduced, unless manganese(IV) fluoride complexes are formed extensively.

The pyrophosphate complex of manganese(III) is stable at lower acidities than is any other manganese(III) species. Since this ligand can undergo ionization both before and after being bound to Mn^{3+}_{aq} in the acidity range used, the pH dependence of the rates of oxidation is complex and rather uninformative.[29] The general observation that oxidations by manganese(III) pyrophosphate are retarded by excess of pyrophosphate shows that the formation of the reaction complex involves displacement of a ligand molecule, and direct kinetic evidence (i.e., Michaelis-Menten type kinetics) has often

[26] H. Taube, *J. Am. Chem. Soc.* **70**, 3928 (1948).

[27] J. A. Ibers and N. Davidson, *J. Am. Chem. Soc.* **72**, 4744 (1950).

[28] R. G. Selim and J. J. Lingane, *Anal. Chim. Acta* **21**, 536 (1959); A. J. Fenton and N. H. Furman, *Anal. Chem.* **32**, 748 (1960); A. J. R. P. Ubbelohde, *J. Chem. Soc.* p. 1605 (1935).

[29] I. M. Kolthoff and J. I. Watters, *Ind. Eng. Chem. Anal. Ed.* **15**, 8 (1943); J. I. Watters and I. M. Kolthoff, *J. Am. Chem. Soc.* **70**, 2455 (1958); J. J. Lingane and R. Karplus, *Ind. Eng. Chem. Anal. Ed.* **18**, 191 (1946).

been obtained for complex formation. The complex cannot be in equilibrium with Mn^{IV}_{aq}, as at the low acidities used precipitation of manganese dioxide would be extremely rapid, but it may, like the sulfate complex, be in equilibrium with a small amount of a manganese(IV) pyrophosphate ion.

Nothing is known of the effect of pH on the nature of any other manganese-(III) or (IV) species. It is reasonable that $Mn(H_2O)_6^{3+}$ should exist in strong acids, and that it should hydrolyze, like $Co(H_2O)_6^{3+}$ at lower acidities. Manganese(IV) may well exist as $Mn(H_2O)_5OH^{3+}$ (cf. Ce^{IV}_{aq}) or as more hydrolyzed species such as MnO^{2+}_{aq}, and the instability of manganese(III) and (IV) solutions can be ascribed to the self-condensation of such species to give first colloidal and later insoluble hydrated manganese dioxide. Reported rates of oxidations by manganese(III) sulfate indicate that no important pH dependent process occurs in accessible regions of acidity.

D. NONAQUEOUS SOLUTION

Very little work has been done on any of these oxidants in nonaqueous solutions, since, in general, complexing agents which would render a metal ion soluble in a nonpolar solvent simultaneously reduce the oxidation potential by complexing more strongly with the metal ion of the upper valence state. Since a change of valence often implies a change in the electrical charge on a metal ion, the former would not be assisted by solvation in a nonpolar solvent. These considerations seriously limit the choice of organic compounds that can be selected for mechanistic study of oxidation processes.

Solutions of vanadium(V) acetate in glacial acetic acid, and of vanadium oxychloride and *tert*-butyl orthovanadate in nonpolar solvents have been used, but they are much less powerful oxidants than aqueous solutions.[30] Various different complexes, and ions such as $VOCl_4^-$, may be present in these media.[31]

Cobalt(III) acetate in glacial acetic acid, which may be a useful oxidant for preparative purposes, is polymeric and invariably contains cobalt(II), so that it is unsuitable for kinetic studies.[32] A relatively simple system for cobalt(III) is a mixture of water and acetonitrile in which it appears that the species present are very like those existing in pure water.[33] For these mixtures it has been found that $\log k$ is linearly dependent on the concentration of acetonitrile if it is below 40%.

[30] J. S. Littler, D.Phil. Thesis, University of Oxford, England, 1960.

[31] K. A. Kraus, F. Nelson, and G. W. Smith, *J. Phys. Chem.* **58**, 11 (1954).

[32] J. A. Sharp and A. G. White, *J. Chem. Soc.* p. 110 (1952); J. A. Sharp, *J. Chem. Soc.* p. 2030 (1957); D. Peschanski and Y. Wormser, *Compt. Rend. Acad. Sci.* **252**, 1607 (1961); Y. Wormser and D. Peschanski, *Bull. Soc. Chim. France* p. 876 (1962); E. Koubek and J. O. Edwards, *J. Inorg. Nucl. Chem.* **25**, 1401 (1963).

[33] D. G. Hoare and W. A. Waters, *J. Chem. Soc.* pp. 2552, 2560 (1964).

Manganese(III) acetate has also been used in glacial acetic acid,[34] but it suffers from the same disadvantages as cobalt(III) acetate.[35]

E. ANALYTICAL METHODS

Very simple analytical methods are available for following the reactions of the three oxidants, V^V, Co^{III}, and Mn^{III}. They all oxidize ferrous ions to ferric ions virtually instantaneously, and so aliquots from reaction mixtures can be run into an excess of ferrous sulfate solution, and the excess of Fe^{2+} ion can then be determined by titration with permanganate or, better, by cerium(IV) or vanadium(V) itself.[36] Iodometric methods are possible, provided that errors due to air oxidation are minimized,[37] and these are especially useful if measurements of concurrent peroxide formation under aerobic conditions are required.[8] However, spectrophotometric methods easily distinguish between the oxidized and the reduced forms of these transition metal ions, and are the best procedures for the analysis of mixtures; data on this are given in various references (for vanadium,[12] for cobalt,[38] and for manganese[28, 39]).

III. Reduction by Inorganic Species

Although this review is primarily concerned with redox processes in organic chemistry, it is instructive to consider what is known of the kinetics and mechanism of inorganic redox processes involving these metals.

A. REDUCTION OF VANADIUM(V)

The vanadium(V)–vanadium(IV) exchange reaction has been studied, by nuclear magnetic resonance techniques, but most of the data have been obtained from solutions in which chloride complexing must have affected the mechanism.[40] Reduction of vanadium(V) by iodide gives iodine atoms, as is shown by their reaction with oxygen,[37] and so can be represented simply as:

$$V^V + I^- \rightarrow V^{IV} + I\cdot$$

The oxidation of hydrazine shows behavior intermediate between that of typical one-equivalent oxidants, which oxidize it according to the equation

$$2 N_2H_4 - 2 e^- \rightarrow N_2 + 2 NH_3 + 3 H^+$$

[34] K. Julian, D.Phil. Thesis, University of Oxford, England, 1962.
[35] R. F. Weinland and G. Fischer, *Z. Anorg. Allgem. Chem.* **120**, 161 (1921).
[36] A. Morette and G. Gaudefroy, *Bull. Soc. Chim. France* p. 956 (1954).
[37] M. H. Boyer and J. B. Ramsey, *J. Am. Chem. Soc.* **75**, 3802 (1953).
[38] G. Hargreaves and L. H. Sutcliffe, *Trans. Faraday Soc.* **51**, 786 (1955).
[39] A. Y. Drummond and W. A. Waters, *J. Chem. Soc.* p. 435 (1953).
[40] C. R. Guiliano and H. M. McConnell, *J. Inorg. Nucl. Chem.* **96**, 171 (1959).

and that of the two-equivalent oxidants, for which the reaction[6] is

$$N_2H_4 - 4\,e^- \rightarrow N_2 + 4\,H^+$$

A similar study using sulfur dioxide as a selective reductant also gave ambiguous results,[7] but the oxidation of stannous ions,[41] though mainly a two-equivalent change,

$$V^V + Sn^{II} \rightarrow V^{III} + Sn^{IV}$$

involved a small percentage of reaction via the high energy Sn^{III} state. Arsenic(III) and thallium(I), in contrast, are not sufficiently powerful as reducing agents to change vanadium(V) to vanadium(III),[42] though arsenic(III) is oxidized to arsenic(V) by vanadium(V) in a reaction which is second order in vanadium(V). This may be a genuine termolecular reaction, or alternatively it may involve the reversible formation of a trace of a transient arsenic(IV) species. It is not surprising that with a weak reducing agent such as arsenic(III), or with organic compounds in general, the two-equivalent process is kinetically unfavorable. The oxidation of Fe^{2+}_{aq} by $VO_2^+{}_{aq}$ in aqueous solution has been studied recently, and found to be acid catalyzed in the same way as are the oxidations of organic compounds.[43]

B. REDUCTION OF COBALT(III) AND MANGANESE(III)

Quantitative one-equivalent oxidation of hydrazine is observed when cobalt(III) and manganese(III) [except manganese(III) acetate[44]] are used, and the corresponding oxidations of sulfur dioxide are similar. Radioactive ions of manganese(II) and (III) exchange rapidly,[3] and the disproportion to manganese(II) + (IV) is of great importance in the reaction of manganese(III) with mercurous perchlorate.[25] Manganese(III) will also catalyze the ligand exchange of chromium(III) halides, presumably by effecting a reversible oxidation to chromium(IV) which can exchange its ligands rapidly.[45]

Reactions of cobalt(III) involving the amines, and other complexes which do not readily undergo ligand exchange, have been studied extensively, the work of Taube on the reduction of cobalt(III) complexes by one-equivalent reducing agents being particularly important. Electron transfer can be shown to occur both locally and via a conjugated ligand such as a terephthalate ester.[46] If the ligand (e.g., oxalate) can be oxidized, then a two-equivalent

[41] D. J. Drye, W. C. E. Higginson, and P. Knowles, *J. Chem. Soc.* p. 1137 (1962).
[42] M. Bobtelsky and A. Glasner, *J. Am. Chem. Soc.* **64**, 1462 (1942); A. G. Sykes, *J. Chem. Soc.* p. 5549 (1961).
[43] M. J. Nicol and D. R. Rosseinsky, *Proc. Chem. Soc.* p. 16 (1963).
[44] E. J. Cuy, M. E. Rosenberg, and W. C. Bray, *J. Am. Chem. Soc.* **46**, 1796 (1924).
[45] A. E. Ogard and H. Taube, *J. Phys. Chem.* **62**, 357 (1958).
[46] R. T. M. Fraser, *J. Am. Chem. Soc.* **83**, 4920 (1961), and references therein; W. F. Libby, *J. Chem. Phys.* **38**, 420 (1963).

oxidant can do this without reducing the cobalt(III), whereas a one-equivalent oxidant may induce the reduction of the cobalt(III) in the complex[47]:

$$Co^{2+}(NH_3)_5\text{—OCO—}\langle\text{ring}\rangle\text{—COOH} + Cr^{2+} \longrightarrow$$
$$Co^{2+} + 5\ NH_3 + C_6H_4(COOH)_2 + Cr^{3+}$$

$$Co^{2+}(NH_3)_5\text{—OCOCOOH} + Co^{3+}{}_{aq} \longrightarrow 2\ Co^{2+} + 5\ NH_3 + 2\ CO_2$$

$$Co(NH_3)_5\text{—OCOCOOH} + Cl_2 \longrightarrow Co(NH_3)_5OH_2{}^{3+} + 2\ Cl^- + 2\ CO_2$$

$$Co^{2+}(NH_3)_5I + Co^3{}_{aq} \longrightarrow Co(NH_3)_5OH_2{}^{3+} + I^{\cdot} + Co^{2+}$$

$$Co^{2+}(NH_3)_5I + I^{\cdot} \longrightarrow Co^{2+} + 5\ NH_3 + I_2$$

$$Co^{2+}(NH_3)_5I + HO^{\cdot} \longrightarrow Co^{2+} + 5\ NH_3 + HOI$$

Reductions of $Co^{3+}{}_{aq}$ and $CoOH^{2+}{}_{aq}$ by cerium(III),[48] cobalt(II),[49] iron(II),[50] mercury(I), vanadium(III), and vanadium(IV)[51] in perchloric acid, and by chromium(II) in acetic acid,[52] have all been studied kinetically. It is generally found that the $(CoOH)^{2+}{}_{aq}$ species is much more active than $Co^{3+}{}_{aq}$ itself; in the case of the isotope exchange, it has been suggested that direct electron transfer occurs between $Co^{3+}{}_{aq}$ and $Co^{2+}{}_{aq}$, but that $(CoOH)^{2+}{}_{aq}$ and $Co^{2+}{}_{aq}$ form a hydroxyl-bridged transition state. Solvent isotope effects are not very informative in determining whether a hydrogen nucleus has been transferred; even if a reduction of the reaction rate is observed in deuterium oxide solution, it may be due not to a primary isotope effect nor to the effect on the hydrolysis equilibrium of $Co^{3+}{}_{aq}$, but rather to effects on the solvation of the ions or of the transition state of the reaction.[53]

Reduction by the solvent (water) is an important reaction of aquo-cobaltic ions at lower acidities, i.e.,

$$Co^{3+}{}_{aq} \rightarrow Co^{2+}{}_{aq} + H^+ + \cdot OH$$

and it appears to follow a similar type of kinetics to the other reductions above, though there is also evidence that $Co^{III}\text{—}O\text{—}Co^{III}$ dimer formation is important.[22, 54]

[47] P. Saffir and H. Taube, *J. Am. Chem. Soc.* **82**, 13 (1960); A. Haim and H. Taube, *J. Am. Chem. Soc.* **85**, 495 (1963); J. P. Candlin and J. Halpern, *J. Am. Chem. Soc.* **85**, 2518 (1963).

[48] L. H. Sutcliffe and J. R. Weber, *Trans. Faraday Soc.* **55**, 1892 (1959).

[49] N. A. Bonner and J. P. Hunt, *J. Am. Chem. Soc.* **82**, 3826 (1960); J. Shankar and B. C. de Souza, *J. Inorg. Nucl. Chem.* **24**, 187 (1962).

[50] L. E. Bennett and J. C. Sheppard, *J. Phys. Chem.* **66**, 1275 (1962).

[51] D. R. Rosseinsky and W. C. E. Higginson, *J. Chem. Soc.* p. 31 (1960).

[52] L. H. Sutcliffe and J. R. Weber, *Trans. Faraday Soc.* **57**, 91 (1961).

[53] J. S. Littler, *J. Chem. Soc.* p. 2190 (1962).

[54] C. E. H. Bawn and A. G. White, *J. Chem. Soc.* p. 331 (1951).

C. SOME REACTIONS WHICH GENERATE FREE RADICALS

Of other inorganic reducing agents, the reactions of hydrogen peroxide have been studied briefly with cobalt(III),[22] and in more detail with vanadium(V),[55] but they differ considerably in type. In the latter case at least two complexes are formed: (i) in acid solution there is a 1:1 complex of formula $VO \cdot O_2^+$ which may be a hydrate $(VO(OH)O_2H)^+$, since a similar complex is formed with organic hydroperoxides, whereas (ii) a 1:2 complex, possibly $(VO_2(O_2)_2)^{3-}$ is formed in neutral solutions. In acid solution, both these probably decompose to give vanadium(IV) and the hydroperoxy radical $HO_2 \cdot$; the cobalt(III) reaction gives this radical also,[22] as does the oxidation of hydrogen peroxide by ceric sulfate.[56]

Free radicals are generated by reduction of acid vanadium(V) by chloride or bromide ions.[57] The bromide reaction may be represented as

$$V^V + Br^- \rightarrow V^{IV} + Br \cdot$$

or more probably

$$V(OH)_2Br_2^+ + Br^- \rightleftharpoons V^{IV} + Br_2^-$$

since the observed kinetic dependence is

$$\frac{-d}{dt}[V^V] = k[VO_2^+][Br^-]^3[H^+]^2$$

The reaction was observed by trapping the bromine atoms formed. They reacted rapidly with an olefin such as crotonic acid, and oxidized both primary and secondary alcohols at a rate independent of the alcohol concentration:

$$C=C + Br \cdot \rightarrow \cdot C-CBr$$

$$R_2CH-OH + Br \cdot \rightarrow R_2\overset{\cdot}{C}(OH) + Br^- + H^+$$

$$HO_3SC_6H_4CHMe_2 + Br \cdot \rightarrow HO_3SC_6H_4\overset{\cdot}{C}Me_2 + Br^- + H^+$$

Hypochlorous acid is also decomposed by cobalt and other transition metals; the mechanism of this reaction is obscure.[58]

IV. Oxidation of Alcohols and Related Compounds

The oxidation of cyclohexanol by vanadium(V) has provided a type reaction for the three oxidants. There is no reason to suspect that primary alcohols behave any differently from secondary alcohols, or that there are large effects

[55] G. Kakabadse and H. J. Wilson, *J. Chem. Soc.* p. 2475 (1960); G. A. Dean, *Can. J. Chem.* **39**, 1174 (1961).

[56] W. T. Dixon and R. O. C. Norman, *Nature* **196**, 891 (1962).

[57] K. Julian and W. A. Waters, *J. Chem. Soc.* p. 818 (1962).

[58] G. H. Ayres and M. H. Booth, *J. Am. Chem. Soc.* **77**, 825 (1955); O. R. Howell, *Proc. Roy. Soc.* **A104**, 135 (1923).

of structure[59]; tertiary alcohols, however, are much more resistant to attack and need separate consideration. The evidence for the formation of a complex of the formula $ROH \cdot V(OH)_3^+$ from any alcohol and an acid solution of vanadium(V) has been presented in Section II,A, and the observed kinetic equation:

$$\frac{-d}{dt}[V^V] = k[ROH][VO_2^+][H_3O^+]$$

corresponds to the slow decomposition of this species to vanadium(IV) and an alcohol radical [Eq. (2)]:

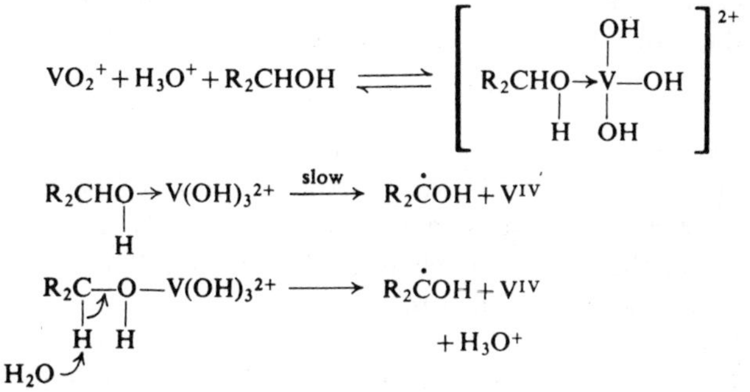

$$VO_2^+ + H_3O^+ + R_2CHOH \rightleftharpoons \left[R_2CHO \underset{\overset{|}{H}\ \overset{|}{OH}}{\rightarrow} V\overset{OH}{\underset{}{-}}OH \right]^{2+} \qquad (1)$$

$$R_2CHO\underset{\overset{|}{H}}{\rightarrow}V(OH)_3^{2+} \xrightarrow{\text{slow}} R_2\overset{\cdot}{C}OH + V^{IV} \qquad (2)$$

$$\underset{H_2O\nearrow}{R_2C\underset{\overset{|}{H}\ \overset{|}{H}}{\overset{\curvearrowright}{-}}O-V(OH)_3^{2+}} \longrightarrow \begin{array}{l} R_2\overset{\cdot}{C}OH + V^{IV} \\ + H_3O^+ \end{array} \qquad (3)$$

The effect of replacing up to 50% v/v of the solvent with acetic acid is to accelerate the reaction. This would be expected, since the formation of the protonated complex [Eq. (1)] should be assisted by the more acidic medium. If the reaction had depended on a solvolysis step [e.g., Eq. (3)] the reduction of the nucleophilicity of the solvent would have retarded the reaction.[30]

The inertness of simple tertiary alcohols toward vanadium(V) indicates that the carbon-bonded H atom of the CHOH group is involved in the reaction, and this has been confirmed by measurements of the primary isotope effect produced by replacing CHOH by CDOH in cyclohexanol.[15] A mechanism (Scheme 1) involving cyclic transfer of this α-hydrogen atom to a portion of the metal ion coordination sphere, can accommodate these facts.

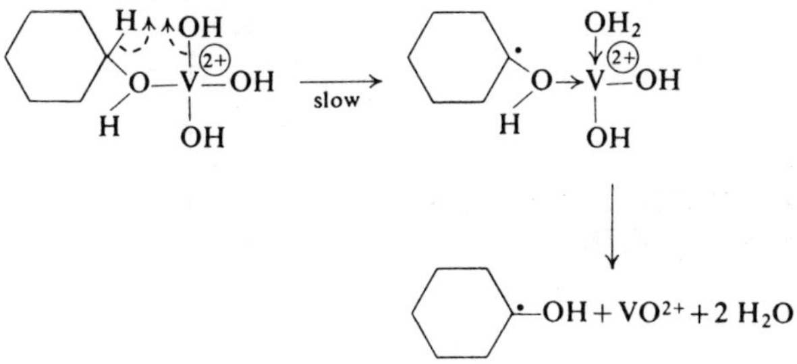

SCHEME 1

[59] J. R. Jones and W. A. Waters, *J. Chem. Soc.* p. 2068 (1962).

The observed value of the isotope effect corresponds to a substantial loss of zero-point energy in the transition state (ca. 0.9 kcal) indicating that the C—H bond is considerably stretched in the transition state. The values of k_H/k_D observed when the same alcohol is oxidized by cobalt(III),[60] manganese(III) sulfate,[53] or cerium(IV)[61] correspond to a much smaller difference of energy (0.3 kcal); with these oxidants the transition state may involve a more strongly bonded hydrogen atom. Manganese(III) pyrophosphate does not attack alcohols, and although manganese(III) acetate in acetic acid does so slowly, the isotope effect is not known.[34]

With each oxidant the reaction has been pictured as proceeding via a complex between the hydroxyl group of the alcohol and the metal ion:

$$\text{ROH} + \text{M}^{n+} \rightleftharpoons \text{RHO} \rightarrow \text{M}^{n+}$$

This complex then decomposes by an internal oxidation switch. The existence of alcohol complexes can be demonstrated from kinetic data (Michaelis-Menten kinetics) when the oxidant is manganese(III) sulfate or cerium(IV) sulfate, but neither the color change [cf. vanadium(V)], nor the extent of complex formation, is sufficient to give direct evidence for similar compound formation with cobalt(III). In all cases, however, the kinetics show that the transition state is comprised of one molecule of alcohol and one of oxidant [CoOH^{2+}_{aq} in the case of cobalt(III)].

The closely related oxidation of formaldehyde, which in water exists as dihydroxymethane $\text{CH}_2(\text{OH})_2$, by cobalt(III) provides a type reaction for these oxidations of alcohols which only show a small CHOH/CDOH isotope effect. It follows the same kinetics as does the oxidation of cyclohexanol, shows the same primary kinetic isotope effect, and yields only formic acid (cf. alcohols, below). In addition it has been found that substitution of OH by OD (by conducting the reaction in deuterium oxide) introduces no primary isotope

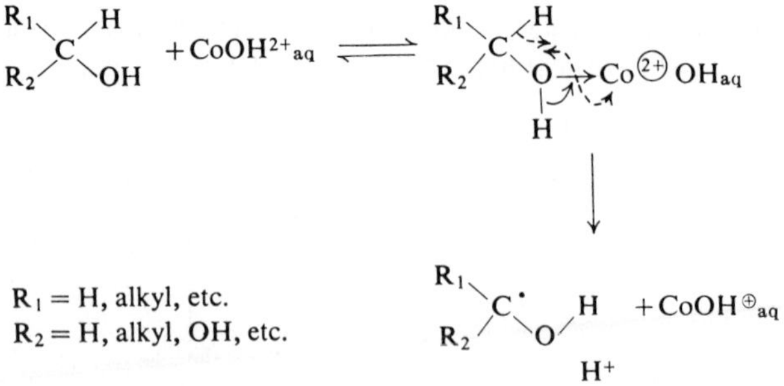

R_1 = H, alkyl, etc.
R_2 = H, alkyl, OH, etc.

SCHEME 2

[60] D. G. Hoare and W. A. Waters, *J. Chem. Soc.* p. 965 (1962).
[61] J. S. Littler, *J. Chem. Soc.* p. 4135 (1959).

effect.[62] The mechanism shown in Scheme 2 involving a 1:2 shift of the C—H hydrogen atom could account for the low isotope effect though it is not the only scheme that could be put forward for other alcohols, and Scheme 1 may exhibit a low isotope effect if a more powerful oxidant than V^V is used, and so be applicable to this reaction also.

Although the O—H bonds of alcohols, formaldehyde, and glycols must be split at some stage of their oxidations, this bond fission has never been correlated with a kinetic isotope effect; so it cannot be decided whether the hydrogen of the O—H group may not be lost during the initial complexing equilibrium, or in a fast subsequent step. As a consequence, the position of such protons indicated in various diagrams in this review must be regarded as tentative, and only illustrative of various possible tautomeric structures:

$$ROH + [Co(H_2O)_5 \cdot OH]^{2+} \rightleftharpoons [ROH, Co(H_2O)_4 \cdot OH]^{2+} \rightleftharpoons [RO \cdot Co(H_2O)_5]^{2+}$$

In both the mechanisms (Schemes 1 and 2) a tervalent carbon radical, $R_2\dot{C}OH$, is obtained; this is normally oxidized further to a ketone by the fast attack of another molecule of the oxidant, though if the conditions are favorable the transient radical can induce polymerization, reduce mercuric chloride, or absorb oxygen.

Since the rate-determining step of these oxidations of alcohols is the formation of a radical, any factors which increase the stability of this radical should increase the ease of oxidation of the parent alcohol. This has been shown directly by the oxidation of allyl and crotyl alcohols by vanadium(V); these react about thirty times faster than the comparable primary or secondary saturated alcohols.[59] Similarly, allyl alcohol, unlike saturated alcohols, is attacked by manganese(III) pyrophosphate.[63] Hyperconjugative stabilization, however, does not affect the rate of the oxidation, as primary and secondary alcohols are attacked at very similar rates.[59, 64]

It may happen, however, that the loss of a stable radical by C—C fission is easier than the removal of the H-atom of a CH(OH) group. An example of this is afforded by the oxidation of β-phenyl ethanol by vanadium(V). This substrate is not oxidized according to the normal sequence:

$$\phi-CH_2CH_2OH \rightarrow \phi CH_2CHOH \rightarrow \phi CH_2CHO \rightarrow \phi-CH_2COOH$$

since no phenylacetic acid is obtained; instead, benzaldehyde is produced via the easily oxidized benzyl alcohol[65]:

$$\phi-CH_2-CH_2OH \rightarrow \phi-CH_2 \cdot + CH_2O \rightarrow \phi CH_2OH \rightarrow \phi CHOH \rightarrow \phi CHO$$

[62] T. J. Kemp and W. A. Waters, *Proc. Roy. Soc.* A**274**, 480 (1963).
[63] H. Land and W. A. Waters, *J. Chem. Soc.* p. 2129 (1958).
[64] W. A. Waters, *Chem. Soc. (London) Spec. Publ.* **19** (1965).
[65] J. R. Jones and W. A. Waters, *J. Chem. Soc.* p. 2772 (1960).

Similarly, *tert*-butyl benzyl alcohol does not give phenyl *tert*-butyl ketone, except by a minor side reaction, but again yields benzaldehyde; evidently the *tert*-butyl radical is lost preferentially:

$$\phi\text{—CH(OH)—CMe}_3 \xrightarrow{\text{V}^{\text{V}}} \phi\text{—CHO} + \cdot\text{CMe}_3$$

Carbon–carbon bond fission in this way provides a route for the oxidation of tertiary alcohols, and indeed does occur if one group can be split off easily as a stable radical. For example, pinacol monomethyl ether can be oxidized by vanadium(V); here the stable radical that is liberated must be $(CH_3)_2\dot{C}OMe$,[66] and similarly (Table I) $Et_2CH(OH)CH_2OMe$ is very easily oxidized by cobalt-(III), with liberation of the radical $\cdot CH_2OMe$.

TABLE I

Relative Ease of Removal of Radicals from an Alcohol by Cobalt(III)[a]

$CH_3\cdot = 1.06 \pm 0.1$	$H\cdot$ (from 2-pentanol) $= 30 \pm 3$	$CH_3OCH_2\cdot = 6310 \pm 40$
$n\text{-}C_3H_7 = 34 \pm 0.5$	$H\cdot$ (from 3-pentanol) $= 36 \pm 0.6$	$iso\text{-}C_3H_7 = 2300 \pm 140$
$n\text{-}C_4H_9 = 28 \pm 6$	$D\cdot$ (from 3-pentanol) $= 12$	$iso\text{-}C_4H_9 = 17.4 \pm 1.2$
$n\text{-}C_5H_{11} = 32 \pm 2.5$		

[a] Ethyl $= 100$.

Obviously the greater the available free energy of the oxidant the less important will be the requirement that the intermediate radical be stabilized. It is not surprising, therefore, that cobalt(III) attacks many tertiary alcohols quite easily, effecting fission of carbon–carbon bonds. The yields of the possible alternative fission products can be used to determine the relative stabilities of the radicals concerned. Even methyl groups are found to exert quite a large influence on the product ratios (see Table I).[33] The carbon–carbon bond fission may be concerted with the oxidation step, but may alternatively be a subsequent reaction of an initially generated alkoxy radical:

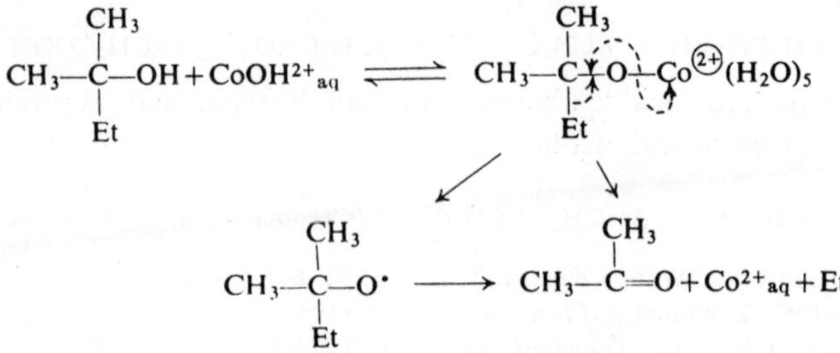

[66] J. R. Jones, W. A. Waters, and J. S. Littler, *J. Chem. Soc.* p. 630 (1961).

The occurrence of carbon–carbon bond fission during oxidations of secondary alcohols has been demonstrated with cobalt(III) (Table II). With

TABLE II

PRODUCTS OF OXIDATION OF SECONDARY ALCOHOLS BY COBALT(III)

Alcohol	Products	Ratios
$CH_3(n\text{-}C_3H_7)CHOH$	$n\text{-}C_3H_7COCH_3:CH_3CHO$	51:49
$(C_2H_5)_2CHOH$	$C_2H_5COC_2H_5:C_2H_5CHO$	15:85
$(C_2H_5)_2CDOH$	$C_2H_5COC_2H_5:C_2H_5CDO$	5:95
$CH_3(iso\text{-}C_3H_7)CHOH$	$iso\text{-}C_3H_7COCH_3:CH_3CHO$	2:98

diethyl carbinol it is noticeable that the distribution of the products changes markedly when CH(OH) is replaced by CD(OH), indicating that, when both C—H and C—C fission paths are available, the path involving CH fission becomes more difficult if CH is replaced by C—D ($k_H/k_D = 3.0 \pm 0.5$). Over-all kinetic isotope effects do not accord with the product ratios, and appear to decrease to unity as the solvent is changed from water to 60% acetonitrile. With cyclohexanol a large proportion of C—H fission occurs under conditions where no kinetic isotope effect is observed, yet with methyl isopropyl carbinol a kinetic isotope effect coexists with a very small proportion of C—H fission.

A scheme of the form

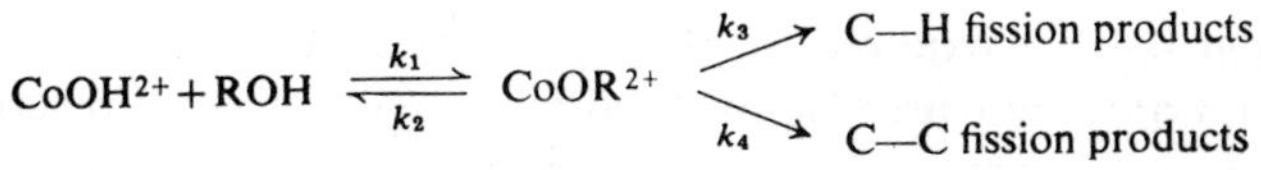

$$CoOH^{2+}+ROH \underset{k_2}{\overset{k_1}{\rightleftharpoons}} CoOR^{2+} \overset{k_3}{\underset{k_4}{\diagup\diagdown}} \begin{array}{l} \text{C—H fission products} \\ \text{C—C fission products} \end{array}$$

can account for the difference between the isotope effects observed in product and in kinetic studies. The effect of deuteration is evidently to reduce k_3 to about one-third of its normal value, but the observed kinetic isotope effect is less than this both because k_4 is not decreased by isotopic substitution, and because k_2 is comparable with k_3+k_4. If increase of the percentage of aceto-nitrile in water increases $(k_3+k_4)/k_2$, there will be a reduction in the kinetic isotope effect. It seems unlikely, however, that k_2 and (k_3+k_4) should have such closely similar values for a wide range of hydroxy compounds (including formaldehyde and formic acid), or for the other oxidants [manganese(III), cerium(IV)] with which low kinetic isotope effects have been observed.

An alternative, and more general, scheme is the following, in which the formation of a cobalt–alcohol complex does not become rate determining:

$$R_2CHO—Co(H_2O)^{2+}{}_5 \begin{cases} \xrightarrow{k_3} R_2\overset{\cdot}{C}OH + Co^{II} \\ \xrightarrow{k_4} R_2CH—O^{\cdot} + Co^{II} \end{cases}$$

$$R_2CHO^{\cdot} + R_2COH \xrightarrow{k_5} R_2CHOH + R_2\overset{\cdot}{C}OH$$

$$R_2CHO^{\cdot} \xrightarrow{k_6} RHC=O + R^{\cdot}$$

$$\left. \begin{array}{l} R_2\overset{\cdot}{C}OH + Co^{III} \longrightarrow R_2C=O + Co^{II} \\ R^{\cdot} + Co^{III} \longrightarrow ROH + Co^{II} \end{array} \right\} \text{fast}$$

The reaction k_3 is the same as has been proposed above for the oxidation of formaldehyde; it has a low isotope effect, and other oxidants than Co^{III} can be used. The sequence $k_4 + k_6$ is the same as the mechanism of oxidation of tertiary alcohols above, except that the two steps are not concerted. Reaction k_5 is likely to be of most importance when k_6 is relatively slow, i.e., when $R \cdot$ is not greatly stabilized, and it must be substantially retarded if $CH(OH)$ is replaced by $CD(OH)$. A kinetic isotope effect is observed when k_3 is greater than or comparable with k_4, and the yield of the C—H fission product is greatly reduced by deuteration if a substantial proportion of it is formed via reaction (5). This scheme is also consistent with observations on the effect of adding acrylamide to trap radical intermediates other than alkoxy radicals. Neither scheme can reconcile the very low yield of the C—H fission product from methyl isopropyl carbinol with the observed isotope effect.

V. The Oxidation of Glycols and Related Compounds

A. OXIDATION BY VANADIUM(V)

Certain glycols are oxidized by $VO_2^+{}_{aq}$ at a rate independent of the acidity of the solution[67]; these are also oxidized by an acid catalyzed reaction that is probably h_0 dependent, and is certainly more strongly acid dependent than the simple $C_{H_3O^+}$ dependent oxidation of alcohols. All these glycols contain a tertiary —OH group. The h_0 dependence indicates that these glycols form chelate complexes with vanadium(V) (see Section II,A), and the slowness of reaction of di-tert-cyclohexane-1,2-diols, compared with pinacol, is to be expected on this hypothesis, as the chelate ring is strained in the structures I or II.

Chelate complexes, analogous to I and II, do not provide a route for the oxidations of disecondary glycols by vanadium(V), for the kinetics of these oxidations are the same as for oxidations of secondary monohydric alcohols,

[67] J. S. Littler, A. I. Mallet, and W. A. Waters, J. Chem. Soc. p. 2761 (1960).

$$
\text{(I)} \qquad\qquad \text{(II)}
$$

and, as shown by the isotope effect and the nature of the products, the CH bond of the CHOH group is broken, rather than the C—C bond. The easy oxidation of tertiary glycols can be accounted for by the stability of the radical product $R_2\dot{C}OH$, which affects the rate of decomposition (k) of the complex:

$$
VO_2^+ + \quad
\begin{array}{c}
H_3C \;\; CH_3 \\
\diagdown \diagup \\
C-OH \\
| \\
C-OH \\
\diagup \diagdown \\
H_3C \;\; CH_3
\end{array}
\;\underset{K}{\rightleftharpoons}\;
\begin{array}{c}
H_3C \;\; CH_3 \\
\diagdown \diagup \\
C-O \\
| \quad V \\
C-O \\
\diagup \diagdown \\
H_3C \;\; CH_3
\end{array}
\;\xrightarrow{k}\;
\begin{array}{c}
(CH_3)_2CO \\[4pt]
(CH_3)_2\dot{C}\,OH
\end{array}
\; + V^{IV}
$$

In the case of the 1,2-dimethylcyclohexane-1,2-diols, K is reduced by steric effects, though k may be similar to k for pinacol, and the over-all reaction is thus diminished in rate. 2-Methylbutane-2,3-diol occupies an intermediate, critical position. Fission of the C—C bond occurs, but the rate of oxidation is much less than that of pinacol; if the stability of the leaving radical were the only factor of importance, then k should be comparable with that for pinacol; K, however, will be lower than for pinacol because there are only three methyl groups to exert inductive effects. Conformational effects should balance, for though the smaller methyl–methyl interaction in the complex might increase K, this would be compensated by a decrease in k. The rate of decomposition of the complex may also be increased by the increased stabilization of the incipient carbonyl group in $(CH_3)_2CO$ as compared with CH_3CHO or CH_2O. It appears that even with vanadium(V), sufficient radical character is developed in the transition state of these glycol fission reactions for the hyperconjugative stabilization of both the radical and the carbonyl compound being produced to be noticeable.

In the case of vanadium(V) oxidation, chelate complexing has been confirmed for pinacol by isotopic substitution and by half methylation, and the alcohol mechanism for primary and secondary glycols has been confirmed similarly.[68] The observed reactivity of ditertiary glycols toward one-equivalent oxidants is in contrast to the oxidation of glycols by both lead tetraacetate and periodic acid. These reagents effect C—C fission of most 1,2-glycols, but do not easily attack monohydric alcohols. Both types of reagent can form chelate

[68] J. S. Littler and W. A. Waters, *J. Chem. Soc.* p. 2767 (1960).

complexes with 1,2-glycols, but in order to facilitate the cyclic movement of electrons the two-equivalent oxidations must involve a transition state which has a planar chelate ring. With the one-equivalent reagents, this ring planarity is not essential. Hence steric interactions in the transition state are the more important with the two-equivalent processes, and favor the oxidation of less substituted glycols, e.g., $RCH(OH)$—CH_2OH. Also a concerted two-equivalent process need not require the development of any high degree of unsaturation, so that stabilization by hyperconjugation of the transition state is relatively unimportant. This results in fission of glycols by two-equivalent oxidants, as by chromic acid, at relative rates which can be correlated with the standard free energy of the process [69, 70]:

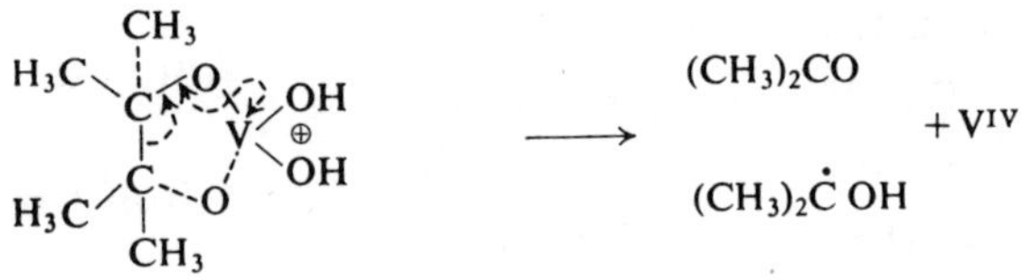

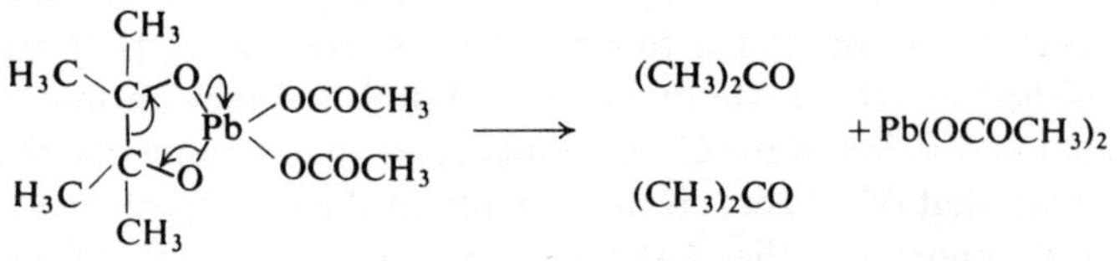

B. OXIDATION BY MANGANESE(III) AND COBALT(III)

Too few oxidations of glycols by manganese(III) pyrophosphate [71] have been examined for comparative study to be of value; the reactions are rather more difficult to compare, as the rate laws are not all identical, and rapid secondary reactions vitiate kinetic evidence with secondary glycols. Complexing between the glycol and the oxidant has been established kinetically in some cases, including pinacol which is oxidized extremely easily. In this case the liberation of the radical $Me_2\dot{C}OH$ has been established, since polymer is formed and the rate of reduction of manganese(III) is decreased when acrylonitrile is present; again, added mercuric chloride is reduced to mercurous chloride. No kinetic studies have yet been carried out with cobalt(III) or manganese(III) sulfate, but it appears that pinacol is oxidized by cobalt(III) at a rate qualitatively similar to that of monohydric secondary alcohols.

[69] J. Roček and F. H. Westheimer, *J. Am. Chem. Soc.* **84**, 2241 (1962).
[70] M. C. R. Symons, *J. Chem. Soc.* p. 4331 (1963).
[71] A. Y. Drummond and W. A. Waters, *J. Chem. Soc.* p. 3119 (1953); P. Levesley, W. A. Waters, and A. N. Wright, *J. Chem. Soc.* p. 840 (1956).

Manganese(III) acetate oxidizes pinacol very easily,[34, 72] but this is an isolated observation.

C. OXIDATION OF α-HYDROXY ACIDS

The oxidation of α-hydroxy acids has been studied with both manganese(III) pyrophosphate[73] and vanadium(V).[66] In the oxidation by vanadium(V), both VO_2^+ and a protonated species are active; and as h_0 dependence is observed for the acid-catalyzed reaction, it is reasonable to again postulate cyclic complex formation:

$$
RCH(OH)COOH + VO_2^+ \rightleftharpoons
\begin{array}{c}
R\ \ H \\
\backslash / \\
C-O \\
| \quad\ \ \ \ \ V \\
C-O \\
\| \\
O
\end{array}
\oplus
\begin{array}{c}
OH \\
OH
\end{array}
\longrightarrow
\begin{array}{c}
R\ \ H \\
\backslash / \\
\overset{\cdot}{C}-OH
\end{array} + V^{IV}
$$

$$+ CO_2$$

$$\Big\updownarrow H^+$$

$$
\begin{array}{c}
R\ \ H\ \ H \\
\backslash /\ / \\
C-O \\
| \quad\ \ \ \ \ V \textcircled{2+} \\
C-O \\
\| \\
O
\end{array}
\begin{array}{c}
OH \\
OH
\end{array}
$$

$$\Big\downarrow V^V$$

$$RCHO$$

Tests with acrylonitrile have confirmed the formation of an organic radical and thus the immediate liberation of carbon dioxide. These mechanisms receive support from the observation that when R is a phenyl group the reaction velocity is considerably enhanced as a result of the stabilization of the intermediate $R\dot{C}HOH$ radical. The extra carboxyl group in malic acid $(R = CH_2COOH)$ appears to cause a slight increase in reaction velocity, which might be due to the malic acid acting as a tridentate ligand. With α-hydroxy-isobutyric acid, there appears to be an acyclic component ($C_{H_3O^+}$ dependent) to the acid catalyzed reaction. The isotope effect arising from substitution of the α-hydrogen by deuterium to give $RCDOH$—$COOH$ is very small, confirming the above mechanism for oxidation by vanadium(V) and extending it to oxidation by manganese(III) sulfate (Table III).

When the oxidation of α-hydroxy acids is effected by manganese(III) pyrophosphate, the first step of the reaction is again decarboxylation with formation of a free radical; the main difference from vanadium(V) is that the

[72] R. Criegee, L. Kraft, and B. Rank, *Ann.* **507**, 159 (1933); S. A. Zonis and Yu. I. Kornilova, *J. Gen. Chem. USSR (Engl. Transl.)* **20**, 1301 (1950); S. A. Zonis, *ibid.* **24**, 814 (1954); S. A. Zonis, *Chem. Abstr.* **49**, 5414 (1955); S. A. Zonis and A. G. Pesina, *J. Gen. Chem. USSR (Engl. Transl.)* **20**, 1223 (1950).

[73] P. Levesley and W. A. Waters, *J. Chem. Soc.* p. 217 (1955).

TABLE III

Isotope Effects

Oxidant	Substrate	Medium	k_H/k_D	Temperature (°C)	$\Delta\Delta G^{\ddagger}$ (H—D)	Reference
Manganese	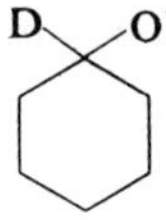	H_2SO_4	1.6	50	0.30	53
	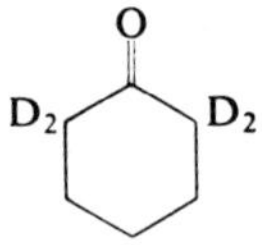	H_2SO_4	4.1	10.8	0.80	90
	DCOOH + Mn^{III}	H_2SO_4	2.2	50	0.51	80
	DCOOH + 3 Mn^{III}	H_2SO_4	4.3	25	0.87	80
	$C_6H_5CDOHCOOH$	H_2SO_4	1.1	23	0.06	80
Vanadium	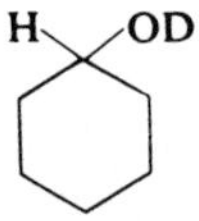	H_2SO_4	4.5	50	0.94	15
		$HClO_4$	3.6	50	0.84	15
	CH$_3$CDOH | CH$_3$CDOH	H_2SO_4	2.7	50	0.64	68
	CD_2O	$HClO_4$	3.9	50	0.88	62
	DCOOH	H_2SO_4	4.1	60	0.93	80
	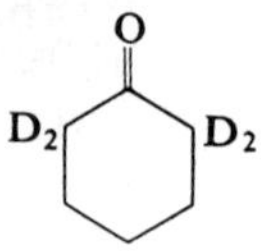	H_2SO_4	4.2	50	0.92	90
	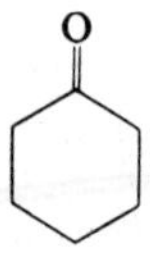	D_2SO_4	0.42	50	−0.56	90
	Pinacol	D_2SO_4 2.9 M 0.5 M	0.89 0.81	25 30	−0.07 −0.13	68 68

TABLE III—*continued*

Oxidant	Substrate	Medium	k_H/k_D	Temperature (°C)	$\Delta\Delta G^{\ddagger}$ (H—D)	Reference
Vanadium	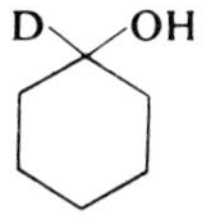 1-D-cyclohexanol (D, OH on C1)	D_2SO_4	0.68	50	−0.25	68
	$C_6H_5CDOHCOOH$	H_2SO_4	2.0	23	+0.43	80
Cobalt	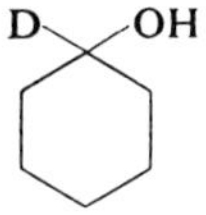 1-D-cyclohexanol (D, OH on C1)	$HClO_4$	1.7	10	0.30	60
	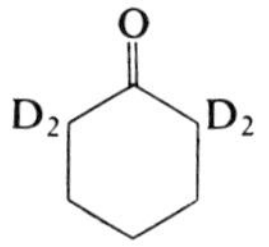 2,2,6,6-D_4-cyclohexanone (D_2, D_2)	H_2SO_4	0.9	25	−0.06	90
	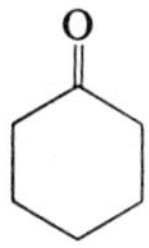 cyclohexanone	D_2SO_4	0.94	25	−0.04	90
	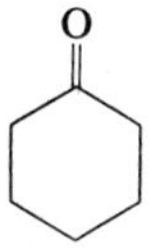 cyclohexanone	$DClO_4$	2.2	0.5	+0.43	90
	$(CH_3CD_2)_2CO$	$HClO_4$	1.0	10	0.0	23
	CD_2O	$HClO_4$	1.5	25	0.24	62
	$m\text{-}NO_2C_6H_4CDO$	$HClO_4$	2.3	10	0.47	85
	$DCOOH$	$HClO_4$	1.5	25	0.24	62
	$CH_3CDOH\ CH(CH_3)_2$	$HClO_4$	1.4	15	0.21	33
	$(C_2H_5)_2\ CDOH$	$HClO_4$	1.0	15	0.0	33
	$C_6H_5CDOHCOOH$	$HClO_4$	1.04	15	0.02	109
	$C_6H_5CD_2COOH$	$HClO_4$	1.24	15	0.12	109

TABLE IV

Redox Potentials in Acid Solutions[a]

Couple		Potential (volts)	Reference
$Mn^{III}-Mn^{II}$	Sulfate	1.5	15
$Mn^{III}-Mn^{II}$	Pyrophosphate	1.0	29
$Mn^{III}-Mn^{II}$	Oxalate	1.2	99
$Mn^{IV}-Mn^{III}$	15 N Sulfuric acid	1.65	1
MnO_2-Mn^{II}		1.23	2
$VO_2^+-VO^{2+}$		1.00	5
$VO^{2+}-V^{3+}$		0.361	5
$Co^{3+}{}_{aq}-Co^{2+}{}_{aq}$		1.842	5
$Co(NH_3)_6{}^{3+}-Co(NH_3)_6{}^{2+}$		0.1	5
CH_2O-CH_3OH		0.19	5
$HCOOH-CH_2O$		0.056	5
$CO_2-HCOOH$		-0.196	5

[a] Potentials are quoted throughout this review using the convention that a more positive value indicates a more powerful oxidant, as above.

extent of preliminary complex formation is enough to be detected in the kinetics. As a pyrophosphate ligand must be displaced in order to form the cyclic complex, the reaction is inhibited by excess pyrophosphate.

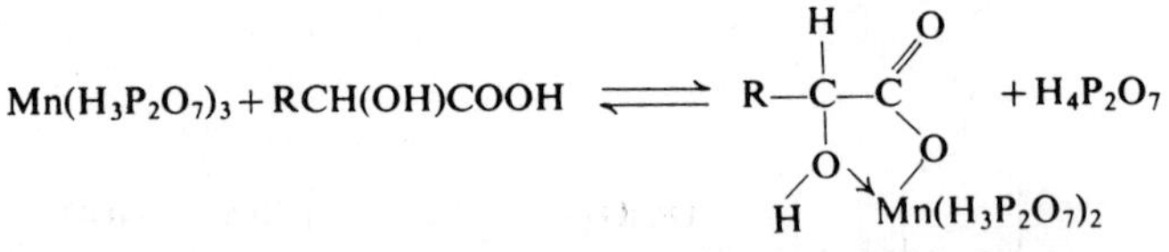

$$Mn(H_3P_2O_7)_3 + RCH(OH)COOH \rightleftharpoons R-\underset{\underset{H}{|}}{\overset{\overset{H}{|}}{C}}-\overset{O}{\underset{O}{C}} \quad + H_4P_2O_7$$

Apart from the observation of retardation of the reaction by manganese(II), probably due to complexing between it and the hydroxy acid, the kinetics are identical with those observed in the oxidation of pinacol. In the oxidations of racemic and *meso*-tartaric acids it was concluded that the *meso* acid formed the stronger complex. Both these acids were oxidized more rapidly than was malic acid, and dimethyltartarate was not attacked, so the reactivity of the tartaric acids must be due to their behaving as polydentate ligands rather than as α-glycols.

D. OXIDATION OF HYDROXY KETONES

Only with vanadium(V) have detailed studies been made of the oxidation of hydroxy ketones.[74] They are also attacked by manganese(III) acetate.[72] In the

[74] J. R. Jones and W. A. Waters, *J. Chem. Soc.* p. 1629 (1962).

case of manganese(III) pyrophosphate, comparative measurements have shown that 2-hydroxycyclohexanone is oxidized about 10 times more slowly than cyclohexanone.[75] On the other hand, with vanadium(V), the hydroxy ketone is oxidized about 200 times more rapidly.[76] With this oxidant both acetoin and methylacetoin (3-hydroxy-3-methylbutan-2-one) show acid catalysis dependent on h_0, which is some indication of chelate complex formation. In addition, methylacetoin, like the hydroxy acids and tertiary glycols discussed above, can be oxidized by the ion VO_2^+ at a rate independent of acidity at low acid concentration. Acetoin yields biacetyl as the first product, but methylacetoin gives acetone and acetaldehyde. To account for these facts the mechanism below has been written:

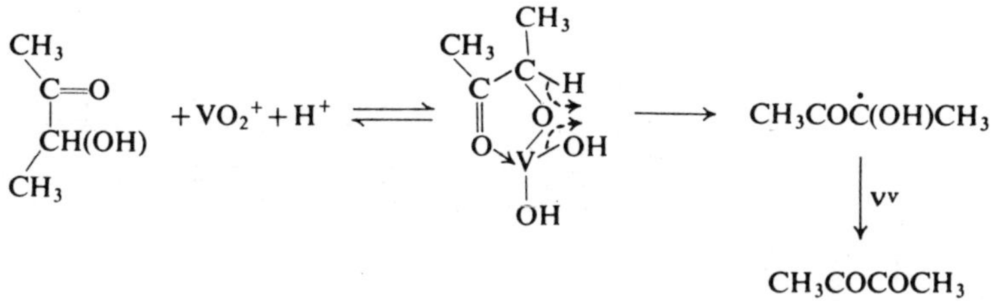

This is a combination of the alcohol and ketone (see below) oxidation mechanisms; the radical formed is of course stabilized by both the OH and the adjacent C=O. For methylacetoin, the pinacol-like mechanism below is possible. The stabilizing effect of the extra methyl group on the transition state must facilitate the VO_2^+ reaction by a factor of at least ten, even though it blocks a possible route for the catalyzed reaction:

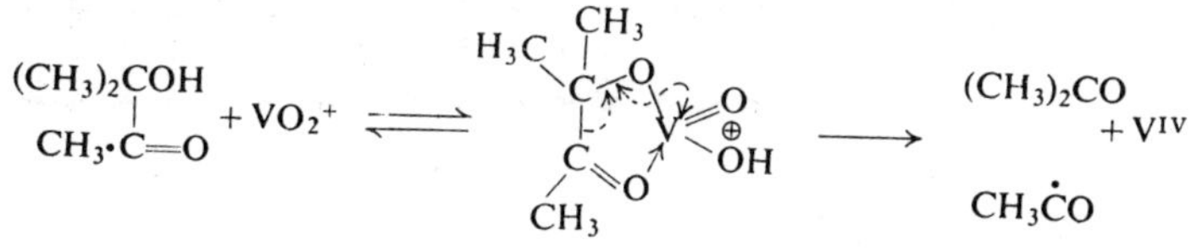

Hence the same factors which facilitate fission of tertiary glycols also facilitate fission of methylacetoin.

VI. Aldehydes

A. ALIPHATIC ALDEHYDES

Oxidations of aliphatic aldehydes can in general occur by two routes, i.e., by terminal oxidation (R·CHO → R·COOH) or by attack at the α-position [R·CH₂CHO → RCH(OH)CHO]. Most oxidants including cobalt(III)

[75] A. Y. Drummond and W. A. Waters, *J. Chem. Soc.* p. 497 (1955).
[76] J. S. Littler and W. A. Waters, *J. Chem. Soc.* p. 3014 (1959).

TABLE V

KINETIC DATA[a]

1. Manganese Compounds

A. Manganese Complexes

					Ref.
$Mn^{III} + C_2O_4^{2-} \rightleftharpoons Mn(C_2O_4)^+$	$K_1 = 4.8 \times 10^8$	25°C	$2M$ Cl$^-$	$\Delta H = 6$	102
	$K_1 = 9.5 \times 10^9$	25°C	$2M$ ClO$_4^-$		26
$Mn(C_2O_4)^+ + C_2O_4^{2-} \rightleftharpoons Mn(C_2O_4)_2^-$	$K_2 = 4.0 \times 10^6$	25°C	$2M$ Cl$^-$		102
	$K_2 = 3.9 \times 10^6$	25°C	$2M$ ClO$_4^-$		26
$Mn(C_2O_4)_2^- + C_2O_4^{2-} \rightleftharpoons Mn(C_2O_4)_3^{3-}$	$K_3 = 7.1 \times 10^2$	25°C	$2M$ Cl$^-$		102
	$K_3 = 7.1 \times 10^2$	25°C	$2M$ ClO$_4^-$		26
	$K_3 = 1.14 \times 10^3$	25°C	$1M$ ClO$_4^-$		4
$Mn^{3+} + Cl^- \rightleftharpoons MnCl^{2+}$	$K_1 = 9$	25°C	$2M$ ClO$_4^-$		26
$Mn^{3+} + HF \rightleftharpoons MnF^{2+} + H^+$	$K_1^* = 320$	25°C	$2M$ ClO$_4$		26
$Mn(C_2O_4)^+$	$k'K_\beta = 6.3 \times 10^{-8}$	25°C	$1M$ ClO$_4^-$		4
	$k' = 1.9 \times 10^{-1}$	25°C	$2M$ Cl$^-$	$E = 18.3; \Delta S^\ddagger = -2.6$	102
$Mn(C_2O_4)_2^-$	$k' = 7.7 \times 10^{-4}$	25°C	$2M$ Cl$^-$		102
	$k' = 1.51 \times 10^{-3}$	25°C	$1M$ ClO$_4^-$		4
	$k' = 8 \times 10^{-4}$	20°C	$0.4M$ NO$_3^-$	$E = 25; \Delta S^\ddagger = +3.2$	142
$Mn(C_2O_4)_3^{3-}$	$k' = 3.41 \times 10^{-4}$	25°C	$2M$ Cl$^-$	$E = 22.2; \Delta S^\ddagger = -2.7$	102
	$k' = 4.9 \times 10^{-4}$	25°C	$1M$ ClO$_4^-$		4
$Mn(tartarate)_x$	$k' = 8 \times 10^{-5}$	40°C	$0.5M$ tartarate	$E = 28$	143
$Mn(glycolate)_x$	$k' = 1.2 \times 10^{-5}$	40°C	$1M$ glycolate	$E = 18$	143

B. Oxidations by Manganese(III) Pyrophosphate

Substrate	K	rate constant	Temp.	Conditions	Ref.
Pinacol	$K = 1.5$	$k' = 0.7 \times 10^{-4}$	30°C	py $= 0.165\,M$; pH $= 0.52$	71
	$K = 2.1$	$k' = 2.7 \times 10^{-5}$	35°C	py $= 0.107\,M$; pH $= 1.36$	71
trans-1,2-Dimethylcyclopentane-1,2-diol		$k'' = 1.9 \times 10^{-5}$	40°C	py $= 0.119\,M$; pH $= 0.10$	71
trans-1,2-Dimethylcyclohexane-1,2-diol		$k'' = 2.8 \times 10^{-5}$	40°C	py $= 0.109\,M$; pH $= 0.04$	71
cis-Cyclohexane-1,2-diol $+ (Mn^{III})_2$		$k''' = 1.48 \times 10^{-3}$	40°C	py $= 0.12\,M$; pH $= 0.19$	71
Allyl alcohol		$k'' = 2 \times 10^{-4}$	45°C	py $= 0.086\,M$; pH $= 0.10$	63
Pyruvic acid	$K = 0.4$	$k' = 9 \times 10^{-4}$	10°C	py $= 0.435\,M$; pH $= 1.30$	73
dl-Malic acid	$K = 1.83$	$k' = 1.22 \times 10^{-4}$	35°C	py $= 0.175\,M$; pH $= 1.3$	73
dl-Tartaric acid	$K = 6.6$	$k' = 1.89 \times 10^{-4}$	35°C	py $= 0.29\,M$; pH $= 1.9$	73
Mesotartaric acid	$K = 14.2$	$k' = 1.78 \times 10^{-4}$	35°C	py $= 0.29\,M$; pH $= 1.9$	73
Malonic acid $+ (Mn^{III})_2$	$K = 3$	$k''' = 5 \times 10^{-3}$	30°C	py $= 0.146\,M$; pH $= 0.92$; $Mn^{2+} = 4 \times 10^{-3}\,M$	8

C. Oxidations by Manganese(III) Sulfate

Substrate	rate constant	Temp.	Conditions	Thermodynamic	Ref.
Cyclohexanone	$k'' = 2 \times 10^{-2}$	25°C	$H_2SO_4 = 4.8\,M$		90
Formaldehyde	$k'' = 1.45 \times 10^{-2}$	25°C	$H_2SO_4 = 3.5\,M$	$E = 17.1$; $\Delta S^{\ddagger} = -12$	80
	$k'' = 2.17 \times 10^{-4}$	25°C	$H_2SO_4 = 2.025\,M$	$E = 25.2$; $\Delta S^{\ddagger} = +7.4$	80

[a] Key: K = equilibrium constant for complex formation (modifying symbols as in International Tables[103]).

$$k' = \text{first order rate constant (sec}^{-1}) = \left(-\frac{d}{dt}[\text{oxidant}] \right) \Big/ [\text{oxidant}]$$

k'' = second order rate constant (liters mole^{-1} sec^{-1})

k''' = third order rate constant (liters mole^{-2} sec^{-1}) and so on

Thermodynamic parameters ΔH, E in kcal., $\Delta S^{\ddagger}$ in cal deg^{-1} mole^{-1}.

Rates dependent on the Hammett acidity function h_0 are quoted at $1\,M$ acidity.

Rates are the observed rates of disappearance of the oxidant, not of the substrate. The first column gives the equilibrium concerned, the substrate, the species decomposing, or the composition of the transition state, as appropriate. The reactions are first order in oxidant in the absence of any contrary indication. The second column gives the equilibrium rate constant; the third, an indication of the conditions under which the reaction was carried out; the fourth, the thermochemical parameters, and the fifth, the reference.

TABLE V—continued

1. Manganese Compounds—continued

C. Oxidations by Manganese(III) Sulfate—continued

					Ref.
Cyclohexanol	$K = 1.03$ $k' = 1.21 \times 10^{-4}$	50° C	$H_2SO_4 = 4.8\,M$		53
	$k'' = 2.5 \times 10^{-5}$	24.5° C	$H_2SO_4 = 2\,M$	$E = 28.9;\ \Delta S^{\ddagger} = +20$	80
Formic acid + Mn^{III}	$k'' = 3.6 \times 10^{-5}$	25° C	$H_2SO_4 = 2.22\,M$	$E = 22.9;\ \Delta S^{\ddagger} = -4$	80
Formic acid + $(Mn^{III})_3$	$k''' = 0.72$	25° C	$H_2SO_4 = 1.2\,M$	$E = 21.9;\ Mn^{2+} = 0.325\,M$	80
α-Hydroxyisobutyric acid	$k'' = 0.54$	24.4° C	$H_2SO_4 = 3.35\,M$	$E = 20.0;\ \Delta S^{\ddagger} = 5.3$	80
Mandelic acid	$k'' = 1.42$	24.4° C	$H_2SO_4 = 3.35\,M$		80
Malonic acid + $(Mn^{III})_2$	$k''' = 2.7 \times 10^{2}$	25° C	$H_2SO_4 = 2.95\,M$	$Mn^{2+} \rightarrow 0$	107
Toluene	$k'' = 4 \times 10^{-4}$	25° C	Sulfate	$E = 31$	116

2. Vanadium Oxidations

					Ref.
Oxalic acid + h_0	$k'' = 6.6 \times 10^{-4}$	50° C	$5\,M\ ClO_4^{-}$		106
$VO(C_2O_4)_2^{-}$ + oxalic acid	$k'' = 1.4 \times 10^{-2}$	40° C	$2.1\,M\ ClO_4^{-}$		106
VO_2^{+} + (oxalic acid)$_2$	$k''' = 10^{-2}$	40° C	$3.1\,M\ ClO_4^{-}$		106
Lactic acid	$k'' = 6.5 \times 10^{-4}$	25° C	$5\,M\ ClO_4^{-}$	$\Big\}\ E = 16.5;\ \Delta S^{\ddagger} = -24$	66 / 146
Lactic acid + h_0	$k'' = 1.4 \times 10^{-3}$	25° C	$5\,M\ ClO_4^{-}$		66
Malic acid	$k'' = 8.8 \times 10^{-4}$	25° C	$5\,M\ ClO_4^{-}$		66
Malic acid + h_0	$k'' = 1.6 \times 10^{-3}$	25° C	$5\,M\ ClO_4^{-}$		66
α-Hydroxyisobutyric acid	$k'' = 9.0 \times 10^{-4}$	25° C	$5\,M\ ClO_4^{-}$		66
α-Hydroxyisobutyric acid + h_0	$k'' = 1 \times 10^{-4}$	25° C	$5\,M\ ClO_4^{-}$		66
Mandelic acid	$k'' = 3.2 \times 10^{-2}$	25° C	$5\,M\ ClO_4^{-}$		66

Reaction	k''	Temp.	Medium		Ref.
Mandelic acid + h_0	$k'' = 1.14 \times 10^{-2}$	25°C	5 M ClO$_4^-$		66
Mandelic acid (both paths combined)					144
Pinacol	$k'' = 4.1 \times 10^{-3}$	30°C	3 M HSO$_4^-$	$E = 14;\ \Delta S^{\ddagger} = -20$	119
	$k'' = 1.6 \times 10^{-1}$	60°C	3 M HSO$_4^-$		119
	$k'' = 3.3 \times 10^{-2}$	25°C	5 M ClO$_4^-$		66
Pinacol + h_0	$k'' = 5.7 \times 10^{-3}$	25°C	5 M ClO$_4^-$		66
Methyl acetoin	$k'' = 8.5 \times 10^{-3}$	25°C	5.1 M ClO$_4^-$		74
Methyl acetoin + h_0	$k'' = 1.7 \times 10^{-3}$	25°C	5.1 M ClO$_4^-$		74
Acetoin + h_0	$k'' = 3.1 \times 10^{-2}$	25°C	3.1 M ClO$_4^-$		74
trans-1,2-Dimethylcyclohexane-1,2-diol + h_0	$k'' = 2.1 \times 10^{-4}$	60°C	1 M HSO$_4^-$		74
trans-1,2-Dimethylcyclohexane-1,2-diol + h_0	$k'' = 3.2 \times 10^{-4}$	60°C	1 M HSO$_4^-$		67
cis-1,2-Dimethylcyclohexane-1,2-diol	$k'' = 4.7 \times 10^{-4}$	60°C	1 M HSO$_4^-$		67
cis-1,2-Dimethylcyclohexane-1,2-diol + h_0	$k'' = 6.0 \times 10^{-4}$	60°C	1 M HSO$_4^-$		67
2-Methyl butane-2,3-diol	$k'' = 1.63 \times 10^{-3}$	60°C	1 M HSO$_4^-$		67
2-Methyl butane-2,3-diol + h_0	$k'' = 8.2 \times 10^{-4}$	60°C	1 M HSO$_4^-$		67
cis-Cyclohexane-1,2-diol + H$_3$O$^+$	$k'' = 5.7 \times 10^{-4}$	60°C	1 M HSO$_4^-$		67
trans-Cyclohexane-1,2-diol + H$_3$O$^+$	$k'' = 1.7 \times 10^{-4}$	60°C	1 M HSO$_4^-$		67
Ethylene glycol + H$_3$O$^+$	$k'' = 1.4 \times 10^{-4}$	60°C	1 M HSO$_4^-$		67
Propane-1,2-diol + H$_3$O$^+$	$k'' = 2.0 \times 10^{-4}$	60°C	1 M HSO$_4^-$		67
Butane-2,3-diol + H$_3$O$^+$	$k'' = 3.6 \times 10^{-4}$	60°C	1 M HSO$_4^-$		67
Cyclohexanol + H$_3$O$^+$	$k'' = 1.08 \times 10^{-4}$	50°C	6 M ClO$_4^-$		15
	$k'' = 1.78 \times 10^{-4}$	50°C	6 M HSO$_4^-$		15
	$k'' = 8.2 \times 10^{-4}$	60°C	1 M HSO$_4^-$		67
n-Propanol + H$_3$O$^+$	$k'' = 2.4 \times 10^{-5}$	50°C	3 M ClO$_4^-$		59
n-Butanol + H$_2$O$^+$	$k'' = 2.3 \times 10^{-5}$	50°C	3 M ClO$_4^-$		59
Isopropanol + H$_3$O$^+$	$k'' = 7.6 \times 10^{-6}$	50°C	3 M ClO$_4^-$		59
Allyl alcohol + H$_3$O$^+$	$k'' = 7.2 \times 10^{-4}$	50°C	3 M ClO$_4^-$		59
Crotyl alcohol + H$_2$O$^+$	$k'' = 7.3 \times 10^{-4}$	50°C	3 M ClO$_4^-$		59
Cyclopentanone + H$_3$O$^+$	$k'' = 4.05 \times 10^{-4}$	40°C	1 M HSO$_4^-$		76

TABLE V—continued

2. Vanadium Oxidations—continued

					Ref.
Cyclohexanone + H_3O^+		$k''' = 1.83 \times 10^{-3}$	35°C	1.2 M HSO_4^-	76
		$k''' = 3.0 \times 10^{-4}$	35°C	1.2 M ClO_4^-	76
		$k'' = 2.3 \times 10^{-4}$	30.2°C	1.67 M ClO_4^- $E = 19.4$; $\Delta S^{\ddagger} = -13$	80
Propanal + H_3O^+	$K = 1.4$	$k'' = 3.8 \times 10^{-4}$	25°C	3.1 M ClO_4^-	79
n-Butanal + H_3O^+	$K = 1.3$	$k'' = 3.3 \times 10^{-4}$	25°C	3.1 M ClO_4^-	79
Isobutanal	zero order in vanadium(V)			3.1 M ClO_4^-	79
Glycerol + H_3O^+ (?)		$k'' = 110 \times 10^{-4}$	100°C	3.4 M HSO_4^- $E = 19$	145
Pinacol monomethyl ether + H_3O^+		$k'' = 1.6 \times 10^{-3}$	50°C	5 M ClO_4^-	66
Formaldehyde + H_3O^+		$k''' = 2.3 \times 10^{-5}$	50°C	5 M ClO_4^- &nbrace; $E = 22$ (composite value)	62
Formaldehyde + (VO_2^+) + $(H_3O^+)_2$		$k'''' = 11.2 \times 10^{-5}$	50°C	5 M ClO_4^-	62
Formic acid		$k'' = 3.3 \times 10^{-6}$	57.9°C	2.6 M HSO_4^- 6.6 M HCOOH $\{ E = 22.8$ (composite values)	107
Formic acid + H_3O^+		$k'' = 8.1 \times 10^{-7}$	57.9°C	2.6 M HSO_4^- 6.6 M HCOOH $\{ \Delta S^{\ddagger} = -17$	107
Malonic acid + $(VO_2^+)_2$ + $(H_3O^+)_2$ (?)		$k'' = 5.8 \times 10^{-4}$	56.5°C	1.8 M HSO_4^- $E = 19.7$	107

3. Cobalt(III) Oxidations

					Ref.
$Co(C_2O_4)_2(H_2O)_2^-$	$k' = 8.9 \times 10^{-4}$	25°C	0.01 M $K_2C_2O_4$	$E = 17.8$; $\Delta S^{\ddagger} = -17.4$	100
$Co(C_2O_4)_3^{3-}$				$E = 30.2$; $\Delta S^{\ddagger} = +17.4$	100
	$k' = 4.2 \times 10^{-6}$	40°C	1.5 M $NaClO_4$	$E = 30.0$; $\Delta S^{\ddagger} = +9.0$	104
				$E = 33.0$; $\Delta S^{\ddagger} = +22.8$	99
$Co(C_2O_4)_3^{3-}$ + H^+	$k'' = 3.3 \times 10^{-5}$	25°C	1.5 M ClO_4^-	$E = 23.2$; $\Delta S^{\ddagger} = +7.3$	100
				$E = 31.9$; $\Delta S^{\ddagger} = -18.2$	99
				$E = 30.0$; $\Delta S^{\ddagger} = +19.0$	104

Compound	k	Temp	Medium	Activation parameters	Ref
tert-Butanol	$k''[H^+] = 1.8 \times 10^{-3}$	10°C	3.5 M ClO$_4^-$		60
	$k'' = 2.16 \times 10^{-3}$	15°C	1.57 M HClO$_4$	$E = 32.1;\ \Delta S^\ddagger = 38.7$	33[c]
tert-Amyl alcohol	$k'' = 50 \times 10^{-3}$	15°C	1.57 M HClO$_4$		33
Dimethyl isopropyl carbinol	$k'' = 74.8 \times 10^{-3}$	15°C	1.57 M HClO$_4$		33
Dimethyl *tert*-butyl carbinol	$k'' = 11.3 \times 10^{-3}$	15°C	1.57 M HClO$_4$		33
Methyl ethyl *n*-propyl carbinol	$k'' = 64.6 \times 10^{-3}$	15°C	1.57 M HClO$_4$		33
Methyl ethyl *n*-amyl carbinol	$k'' = 82.6 \times 10^{-3}$	15°C	1.57 M HClO$_4$		33
Diethyl methoxymethyl carbinol	$k'' = 160 \times 10^{-3}$	15°C	1.57 M HClO$_4$		33
Ethanol	$k'' = 286 \times 10^{-3}$	15°C	1.57 M HClO$_4$		33
Methanol	$k'' = 118 \times 10^{-3}$	15°C	1.57 M HClO$_4$		33
Isopropanol	$k'' = 37 \times 10^{-3}$	15°C	1.57 M HClO$_4$	$E = 29.6;\ \Delta S^\ddagger = 35.5$	33
sec-Butanol	$k'' = 63.5 \times 10^{-3}$	15°C	1.57 M HClO$_4$		33
Methyl *n*-propyl carbinol	$k'' = 63.1 \times 10^{-3}$	15°C	1.57 M HClO$_4$		33
Cyclohexanol	$k'' = 49.7 \times 10^{-3}$	15°C	1.57 M HClO$_4$		33
Cyclohexanol	$k''[H^+] = 53 \times 10^{-3}$	10°C	3.4 M ClO$_4^-$	$E = 31.5;\ \Delta S^\ddagger = 43.0$	60
Diethyl carbinol	$k'' = 106 \times 10^{-3}$	15°C	1.57 M HClO$_4$		33[c]
Methyl isopropyl carbinol	$k'' = 33.7 \times 10^{-3}$	15°C	1.57 M HClO$_4$	$E = 29.8;\ \Delta S^\ddagger = 38.5$	33
Benzyl alcohol	$k''[H^+] \approx 400$	15°C	1.1 M HClO$_4$; 3.14 M ClO$_4^-$		109
Isobutyl alcohol	$k''[H^+] = 0.72$	15°C	1.1 M HClO$_4$; 3.14 M ClO$_4^-$		109
Methyl α-hydroxy-α-methyl butyrate	$k'' = 8.59 \times 10^{-3}$	15°C	1.57 M HClO$_4$		33
Isobutyric acid	$k'' = 227 \times 10^{-3}$	15°C	1.57 M HClO$_4$		33
α-Hydroxyisobutyric acid	$k'' = 1.44$	15°C	1.57 M HClO$_4$		33
Isobutylenediol	$k'' = 1.42$	15°C	1.57 M HClO$_4$		33
Methyl acetoin	$k'' = 0.339$	15°C	1.57 M HClO$_4$		33
Cyclohexanone	$k'' = 0.150$	15°C	0.34 M HClO$_4$		33
	$k'' = 1.08$	25°C	0.21 M H$_2$SO$_4$		90
	$k'' = 0.016$	0.5°C	0.33 M HClO$_4$		90
Diethyl ketone	$k''[H^+] = 4.15 \times 10^{-3}$	10°C	3.4 M ClO$_4^-$		23
	$k''[H^+] = 2.15 \times 10^{-3}$	10°C	3.4 M HSO$_4^-$		23

TABLE V—continued

3. Cobalt(III) Oxidations—continued

Compound	Rate	Medium	Temp	Activation	Ref.
Acetone	$k'' = 0.103 \times 10^{-3}$	$1.35\,M$ HClO$_4$	10°C		33
Benzaldehyde	$k'' = 0.02$		26°C	$E = 15$	84
	$k'' = 0.023$	45% CH$_3$CN; 1.65 M HClO$_4$	10°C		127
p-Nitrobenzaldehyde	$k'' = 0.13$	45% CH$_3$CN; 1.65 M HClO$_4$	10°C	$E = 20.7$; $\Delta S^\ddagger = 13$	127
m-Nitrobenzaldehyde	$k'' = 7.4 \times 10^{-2}$	45% CH$_3$CN; 1.65 M HClO$_4$	10°C	$E = 21.3$; $\Delta S^\ddagger = 14$	127
Acetaldehyde	$k''[H^+] = 0.58$	$3.14\,M$ ClO$_4^-$	15°C		109
Formaldehyde	$-k'' = 15$	$1\,M$ HClO$_4$; $6\,M$ ClO$_4^-$	22.2°C	$E = 22$	38
	$k'' = 4$	$1\,M$ H$_2$SO$_4$; $3.5\,M$ HSO$_4^-$	22.2°C	$E = 28$	38
Formic acid	$k'' = 17.2$	$1\,M$ HClO$_4$	25°C		62
	$k''[H^+] = 0.14$	$4\,M$ ClO$_4^-$	25.6°C	$E = 21.7$	82
	$k'' = 0.11$	$1\,M$ HClO$_4$	25°C		62
Acetic acid	$k''[H^+] = 1.1 \times 10^{-3}$	$3.14\,M$ ClO$_4^-$; 33% v/v CH$_3$CN	15°C		109
Propionic acid	$k''[H^+] < 2 \times 10^{-4}$	$3.14\,M$ ClO$_4^-$	15°C	$E = 26$; $\Delta S^\ddagger = 21$	109
Isobutyric acid	$K[H^+] = 0.72$; $k' = 0.01$	$3.14\,M$ ClO$_4^-$	15°C		109
Pivalic acid	$k''[H^+] = 0.84$	$3.14\,M$ ClO$_4^-$	15°C		109
	$k''[H^+] = 1.8$	$3.14\,M$ ClO$_4^-$	15°C		109
Phenylacetic acid	$K[H^+] = 27.7$; $k' = 0.11$	$3.14\,M$ ClO$_4^-$	15°C		109
Diphenylacetic acid	$k''[H^+] = 1.1$	$3.14\,M$ ClO$_4^-$; 39% v/v CH$_3$CN	15°C		109
β-Phenylpropionic acid	$k''[H^+] = 0.19$	$3.14\,M$ ClO$_4^-$	15°C		109
Malonic acid	$K[H^+] = 4.05$; $k' = 0.029$	$3.14\,M$ ClO$_4^-$	15°C		109
Lactic acid	$k''[H^+] = 0.42$	$3.14\,M$ ClO$_4^-$	15°C		109
Mandelic acid	$k''[H^+] = 2.1$	$3.14\,M$ ClO$_4^-$	15°C		109

					Ref.
2-Methylbut-2-ene	25°C	0.09 M H$^+$; 2 M HSO$_4^-$	$k'' = 2.2^b$	$E = 27$; $\Delta S^{\ddagger} = 32.2$	112
Pent-2-ene	25°C	0.09 M H$^+$; 2 M HSO$_4^-$	$k'' = 0.9^b$		112
2-Ethyl but-1-ene	25°C	0.09 M H$^+$; 2 M HSO$_4^-$	$k'' = 0.75^b$		112
Hex-1-ene	25°C	0.09 M H$^+$; 2 M HSO$_4^-$	$k'' = 0.32^b$	$E = 29$; $\Delta S^{\ddagger} = 34.8$	112
Hept-1-ene	25°C	0.09 M H$^+$; 2 M HSO$_4^-$	$k'' = 0.37^b$		112
Oct-1-ene	25°C	0.09 M H$^+$; 2 M HSO$_4^-$	$k'' = 0.37^b$	$E = 28.5$; $\Delta S^{\ddagger} = 33.6$	112
Styrene	25°C	0.09 M H$^+$; 2 M HSO$_4^-$	$k'' = 7.4^b$		112
Isoprene	25°C	0.09 M H$^+$; 2 M HSO$_4^-$	$k'' = 6.2^b$		112
2-Methyl but-2-ene and other olefins	20°C	90% CH$_3$COOH; 10% H$_2$SO$_4$ [cobalt(III) acetate]	Zero order in olefin		112
Benzene			k''^b k''[H$^+$]	$E = 23$ $E = 40$	114 114
Crotonic acid	25°C	H$_2$SO$_4$	$k'' = 1.1 \times 10^{-2}$		112
tert-Butyl hydroperoxide	20°C	H$_2$SO$_4$	k''[H$^+$] = 1.42		134
Cobaltic acetate (acid catalyzed decomp.)	20°C	glacial CH$_3$COOH	$k'' = 0.43 \times 10^{-3}$		134
	17°C	H$_2$SO$_4$	$k'' = 17 \times 10^{-4}$		32

4. Catalyzed Reactions

					Ref.
Malonic acid + vanadium(V) + Mn^{2+}				$E = 6.9$	107
Oxalic acid + vanadium(V) + Mn^{2+}				$E = 4.7$	107

^{b} Reaction rate is independent of acidity.

^{c} k'' = rate at given acidity; in water or water/acetonitrile mixture, extrapolated to pure water, as for most data from reference 33.

sulfate give a mixture of products.[77] When manganese(III) pyrophosphate is used, the oxidations of propanal and n-butanal are of zero order with respect to the concentration of oxidant. As they are also acid catalyzed oxidations, it would appear that the first rate-determining step does not involve the oxidant, and so must be an enolization. Attack on the enol results in α-oxidation and the uptake of about four equivalents of oxidant.[78] Similarly, the rate of oxidation of isobutanal by vanadium(V) is independent of the concentration of oxidant, and is the same as is observed in halogenation (after allowance for terminal oxidation by the halogens). Again, no isobutyric acid could be found, and extensive degradation occurs.[79]

However, when vanadium(V) reacts with propanal and n-butanal, the oxidation is slower than enolization and there is kinetic evidence for extensive complexing between the reagents. As there is also an induction period, comparable with that which would be expected if enol had to first form and then complex with the metal ion, the oxidation may well involve an enol–vanadium(V) complex:

$$RCH_2-CHO \xrightleftharpoons{H^+} RCH=CH-OH$$

$$RCH=CH-\underset{\underset{H}{|}}{O} + VO_2^+ + H_3O^+ \rightleftharpoons RCH=CH-\overset{(2+)}{\underset{H}{O}} V \overset{OH}{\underset{OH}{-OH}}$$

$$R\overset{\bullet}{C}H-CH=O \longleftrightarrow RCH=CH-\overset{\bullet}{O} + V^{IV}$$

$$\downarrow V^V$$

$$RCH(OH)CHO$$

It is notable that these are the only reactions of vanadium(V) other than that with oxalic acid in which a kinetically significant degree of complexing has been observed. The acid dependence is on $C_{H_3O^+}$ as would be expected, as no chelate complexes can form, but an acceleration over and above this is observed at high acidities. This could be due to an increase in the concentration of the un-hydrated aldehyde, resulting from the reduced activity of water in strong acids.

B. FORMALDEHYDE

Formaldehyde which obviously cannot enolize is oxidized only very slowly by vanadium(V), but the reaction has been the subject of two investigations.[42, 62]

[77] J. B. Conant and J. G. Aston, *J. Am. Chem. Soc.* **50**, 2783 (1928).
[78] A. Y. Drummond and W. A. Waters, *J. Chem. Soc.* p. 440 (1953).
[79] J. R. Jones and W. A. Waters, *J. Chem. Soc.* p. 352 (1963).
[80] T. J. Kemp and W. A. Waters, *J. Chem. Soc.* pp. 339, 1192, and 1610 (1964).

The kinetics are complicated, but clearly show that reaction occurs by way of the hydrate $CH_2(OH)_2$, which does not protonate at the acidity used. Two terms are required to express the vanadium dependence, one first and the other second order in $V(OH)_3{}^{2+}$. This also occurs with chloral hydrate. The kinetic isotope effect shows that C—H fission is involved in the rate-determining step and the kinetics can be accounted for if two paths are possible, one following the normal mechanism of oxidation of alcohols, and the other involving a further vanadium(V) ion complexed to the hydrated diol form, $CH_2(OH)_2$, which provides two nucleophilic centers for complexing with vanadium ions:

$$CHR(OH)_2 + V(OH)_3{}^{2+} \rightleftharpoons CHROH\!-\!\underset{H}{O} \rightarrow V(OH)_3{}^{2+}$$

$$CHROH\!-\!\underset{H}{O} \longrightarrow V(OH)_3{}^{2+} + V(OH)_3{}^{2+} \rightleftharpoons CHR\!\!\begin{array}{l} \diagup OH \rightarrow V(OH)_3{}^{2+} \\ \diagdown OH \rightarrow V(OH)_3{}^{2+} \end{array}$$

$$HO\overset{H}{\underset{O \rightarrow V - OH}{C}R \quad OH} \longrightarrow HO\overset{\bullet}{C}ROH + V^{IV}$$

$$(HO)_3\overset{(2+)}{V} \cdots \underset{H}{O} \cdots \overset{H}{CR} \quad OH \longrightarrow V^{IV} + O\!=\!CROH + V^{IV}$$

$$R = H \text{ or } CCl_3$$

A similar concerted oxidation involving two one-equivalent oxidizing centres is involved in the oxidation of "bound" *p*-aldehydobenzoate by cobalt(III)[81] (see below).

The oxidation of formaldehyde by cobalt(III) has also been studied several times.[62, 82] As in alcohol oxidations, the $CoOH^{2+}{}_{aq}$ species is the most active one, and the C—H isotope effect is of much the same magnitude as that found for cyclohexanol so there is no reason to suppose that the mechanisms are different (see p. 200). Some evidence of second order dependence has been found in sulfuric acid.[82]

Manganese(III) sulfate oxidizes formaldehyde in a simple manner, very similar to its attack on alcohols. Most of the reaction is dependent only on the manganese(III) concentration, but at very low manganese(II) concentrations a manganese(II) retarded term appears, presumably due to attack by manganese(IV).

[81] R. T. M. Fraser and H. Taube, *J. Am. Chem. Soc.* **82**, 4152 (1960); J. P. Candlin and J. Halpern, *J. Am. Chem. Soc.* **85**, 2518 (1963).
[82] C. E. H. Bawn and A. C. White, *J. Chem. Soc.* pp. 339, 343 (1951).

C. OTHER ALDEHYDES

Acraldehyde, crotonaldehyde and α-methyl acraldehyde cannot enolize in the normal manner; they can, however, take up a molecule of water to form an enol:

$$CH_2\!=\!CH\!-\!CHO \underset{\longleftarrow}{\overset{H^+,\ H_2O}{\rlap{\longrightarrow}}} HO\!-\!CH_2\!-\!CH\!=\!CHOH$$

This common enol is formed more rapidly from crotonaldehyde than from its alternative precursor, 3-hydroxypropanal, and its rate of formation determines the rate of oxidation of crotonaldehyde [83] by manganese(III) pyrophosphate. The initial product of oxidation is glyceric acid, but this is also easily oxidized, and extensive degradation eventually occurs.

Aldehydes which can neither enolize nor hydrate easily have been granted few kinetic studies. Attack on such an aldehyde is an essential step in the cobalt catalyzed autoxidation of benzaldehyde [84]

$$ArCHO + Co^{3+} \rightarrow ArC\!=\!O + Co^{2+} + H^+$$

and a similar hydrogen atom removal must occur in the oxidation by cobalt(III) of the cobaltic p-aldehydobenzoatopentammine cation. [81]

This latter reaction results in reduction of both the cobalt(III) ions involved, and subsequently in liberation of the ligands, which are found to include terephthalic acid:

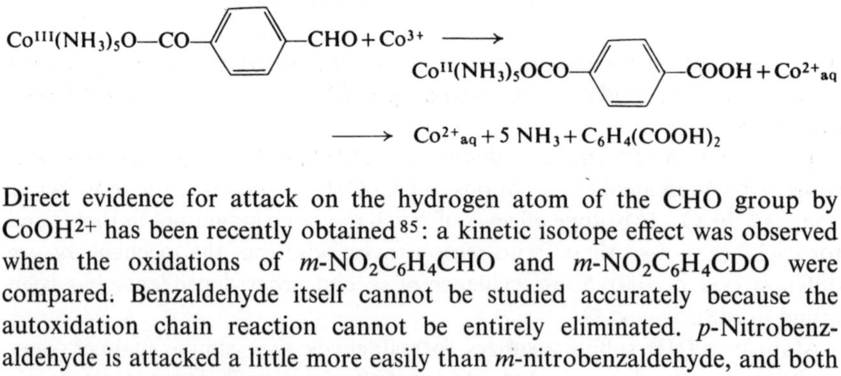

Direct evidence for attack on the hydrogen atom of the CHO group by $CoOH^{2+}$ has been recently obtained [85]: a kinetic isotope effect was observed when the oxidations of $m\text{-}NO_2C_6H_4CHO$ and $m\text{-}NO_2C_6H_4CDO$ were compared. Benzaldehyde itself cannot be studied accurately because the autoxidation chain reaction cannot be entirely eliminated. p-Nitrobenzaldehyde is attacked a little more easily than m-nitrobenzaldehyde, and both are oxidized faster than benzaldehyde, a result in accord with the greater stability of the radical formed from the former compound. The value observed

[83] H. Land and W. A. Waters, *J. Chem. Soc.* p. 4312 (1957).

[84] C. E. H. Bawn and J. E. Jolley, *Proc. Roy. Soc.* A237, 297 (1956); C. E. H. Bawn, *Discussions Faraday Soc.* 14, 181 (1953); C. E. H. Bawn, T. P. Hobin, and L. Raphael, *Proc. Roy. Soc.* A237, 313 (1956).

[85] T. A. Cooper and W. A. Waters, *J. Chem. Soc.* p. 1538 (1964).

for the kinetic isotope effect is comparable with that observed in the oxidations of alcohols, formic acid, or formaldehyde, and a similar mechanism may be suggested.

VII. Ketones

A. THE MECHANISM OF THE OXIDATION

The oxidation of ketones has been studied in considerable detail with all three oxidants. In the case of manganese(III) pyrophosphate, the oxidation rate of cyclohexanone reaches a limit at high oxidant concentrations which is independent of the oxidant concentration but which is comparable with the rate of enolization measured under the same conditions.[75] This demonstrates that the enol is attacked. On the basis of this, and by analogy with suggested mechanisms of oxidation by cerium(IV),[86] permanganate,[87] and chromium (VI)[88] in acid, and by ferricyanide in alkaline solution,[89] and with the evidence furnished by the oxidation of aldehydes by manganese(III) pyrophosphate,[78] it has been suggested[75] that all one-equivalent oxidants attack the enol tautomer, and do not attack the ketone directly.

However, when manganese(III) sulfate was used, the rate of consumption of cyclohexanone was found to be twice as great as that observed in the enolization-limited iodination reaction; moreover the manganese(III) oxidation remained first order with respect to the oxidant.[90] These facts exclude a mechanism involving attack on the enol unless the initial attack by manganese(III) is immediately followed by a long sequence of secondary reactions, which definitely is not the case with manganese(III) pyrophosphate.

Oxidation of cyclohexanone by cobalt(III) in both perchloric and sulfuric acids was found to be much faster than the enolization rate, so in this reaction also it can be inferred that the ketone is directly attacked. In both these reactions, and also in the oxidation of cyclohexanone by vanadium(V), which is slower than the enolization rate, the isotope effect resulting from replacement of α-H by deuterium has been measured. If the isotope effect was due to a rate-determining enolization step, it would be expected to be the same as that observed for the acid catalyzed enolization such as measured by halogenation (1.17 kcal), but in fact it was found to have a rather lower value (0.92 kcal)

[86] J. Shorter and C. N. Hinshelwood, *J. Chem. Soc.* p. 3276 (1950); J. Shorter, *J. Chem. Soc.* p. 3425 (1950); p. 1868 (1962); I. C. Fromageot, *Compt. Rend. Acad. Sci.* **182**, 1240, 1411 (1926); *Bull. Soc. Chim. France* **39**, 1207 (1926).

[87] G. Lejeune, *Compt. Rend. Acad. Sci.* **182**, 694 (1926).

[88] G. Petit, *Bull. Soc. Chim. France* **12**, 568 (1945).

[89] P. T. Speakman and W. A. Waters *J. Chem. Soc.* p. 40 (1955).

[90] J. S. Littler, *J. Chem. Soc.* pp. 827, 832 (1962); A. J. Green, T. J. Kemp, J. S. Littler, and W. A. Waters, *J. Chem. Soc.* p. 2772 (1964).

and in the case of the cobalt(III) oxidations of diethyl ketone and cyclo-hexanone it was negligibly small. However, these observations are not suf-ficient to determine whether the enolic or the ketonic form of cyclohexanone is attacked by vanadium(V). In this case the isotope effect could be due either to a kinetic effect operating in a direct attack on the ketone, or to an equilibrium isotope effect, altering the enol content of the solution of deuterated ketone in (light) water. This latter can be estimated by considering the various steps of the acid catalyzed enolization and ketonization processes.[91]

If a deuterated ketone is dissolved in water (either protio or deuterio), then the enolization process is retarded by the primary isotope effect in the C—H (C—D) bond breaking step; the reverse process is not retarded, with the result that there is a shift in the keto–enol equilibrium as compared with its position using protio–ketone in the same solvent. This kinetic disturbance of the keto–enol equilibrium is only maintained so long as the ketone and solvent have not reached equilibrium as regards isotopic exchange. This takes quite a long time—in fact, much longer than the formation of an equilibrium mixture of ketone and enol in the absence of exchange. The apparent isotope effect in a reaction which proceeds via an enol necessarily reflects this equilibrium shift; thus, the observed isotope effect, if it is of the same size as the expected equilibrium shift, as in the case of vanadium(V), cannot be used to distinguish a direct attack on a ketone from an attack on its enol.

On the other hand, the solvent isotope effect, k_{H_2O}/k_{D_2O}, can discriminate between these two mechanisms. Acid catalyzed enolization of either protio or deuterio ketone is accelerated in deuterium oxide, owing to the well-known phenomenon that acids are weaker in deuterium oxide than in water,[92] whereas the rate of ketonization of an enol is independent of the solvent, as it depends not on an equilibrium protonation but on a rate-determining protona-tion, which is equally rapid in both solvents.[93]

Consequently the solvent isotope effect measured before isotopic exchange becomes significant, can be compared with that predicted from the known acid dependence of the oxidation reaction; if they agree the attack must be on the

[91] P. A. Best, J. S. Littler, and W. A. Waters, *J. Chem. Soc.* p. 822 (1962).

[92] C. K. Rule and V. K. LaMer, *J. Am. Chem. Soc.* **60**, 1974 (1938).

[93] F. A. Long and D. Watson, *J. Chem. Soc.* p. 2019 (1958); Y. Pocker, *Proc. Chem. Soc.* p. 17 (1960).

ketone itself, but if there is evidence from the isotopic effect of a higher order of acid catalysis than the kinetics show, this is due to the acid catalyzed enolization step, and attack must be on the enol.

Measurements of these solvent isotope effects provide confirmatory evidence of direct attack on the ketonic form of cyclohexanone in the oxidations by manganese(III) sulfate, and by both cobalt(III) sulfate and perchlorate. They also show that vanadium(V) [and cerium(IV)] attack the ketone directly, whereas chromium(VI) can be shown to attack the enol.[91] It is therefore possible to postulate the following mechanism for attack on cyclohexanone by manganese(III) sulfate and by vanadium(V); for cobalt(III) the mechanism cannot involve C—H fission in a rate-determining step.

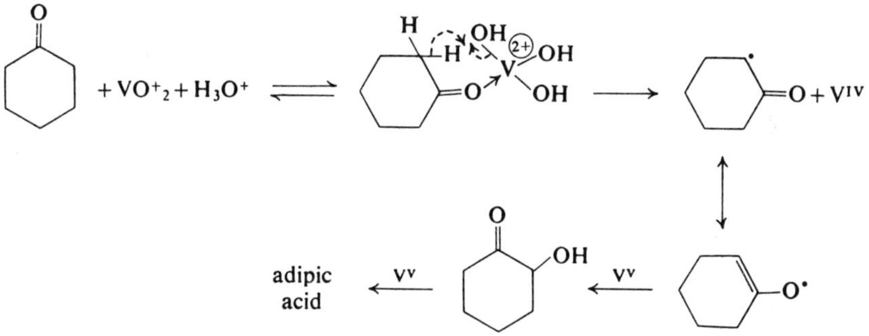

The nature of the radical has been confirmed by infrared investigation of the polyacrylonitrile obtained from the oxidation of cyclopentanone by vanadium in the presence of acrylonitrile: the typical absorption of a carbonyl group in a five-membered ring can be seen. In the case of cobalt(III), the rate-determining step could be either the initial substitution of the ketone in the cobalt(III) coordination sphere or the electron removal from the carbonyl group. The latter could be a direct ("outer sphere") process or, alternatively, an inner sphere process subsequent to the substitution step, and it would leave a radical ion that could achieve stability by hydration followed by fission, or by subsequent loss of an α-proton (see p. 226).

Evidently, manganese(III) pyrophosphate is an exception to the rule of direct attack in acid conditions. One possible explanation might be that the solution could contain a small amount of manganese(IV) pyrophosphate, which would be expected to be a two-equivalent oxidant and, like bromine, etc., attack the enol form rapidly. The observed kinetics would not preclude this, though the evidence for some contribution by a radical mechanism is extremely strong. Similar kinetics are observed in oxidation of ketones by manganese(III) acetate.[94] The oxidation by manganese(III) sulfate is first

[94] R. van Helden and E. C. Kooyman, *Rec. Trav. Chim.* **80**, 57 (1961); R. van Helden, A. F. Bickel, and E. C. Kooyman, *Rec. Trav. Chim.* **80**, 1237, 1257 (1961).

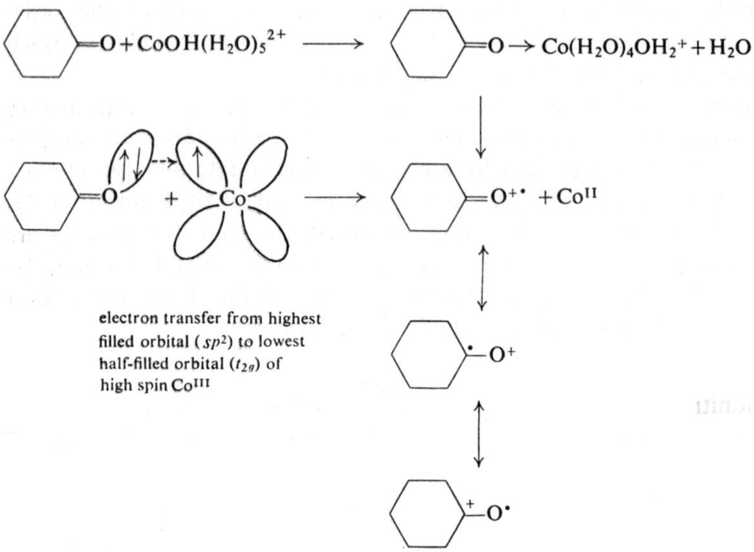

electron transfer from highest
filled orbital (sp^2) to lowest
half-filled orbital (t_{2g}) of
high spin Co^{III}

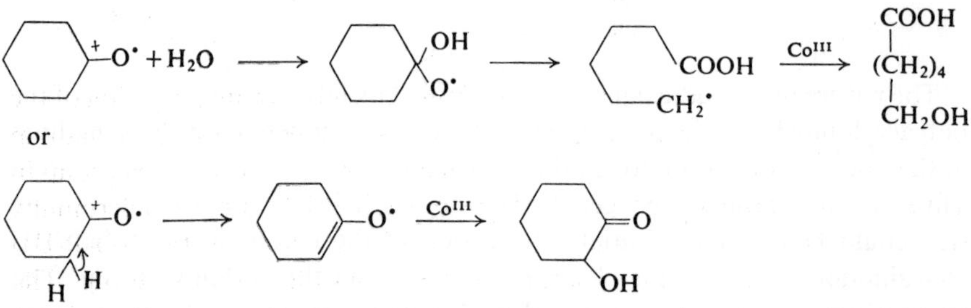

or

order in manganese(III) and not affected by manganese(II), so manganese(IV) is not important under these conditions.

The oxidations of keto acids and 1,2-diketones[95] are too fast for convenient study with vanadium(V),[30] but the oxidations of pyruvic acid[75] and (briefly) mesoxalic acid[8] by manganese pyrophosphate has been studied kinetically. Complexing was kinetically detectable, and so homolytic fission of a chelate complex provides a rational mechanism[36]:

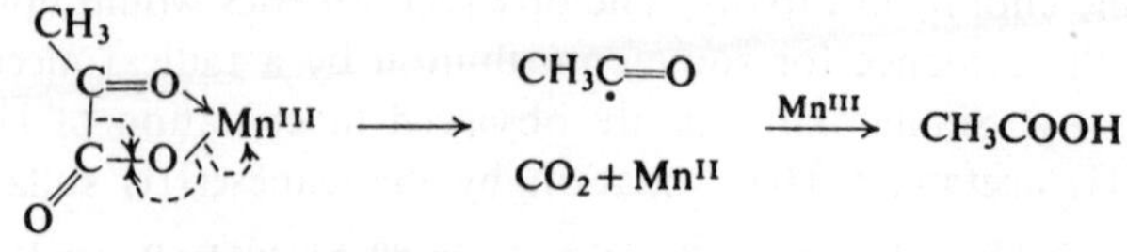

[95] H. Funk, W. Weiss, and M. Zeising, Z. Anorg. Allgem. Chem. 296, 36 (1958).

B. PRODUCT STUDIES

The immediate products of oxidation of ketones are often difficult to determine, owing to their ease of further oxidation. From cyclohexanone and manganese(III) pyrophosphate, 2-hydroxycyclohexanone has been isolated[75]; if manganese(III) sulfate is used, adipic acid has been isolated in good yield; although intermediates could not be isolated, it has been shown that the α-hydroxy ketone was readily oxidized to 1,2-cyclohexanedione which is readily oxidized by C—C fission to adipic acid. Had such fission occurred in the first stage it should have been possible to isolate ω-hydroxyhexanoic acid or rather the lactone or polymeric ester derived from it. Cyclopentanone was more extensively degraded by vanadium(V) and gave some formic acid. The amount of vanadium reduced was consistent with eventual oxidation to succinic acid. Methyl cyclohexanone and menthone have been oxidized by vanadium(V) to keto acids[96]:

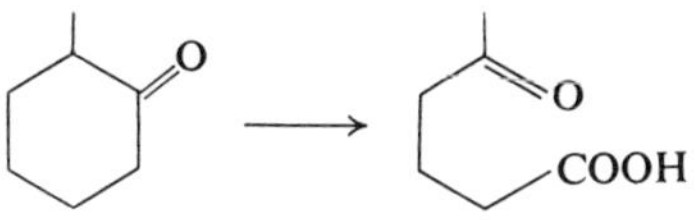

mesityl oxide undergoes extensive degradation to acetone and acetic acid, whereas methyl isopropyl ketone gave no isobutyric acid, and only traces of formic acid, so that the initial attack takes place at the tertiary H atom:

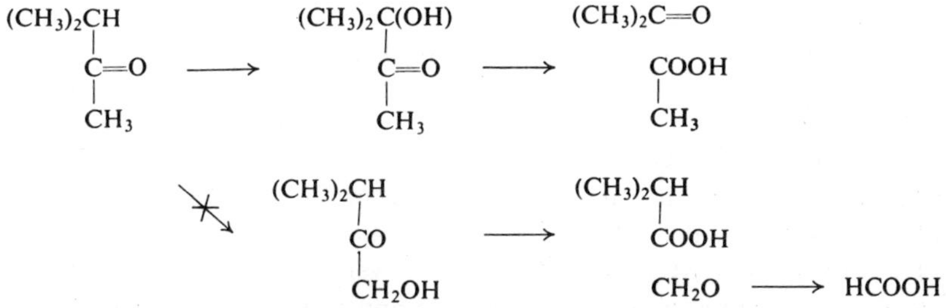

Acetone itself is rather resistant to oxidation, but under vigorous oxidation conditions it gives acetic and formic acids, together with a trace of formaldehyde.[97] In nonaqueous solution (vanadium oxytrichloride in carbon tetrachloride), cyclohexanone gives a mixture of chloroketones (up to 35% yield of α-chlorocyclohexanone), and with the oxychloride in acetic acid, acetylated products are also formed.[30]

[96] J. R. Jones, Thesis, University of Oxford, England, 1959.
[97] G. Gaudefroy, *Ann. Pharm. Franc.* **13**, 51 (1955); *Chem. Abstr.* **49**, 10784 (1955).

The oxidations of benzyl phenyl ketone by manganese(III) in acetic acid yield dimeric products, and this has been interpreted as evidence for the formation of an intermediate free radical[94] that is not easily further oxidized:

$$\begin{array}{ccc} \phi\!-\!CH_2 & & \phi\!-\!CH^{\cdot} & & \phi\!-\!CH\!-\!CH\!-\!\phi \\ | & +\ Mn^{III} \longrightarrow & | & \longrightarrow & |\quad\quad| \\ \phi\!-\!CO & & \phi\!-\!C\!=\!O & & \phi\!-\!CO\quad CO\!-\!\phi \end{array}$$

However, dimeric products have been obtained in oxidations of ketones by lead(IV) acetate[98] ($10°$ C, in benzene), and there is no evidence for the generation of free radicals from this oxidant under these mild conditions. A two-equivalent mechanism could account for the products in both these oxidations:

$$\begin{array}{c} \phi\!-\!C\overset{O}{\diagdown}\\ \quad CH\!-\!M(OAc)_3 \\ \phi \diagup \ \ OAc \end{array} \longrightarrow \begin{array}{c} \phi\!-\!C\overset{O}{\diagdown}\\ \quad CHOAc + M^{II}(OAc)_2 + OAc^- \\ \phi\diagup \end{array}$$

or

$$\begin{array}{c} \phi\!-\!C\overset{O}{\diagdown}\\ \quad\quad M(OAc)_3^+ \\ CH \\ \phi\diagup \end{array} + \begin{array}{c} \phi\ \ OH \\ \diagdown C\diagup \\ || \\ CH \\ \phi\diagup \end{array} \longrightarrow \begin{array}{c} \phi\ \diagdown C\diagup O \diagdown C\diagup \phi\\ \ \ || \quad\quad ||\\ CH\!-\!CH \\ \phi\diagup \ \ \ \diagdown\phi \end{array} + M(OAc)_2$$

where $M = Mn^{IV}$ or Pb^{IV}.

VIII. Carboxylic Acids

A. OXALIC ACID

The oxidations of oxalic acid are strongly influenced by its ease of complex formation with transition metals. This reduces the redox potential of the $Co^{III}\!-\!Co^{II}$ couple to about 1.0–1.3 volts.[99] Similarly, both manganese(III) and (IV) are considerably stabilized. This effect is very important in the oxidation of oxalate by permanganate, as the decomposition of the manganese(III) oxalate complex provides the main route for the oxidation.[3, 100] The manganese(II)–manganese(III)–manganese(IV) exchange reaction, important as a step in the Guyard reaction, is catalyzed by oxalate, presumably by formation

[98] W. Cocker and J. C. P. Schwarz, *Chem. & Ind.* (*London*) p. 390 (1951); G. W. K. Cavill and D. H. Solomon, *J. Chem. Soc.* p. 4426 (1955); G. W. K. Cavill and D. H. Solomon, *J. Chem. Soc.* p. 3943 (1954); D. I. Davies, *J. Chem. Soc.* p. 2351 (1963).

[99] T. B. Copestake and N. Uri, *Proc. Roy. Soc.* **A228**, 252 (1955).

[100] W. V. Bhagwat and N. R. Dhar, *Z. Anorg. Allgem. Chem.* **197**, 18 (1931); I. C. Murgulescu and T. Oncescu, *Z. Physik. Chem.* (*Leipzig*) **214**, 238 (1960).

of the manganese(III) and (IV)–oxalate complexes,[101] and it has been shown that these oxalate complexes undergo both photochemical and thermal redox decomposition.

Again, manganese(III) pyrophosphate oxidizes oxalic acid, and of the complexes formed between manganese(III) and oxalic acid the monoxalate complex is the most reactive, and the trioxalate the least. Taube[102] has rationalized this on the supposition that $Mn^{III}(C_2O_4)_n$ complexes more strongly with a further oxalate ligand than does $Mn^{II}(C_2O_4)_{(n-1)}$, the product of the oxidation, so that as n increases from 1 to 3, the free energy of the reaction becomes less negative, and this is reflected in an increase in the activation energy. The stability constants of the manganese(II) and (III)–oxalate complexes are now known to be compatible with this reasoning.[103] The same factors may be operating in the cobalt series since the dioxalate complex of cobalt(III), $Co(C_2O_4)_2^-$, is more reactive than the tris-oxalate one $Co(C_2O_4)_3^{3-}$ at room temperature, whereas the direct reaction between Co^{3+}_{aq} and oxalic acid does not appear to have been measured. However there is a very big difference in the activation entropies for the decomposition of $Co(C_2O_4)_2(OH_2)_2^-$ and $Co(C_2O_4)_3^{3-}$, which suggests that the mechanisms of decomposition of the bis- and tris-oxalate complexes may not be comparable. In fact there is evidence[104] that a preliminary step involving $Co(C_2O_4)_3^{3-} \rightleftharpoons Co^{2-}(C_2O_4)_2OH_2—OCOCOO^-$ may be required: this is consistent with the entropy data. The second step forms $CO_2 + CO_2^-$, rather than $C_2O_4^-$, as is shown by the lack of exchange between the liberated radical and isotopically labeled oxalate in the solution. The same intermediate provides a path for the exchange of cobalt(II) and cobalt(III) in oxalate solution. An earlier suggestion[105] that the $C_2O_4^-$ radical is generated reversibly

$$Co(C_2O_4)_3^{3-} \rightleftharpoons Co(C_2O_4)_2^{2-} + C_2O_4^-$$

does not seem to be borne out by this more recent work.

In the oxidations by vanadium(V),[106] only the dioxalate complex is extensively formed

$$\beta_2 = \frac{[VO_2(C_2O_4)_2^{3-}]}{[VO_3^-][C_2O_4H^-]^2} = \text{ca. } 5 \times 10^7 \text{ from ref. 106, cf. 103, } \log\beta_2 = 7.6$$

[101] G. H. Cartledge and W. B. Ericks, *J. Am. Chem. Soc.* **58**, 2061, 2065, 2069 (1936).

[102] H. Taube, *J. Am. Chem. Soc.* **70**, 1216 (1948).

[103] "Stability Constants," Chem. Soc. Spec. Publ. No. 6 (1957).

[104] F. S. Dainton, G. S. Laurence, W. Schneider, D. R. Stranks, and M. S. Vaidya, *Proc. UNESCO Isotope Conf., Paris*, 1957 (R. C. Extermann, ed.) Vol. II, p. 305. Macmillan (Pergamon), New York; W. Schneider, *Helv. Chim. Acta.* **46**, 1863 (1963).

[105] A. W. Adamson, H. Ogata, J. Grossman, and R. Newbury, *J. Inorg. Nucl. Chem.* **6**, 319 (1958).

[106] J. R. Jones and W. A. Waters, *J. Chem. Soc.* p. 4757 (1961); H. Kurihara and T. Nozaki, *J. Chem. Soc. Japan* **83**, 708 (1962).

and it is stable unless it is multiply protonated. However cationic mono- and dioxalate complexes, and a trisoxalate complex, all appear to be unstable to thermal redox decomposition. It would not be expected that any simple relationship between oxidation rate and degree of complexing would be found in this system, in which the extent of hydrolysis and the coordination numbers of both vanadium(IV) and (V) may be variable.

There are three paths for the oxidation of oxalic acid by vanadium(V). In strong acid, an acid catalyzed path is observed, which corresponds to the decomposition of a complex of formula $[V(OH)_3H_2C_2O_4]^{2+}$; at lower acidities $(0.5\,M)$ the reaction rate decreases with increasing acidity and has an approximately second order dependence on oxalic acid; the following scheme can account for this:

$$VO_2^+ + 2\,H_2C_2O_4 \rightleftharpoons VOH(C_2O_4)_2 + H_3O^+$$

$$VOH(C_2O_4)_2 \xrightarrow{\text{slow}} V^{IV} + C_2O_4^- \qquad \text{etc.}$$

These two processes combine to produce a minimum rate in 2–$3\,M$ acid. A third mechanism prevails at about pH 1. Here almost all the vanadium is present as a dioxalate complex. Such a complex exists within the pH range from 2 to 6, and has the formula $[V(C_2O_4)_2O_2]^{3-}$. This, or a more protonated species, reacts at a rate independent of the acidity, with undissociated oxalic acid, such as:

$$VO(C_2O_4)_2^- + H_2C_2O_4 \rightleftharpoons V(C_2O_4)_3^- + H_2O$$

$$V(C_2O_4)_3^- \rightarrow \text{products}$$

No oxidation occurs at acidities below pH 2 since no undissociated oxalic acid is present.

The reaction is also strongly catalyzed by manganese(II), perhaps by formation and decomposition of a manganese(III) oxalate complex. The catalyzed reaction has a remarkably low activation energy. A possible reason is that the rate-determining step may be the electron transfer[107]:

$$V^V + Mn^{II}(C_2O_4)_n \rightarrow V^{IV} + Mn^{III}(C_2O_4)_n$$

B. FORMIC ACID

Formic acid can also be considered as an aldehyde, and these oxidants attack it, though it is generally much more susceptible to attack by two-equivalent oxidants. Both the acid and its anion can be attacked. With manganese(III) sulfate the free acid is attacked both by a first order reaction, and also by a path which is both third order in manganese(III) and retarded by manganese(II).[80] In addition, formic acid forms a complex with manganese(III) which affects the observed kinetics.

Both paths show a C—H (C—D) isotope effect. The direct attack resembles that for formaldehyde oxidation, whereas the third order term implies that both manganese(III) and (IV) are involved. Manganese(IV) alone cannot be involved but a concerted mechanism such as

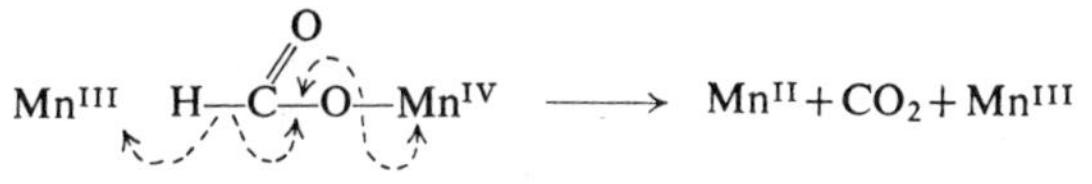

$$Mn^{III} \quad H\!-\!\overset{\displaystyle O}{\underset{}{C}}\!-\!O\!-\!Mn^{IV} \quad \longrightarrow \quad Mn^{II}+CO_2+Mn^{III}$$

can account for the kinetics.

Vanadium(V) oxidation of formic acid is first order in vanadium(V) and a C—H (C—D) isotope effect is observed of similar magnitude to that which occurs in oxidations of alcohols. Manganese(II) does not interfere with this reaction, so the inhibition by manganese(II) observed in the manganese(III) oxidation is unlikely to be due to the oxidative properties of an intermediate free radical:

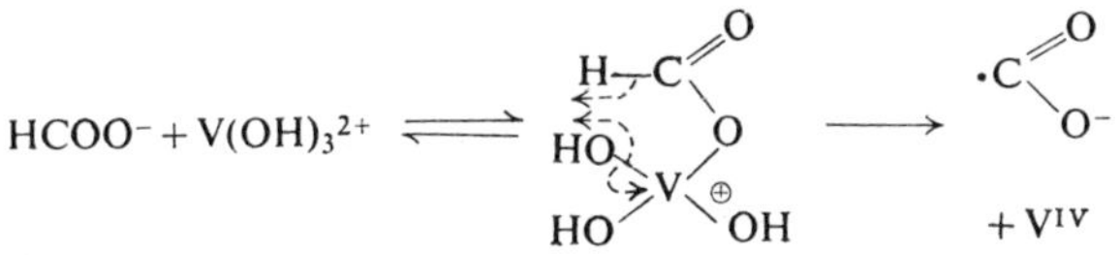

$$HCOO^- + V(OH)_3^{2+} \rightleftharpoons \underset{\underset{HO}{HO}\diagdown V \diagup OH}{\overset{H\!-\!C\diagup O}{\overset{\diagup}{\underset{\oplus}{}}}} O \longrightarrow \overset{\cdot C\diagup O}{\underset{O^-}{}} + V^{IV}$$

The kinetics and isotope effect observed in the cobalt(III) oxidation of formic acid are almost identical to those observed in the oxidations of secondary alcohols or formaldehyde. A similar mechanism can be written involving attack by Co^{3+}_{aq} and $CoOH^{2+}_{aq}$ on formic acid, though it is not possible to show that reaction between Co^{3+} and $HCOO^-$ does not also occur. The oxidation of the formate ligand in the cobalt(III) complex $Co(NH_3)_5 \, O\cdot CO\cdot H^{2+}$ by the permanganate ion does not appear to be concerted with the reduction of the cobalt(III) center, but such reduction can occur in a subsequent step[81]:

$$MnO_4^- + (NH_3)_5 \, CoOCOH^{2+} \rightarrow HMnO_4^- + (NH_3)_5CoOCO^{2+}$$

$$(NH_3)_5CoOCO^{2+} + H_2O \rightarrow (NH_3)_5Co^{2+}OH_2 + CO_2$$

$$(NH_3)_5CoOCO^{2+} + MnO_4^- \rightarrow (NH_3)_5Co^{3+}OH_2 + CO_2 + Mn^{VI}$$

This system may provide an analogy for the manganese(III) formate reaction above.

C. MALONIC ACID

Malonic acid is oxidized by all these reagents.[36] The first to be investigated was the oxidation by manganese(III) pyrophosphate. The observed kinetics were unusual in that the reaction was second order in manganese(III) and retarded by manganese(II), and this was accounted for as follows:

(i) the formation of a complex between the reagents by a fast equilibration:

Mn^{III} pyrophosphate $+ CH_2(COOH)_2 \rightleftharpoons$
$\quad\quad Mn^{III}CH_2(COOH)_2$ pyrophosphate ($Py_2Mn^{III}Ma$ for brevity) $+$ pyrophosphate

(ii) its *reversible* decomposition:

$$Py_2Mn^{III}Ma \underset{k_2}{\overset{k_1}{\rightleftharpoons}} Mn^{II} + \cdot CH(COOH)_2$$

(iii) the oxidation of some of the radicals:

$$Mn^{III} + \cdot CH(COOH)_2 \overset{k_3}{\longrightarrow} Mn^{II} + CHOH(COOH)_2$$

where k_2 and k_3 are comparable and either k_1 or k_3 may be rate determining.

This mechanism accounts for the observed kinetics, except for a very small term in $(Mn^{III})^3$, and explains the strong evidence for the presence of an oxidizing intermediate radical, which can: (a) attack a variety of alcohols and ethers which are otherwise inert; (b) react with oxygen; and (c) polymerize acrylonitrile.

However, since ethylmalonic acid and benzylmalonic acid are both oxidized by a much simpler mechanism which is first order in manganese(III) and not retarded by manganese(II), it was concluded that the redox potential of the $\cdot CH(COOH)_2$—$CH_2(COOH)_2$ couple must be only slightly higher than that of the manganese(III)–manganese(II) pyrophosphate couple, and must be reduced below it by the inductive effect of the alkyl group.

Later work has shown that the malonate radical does not reoxidize vanadium(IV) to (V), though the redox potential for this system is very similar to that of manganese(III) pyrophosphate. Again, manganese(II) does not retard the oxidation of malonic acid by vanadium(V), but in fact is a positive catalyst. The oxidation of malonic acid by manganese(III) in sulfate solutions follows the same kinetics as does the oxidation in pyrophosphate solutions, although the redox potential of the manganese(III)–manganese(II) couple is so much higher that the radical $\cdot CH(COOH)_2$ should then be unable to oxidize the manganese(II) ion.[107]

The following scheme is consistent with all these observations (L = a bidentate ligand, i.e., sulfate or pyrophosphate):

$$MnL_3^{III} + CH_2(COOH)_2 \overset{K}{\rightleftharpoons} MnL_2Ma^{III} + L$$

$$MnL_2Ma^{III} + Mn^{III} \underset{k_2}{\overset{k_1}{\rightleftharpoons}} MnL_2Ma^{IV} + Mn^{II}$$

$$MnL_2Ma^{IV} \overset{k_4}{\longrightarrow} Mn^{II} + \text{products}$$

$$MnL_2Ma^{IV} + Mn^{III} \overset{k_3}{\longrightarrow} Mn^{II} + Mn^{III} + \text{products}$$

[107] T. J. Kemp and W. A. Waters, *J. Chem. Soc.* pp. 1489, 3101, 3193 (1964).

The active intermediate may be the $Mn^{IV}L_2Ma$ complex, which can behave as a free radical complex of manganese(III) because the t_{2g} orbitals of the metal can interact with the π system of the ligand, and so the complex can react with oxygen, acrylonitrile, alcohols, etc. (cf. ref. 108):

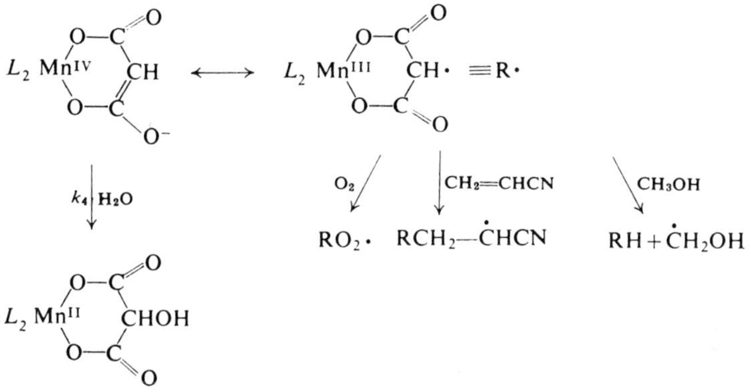

$$L_2\ Mn^{IV}\ \text{(chelate)} \quad\longleftrightarrow\quad L_2\ Mn^{III}\ \text{(chelate)} \quad CH\cdot \equiv R\cdot$$

$$\big| k_4\ H_2O$$

$$O_2 \Big/ \quad \Big| CH_2{=}CHCN \quad \Big\backslash CH_3OH$$

$$RO_2\cdot \quad RCH_2{-}\dot{C}HCN \quad RH+\dot{C}H_2OH$$

$$L_2\ Mn^{II}\ \text{(CHOH chelate)}$$

Reaction k_4 could be perhaps split into the sequence

$$Mn^{IV}MaL_2 \underset{k_6}{\overset{k_5}{\rightleftharpoons}} Mn^{III}+R\cdot \qquad R = \text{malonic acid radical}$$

$$R\cdot + Mn^{III} \xrightarrow{k_7} Mn^{II} + \text{products}$$

This would liberate the malonic acid radical, but requires that k_6 be greater than k_7 if induced oxidation (of alcohols, etc.) is to accelerate the reduction of manganese(III). This condition is unlikely to hold when L is the sulfate group, even if it does when L is the pyrophosphate group. The cage effect must also reduce the chances of $R\cdot$ becoming sufficiently free to cause induced oxidations.

Reaction k_3 is necessary to account for the small third order term; although it, as written above, has Mn^{III} on each side of the equation, it should be viewed as an attack by Mn^{III} on a chelate complex of radical character. This is similar to the scheme suggested for the oxidation of formic acid:

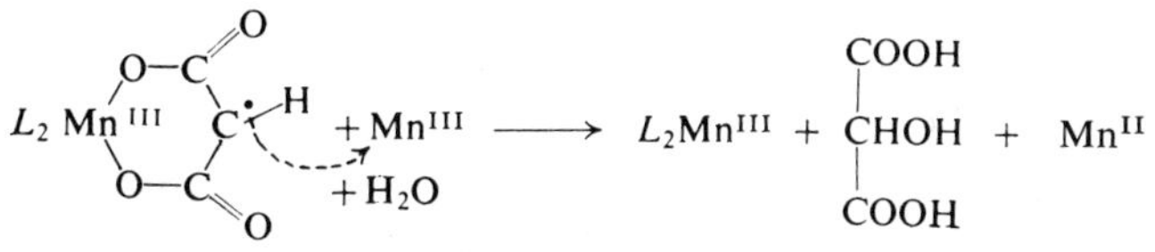

$$L_2\ Mn^{III}\ \text{(chelate, } \dot{C}H) + Mn^{III} + H_2O \longrightarrow L_2Mn^{III} + \begin{array}{c}COOH\\|\\CHOH\\|\\COOH\end{array} + Mn^{II}$$

The oxidation of malonic acid by vanadium(V) sulfate is relatively slow,[80] showing no kinetic evidence for complex formation, and it is not very sensitive

[108] E. M. Arnett and M. A. Mendelsohn, *J. Am. Chem. Soc.* **84**, 3821, 3824 (1962).

to the acidity of the medium. Like the oxidation of formaldehyde, however, the reaction is, for the greater part, second order in vanadium(V), although it is not [unlike the above manganese(III) oxidation] retarded by the lower valence of the oxidant. Thus the transition state contains two vanadium(V) ions and a malonic acid molecule; consequently, a cyclic mechanism such as the following seems indicated:

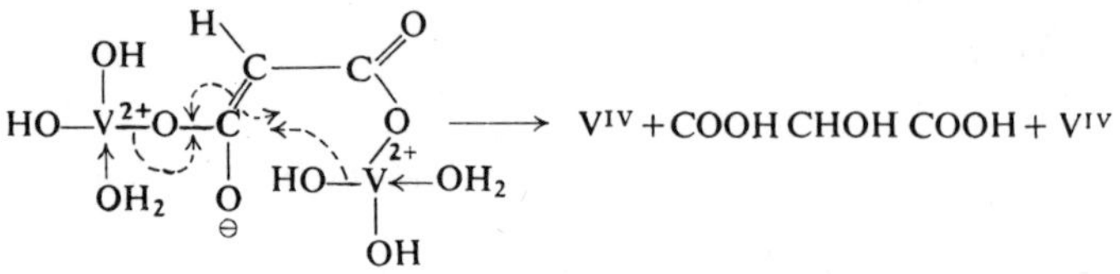

This reaction is strongly catalyzed by the addition of manganese(II).[107] It then ceases to be second order in vanadium(V), and becomes inhibited by vanadium(IV). The kinetic data are consistent with the extensive formation of a manganese(II) malonic acid complex, which is oxidized by vanadium(V) to manganese(III) and then decomposes. Under these conditions, the decomposition of a manganese(IV) complex is not observed, as the equilibrium manganese(III) concentration is too low. Chromium(VI) can replace vanadium(V) in this process, and a marked catalysis by manganese(II) of oxidation of hydroxy acids by chromium(VI) can be explained by the rapid decomposition of reversibly formed manganese(III)–hydroxy acid complexes.[80, 107]

The oxidation of malonic acid by cobalt(III) is another reaction in which complexing between Co^{3+}_{aq} and an organic substrate has been detected kinetically. Evidently in these cases substitution in the coordination sphere cannot be rate determining. The reaction is comparable in speed to other oxidations of carboxylic acids by cobalt(III).[109] Malonate, like oxalate, can form a conjugated bridge between two metal ions if it is in the enol form, and electron-transfer reactions involving such a bridge are known.[110]

D. OTHER ACIDS

Manganese(III) is not recorded as oxidizing any aliphatic carboxylic acids or even unsaturated acids.[39] These are also very resistant to attack by vanadium(V), though branched chain and unsaturated acids are somewhat attacked.[36] Cobalt(III) (as $CoOH^{2+}_{aq}$), however, is a sufficiently powerful oxidant, at least when a relatively stable radical may be formed, as is the case in oxidation of phenylacetic,[109] isobutyric, or pivalic acids. β-Phenyl propionic

[109] A. A. Clifford and W. A. Waters, J. Chem. Soc. p. 2796 (1965).
[110] G. Svatos and H. Taube, J. Am. Chem. Soc. 83, 4172 (1961).

acid, and even acetic acid, which do not give stabilized radicals, are oxidized less easily. $C_6H_5C(CH_3)_2CH_2COOH$ is oxidized to products $[C_6H_5CHO+(CH_3)_2CO]$ which show that a rearrangement has occurred, and a radical, presumably C_2H_5, generated by the oxidation of propionic acid, can attack toluene and so catalyze its oxidation. The formation of complexes between the reagents is sometimes detectable kinetically. Manganese(III) acetate can also attack phenylacetic acid, giving products[94] such as $C_6H_5CH_2OCOCH_2C_6H_5$ which can be visualized as arising via the benzyl radical.

It is noticeable that the relative ease of oxidation of carboxylic acids by cobalt(III) in no way parallels their ease of oxidation by chromium(VI).[111] The latter oxidant preferentially attacks tertiary hydrogen atoms, whether they are close to or remote from the carboxyl group, whereas the behavior of the former oxidant is in accord with a mechanism such as

$$RCOO^- + Co^{III} \rightarrow R\cdot + CO_2 + Co^{II}$$

in which the whole decomposition is a concerted process.[109]

IX. Other Oxidations

A. HYDROCARBONS

Although vanadium(V) in aqueous acid is reduced by olefins, it is not certain to what extent traces of hydroperoxide catalyze the reaction. Also, if kinetics are to be studied, some solvent must be used which can dissolve both the olefin and the oxidant. The simplest vanadium(V) compound which is soluble in nonaqueous solvents is the oxytrichloride $VOCl_3$; an acetate can also be obtained in glacial acetic acid solution.

Exploratory work has shown that neither of these reagents is sufficiently powerful to attack olefins, or even alcohols, unless a Lewis acid such as BF_3, $POCl_3$, or acetyl chloride is also present.[30] When $POCl_3$ was used, an 80% yield of 1:2 dichlorohexane (mainly *trans*) was obtained from cyclohexene. Oxidative degradation was by no means so extensive in these solutions as in aqueous media. This is to be expected since chlorinated or acetylated products, resistant to further oxidation, are formed.

In contrast, cobalt(III) oxidizes olefins at a measurable rate, and the reaction has been studied in aqueous solution.[112] Unlike the other oxidations of organic compounds by cobalt(III), this reaction is independent of the

[111] F. Mareš and J. Roček, *Collection Czech. Chem. Commun.* **26**, 2389 (1961); K. Nakanishi and L. F. Feiser, *J. Am. Chem. Soc.* **74**, 3910 (1952).
[112] C. E. H. Bawn and J. A. Sharp, *J. Chem. Soc.* pp. 1854, 1866 (1957).

acidity, and of first order with respect to both cobalt(III) and the olefin, and so it has been represented as

$$Co_{aq}^{3+} + R—CH=CH_2 \xrightarrow{\text{slow}} R—CH—CH_2^+ + Co^{2+}$$

$$R—\overset{\cdot}{C}H—CH_2^+ + Co^{3+} + 2H_2O \longrightarrow R—CHOH—CH_2OH + Co^{2+} + 2\,H^+$$

$$\overset{Co^{3+}}{\searrow} \text{further products}$$

Cobalt(III) does not attack olefins in glacial acetic acid, although in aqueous acid, cobalt(III) acetate attacks olefins at a rate independent of the olefin concentration, which is evidently due to some process of activation of cobaltic acetate. Cobalt(III) also attacks acetylene,[113] and its oxidation of benzene in aqueous solution has been studied kinetically.[114] This is first order in each reactant, and the reactions due to Co^{3+}_{aq} and $CoOH^{2+}_{aq}$ are each measurable. Presumably the reaction generated the phenyl radical, but this was oxidized so rapidly that no diphenyl was detected. The ultimate products were p-benzoquinone and muconic acid

$$COOH—CH=CH—CH=CH—COOH$$

The following equations have been written, but need confirmation by some independent experimental test:

$$C_6H_6 + Co^{3+} \to C_6H_5\cdot + H^+ + Co^{2+}$$

$$C_6H_5\cdot + Co^{3+} + H_2O \to C_6H_5OH + Co^{2+} + H^+$$

Although aqueous vanadium(V) will not attack benzene itself, it will oxidize naphthalene and other polycyclic aromatic hydrocarbons, provided that acetic acid is present as a cosolvent.[96] At 50° C in 6 M sulfuric acid, phenanthrene yielded up to 38 % of the quinone, and acenaphthene 25 %, but very little acidic material was obtained. Manganese(III) acetate will also acetoxylate anthracene and give a dimer from anthrone,[115] but it does not attack cyclohexene or stilbene. However, manganese(III) sulfate, generated electrolytically in situ has been used to oxidize toluene to benzoic acid, and toluic acid to phthalic acid,[116] whereas manganese(III) acetate oxidizes dibenzyl and triphenylmethane[115]; one can assume that Co^{III} can also do this.

There is little direct evidence for attack on saturated aliphatic hydrocarbons by any of these ions. However, their use as autoxidation catalysts suggests that a sufficient attack of the general type

$$RH + Ox \to R\cdot + HOx$$

[113] S. Swann and T. S. Xanthakos, J. Am. Chem. Soc. 53, 400 (1931).
[114] J. H. Baxendale and C. F. Wells, Discussions Faraday Soc. 14, 239 (1953).
[115] S. A. Zonis, Chem. Abstr. 49, 5414 (1955).
[116] C. F. Cullis and J. W. Ladbury, J. Chem. Soc. pp. 555, 2850 (1955); M. S. Venkatachalapathy, R. Ramaswamy, and H. V. K. Udupa, Chem. Abstr. 54, 22461 (1960).

might occur either thermally or photochemically, to initiate autoxidation chain reactions. Alternatively, the catalysis of autoxidation by an active transition metal cation might follow attack on the solvent to form a simple free radical such as:

$$Co^{III} + H_2O \rightarrow Co^{II} + \cdot OH + H^+$$

$$Co^{III} + CH_3COOH \rightarrow Co^{II} + H^+ + CO_2 + CH_3 \cdot$$

$$Co^{III} + HBr \rightarrow Co^{II} + H^+ + Br \cdot$$

from which an autoxidation chain might arise as follows[117]:

$$RH + CH_3 \cdot \rightarrow R \cdot + CH_4$$

$$R \cdot + O_2 \rightarrow RO_2 \cdot \quad \text{etc.}[118]$$

The recent demonstration by Clifford and Waters[109] of the formation of free radicals by the direct oxidation of organic acids by cobalt(III) perchlorate provides a simple interpretation of the initiation of these autoxidations.[64]

Chelate complexes of both cobalt and manganese are very good autoxidation catalysts, but many of these are effective only in the presence of preformed peroxides.

B. PHENOLS

Phenols are easily oxidized by all these systems. However, the reactions are very rapid and have not been studied as to either their kinetics or their products. A brown color is formed initially in the manganese(III) phenol reaction, as in the cerium(IV) phenol and iron(III) phenol reactions, due to the formation of a complex which exhibits a strong charge-transfer absorption. Such a complex is not detectable with vanadium and simple phenols.[119] The product of oxidation must be a phenoxy radical, which can undergo a variety of reactions.[120] In nonpolar solvents, vanadium oxytrichloride forms phenolic esters which can be isolated,[95] although they are sensitive both to photochemical decomposition and to hydrolysis. These are similar in reactivity to the vanadic esters of monohydric alcohols and glycols.[30] Vanadium(V) oxidation of hydroquinones to quinones has been used as a method of analysis.[121] The attack of manganese(III) on phenols appears to be the rate-determining step in their oxidation by permanganate,[122] and when *p*-methyl

[117] D. A. S. Ravens, *Trans. Faraday Soc.* **55**, 1768 (1959).

[118] W. A. Waters, *Progr. Org. Chem.* **5**, 1 (1961); K. U. Ingold, *Chem. Rev.* **61**, 563 (1962); N. Uri, "Free Radicals in Organic Chemistry," p. 102. *Advan. Chem. Ser.* (1962).

[119] J. S. Littler and W. A. Waters, *J. Chem. Soc.* p. 1299 (1959); J. S. Littler, Thesis, University of Oxford, England, 1959.

[120] K. S. Panwar and J. N. Gaur, *Naturwissenschaften* **48**, 602 (1961).

[121] G. G. Rao, V. B. Rao, and M. N. Sastri, *Current Sci. (India)* **18**, 381 (1949); *Chem. Abstr.* **44**, 2892 (1950); M. Narasimhasastri, J. V. S. Ramanjaneyulu, and G. G. Rao, *Current Sci. (India)* **18**, 169 (1949); *Chem. Abstr.* **43**, 7376 (1949).

[122] E. A. Alexander and F. C. Tompkins, *Trans. Faraday Soc.* **35**, 1156 (1936).

o-di-*tert*-butyl-phenol is used, acetoxylation of the p-CH$_3$ group by manganese(III) acetate can occur.[94] This is in agreement with the known reaction of hindered phenol radicals which can be generated by one-electron oxidants and detected by electron spin resonance.[123]

C. COMPOUNDS CONTAINING NITROGEN

It is to be expected that nitrogen-containing functional groups are not vulnerable to oxidation by these reagents, as under the conditions of acidity required the nitrogen atom will be almost entirely in quadricovalent form. This absence of unshared electrons explains the considerable resistance of amino acids to oxidation. However, oxidations of aliphatic amines by vanadium(V)[119] or manganese(III)[39] and a rapid attack on aromatic amines by vanadium have been reported. Also, ethylenediamine tetraacetic acid (EDTA) can both be oxidized by, and form complexes with, all three metals. The cobalt complex decomposes on heating to give formaldehyde, and it is probable that even in the presence of a ligand such as

$$[(NH_2CH_2CH_2)_2N—CH_2]_2,$$

which preferentially stabilizes the cobalt(III) state to a very large extent, some oxidation can occur under extreme conditions, to give cobalt(II) and provide a route for ligand exchange via electron transfer.[124, 125] The manganese(III) EDTA complex also decomposes, giving formaldehyde; interestingly, it oxidizes free excess EDTA in preference to the bound material.[126] EDTA is oxidized by vanadium(V).[117, 126] Oxidation of α-amino acids by manganese(III) acetate has been studied kinetically. It is second order in manganese(III) and inhibited by manganese(II), indicating either attack by manganese(IV) acetate, or a reversible first step, as in Drummond and Waters' mechanism for the oxidation of malonic acid. The CH(NH$_2$)COOH group must be present if attack is to be easy.[34] Hydrazine and hydrazine derivatives are of course readily oxidized by these reagents.

D. CATALYZED OXIDATIONS

Several industrial processes are catalyzed by vanadium in homogeneous solution. One is the preparation of chlorine dioxide from sodium chlorate, by reduction by a variety of waste organic materials, for which a vanadium or cobalt catalyst is used in strong acid[127]; a chlorate–vanadium mixture has also

[123] T. J. Stone and W. A. Waters, *Proc. Chem. Soc.* p. 253 (1962); *J. Chem. Soc.* p. 213 (1964).
[124] G. Schwarzenbach, *Helv. Chim. Acta* **32**, 839 (1949).
[125] R. G. Wilkins, *Quart. Rev. (London)* **16**, 316 (1962).
[126] R. E. Hamm and K. Schroeder, *Inorg. Chem.* **3**, 391 (1964); G. Kakabadse and H. J. Wilson, *Analyst* **86**, 402 (1961).
[127] N. A. Milas, *J. Am. Chem. Soc.* **50**, 493 (1928); G. A. Day and E. F. Fenn, U.S.P. 2736636; *Chem. Abstr.* **50**, 13386 (1956).

been used as a preparative oxidant.[128] A second is the oxidation of cyclo-hexanol to adipic acid in 40–50 % nitric acid.[129] Nitric acid has been found to accelerate oxidations by vanadium when it is not free from nitrous acid.[34, 42] The vanadium-catalyzed nitric acid oxidation is advantageous in that it gives very few by-products. A similar oxidation of cyclohexene has been reported, in which the vanadium(V) is assumed to intervene after the initial attack of nitric acid on the olefin. In the absence of vanadium, the main product is oxalic acid, but in its presence adipic acid is the main product.[130]

Oxidations by hydroperoxides and hydrogen peroxide, catalyzed by vanadium,[131] have been studied repeatedly, though vanadium(V) has not often been found to offer decisive advantages over alternative catalysts. The oxidation may involve both $HO_2 \cdot$ or $RO_2 \cdot$ radicals generated by reduction of the vanadium by the peroxide, and radicals generated by attack of the vanadium on the substrate or a peroxide formed from it. Among other compounds, t-butanol, methanol, acetone, dioxane, and olefins[132, 133] are oxidized at acidities at which the direct attack by vanadium(V) is undetectable. The reactions between cobalt and hydroperoxides have also been studied, as the radicals formed may initiate autoxidations.[134]

A detailed study of the products of the catalytic decomposition of a cyclo-hexanone peroxide by vanadium(V) has been recently made.[132] The mixture includes α-hydroxy ketone, α-diketone, ω-caprolactone, adipic and other acids, and, most interestingly, a small yield of cyclohexane-1,4-dione and 4-hydroxy-cyclohexanone, by a transannular hydrogen atom abstraction mechanism. Oxidation of the $\cdot CH_2$—$(CH_2)_4 COOH$ radical was evidently faster than its dimerization, as no dimer was found.

Most of the technical applications of these metals as catalysts involve oxide catalysts in heterogeneous systems, and so are not directly approach-able by the methods of homogeneous solution kinetics. Autoxidations of most types of organic compound can be catalyzed by ions of manganese, cobalt, and vanadium, but these will be discussed in another section of this treatise.

[128] N.A. Milas, *J. Am. Chem. Soc.* **50**, 493 (1928).
[129] E. Harrison and R. May, B.P. 567525; *Chem. Abstr.* **41**, 2747 (1947); W. J. Asselt and D. W. van Krevelen, *Rec. Trav. Chim.* **82**, 51, 438 (1963).
[130] J. E. Franz and W. S. Knowles, *Chem. & Ind.* (*London*) p. 250 (1961); J. E. Franz, J. F. Herber, and W. S. Knowles, *J. Org. Chem.* **30**, 1488 (1965).
[131] W. Treibs, *Ber.* **72**, 1194 (1930); N. A. Milas and S. Sussman, *J. Am. Chem. Soc.* **59**, 2345 (1937) and earlier papers.
[132] J. M. Mellor, D.Phil. Thesis, University of Oxford, England, 1962.
[133] M. Mugdan and D. P. Young, *J. Chem. Soc.* p. 2988 (1949).
[134] M. H. Dean and G. Skirrow, *Trans. Faraday Soc.* **54**, 849 (1958); J. A. Sharp, *J. Chem. Soc.* p. 2026 (1957).

X. Biochemical Significance

Vanadium has been detected in a blood pigment (oxygen carrier) in the Ascidiae, a group of marine worms,[135] in place of the normal iron-containing hemin. In higher animals it assists the mineralization of bone and increases the resistance of teeth to caries, and it also reduces the cholesterol level in the aorta.[136] It occurs in mineral oils as a porphyrin complex; this may be due not to its originating as such in any biological oil-producing materials, but to the vanadium(IV) displacing other metals from their porphyrin complexes. Thus, vanadium cannot be regarded as an essential trace element for higher animals.

Cobalt and manganese, however, are undoubtedly essential in the zoological world. It is rational to suspect that this might be related to their ability to undergo one-equivalent reductions. However, there is little experimental evidence to support this view.

Manganese(II) appears to be involved as a catalyst in many enzyme hydrolyses (in particular, it is a natural component of arginase[137]) which however do not involve valency changes. In fact, manganese(II) can often play a similar biological role to zinc(II) which acts as a coordinating center, holding the reactants together. Manganese, however, is present in a blood pigment in some shellfish.[138]

Cobalt is present in vitamin B_{12}, which does indeed appear to be involved in redox reactions involving one-carbon units, and in isomerization reactions which might have a hydride transfer mechanism:

$$CH_3CHOH—CH_2OH \longrightarrow CH_3CH_2CHO$$

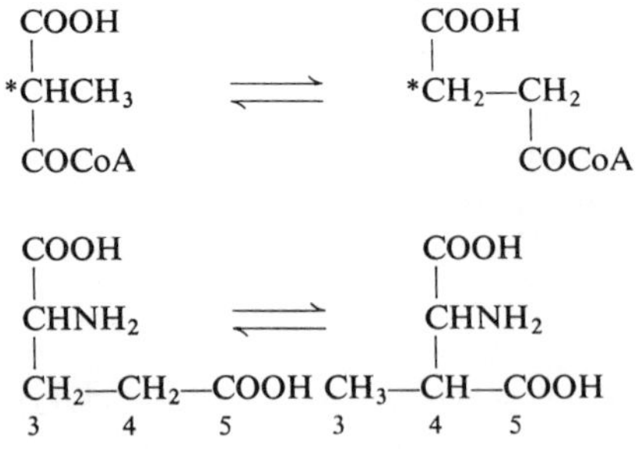

$$\begin{array}{ccc} COOH & & COOH \\ | & & | \\ *CHCH_3 & \rightleftharpoons & *CH_2—CH_2 \\ | & & | \\ COCoA & & COCoA \end{array}$$

$$\begin{array}{ccc} COOH & & COOH \\ | & & | \\ CHNH_2 & \rightleftharpoons & CHNH_2 \\ | & & | \\ CH_2—CH_2—COOH & & CH_3—CH—COOH \\ _3 _4 _5 & & _3 _4 _5 \end{array}$$

Isotopic labeling has indicated that carbon atoms are transferred in the way shown above, and that deuterium is not incorporated in the organic compounds

135 M. Henze, Z. Physiol. Chem. 72, 494 (1911).
136 O. Rygh, Bull. Soc. Chim. Biol. 33, 133 (1951); E. Maschitelli-Coriandoli and C. Citterio, Nature 183, 1527 (1959).
137 S. J. Bach and D. B. Whitehouse, Biochem. J. 57, xxxi (1954).
138 A. B. Griffiths, Compt. Rend. Acad. Sci. 114, 840 (1892).

if the reaction is carried out in deuterium oxide. It has been found that the vitamin is present *in vivo* as a coenzyme, a cobalt(III) complex involving a metal–carbon bond,[139] so it may be involved in two-equivalent redox processes rather than in radical mechanisms. However, the cobalt–carbon bond can be broken photochemically to give cobalt(II) and a free radical.[140] Alternatively, the role of cobalt(III) in these molecules may be largely that of a coordinating center to hold together the components of the very large biological system as a resonance stabilized unit.

Cobalt and manganese are well tolerated when present in excess of the normal (trace) requirement, but covalent vanadium(V) compounds, the oxytrichloride especially, are highly toxic both when the vapor is inhaled and when they are absorbed through the skin.[141]

[139] "Vitamin B_{12} and Intrinsic Factor: 2nd European Symposium," Enke, Stuttgart, 1961; E. Lester Smith, "Vitamin B_{12}." Methuen, London, 1960; A. M. White, *Ann. Rep. Progr. Chem. (Chem. Soc. London)* **59**, 400 (1962); J. A. Hill, J. M. Pratt, and R. J. P. Williams. *J. Chem. Soc.* p. 5149 (1964); J. M. Pratt, *J. Chem. Soc.* p. 5154 (1964).

[140] A. W. Johnson, E. Lester Smith, L. Mervyn, and N. Shaw, *Abstr. 19th Intern. Congr. Pure and Appl. Chem.* 1963 p. 167; A. W. Johnson, D. Oldfield, R. Rodrigo, N. Shaw, *J. Chem. Soc.* p. 4080 (1964).

[141] A. Lambert, I.C.I. Dyestuffs Division, personal communication.

[142] F. R. Duke, *J. Am. Chem. Soc.* **69**, 2885 (1947).

[143] T. N. Srivastava, *Z. Physik. Chem. (Leipzig)* **209**, 22 (1958); **211**, 251 (1959).

[144] R. Shanker and S. N. Swami, *J. Indian Chem. Soc.* **40**, 105 (1963).

[145] D. M. West and D. A. Skoog, *J. Am. Chem. Soc.* **82**, 280 (1960).

[146] U. S. Mahnot, R. Shanker, and S. N. Swami, *Z. Physik. Chem. (Leipzig)* **222**, 240 (1963).

CHAPTER **IV**

Ceric Ion Oxidation of Organic Compounds

William H. Richardson

	I. Introduction	.	.	.	.	.	.	.	.	.	.	.	.	.	.	244
II.	Inorganic Chemistry of Ceric Ion	.	.	.	.	.	.	.	.	.	.	244
	A. Structure of Ceric Ions and Oxidation Potentials	.	.	.	.	.	244
	B. Coordination Number and Stereochemistry of Cerium(IV)	.	.	.	246
III.	Oxidation of Alcohols	.	.	.	.	.	.	.	.	.	.	.	.	247
	A. Cerium(IV)–Alcohol Complexes	.	.	.	.	.	.	.	.	247
	B. Reactive Cerium(IV) Species in Perchloric Acid	.	.	.	.	.	248
	C. The Rate-Determining Step	.	.	.	.	.	.	.	.	.	248
	D. Cerium(IV) Alkoxides	.	.	.	.	.	.	.	.	.	.	249
IV.	Oxidation of Glycols and Other Polyhydric Alcohols	.	.	.	.	.	250
	A. Scope	.	.	.	.	.	.	.	.	.	.	.	.	.	.	250
	B. Cerium(IV)–Glycol Complexes	.	.	.	.	.	.	.	.	.	251
	C. The Rate-Determining Step	.	.	.	.	.	.	.	.	.	253
	D. Structure of Cerium(IV)–Glycol Complexes	.	.	.	.	.	255
V.	Oxidation of Aldehydes and Ketones	.	.	.	.	.	.	.	.	255
	A. Introduction	.	.	.	.	.	.	.	.	.	.	.	.	255
	B. Aliphatic Ketones	.	.	.	.	.	.	.	.	.	.	.	255
	C. Aliphatic Aldehydes	.	.	.	.	.	.	.	.	.	.	.	259
	D. Aromatic Aldehydes	.	.	.	.	.	.	.	.	.	.	.	262
VI.	Oxidation of Carboxylic Acids	.	.	.	.	.	.	.	.	.	.	264
	A. Monofunctional Acids	.	.	.	.	.	.	.	.	.	.	264
	B. Dicarboxylic Acids	.	.	.	.	.	.	.	.	.	.	.	265
	C. Hydroxycarboxylic Acids	.	.	.	.	.	.	.	.	.	265
VII.	Oxidation of Hydroperoxides	.	.	.	.	.	.	.	.	.	.	267
VIII.	Oxidation of Nitrogen-Containing Compounds	.	.	.	.	.	269
IX.	Oxidation of Sulfur-Containing Compounds	.	.	.	.	.	.	270
X.	Oxidation of Stable Free Radicals	.	.	.	.	.	.	.	.	.	271
XI.	Oxidation of Hydrocarbons	.	.	.	.	.	.	.	.	.	.	.	271
XII.	Indirect Oxidations with Ceric Ions	.	.	.	.	.	.	.	.	.	272
	A. Cerium(IV) and Chromium Ions	.	.	.	.	.	.	.	.	272
	B. Cerium(IV) and Bromide Ions	.	.	.	.	.	.	.	.	273
	C. Cerium(IV) and Radiation	.	.	.	.	.	.	.	.	.	274
	D. Cerium Ion Catalysis of Autoxidation	.	.	.	.	.	.	.	274
	E. Cerium(IV) and Hydrogen Peroxide	.	.	.	.	.	.	.	276

I. Introduction

The use of ceric ion as an oxidant for organic compounds first gained prominence as an analytical reagent, and this subject was reviewed in 1942 by G. F. Smith.[1a] More recently an inherent interest in these reactions has developed, and two additional reviews of ceric ion oxidation of organic compounds have appeared.[1b,c] Most of the reactions considered involve direct oxidation of the organic compound by cerium(IV). However, some indirect oxidations are considered where cerium(IV) produces the active oxidant.

Excluded from discussion are heterogeneous cerium(IV) reactions. The use of ceric ion to initiate polymerization is not considered unless this is pertinent to understanding the reaction mechanism. Some attention is given to ceric ion as an autoxidation catalyst, but an exhaustive treatment is beyond the scope of this review.

The subject matter is organized according to organic functional groups which undergo oxidation by ceric ion. Indirect oxidations are considered separately. Whenever possible the reaction mechanism is explored and considerable emphasis is given to this topic. As an aid to understanding cerium(IV) oxidation, a survey of the structure and properties of cerium salts is given.

II. Inorganic Chemistry of Ceric Ion

A. STRUCTURE OF CERIC IONS AND OXIDATION POTENTIALS

The common valences of cerium salts are three and four,[2] in which the most probable unhybridized electronic configurations are[3] $5s^25p^64d^{10}4f^1$ and $5s^25p^64d^{10}$, respectively. Monomeric cerium(IV) will then be a one-electron oxidant. The oxidation potential of the cerium(IV)–(III) couple is ligand dependent. For example, the oxidation potentials are -1.70 to -1.71, -1.61, -1.44, and -1.28 volts in $1 N$ perchloric, nitric, sulfuric, and hydrochloric acids, respectively.[4] The oxidation potential in hydrochloric acid is

[1] (a) G. F. Smith, "Cerate Oxidimetry." G. Frederick Smith Chemical Co., Columbus, Ohio, 1942; (b) Y. Ogata and I. Tabushi, *Kagaku no Ryoiki* **12**, 489 (1958); *Chem. Abstr.* **53**, 1093c (1958); (c) O. Kovács and G. Bernáth, *Chemie (Prague)* **10**, 1022 (1958); *Chem. Abstr.* **54**, 1250g (1960).

[2] R. E. Connick, *J. Chem. Soc.* (Suppl. 2), S235 (1949).

[3] D. M. Yost, H. Russell, Jr., and C. S. Garner, "The Rare-Earth Elements and Their Compounds," p. 5. Wiley, New York, 1947.

[4] (a) G. E. Smith and C. A. Getz, *Ind. Eng. Chem. Anal. Ed.* **10**, 191 (1938); (b) M. S. Sherrill, C. G. King, and R. C. Spooner, *J. Am. Chem. Soc.* **65**, 170 (1943); (c) F. B. Baker, T. W. Newton, and M. Kahn, *J. Phys. Chem.* **64**, 109 (1960); (d) A. A. Noyes and C. S. Garner, *J. Am. Chem. Soc.* **58**, 1264 (1936); (e) A. H. Kunz, *ibid.* **53**, 98 (1931).

probably low (in the negative sense), because reaction at the platinum electrode is not reversible.[5] Increasing the acid concentration from $1 N$ to $8 N$ increases the oxidation potential in perchloric acid to -1.87 volts, whereas a decrease to -1.56 and -1.42 volts is noted in nitric and sulfuric acids, respectively.[4a, b] The increase in potential with increasing perchloric acid concentration is in part attributed to cerium(IV) hydrolysis products. The decrease in potential in sulfuric and nitric acids with increasing acid concentration can be attributed to complexing of cerium ions with sulfate and nitrate anions. These predictions have been verified quantitatively for perchloric and sulfuric acid solutions. The standard potential (E_0) in sulfuric acid was calculated to be -1.74 volts [5] when account was made for bisulfate dissociation and the equilibria (Eqs. 1–4).

$$Ce^{4+} + HSO_4^- \;\rightleftharpoons\; CeSO_4^{2+} + H^+ \qquad K_1 = 3500 \qquad (1)^6$$

$$CeSO_4^{2+} + HSO_4^- \;\rightleftharpoons\; Ce(SO_4)_2 + H^+ \qquad K_2 = 200 \qquad (2)^6$$

$$Ce(SO_4)_2 + HSO_4^- \;\rightleftharpoons\; Ce(SO_4)_3^{2-} + H^+ \qquad K_3 = 20 \qquad (3)^6$$

$$CeSO_4^+ \;\rightleftharpoons\; Ce^{3+} + SO_4^{2-} \qquad (4)^7$$

$$Ce^{4+} + H_2O \;\rightleftharpoons\; Ce(OH)^{3+} + H^+ \qquad K_5 = 5.2 \qquad (5)$$

$$2Ce(OH)^{3+} \;\rightleftharpoons\; CeOCe^{6+} + H_2O \qquad K_6 = 16.5 \qquad (6)$$

Accounting for hydrolysis of cerium(IV) (Eq. 5) and dimerization of the hydrolysis product (Eq. 6),[8] the standard potential in perchloric acid was calculated to be -1.75 volts,[5] which is in excellent agreement with the value in sulfuric acid. A correlation was made between ionic strength and oxidation potential to explain the increase in potential with increasing perchloric acid concentration.[5]

The cerium(IV) equilibria (Eqs. 1–3, 5, and 6), which were determined spectrally,[6, 8] are important in interpreting oxidation of organic compounds.[9] Kinetic and additional spectral measurements also indicate that the degree of ceric perchlorate association depends on acid concentration.[10, 11] However, a monomer–dimer equilibrium may be an oversimplification, since above pH 0.7 colloidal polymers slowly form.[12] Confirmation of complex formation

[5] E. Wadsworth, F. R. Duke, and C. A. Goetz, *Anal. Chem.* **29**, 1824 (1957).

[6] T. J. Hardwick and E. Robertson, *Can. J. Chem.* **29**, 828 (1951).

[7] T. W. Newton and G. M. Arcand, *J. Am. Chem. Soc.* **75**, 2449 (1953).

[8] T. J. Hardwick and E. Robertson, *Can. J. Chem.* **29**, 818 (1951).

[9] Potentiometric studies [4c] have suggested that Eq. (5) is 85% complete in $2 M$ perchloric acid rather than 72% as indicated by spectral methods.[8]

[10] (a) F. L. King and M. L. Pandow, *J. Am. Chem. Soc.* **74**, 1966 (1952); (b) L. J. Heidt and M. E. Smith, *ibid.* **70**, 2476 (1948).

[11] M. Ardon, *J. Chem. Soc.* p. 1811 (1957).

[12] M. Ardon and G. Stein, *J. Chem. Soc.* p. 104 (1956).

of cerium(IV) with sulfate[13] and nitrate[14] ions has been reported. At higher sulfuric acid concentrations, $H_4Ce(SO_4)_4$ has also been suggested.[13c] Ceric nitrate equilibria are complicated by dimerization, hydrolysis, and association with cerium(III).[14] This could provide an added complexity in cerium(IV) oxidations where appreciable quantities of cerium(III) are formed.

B. COORDINATION NUMBER AND STEREOCHEMISTRY OF CERIUM(IV)

It is apparent from the preceding that the number of anions associated with cerium(IV) ion varies. This is also evident from isolable cerium(IV) salts such as the double salt ceric ammonium sulfate $Ce(SO_4)_2 \cdot 2(NH_4)_2SO_4 \cdot 2H_2O$,[15] the complex salt hexanitratoammonium cerate $(NH_4)_2Ce(NO_3)_6$,[15] cerium(IV) acetylacetonate $Ce(Ac)_4$,[16] cerium(IV) tetrakisdibenzoylmethane $Ce(C_6H_5-CO—CH—COC_6H_5)_4$,[17] and cerium(IV) disalicylalpropylenediamine $Ce(o-C_6H_5(O)CH{=}N—CH(CH_3)CH_2N{=}CH(O)C_6H_5-o)_2$.[18] From casual examination, the coordination number of cerium(IV) is not apparent, although the last three salts suggest eight. Indeed, X-ray diffraction studies have shown that $Ce(C_6H_5COCH—COC_6H_5)_4$[17] and basic cerium(IV) salts[19] have a coordination number of eight, which agrees with theoretical prediction.[20] It seems most likely that the sulfate[21] and nitrate salts are also eight-coordinated, whereby more than one coordination site may be occupied by the oxygen atoms of a single nitrate or sulfate anion. In solution, the solvent may occupy coordination sites so that eight-coordination is maintained.

The stereochemistry of eight-coordination can be accommodated by several polyhedral arrangements.[22] From X-ray diffraction studies, both square antiprism (I)[19] and dodecahedral (II)[17] geometry have been proposed.

13 (a) R. L. Moore and R. C. Anderson, *J. Am. Chem. Soc.* **67**, 167 (1945); (b) W. H. McCurdy, Jr., and G. G. Gilbault, *J. Phys. Chem.* **64**, 1825 (1960); (c) E. G. Jones and F. G. Soper, *J. Chem. Soc.* p. 802 (1935).

14 B. D. Blaustein and J. W. Gryder, *J. Am. Chem. Soc.* **79**, 540 (1957); M. K. Dorfman and J. W. Gryder, *Inorg. Chem.* **1**, 799 (1962).

15 G. F. Smith, V. R. Sullivan, and G. Frank, *Ind. Eng. Chem. Anal. Ed.* **8**, 449 (1936).

16 G. Scagliarini, *Atti. Accad. Lincei* [6] **4**, 204 (1926); L. E. Murchi, W. C. Fernelius, and J. P. McReynolds, *J. Am. Chem. Soc.* **65**, 329 (1943).

17 L. Wolf and H. Barnighausen, *Acta Cryst.* **13**, 778 (1960); J. L. Hoard and J. V. Silverton, *Inorg. Chem.* **2**, 235 (1963).

18 H. R. Baker, J. G. O'Rear, P. J. Sniegaski, and R. E. Kagarise, U.S. Naval Res. Lab. Rept. 5641 (September, 1961).

19 G. Lundgren, *Rec. Trav. Chim.* **75**, 585 (1956); *Arkiv Kemi* **6**, 59 (1953).

20 L. Pauling, "Nature of the Chemical Bond," p. 546. Cornell Univ. Press, Ithaca, New York, 1960.

21 W. G. Penny and J. S. Anderson, *Trans. Faraday Soc.* **33**, 1363 (1937).

22 T. D. O'Brien, *in* "The Chemistry of the Coordinate Compounds" (J. C. Bailar, Jr., ed.), p. 394. Reinhold, New York, 1956; R. J. Gillespie, *in* "Advances in the Chemistry of the Coordination Compounds" (S. Kirschner, ed.), p. 38. Macmillan, New York, 1961.

Cerium(IV) resides in the center of the polyhedra I and II, and the apexes represent coordination sites. Molecular orbital calculations for I and II predict sp^3d^4 hybridization with about the same energy for each[23, 24]; however, the barrier to interconversion may be large.[23a]

(I)   (II)

III. Oxidation of Alcohols

A. CERIUM(IV)–ALCOHOL COMPLEXES

The intermediacy of cerium(IV)–alcohol complexes was first suspected from the appearance of a red-shift in the visible spectrum upon adding ethanol to cerium(IV) solutions.[25, 26] More recently, kinetic data have confirmed this suspicion, and the following mechanism was proposed[27]:

$$Ce^{IV}(H_2O)_8{}^{4+} + C_2H_5OH \rightleftharpoons Ce^{IV}(H_2O)_7(C_2H_5OH)^{4+} + H_2O \qquad (7)[28]$$

$$Ce^{IV}(H_2O)_7(C_2H_5OH)^{4+} \rightarrow Products \qquad (8)$$

A first-order dependence on ceric perchlorate was observed and a plot of $1/k_{obs}$ versus $1/[C_2H_5OH]$ was linear, which is consistent with the mechanism. This can be seen by considering the derived rate law,

$$\frac{-d[Ce^{IV}]_T}{dt} = k_8 K_7 [Ce^{IV}] [ROH] \qquad (9)$$

where $[Ce^{IV}]_T$ is the total cerium(IV) concentration, $[Ce^{IV}]$ is the concentration of cerium(IV) not complexed with alcohol, and R is C_2H_5. Total cerium(IV) concentration is given by Eq. (10). Upon solving for $[Ce^{IV}]$ and substituting into Eq. (9), rate law (11) results,

$$[Ce^{IV}]_T = [Ce^{IV}] + K_7[Ce^{IV}][ROH] \qquad (10)$$

$$\frac{-d[Ce^{IV}]_T}{dt} = \frac{k_8 K_7 [Ce^{IV}]_T [ROH]}{1 + K_7[ROH]} \qquad (11)$$

[23] (a) G. H. Duffey, *J. Chem. Phys.* **18**, 1444 (1950); (b) **18**, 746 (1950).

[24] G. E. Kimball, *J. Chem. Phys.* **8**, 188 (1940).

[25] R. J. Meyers and R. Jacoby, *Z. Anorg. Chem.* **27**, 359 (1901).

[26] F. R. Duke and G. F. Smith, *Ind. Eng. Chem. Anal. Ed.* **12**, 201 (1940).

[27] M. Ardon, *J. Chem. Soc.* p. 1811 (1957).

[28] Six-coordinated cerium(IV) was assumed by the author,[27] without support. We feel eight-coordinated cerium(IV) is more reasonable (cf. Section II,B).

where $k_{obs} = k_8 K_7[ROH]/(1 + K_7[ROH])$. The latter predicts a linear plot between $1/k_{obs}$ and $1/[ROH]$. From the intercept and slope of such a plot, $K_7 = 4.3 \pm 0.4$ liters mole^{-1} and $k_8 = 7 \pm 0.7 \times 10^{-3}$ sec^{-1} at 20°C for ceric perchlorate oxidation of ethanol in 3.2 N perchloric acid. Further confirmation of the cerium(IV)–alcohol complex is given by observing the dependence of optical density on ethanol concentration at low ceric ion concentration where oxidation is slow. Assuming only one ethanol molecule is complexed with a ceric ion, the equilibrium constant of Eq. (7) is 4.3 ± 0.7 which is the same as the value from kinetic data. At higher alcohol concentrations, it was suggested[27] that more than one alcohol molecule may complex with a ceric ion.

A limited amount of data substantiates cerium(IV)–alcohol complex formation in the ceric sulfate oxidation of ethanol.[29] At least one of the complexes appears to resist oxidation, since increasing ethanol concentration decreases the rate. If all the cerium(IV)–alcohol complexes undergo oxidation, increasing the alcohol concentration should increase the rate.

Ceric sulfate oxidation of cyclohexanol does *not* show a decreasing rate with increasing alcohol concentration.[29] Instead, rate law (11) is obeyed, where $R = C_6H_{11}$, which indicates cerium(IV)–alcohol complex formation. The constants from rate law (11) are $K_7 = 13.0$ liters mole^{-1} and $k_8 = 1.38 \times 10^{-4}$ sec^{-1} at 50°C in 0.24 N sulfuric acid.

B. REACTIVE CERIUM(IV) SPECIES IN PERCHLORIC ACID

Cerium(IV) in perchloric acid may exist as $Ce(H_2O)_8^{4+}$, $Ce(OH)(H_2O)_7^{3+}$, and $[(H_2O)_7CeOCe(H_2O)_7]^{6+}$ (cf. Section II,A). It was concluded that cerium(IV) dimers are in low concentration and unimportant in the oxidation of ethanol under the conditions employed.[27] Furthermore, it was concluded that $Ce(H_2O)_8^{4+}$ and not $Ce(OH)(H_2O)_7^{3+}$ is the active oxidant, since the equilibrium constant K_7 increased with increasing acid concentration in the same manner as the $Ce(H_2O)_8^{4+}/Ce(OH)(H_2O)_7^{3+}$ ratio.

C. THE RATE-DETERMINING STEP

Although a one-electron oxidation is indicated in reaction (8), the structure of the organic radical and its mode of formation need to be specified. In an attempt to resolve this problem, the deuterium isotope effect for ceric sulfate oxidation of α-deuterocyclohexanol was measured.[30] The isotope effect (k_H/k_D) of 1.9 indicates α-carbon–hydrogen bond breaking in the rate-determining step. A cyclic activated complex (III) was suggested to explain the low value.[30, 31] The activated complex is unknown. The possibility of some

[29] J. S. Littler and W. A. Waters, *J. Chem. Soc.* p. 2767 (1960).
[30] J. S. Littler, *J. Chem. Soc.* p. 4135 (1959).
[31] F. H. Westheimer, *Chem. Rev.* **61**, 265 (1961).

attack at the oxygen–hydrogen bond was also suggested to explain the low isotope effect. Rates were not measured in deuterium oxide to confirm this proposal.

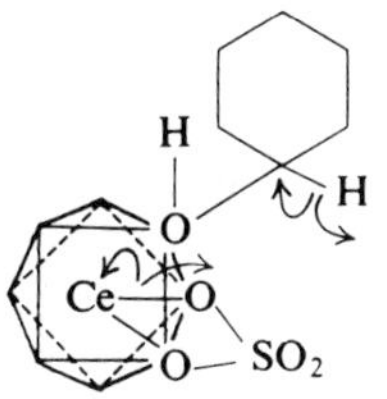

(III) 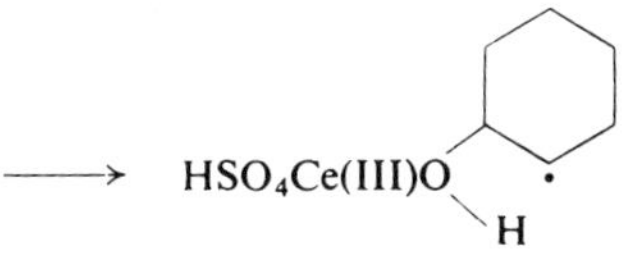   (IV)

Further oxidation of IV gives the product, cyclohexanone. The yield of cyclohexanone was not reported, but ethanol is oxidized to acetaldehyde in 90 % yield.[27]

As yet, the effect of alcohol structure on reactivity has not been thoroughly investigated. One report gives activation energies (E_a) for ceric sulfate oxidation of a series of alcohols.[32] Unfortunately, the activation energy refers to the sum of the equilibrium (Eq. 7) and unimolecular (Eq. 8) steps. However, for the most part, the data are explicable on the basis of free radical character developing in the activated complex at the α-carbon atom.[33] For example, E_a for *n*-propyl alcohol (20.1 kcal/mole) > isopropyl alcohol (19.0 kcal/mole) > benzyl alcohol (18.5 kcal/mole). The oxidation mechanism of a tertiary alcohol is not clear; however, the presence of an α-hydrogen atom for *facile* oxidation is seen by comparing the rates for *tert*-butyl alcohol and ethanol. With identical ceric sulfate ($4.4 \times 10^{-3} M$) and acid ($0.272 M$) concentrations, the first-order rate constants for ethanol and *tert*-butyl alcohol are 2.57×10^{-4} and 0.05×10^{-4} sec^{-1}, when the alcohol concentrations are $0.100 M$ and $0.058 M$, respectively.[29]

D. CERIUM(IV) ALKOXIDES

Although cerium(IV)–alcohol complexes are no doubt intermediates in the oxidation of alcohols, stable alkoxides of cerium(IV) can be isolated.[34] They can be prepared from hexachlorobis(pyridine)cerium(IV) and the alcohol in the presence of ammonia or by alcohol interchange with a cerium(IV) alkoxide. Primary, secondary, and tertiary alcohols can be used, and the resulting alkoxides are stable to about 200° C under vacuum. The basic structural unit

[32] S. M. Chou and S. V. Gorbachev, *Zh. Fiz. Khim.* **32**, 635 (1958).

[33] See W. H. Urry, F. W. Stacey, E. S. Huyser, and O. O. Juveland, *J. Am. Chem. Soc.* **76**, 450 (1954).

[34] (a) D. C. Bradley, A. K. Chatterjee, and W. Wardlaw, *J. Chem. Soc.* p. 2260 (1956); (b) p. 2600 (1957).

in all cases is the tetraalkoxide, $Ce(OR)_4$, but these units are associated depending on alkoxide structure. Highly substituted tertiary alkoxides are monomeric in boiling benzene, whereas primary alkoxides contain about 4.2 cerium(IV) alkoxide units. The reason for association is no doubt an attempt to satisfy eightfold cerium(IV) coordination. Stability of cerium(IV) alkoxides is consistent with the observation that strongly complexing ligands stabilize the higher valence state of a metal ion relative to the lower state.[35] Since alkoxide ions complex more strongly than alcohols with cerium(IV), the former are stable and the latter are readily oxidized.

IV. Oxidation of Vicinal Glycols and Other Polyhydric Alcohols

A. SCOPE

The use of cerium(IV) as an effective reagent for polyhydric alcohol cleavage has been known for some time. Yields are usually excellent and the oxidation has been used in synthesis and as an analytical reagent.[36] For example, pinacol is quantitatively cleaved to acetone by ceric sulfate.[37] Glucose phenylosotriazole (V) is oxidized quantitatively to 2-phenyl-1,2,3-triazole-4-carboxylic acid (VI) with ceric sulfate.[36a] Ceric perchlorate oxidation of glycerol to formic acid proceeds nearly quantitatively and has been used as an analytical

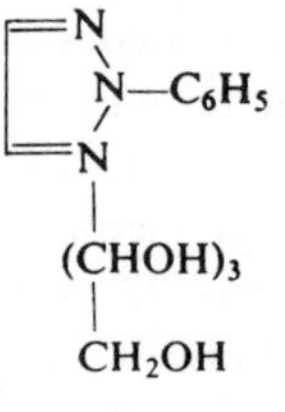

(V) 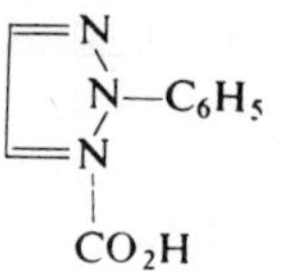   (VI)

procedure.[36b] Further oxidation of formic acid is slow so that excess ceric ion can be titrated after completion of glycerol oxidation. The stoichiometry of ceric perchlorate oxidation of several other polyhydric alcohols is reported to be nearly quantitative and the reaction is summarized:[38]

$$HOCH_2(CHOH)_nCH_2OH + (6+2n)Ce^{IV} + (2+n)H_2O \rightarrow (2+n)HCO_2H + (6+2n)H^+ \quad (12)$$

[35] F. Basolo and R. G. Pearson, "Mechanisms of Inorganic Reactions," p. 60. Wiley, New York, 1958.

[36] (a) S. P. Rao, J. N. Gaur, and S. K. Sharma, *Naturwissenshaften* **48**, 98 (1961); (b) G. F. Smith and F. R. Duke, *Ind. Eng. Chem. Anal. Ed.* **13**, 558 (1941); (c) R. C. Huston, G. L. Goerner, and H. H. György, *J. Am. Chem. Soc.* **70**, 389 (1948); **68**, 2504 (1946); (d) H. Süllmann, *Enzymologia* **5**, 326 (1938); *Chem. Abstr.* **33**, 1354 (1939).

[37] G. Mino, S. Kaizerman, and E. Rasmussen, *J. Am. Chem. Soc.* **81**, 1494 (1959).

[38] G. F. Smith and F. R. Duke, *Ind. Eng. Chem. Anal. Ed.* **15**, 120 (1943).

In general, hydroxyl groups at primary and secondary positions give acids while tertiary attachment leads to ketones.

B. CERIUM(IV)–GLYCOL COMPLEXES

Mechanism of glycol oxidation has been studied by several workers.[29, 37, 39] By analogy from alcohol oxidation, one might expect cerium(IV)–glycol complexes as intermediates. However, complex formation appears to be dependent on the anion associated with cerium(IV) and on the type of glycol.

With ceric sulfate, although ethylene glycol appears to be oxidized via complex formation,[29] there is no evidence for such complexes with pinacol, 2,3-butanediol,[29] or glycerol.[40] With ceric sulfate and pinacol, first-order dependence is observed (Fig. 1).[37]

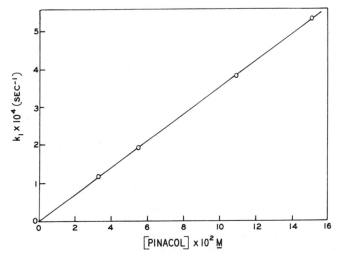

FIG. 1. First-order plot in pinacol for ceric sulfate oxidation, where $-d[Ce^{IV}] = k_2 [Ce^{IV}]$ [pinacol] and $k_1 = k_2$ [pinacol]. Rates were measured with $[Ce^{IV}] = 0.01\,M$, $[SO_4^{2-}]$ $= 0.29\,M$, and pH $= 0.97$ at $25°\,C.[37]$

With ceric perchlorate, kinetic evidence indicates that both glycerol[40] and 2,3-butanediol[39a] are oxidized via complex formation. The glycerol complexes are also supported by spectral evidence. The plot for ceric perchlorate and 2,3-butanediol (Fig. 2) shows curvature indicating nonfirst-order dependence on glycol.[39a] However, a plot of $1/k$ versus $1/[2,3$-butanediol] (Fig. 3) is reasonably linear, indicating complex formation (Section III,A).

[39] (a) F. R. Duke and R. F. Bremer, *J. Am. Chem. Soc.* **73**, 5179 (1951); (b) F. R. Duke and A. A. Forist, *ibid.* **71**, 2790 (1949).

[40] G. G. Guelbault and W. H. McCurdy, Jr., *J. Phys. Chem.* **67**, 283 (1963).

A somewhat better correlation is obtained if, in addition to the $1:1$ cerium(IV)–glycol complex, a $1:2$ complex is included. Ceric perchlorate oxidation of 2,3-butanediol (G) can then be explained by Eqs. (13)–(16).

$$Ce(H_2O)_8^{4+} + G \;\rightleftharpoons\; Ce(H_2O)_7(G)^{4+} + H_2O \qquad (13)[28]$$

$$Ce(H_2O)_7(G)^{4+} + G \;\rightleftharpoons\; Ce(H_2O)_6(G)_2^{4+} + H_2O \qquad (14)$$

$$Ce(H_2O)_7(G)^{4+} \;\rightarrow\; Products \qquad (15)$$

$$Ce(H_2O)_6(G)_2^{4+} \;\rightarrow\; Products \qquad (16)$$

Rapid oxidation of the free radical produced in Eqs. (15) and (16) by cerium(IV) completes the oxidation.

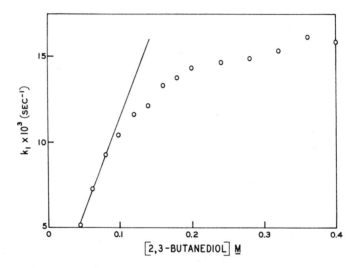

FIG. 2. Attempted first-order plot in 2,3-butanediol, with $[Ce^{IV}] = 0.01\,M$, $[ClO_4^-]$ $= 1.0\,M$, $[Na^+] = 0.9\,M$, and $[H^+] = 0.1\,M$ at $0°$ C.[39a]

An insight into the nature of the cerium(IV)–2,3-butanediol complex can be given from the effect of perchloric acid concentration on reaction rate. It is concluded that 2,3-butanediol oxidation does not proceed via VII[39a]:

$$Ce(H_2O)_8^{4+} + B \;\rightleftharpoons\; Ce(H_2O)_7(OH)^{3+} + BH^+ \qquad (17)$$

$$Ce(H_2O)_7(OH)^{3+} + G \;\rightleftharpoons\; Ce(H_2O)_6(OH)(G)^{3+} + H_2O \qquad (18)$$

$$(VII)$$

Increasing the acid concentration increases the equilibrium constant for ceric perchlorate–2,3-butanediol complex formation, which also indicates that oxidation proceeds through the hydrated complex rather than through VII.[39a] A similar result is observed in the ceric perchlorate oxidation of glycerol[40] as well as of the monofunctional alcohol, ethanol (Section III,B).[11]

Ceric nitrate oxidation of 2,3-butanediol also proceeds through complex formation.[39b]

Complex formation depends on the ratio of the formation constant to the decomposition constant (K/k) of the complex. Changing from perchlorate to sulfate ions will reduce K/k, since the hydroxy compound can compete more favorably for cerium(IV) ligand sites in the presence of perchlorate ions. For glycerol[40] and 2,3-butanediol,[29] changing from perchlorate to sulfate ions has such a drastic effect on K/k that no complex formation is observed with sulfate ions. The K/k ratio also depends on the type of hydroxy compound.

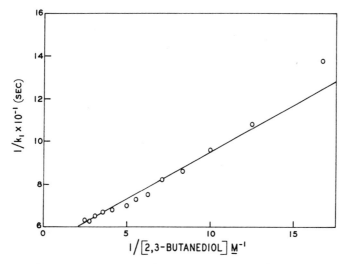

FIG. 3. Data [39a] of Fig. 2 plotted, assuming a 1:1 cerium(IV)–glycol complex intermediate (cf. Section III,A).

The value of K/k for glycerol[40] is considerably less than for ethanol.[11] A similar change is seen by the absence of complexes with 2,3-butanediol in ceric sulfate oxidation,[29] but their presence with ethylene glycol[29,41] and alcohols (Section III,A).

C. THE RATE-DETERMINING STEP

To rationalize variation in complex formation with glycol structure, and their K/k, the rate-determining step (Eqs. 15, 16) must be considered as well as the equilibrium steps (Eqs. 13, 14). Consider ceric sulfate oxidation of 2,3-butanediol and ethylene glycol,[29] where complex formation is observed

[41] From the data of Littler and Waters,[29] the monoglycolated complex equilibrium constant was calculated to be 1.1×10^2 liters mole^{-1} at 50°C for ceric sulfate oxidation. See Section II,A for method of calculation.

with the latter but not with the former. With increased substitution of the carbon atoms bearing the hydroxyl groups, the stability of the incipient radical in the activated complex should increase.[33, 42] This is independent of whether or not reaction proceeds via Eqs. (19) or (20), where R is hydrogen or an alkyl group:

$$\text{Ce}^{\text{IV}}(\text{RCH(OH)CH)(OH)R}) \begin{cases} \longrightarrow \text{Ce}^{\text{III}} + \text{H}^{\oplus} + \text{RCHO} + \text{R}\overset{\bullet}{\text{C}}\text{HOH} & (19) \\ \\ \longrightarrow \text{Ce}^{\text{III}} + \text{H}^{\oplus} + \text{R}\overset{\bullet}{\text{C}}\text{(OH)CH(OH)R} & (20) \end{cases}$$

The prediction that the velocity of the rate-determining step should increase from 2,3-butanediol ($R = CH_3$) to ethylene glycol ($R = H$) is borne out.[29, 41] In addition, steric effects may decrease complex formation with 2,3-butanediol compared with ethylene glycol. This factor and the increase in the rate-determining step both lower K/k for 2,3-butanediol such that complex formation is not kinetically detectable, whereas it is detectable with ethylene glycol.

In the two possible reaction paths given above, one depends on carbon–carbon rupture (Eq. 19) and the other on carbon–hydrogen rupture (Eq. 20). Available data suggest the former may be most important. The isotope effect (k_H/k_D) for ceric sulfate oxidation of 2,3-dideutero-2,3-butanediol is 1.18 ± 0.12 at $50°$ C,[29] which is considerably lower than the value for α-deuterocyclohexanol ($k_H/k_D = 1.9$).[30] A secondary isotope effect in reaction (19) could be responsible for the slower rate with deuterated glycol. Admittedly, a primary isotope effect in reaction (20) cannot be eliminated. Although the data are not directly comparable, the oxidation rate of pinacol may be somewhat faster than for 2,3-butanediol.[43] This shows that carbon–hydrogen rupture (reaction 20) is not essential for glycol oxidation. It is also consistent with reaction (19), since pinacol is expected to be oxidized faster than 2,3-butanediol according to reaction (19) on the basis of radical stability.[33]

Product studies provide further evidence for reaction (19). Acetoin would be the expected primary oxidation product from 2,3-butanediol according to reaction (20). Cerium(IV) oxidation of acetoin gave biacetyl.[29] Neither acetoin nor biacetyl was detected from oxidation of 2,3-butanediol. Instead, essentially pure acetaldehyde was the product, as predicted by reaction (19).[29]

---

[42] Radical intermediates are indicated by initiation of acrylamide polymerization in the ceric sulfate oxidation of pinacol. Acrylamide is stable to ceric sulfate.[36]

[43] Extrapolating to $50°$C from data at $20°$, $25°$, and $35°$C,[36] $k_2 = 13 \times 10^{-2}$ liters mole^{-1} sec^{-1} for pinacol at $[\text{H}^+] = 0.3 M$, $[\text{SO}_4{}^{2-}] = 0.29 M$, and $[\text{Ce}^{\text{IV}}] = 0.01 M$. For 2,3-butanediol,[29] $k_2 = 2.15 \times 10^{-2}$ liters mole^{-1} sec^{-1} at $50°$C, with $[\text{H}^+] = 0.272 M$, $[\text{SO}_4{}^{2-}] = 0.14 M$, and $[\text{Ce}^{\text{IV}}] = 4 \times 10^{-3} M$. In both instances the rate law is first-order in cerium(IV) and in glycol.

Ceric sulfate oxidation of 2,3-butanediol in deuterium oxide showed no isotope effect,[29] which rules out oxygen–hydrogen rupture in the rate-determining step. Usually, acid-catalyzed reactions are faster by a factor of 1.3–3.0 in deuterium oxide,[44] so there is some concern that this may compensate for a primary isotope effect. However, this seems unlikely, since the rate is not noticeably acid dependent over a twofold change in acid concentration.[29]

D. STRUCTURE OF CERIUM(IV)–GLYCOL COMPLEXES

Two possible complex structures should be considered, where cerium(IV) is associated with both oxygen atoms (VIII) or with only one (IX). Undefined

(VIII)   (IX)

ligands are represented by L. Structure VIII is not required, since ethylene glycol and 2-methoxyethanol are oxidized by ceric sulfate at about the same rate.[29] Both are oxidized via complex formation.

V. Oxidation of Aldehydes and Ketones

A. INTRODUCTION

In this group of carbonyl compounds, cerium(IV) oxidation of aliphatic ketones has received the most attention, followed by oxidation of aliphatic aldehydes. Oxidation of aromatic aldehydes has been studied to some extent; however, no reports are made of aralkyl or diaryl ketone oxidation. No synthetic utility has been made of these reactions. Acyloin intermediates are suggested in aliphatic ketone oxidation, but they are rapidly oxidized and have not been isolated.

B. ALIPHATIC KETONES

1. CERIUM(IV)–KETONE COMPLEXES AND THE ENOL MECHANISM

Several papers have been devoted to elucidating the mechanism of aliphatic ketone oxidation. Kinetic studies show the oxidation rate to be dependent on both ketone and cerium(IV) concentration.[45, 46] Initially, an enol mechanism

[44] K. B. Wiberg, *Chem. Rev.* **55**, 713 (1955).
[45] (a) J. Shorter and C. N. Hinshelwood, *J. Chem. Soc.* p. 3276 (1950); (b) J. Shorter, *ibid.* p. 3425 (1950); (c) S. Venkatakrishnan and M. Santappa, *Z. Physik. Chem. (Frankfurt)* **16**, 73 (1958); (d) J. Shorter, *J. Chem. Soc.* p. 1868 (1962).
[46] J. S. Littler, *J. Chem. Soc.* p. 832 (1962).

was proposed,[45] which appears unique in comparison with ketone halo-genation (a two-electron oxidation). Here reaction via an enol intermediate is first-order in ketone and zero-order in halogen.[47] Recently,[46] evidence has been presented against the enol mechanism.

The most devastating argument against the enol mechanism is that the rate of ceric sulfate oxidation of cyclohexanone is 61-fold faster than enolization.[46] A kinetic isotope effect (k_H/k_D) of 6.0 for 2,2,6,6-tetradeuterocyclohexanone in light water shows that α-carbon–hydrogen bond breaking occurs in the rate-determining step. The mechanism shown (Eqs. 21–23) was proposed,[46] where X may be hydrogen, $-SO_2O^\ominus$, or $-SO_2OH$, and L is an unspecified ligand:

$$\text{(cyclohexanone)}{=}O + Ce^{IV}(OX)L_7 \longrightarrow \text{(cyclohexanone)}{=}\overset{..}{\underset{..}{O}}{:}Ce^{IV}(OX)L_6 + L \qquad (21)$$

$$\text{(cyclohexanone)}{=}\overset{..}{\underset{..}{O}}{:}Ce^{IV}L_6 \xrightarrow{\text{slow}} \text{(cyclohexanone)}{=}O + HOX + Ce^{III} \qquad (22)$$

$$\text{(cyclohexanone)}{=}O + Ce^{IV}(H_2O)L_7 \xrightarrow{\text{fast}} \text{(cyclohexanone with OH)}{=}O + Ce^{III} + H^\oplus \qquad (23)$$

Alternatively, the cerium(IV) species may add across the carbonyl double bond, giving a cerium(IV)–ketone complex with a tetrahedral carbon atom (cf. Section V,D). Complex formation between methyl ethyl ketone and acetone with ceric nitrate in perchloric acid was demonstrated by a linear plot of the reciprocal rate constant for oxidation versus the reciprocal ketone concentration.[45c,48] Using the data of Venkatakrishnan and Santappa[45c] for ceric nitrate (0.01 M) oxidation of acetone in 1 M perchloric acid at 30° C, K (cf. reaction 21) is 2.0 liters mole^{-1} and k (cf. reaction 22) is 1.8×10^{-3} sec^{-1}. The values of K for acetone and methyl ethyl ketone from spectral data, where the oxidation rate is slow, agree reasonably well with the values from kinetic data.[45c] Using the data of Shorter and Hinshelwood[45a] for ceric sulfate oxidation of acetone at 70° C, $1/k_{obs}$ versus $1/[\text{acetone}]$ plots were linear (Fig. 4). At $[H^+] = 4.4 \times 10^{-3}\,N$, K (cf. reaction 21) is 7.3 liters mole^{-1}, and k (cf. reaction 22) is 1.22×10^{-1} sec^{-1}. With $[H^+] = 1.003\,N$, $K = 16.4$ liters mole^{-1} and $k = 5.36 \times 10^{-2}$ sec^{-1}. However, simple first-order dependence in cyclo-hexanone, over a 3.4-fold concentration range, was observed with ceric sulfate

[47] J. Hine, "Physical Organic Chemistry," p. 109. McGraw-Hill, New York, 1962.
[48] See Section III,A for derivation in the analogous case with alcohols.

oxidation.[46] Although all the data are not directly comparable, it appears that the degree of complex formation depends on the type of anion and ketone. Similar observations were made in glycol oxidation (Section IV,B).

A comparison was made between the relative rates of ceric sulfate oxidation and bromination of a series of aliphatic ketones to determine the validity of an enol mechanism.[45b] Since bromination is known to proceed via an enol intermediate, a linear correlation would be expected if ceric oxidation also takes this course. No correlation existed. Only when the partial rate of enolization at the most labile α-position was plotted against oxidation rate could any

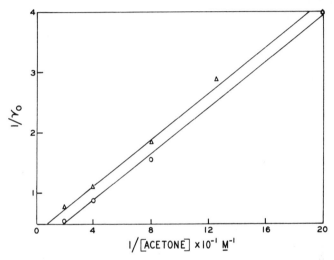

FIG. 4. Cerium sulfate oxidation of acetone at 70°C, where γ_0 is the initial velocity. Legend: $\circ \sim [H^+] = 4.4 \times 10^{-3} N$ and $\triangle \sim [H^+] = 1.003 N$. Ceric sulfate concentration is $0.05 N$ in both instances.

linear correlation be observed. Even in this case, acetone did not fit the plot. This unusual behavior cannot be accommodated by a simple enol mechanism. However, it may not be unreasonable for the cerium(IV)–ketone complex mechanism (reactions 21–23). Here, alkyl groups which flank the carbonyl group can affect the oxidation rate both in complex formation (reaction 21) and hydrogen atom abstraction (reaction 22). A linear relationship between these processes and enolization need not exist.

The cerium complex mechanism (21–23), as well as the enol mechanism, requires first-order dependence on ceric ion. This is observed at low cerium concentrations, but the rate is slower than expected at higher concentrations.[45a, d] This may be due to association of cerium(IV) into less reactive species.

Oxidation of ketones by free hydroxyl radicals, which are produced from ceric ion (reaction 24)

$$Ce^{IV} + H_2O \rightarrow Ce^{III} + H^{\oplus} + OH \tag{24}$$

appear unlikely, since cerium(III) did not inhibit oxidation. Cerous ions would be expected to reduce hydroxyl radicals.[45a, d]

2. ACID DEPENDENCE

The equilibrium constant (K) for complex formation (reaction 21) and the rate constant (k) for complex decomposition (reaction 22) are affected inversely by changing acid concentrations. For ceric sulfate oxidation of acetone, K increases from 7.3 to 16.4 liters mole^{-1} by increasing the acid concentration from $4.4 \times 10^{-3} N$ to $1.003 N$, while k decreases from 1.22×10^{-1} to 5.36×10^{-2} sec^{-1} (Section V,B,1). The increase in K is most reasonably explained by acid-facilitating ligand (L) displacement in reaction (21). A decrease in k with increasing acid concentration suggests that $Ce^{IV}(OH)$ is the reactive oxidant. Higher acid concentrations should suppress this species according to reaction (5):

$$Ce^{4+} + H_2O \rightleftharpoons Ce(OH)^{3+} + H^+ \tag{5}$$

This is in contrast to alcohol (Section III,B) and glycol (Section IV,B) oxidation where Ce^{4+} is the active oxidant. The inverse effect on K and k with changing acid concentration will explain the complex dependence of rate on acid concentration.[45a, d]

3. STOICHIOMETRY AND PRODUCTS

The stoichiometry and products of cerium(IV) oxidation of several ketones has been investigated.[45a, b, d] One mole of acetone required 8.6 equivalents of ceric sulfate, and 1.4 moles of formic acid were produced.[45a] It was proposed that 60% of the reaction proceeded via reactions (25)–(27) and 40% via reactions (25), (28), and (29):

$$CH_3COCH_3 + 2\,Ce^{IV} + H_2O \rightarrow CH_3COCH_2OH + 2\,Ce^{III} + 2\,H^{\oplus} \tag{25}$$

$$CH_3COCH_2OH + 2\,Ce^{IV} \rightarrow CH_3COCHO + 2\,Ce^{III} + 2\,H^{\oplus} \tag{26}$$

$$CH_3COCHO + 2\,Ce^{IV} + 2\,H_2O \rightarrow CH_3CO_2H + HCO_2H + 2\,Ce^{III} + 2\,H^{\oplus} \tag{27}$$

$$CH_3COCH_2OH + 2\,Ce^{IV} + H_2O \rightarrow HOCH_2COCH_2OH + 2\,Ce^{III} + 2\,H^{\oplus} \tag{28}$$

$$HOCH_2COCH_2OH + 8\,Ce^{IV} + 3\,H_2O \rightarrow 2\,HCO_2H + CO_2 + 8\,Ce^{III} + 10\,H^{\oplus} \tag{29}$$

This predicts that one molecule of acetone would require 8.4 equivalents of ceric sulfate and yield 1.4 moles of formic acid. In contrast to the ceric sulfate oxidation at 70° C, one mole of acetone requires 6.01 equivalents of ceric nitrate at 25° C.[45d] Only reactions (25)–(27) are needed to explain the latter stoichiometry.

Higher molecular weight ketones suffer extensive degradation. At 70° C, one molecule of methyl *n*-amyl ketone consumes 18.2 equivalents of ceric sulfate, and 2.75 moles of formic acid are produced.[45b] This requires that the ketone be degraded primarily to acetic and formic acids. In general, ketones are degraded to acetic and formic acids, along with carbon dioxide, with ceric sulfate at 70° C. Table I presents some additional stoichiometric data.

TABLE I

Stoichiometry of Ceric Sulfate Oxidation of Ketones
at 70° C[45b]

Ketone[a]	Equivalents of Ce^{IV} consumed/ mole of ketone	Moles of formic acid produced/ mole of ketone
CH_3COCH_3	8.6	1.40
$CH_3COC_2H_5$	11.95	2.25
$(C_2H_5)_2CO$	13.4	2.85
$CH_3COC_3H_7$-n	14.25	2.75
$CH_3COC_3H_7$-iso	12.4	1.35
$CH_3COC_4H_9$-iso	14.75	2.15
$(iso-C_3H_7)_2CO$	12.3	1.55
$CH_3COC_5H_{11}$-n	18.2	2.75

[a] With $[Ce^{IV}] = 0.05\,N$, $[CH_3COCH_3]_0 = 0.005\,M$, and $[H_2SO_4]_0 = 2\,N$. Values for the remaining ketones are: $[Ce^{IV}]_0 = 0.0667\,N$, $[ketone]_0 = 0.00333\,M$, and $|H_2SO_4| = 2\,N$.

C. ALIPHATIC ALDEHYDES

1. Products and Stoichiometry

Ceric ion oxidation of aliphatic aldehydes has not been studied extensively, even though the reaction was reported a number of years ago.[49] A stoichiometric study showed that one mole of acetaldehyde required 5.75 equivalents of ceric sulfate, and 1.75 moles of formic acid were produced.[45b] The results were explained in terms of two competing reactions by assuming that 10% reaction occurs via reaction (30) and 90% via reaction (31):

$$CH_3CHO + 2\,Ce^{IV} + H_2O \rightarrow CH_3CO_2H + 2\,Ce^{III} + 2\,H^{\oplus} \tag{30}$$

$$CH_3CHO + 6\,Ce^{IV} + 3\,H_2O \rightarrow 2\,HCO_2H + 6\,Ce^{III} + 6\,H^{\oplus} \tag{31}$$

[49] J. B. Conant and J. G. Aston, *J. Am. Chem. Soc.* **50**, 2783 (1928).

α-Hydroxyacetaldehyde and glyoxal were proposed as intermediates. With isobutyraldehyde, α-hydroxyisobutyraldehyde (14% yield) could be detected along with isobutyric acid (22% yield) and acetone.[49]

2. KINETICS AND MECHANISM

It was stated (Section V,B,1) that ketone oxidation could not be accommodated by a simple enol mechanism. Similarly, acetaldehyde oxidation cannot be explained by an enol mechanism. Table II indicates that ceric oxidation is considerably faster than would be expected by an enol mechanism. Although only a limited amount of data is available, it seems most reasonable that the α-oxidation mechanism may be similar to that for ketones (cf. reactions 21–23).

TABLE II[45b]

RELATIVE INITIAL RATES OF CERIC SULFATE OXIDATION (v_0)
AT 70° C[a] AND ENOLIZATION (v_e) AT 25° C

Compound	v_0	v_e	Compound	v_0	v_e
CH_3CHO	5.55	0.388	$CH_3COC_3H_7$-n	2.59	0.94
CH_3COCH_3	≡1.00	≡1.00	$CH_3COC_3H_7$-iso	2.84	0.695
$CH_3COC_2H_5$	3.15	1.04	$CH_3COC_4H_9$-iso	1.61	0.86
$C_2H_5COC_2H_5$	3.12	0.82	iso-$C_3H_7COC_3H_7$-iso	0.748	0.14
			$CH_3COC_5H_{11}$-n	2.26	0.996

[a] $[Ce^{IV}]_0 = 0.05\,N$, [ketone or aldehyde]$_0 = 0.005\,M$, $[H_2SO_4] = 2.00\,N$.

3. FORMALDEHYDE OXIDATION

Ceric ion oxidation of formaldehyde is unique, since there are no α-hydrogen atoms, and is considered separately for this reason. Formic acid is the oxidation product, and two moles of cerium(IV) are required per mole of formaldehyde.[50]

A kinetic study[50] has shown the reaction to be first-order in formaldehyde and in cerium(IV) with either perchlorate or sulfate salts. The dependence of the second-order rate constant (k_2) on perchloric acid concentration is given by equation (32),

$$\frac{1}{k_2} = a + \frac{b}{[H^+]} \tag{32}$$

where a and b are constants. First-order dependence on formaldehyde (over a five-fold concentration range) negates complex formation (see Section III,A)

[50] G. Hargreaves and L. H. Sutcliffe, *Trans. Faraday Soc.* **51**, 1105 (1955).

at low formaldehyde concentrations (to $1.5 \times 10^{-2} M$). At higher concentrations, where the rate was too fast to measure conveniently, color changes which may be indicative of complex formation were observed. Color changes are observed with alcohol complex formation.[25, 26] The mechanism in reactions (33)–(36)

$$Ce(H_2O)_8{}^{4+} + H_2O \; \rightleftharpoons \; Ce(OH)(H_2O)_7{}^{3+} + H_3O^{\oplus} \tag{33}$$

$$H_2C(OH)_2 + H_3O^{\oplus} \; \rightleftharpoons \; H_2\overset{\oplus}{C}OH + 2\,H_2O \tag{34}$$

$$Ce(H_2O)_8{}^{4+} + H_2C(OH)_2 \; \rightarrow \; Ce^{III} + H{-}\overset{\centerdot}{C}(OH)_2 + H^{\oplus} \tag{35}$$

$$Ce^{IV} + H{-}\overset{\centerdot}{C}(OH)_2 \; \rightarrow \; Ce^{III} + H{-}CO_2H + H^{\oplus} \tag{36}$$

was suggested for ceric perchlorate oxidation, where Ce^{IV} may be any cerium(IV) species.[27, 50] Carbon–hydrogen rupture is suggested[51] in the rate-determining step (34) rather than oxygen–hydrogen rupture as originally proposed.[50] By assuming $Ce(H_2O)_8{}^{4+}$ is the active oxidant, the acid dependence given by reaction (32) can be explained, where $a = 1 + K_{34}K_{35}/k_{36}$ and $b = K_{34}/k_{36}$.

As was shown previously, the anion greatly influences the rate of cerium(IV) oxidations. Formaldehyde oxidation was estimated to proceed about 4×10^7 faster in perchloric acid than in sulfuric acid at unit acid concentration.[50] In addition, the rate was third-order in sulfuric acid in contrast to the dependence given by reaction (32) for perchloric acid. These data are suggestive of sulfate complexes with cerium(IV), and the following mechanism was proposed[50]:

$$Ce(SO_4)_4{}^{4-} + H_3\overset{\oplus}{O} \; \rightleftharpoons \; HCe(SO_4)_4{}^{3-} + H_2O \tag{37}$$

$$HCe(SO_4)_4{}^{3-} + H_3\overset{\oplus}{O} \; \rightleftharpoons \; H_2Ce(SO_4)_4{}^{2-} + H_2O \tag{38}$$

$$H_2Ce(SO_4)_4{}^{2-} + H_3\overset{\oplus}{O} \; \rightleftharpoons \; H_3Ce(SO_4)_4{}^{-} + H_2O \tag{39}$$

$$H_3Ce(SO_4)_4{}^{-} + H_3\overset{\oplus}{O} \; \rightleftharpoons \; H_4Ce(SO_4)_4 + H_2O \tag{40}$$

$$H_2C(OH)_2 + H_3\overset{\oplus}{O} \; \rightleftharpoons \; H_2\overset{\oplus}{C}OH + H_2O \tag{34}$$

$$H_4Ce(SO_4)_4 + H_2C(OH)_2 \; \rightarrow \; Ce^{III} + H{-}\overset{\centerdot}{C}(OH)_2 + H^{\oplus} \tag{41}$$

$$Ce^{IV} + H\overset{\centerdot}{C}(OH)_2 \; \rightarrow \; Ce^{III} + HCO_2H + H^{\oplus} \tag{42}$$

[51] Carbon–hydrogen rupture generally occurs rather than oxygen–hydrogen rupture; see ref. 33.

The total cerium concentration $[Ce^{IV}]$ is given by equation (43), which on rearrangement and substitution of the appropriate equilibrium constants gives equation (44):

$$[Ce^{IV}] = [H_4Ce(SO_4)_4] + [H_3Ce(SO_4)_4^-] + [H_2Ce(SO_4)_4^{2-}]$$
$$+ [HCe(SO_4)_4^{3-}] + [Ce(SO_4)_4^{4-}] \qquad (43)$$

$$[H_4Ce(SO_4)_4] =$$

$$\frac{K_{40}K_{39}K_{38}K_{37}[Ce^{IV}][H^+]^4}{K_{40}K_{39}K_{38}K_{37}[H^+]^4 + K_{40}K_{39}K_{38}[H^+]^3 + K_{40}K_{39}[H^+]^2} + K_{40}[H^+] + 1 \quad (44)$$

If one is large compared with the other terms in the denominator of Eq. (44), the rate law is given by Eq. (45),

$$\frac{-d[Ce^{IV}]}{dt} = \frac{k_{41}K_{40}K_{39}K_{38}K_{37}[H_4Ce(SO_4)_4][\text{formaldehyde}][H^+]^4}{1 + K_{34}[H^+]} \qquad (45)$$

where [formaldehyde] is the total formaldehyde concentration. Now if $K_{34}[H^+]$ is large compared with one, third-order dependence on acid concentration is predicted in accordance with the observation. The cerium(IV)-to-sulfate ion ratio was high, so that oxidation by cerium species with fewer than four sulfate ions was apparently unimportant.

D. AROMATIC ALDEHYDES

A preliminary investigation of the ceric perchlorate oxidation of benzaldehyde in 91 % aqueous acetic acid suggests that cerium(IV)–benzaldehyde intermediates are present.[52] As is found in many ceric oxidations, the kinetics were not precise. Nonetheless, the rate law (46) could be obtained:

$$\frac{-d[Ce^{IV}]}{dt} = k_a[Ce^{IV}] + k_b[Ce^{IV}][C_6H_5CHO]^2 \qquad (46)$$

The oxidation is acid dependent, but as yet the order in acid is unknown. A mechanism consistent with the data is given by Eqs. (47)–(54), where AH is benzaldehyde and AOH is benzoic acid:

$$Ce^{IV} + AH \underset{}{\overset{K_1}{\rightleftharpoons}} Ce^{IV}(AH) \qquad (47)$$

$$Ce^{IV}(AH) + AH \underset{}{\overset{K_2}{\rightleftharpoons}} Ce^{IV}(AH)_2 \qquad (48)$$

$$Ce^{IV}(AH)_2 + AH \underset{}{\overset{K_3}{\rightleftharpoons}} Ce^{IV}(AH)_3 \qquad (49)$$

$$Ce^{IV}(AH) \overset{k_1}{\longrightarrow} Ce^{III} + A\cdot + H^\oplus \qquad (50)$$

$$Ce^{IV}(AH)_2 \overset{k_2}{\longrightarrow} Ce^{III}(AH) + A\cdot + H^\oplus \qquad (51)$$

[52] K. B. Wiberg and W. H. Richardson, unpublished results.

$$Ce^{IV}(AH)_3 \xrightarrow{k_3} Ce^{III}(AH)_2 + A \cdot + H^\oplus \tag{52}$$

$$Ce^{IV} + A \cdot \xrightarrow{fast} Ce^{III} + A^\oplus \tag{53}$$

$$A^\oplus + H_2O \longrightarrow AOH + H^\oplus \tag{54}$$

Ligand transfer, rather than electron transfer, may occur in reaction (53) to give AOH directly. Equation (55) gives the derived rate law in terms of total cerium(IV) concentration $[Ce^{IV}]$:

$$\frac{-d[Ce^{IV}]}{dt} = \frac{\begin{aligned}&k_1 K_1[Ce^{IV}][AH] + k_2 K_1 K_2[Ce^{IV}][AH]^2\\&+ k_3 K_1 K_2 K_3[Ce^{IV}][AH]^3\end{aligned}}{[1 + K_1[AH] + K_1 K_2[AH]^2 + K_1 K_2 K_3[AH]^3]} \tag{55}$$

The observed rate law results if $K_1 \gg K_2, K_3$; $K_1[AH] \gg 1$; and $k_2 \ll k_1, k_3$.

A kinetic isotope effect of $k_H/k_D = 3.78$ for the third-order term in Eq. (46) suggests a rate-determining carbon–hydrogen bond breaking in reaction (52). The first-order term in reaction (46) also shows an isotope effect, which may be assigned to reaction (50) by comparing the observed and derived rate laws.

Evidence for radical intermediates, such as $A \cdot$, was given by the polymerization of acrylamide during the reaction of cerium(IV) with benzaldehyde. Without benzaldehyde, polymerization was markedly decreased. Another diagnostic test for hydrogen atom abstraction by cerium(IV) from an aldehyde group was given by the oxidation of triphenylacetaldehyde. Triphenylcarbinol was produced in 75% yield along with 16% recovered aldehyde. Decarbonylation of the acyl radical, which results from one-electron oxidation, occurs to give the trityl radical. Further oxidation of the latter yields triphenylcarbinol. If a two-electron ligand transfer oxidation was operative, which might arise from associated cerium(IV) species, triphenylacetic acid would be the expected product.[53]

Substituent effects are consistent with the proposed mechanism of aryl aldehyde oxidation. If K_1 is large, as was assumed, the equilibrium (reaction 47) will be displaced far to the complex, and substituents will have little effect on reaction (47). Thus, the substituent effect for decomposition of $Ce^{IV}(AH)$ will not be complicated by a prior equilibrium. A ρ-value of about -0.8 would be expected for hydrogen atom abstraction, on the basis of autoxidation of substituted benzaldehydes.[54] This agrees well with the observed value of -0.72 associated with the first term of rate law (46). The substituents groups were p-CH_3O, p-CH_3, p-Cl, m-Cl, and m-NO_2. Assuming the equilibria (48) and (49) are *not* displaced far to the right, substituent effects for the third-order

[53] K. B. Wiberg and W. H. Richardson, *J. Am. Chem. Soc.* **84**, 2800 (1962).
[54] C. Walling and E. A. McElhill, *J. Am. Chem. Soc.* **73**, 2927 (1951).

term of the rate law (46) will arise both from decomposition of $Ce^{IV}(AH)_3$ and the prior equilibria. The ρ-value for cerium(IV)–aldehyde complex formation is unknown. However, if the cerium(IV) species adds to the carbonyl group, a ρ-value for cyanohydrin formation with substituted benzaldehydes ($+1.49$)[55] may be a good approximation. If the ρ-value for decomposition of $Ce^{IV}(AH)_3$ is assumed to be the same as for $Ce^{IV}(AH)$ (i.e., -0.72), a ρ-value of $+0.77$ is predicted for the third-order term of rate law (46). This is in good agreement with the observed value of $+0.74$. If the complex was similar to that proposed for cyclohexanone oxidation[46] ($ArC\overset{..}{H}\overset{..}{O}: \rightarrow Ce^{IV}$), groups that release electrons to the electron-deficient carbonyl carbon atom would facilitate complex formation. Here, a negative ρ-value for complex formation would be predicted.

VI. Oxidation of Carboxylic Acids

A. MONOFUNCTIONAL ACIDS

Simple aliphatic acids (formic, acetic, and propionic acids) are not oxidized by ceric sulfate in refluxing dilute sulfuric acid.[1a, 56] In the presence of a stronger oxidizing agent, ceric perchlorate in $4M$ perchloric acid, formic and acetic acid are slowly oxidized. The second-order rate constants at the indicated temperatures are[1a, 36b]: 1.92×10^{-5} ($51°$ C) and 9.0×10^{-5} ($66°$ C) liters mole^{-1} sec^{-1} for formic acid; and for acetic acid, 7.2×10^{-5} ($55°$ C) and 4.3×10^{-4} ($70°$ C) liters mole^{-1} sec^{-1}.

Oxidative decarboxylation of cyclohepta-2,4,6-trienecarboxylic acid (X) to

(X)

give tropenium salts occurs with various oxidizing agents including ceric ammonium nitrate.[57] In the latter reaction, the tropenium salt was produced in 30% yield and no other products were identified. With some oxidizing agents, it was possible to isolate benzaldehyde and benzoic acid in addition to tropenium salts.

Benzoic acid is reported to be stable to ceric sulfate under reflux, if light is excluded.[58] Another report states that benzoic, phthalic, and salicylic acids are oxidized to a variable extent with ceric sulfate under reflux; however, no attempt was apparently made to exclude light.[56]

[55] H. H. Jaffe, Chem. Rev. 53, 191 (1953).
[56] H. H. Willard and P. Young, J. Am. Chem. Soc. 52, 132 (1930).
[57] M. J. S. Dewar, C. R. Ganellin, and R. Pettit, J. Chem. Soc. p. 55 (1958).
[58] S. P. Rao, T. R. Lodha, and J. N. Gaur, Naturwissenschaften 48, 404 (1961).

B. DICARBOXYLIC ACIDS

Oxidation of oxalic acid, which was found to require two equivalents of cerium(IV) per mole of acid, was one of the early developments in cerimetry.[59] Kinetics of ceric sulfate oxidation of oxalic acid were first reported in 1920[60a] and confirmed more recently.[60b–d] First-order dependence in each reactant was observed.[60] Formation of a stable cerium(IV) oxalate intermediate must not occur, or else kinetics analogous to alcohol oxidation would be observed (Section III,A). A unique oxidation of a complex cobalt(III) oxalate has been reported, whereby cobalt is reduced (reaction 56)[61]:

$$(NH_3)_5Co^{III}C_2O_4H^{2+} + Ce^{IV} + 4\,H^{\oplus} \rightarrow Co^{II} + Ce^{III} + 2\,CO_2 + 5\,NH_4^+ \qquad (56)$$

Evidence for intermediate formation of $(NH_3)_5CoC_2O_4^{2+}$ could not be provided. An analytical method for malonic acid has been developed, where one mole of acid requires 6.66 equivalents of ceric sulfate.[56] Complete oxidation to carbon dioxide and water would require 7.0 equivalents. Other dicarboxylic acids, such as succinic, maleic, and fumaric acids, were stable to refluxing ceric sulfate solutions.[56]

C. HYDROXYCARBOXYLIC ACIDS

A kinetic study indicated first-order dependence on ceric sulfate and on the following α-hydroxy acids: mandelic, malic, and lactic.[62] Thus, cerium(IV)–acid complexes are not present in detectable concentrations (cf. Section III,A) and the mechanism below is suggested, where R is methyl, phenyl, or —CH_2—CO_2H:

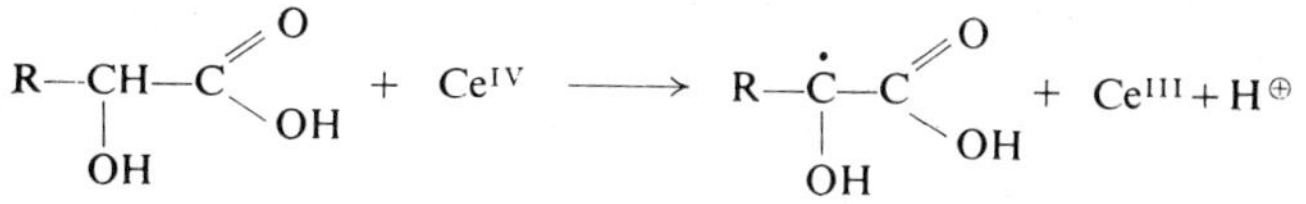

$$\text{(57)}$$

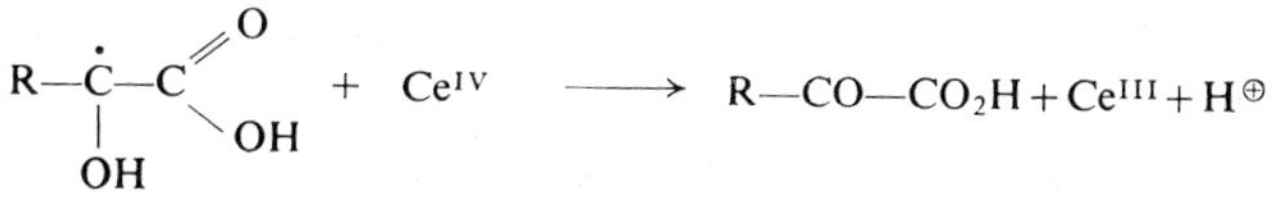

$$\text{(58)}$$

The reactive cerium specie(s) is unknown. Carbon–hydrogen rupture is shown rather than oxygen–hydrogen rupture as was originally suggested[62] (cf. Section III,C). The inability to detect a cerium(IV)–acid complex with ceric

[59] N. H. Furman, *J. Am. Chem. Soc.* **50**, 755 (1928); H. H. Willard and P. Young, *ibid.* **50**, 1322 (1928).

[60] (a) A. Benrath and K. Ruland, *Z. Anorg. Chem.* **114**, 267 (1920); (b) V. H. Dodson and A. H. Black, *J. Am. Chem. Soc.* **79**, 3657 (1957); (c) *J. Chem. Educ.* **33**, 562 (1956); (d) S. D. Ross and C. G. Swain, *J. Am. Chem. Soc.* **69**, 1325 (1947).

[61] P. Saffir and H. Taube, *J. Am. Chem. Soc.* **82**, 13 (1960).

[62] B. Krishna and K. C. Tewari, *J. Chem. Soc.* p. 3097 (1961).

sulfate oxidant is analogous to most glycol oxidations (Section IV,B). If this
analogy, based on the similarity in structure of *vic*-glycols and α-hydroxy
acids, can be extended, complex formation may be observed with ceric
perchlorate or nitrate oxidation. Although rate retardation was observed with
added sulfate ions, this does not necessarily indicate complex formation.[62]
Instead, sulfate ions may merely increase the stability of cerium(IV) relative to
cerium(III), which would reduce the rate (Section II,A).

The stoichiometry of α-hydroxy acid oxidation by ceric sulfate at 25° C
was determined by the amount of cerium(IV) consumed.[62] Mandelic acid
required 2.0 equivalents of ceric ion per mole of acid, which indicates that
oxidation proceeds only to the α-keto acid. With malic and lactic acids, the
stoichiometry is more complex, since 8.50 and 5.75 equivalents of ceric ion
per mole are required, respectively. Oxidation of lactic acid was found to
produce 0.3 mole of formic acid per mole of substrate. The data for lactic acid
oxidation are consistent with 70% reaction via reaction (59) and 30% via
reaction (60):

$$CH_3\underset{\underset{\displaystyle OH}{|}}{C}HCO_2H + 4\,Ce^{IV} + H_2O \longrightarrow CH_3CO_2H + CO_2 + 4\,H^{\oplus} + 4\,Ce^{III} \qquad (59)$$

$$CH_3\underset{\underset{\displaystyle OH}{|}}{C}HCO_2H + 10\,Ce^{IV} + 3\,H_2O \longrightarrow HCO_2H + 2\,CO_2 + 10\,H^{\oplus} + 10\,Ce^{III} \qquad (60)$$

It seems most likely that pyruvic acid is an intermediate in both reactions;
however, pyruvic acid is reported to yield only acetic acid upon cerium(IV)
oxidation.[1a]

An analytical method for hydroxy acids has been reported using ceric
perchlorate.[37] The equivalents of cerium(IV) consumed 1 mole of acid, and
deviations from 100% accuracy were: tartaric acid (6, +0.08%), citric acid
(14, 0.00%), and malic acid (8, +0.02%). The following generalizations were
made[37]:

For polyhydric alcohol monocarboxylic acids

$$HOCH_2(CHOH)_nCO_2H + (4+2n)Ce^{IV} + (n+1)H_2O \rightarrow$$
$$(n+1)HCOOH + (4+2n)H^{\oplus} + (4+2n)Ce^{III} + CO_2 \quad (61)$$

For polyhydric alcohol dicarboxylic acids

$$HOOC—(CHOH)_n—COOH + (4+2n)Ce^{IV} + nH_2O \rightarrow$$
$$nHCOOH + (4+2n)H^{\oplus} + (4+2n)Ce^{III} + 2\,CO_2 \quad (62)$$

An analytical procedure for hydroxy acid has also been developed using
ceric sulfate, but oxidation usually proceeds to a greater extent than with ceric
perchlorate.[56] The equivalents of ceric sulfate required for 1 mole of the
following acids are: tartaric, 7.2; citric, 15.85; malic, 9.25; and glycolic, 3.95.

VII. Oxidation of Hydroperoxides

By analogy to ceric ion oxidation of hydrogen peroxide,[63] hydroperoxides would be expected to yield peroxy radical intermediates. Electron spin resonance (e.s.r.) spectra of ceric ion reactions with *tert*-butyl and cumyl hydroperoxide seem to be consistent with such intermediates.[64] Single lines of width 14 and 6 gauss were reported for the cerium(IV) reaction with *tert*-butyl and cumyl hydroperoxide. A line width of 16–18 gauss has been observed for the *tert*-butyl peroxy radical generated by cobalt ion-catalyzed decomposition of *tert*-butyl hydroxide.[65] The line width reported for the cumyl peroxy radical seems somewhat low, since values of 11–12 gauss have been observed in autoxidation of cumene[66] and cobalt ion decomposition of cumyl hydroperoxide.[65]

Little effort has been invested in studying the products of the cerium(IV)–hydroperoxide reaction. The earliest report indicated that cumyl hydroperoxide gave acetophenone in 8 % yield with ceric sulfate.[67] No other products were given. Ceric ion oxidation of *tert*-butyl hydroperoxide is reported to yield acetone, formaldehyde di-*tert*-butyl peroxide, and oxygen in undisclosed yields.[68] The stoichiometry was observed to be 1 cerium(IV) per mole of *tert*-butyl hydroperoxide. Acetone from *tert*-butyl hydroperoxide and acetophenone from cumyl hydroperoxide suggests an alkoxy radical intermediate.[69] Kinetic data and product yields are needed to establish a complete mechanism; however, the available data suggest that reactions (64) to (69) may contribute to an over-all mechanism, where R is *tert*-butyl or cumyl:

$$ROOH + Ce^{IV} \rightleftharpoons Ce^{IV}(ROOH) \tag{63}$$

$$Ce^{IV}(ROOH) \rightarrow Ce^{III} + ROO\cdot + H^{\oplus} \tag{64}$$

$$ROO\cdot + Ce^{IV}(ROOH) \rightarrow 2\,RO\cdot + O_2 + Ce^{III} + H^{\oplus} \tag{65}$$

$$RO\cdot \rightarrow Ketone + CH_3\cdot \tag{66}$$

$$CH_3\cdot + Ce^{IV}(H_2O) \rightarrow CH_3OH + Ce^{III} + H^{\oplus} \tag{67}$$

$$CH_3OH + 2\,Ce^{IV} \rightarrow CH_2O + 2\,Ce^{III} + 2\,H^{\oplus} \tag{68}$$

$$2\,ROO\cdot \rightarrow ROOR + O_2 \tag{69}[70]$$

[63] M. Ardon and G. Stein, *J. Chem. Soc.* p. 104 (1956); S. Baer and G. Stein, *ibid.* 3176 (1953); A. K. Babko and A. I. Volkova, *Ukr. Khim. Zh.* **20**, 211 (1954), *Chem. Abstr.* **49**, 1465d (1955).

[64] W. T. Dixon and R. O. C. Norman, *Nature* **196**, 891 (1962).

[65] W. H. Richardson, *J. Org. Chem.* (in press).

[66] J. R. Thomas, *J. Am. Chem. Soc.* **85**, 591 (1963).

[67] M. S. Kharasch, A. Fono, W. Nudenberg, and B. Bischof, *J. Org. Chem.* **17**, 207 (1952).

[68] M. S. Kharasch, U.S. Dept. of Commerce Tech. Rept. PB 123737: Cumulative Report for Period July, 1953 to September, 1955. (Contract No. N6 ori-02040.)

[69] C. Walling and A. Padwa, *J. Am. Chem. Soc.* **85**, 1593 (1963); J. K. Kochi, *ibid.* **84**, 1193 (1962).

[70] See G. A. Russell, *in* "Peroxide Reaction Mechanisms" (J. O. Edwards, ed.), Wiley (Interscience), New York, 1962.

To explain the stoichiometry, additional products in a lower oxidation state, e.g., methane and *tert*-butyl alcohol, are required. An alternative mechanism (70–72), which explains the 1:1 cerium(IV)–hydroperoxide stoichiometry, cannot be operative because the yields of oxygen and dialkyl peroxide are not equal.[68] The over-all reaction is given by reaction (73):

$$ROOH + Ce^{IV} \rightarrow ROO\cdot + Ce^{III} + H^{\oplus} \tag{70}$$

$$ROO\cdot + Ce^{IV} \rightarrow R^{\oplus} + O_2 + Ce^{III} \tag{71}$$

$$R^{\oplus} + ROOH \rightarrow ROOR + H^{\oplus} \tag{72}$$

$$2\,ROOH + 2\,Ce^{IV} \rightarrow ROOR + 2\,Ce^{III} + O_2 \tag{73}$$

Since peroxy radicals are produced from ceric ion and hydroperoxides, it was hoped that addition of peroxy radicals to olefins could be accomplished by this means.[68, 71] Products from cerium(IV) decomposition of *tert*-butyl hydroperoxide in the presence of 2,4,4-trimethyl-1-pentene indicate a small amount of addition.[71] The indicated yields are based on hydroperoxide:

$$
\begin{array}{c}
\qquad\qquad\qquad\qquad\qquad\overset{\displaystyle CH_3}{|}\\
Ce^{IV} + tert\text{-}C_4H_9OOH + (CH_3)_3C\!-\!CH_2\!-\!C\!=\!CH_2 \quad \longrightarrow
\end{array}
$$

$$(CH_3)_3CCH_2COCH_3 + (CH_3)_3CCH_2CH(CH_3)CHO + t\text{-}C_4H_9OH + O_2 \tag{74}$$
$$\quad(10\%)\qquad\qquad\qquad(4\%)\qquad\qquad\qquad(55\%)\quad\;(12\%)$$

The same product distribution resulted when the reaction solution was purged with nitrogen, which shows that oxidation products do not arise from oxygen produced in the reaction. The mechanism in reactions (75)–(78) was suggested for aldehyde formation, where R is *tert*-butyl. Reaction (78) was confirmed independently:

$$Ce^{IV} + ROOH \longrightarrow Ce^{III} + ROO\cdot + H^{\oplus} \tag{75}$$

$$
\begin{array}{cc}
\quad\overset{\displaystyle CH_3}{|} & \overset{\displaystyle CH_3}{|}\\
ROO\cdot + (CH_3)_3\!-\!CH_2\!-\!C\!=\!CH_2 \longrightarrow & (CH_3)_3\!-\!CH_2\!-\!C\!-\!CH_2\!-\!OO\!-\!R\\
& \quad\;\;\underset{\textbf{(XI)}}{\cdot}
\end{array} \tag{76}
$$

$$
\begin{array}{c}
\qquad\qquad\qquad\overset{\displaystyle CH_3}{|}\\
XI \longrightarrow (CH_3)_3\!-\!CH_2\!-\!C\!-\!CH_2 + RO\cdot\\
\qquad\qquad\qquad\;\underset{O}{\diagdown\;\diagup}\\
\qquad\qquad\qquad\;\;\textbf{(XII)}
\end{array} \tag{77}
$$

$$
\begin{array}{c}
\qquad\qquad\qquad\overset{\displaystyle CH_3}{|}\\
XII + Ce^{IV} \longrightarrow (CH_3)_3\!-\!CH_2\!-\!CH\!-\!CHO
\end{array} \tag{78}
$$

[71] W. F. Brill, *J. Am. Chem. Soc.* **85**, 141 (1963).

Ceric ion reactions with other peroxides have not been reported. However, it is known that hydrogen peroxide is oxidized much faster by ceric ion than peracids, diacyl, or dialkyl peroxides.[72]

VIII. Oxidation of Nitrogen-Containing Compounds

With the exception of chlorophyll oxidation,[73] all the reported cerium(IV) oxidations of nitrogen-containing compounds have been performed on aromatic amines. Leuco malachite green (XIII), a tertiary amine, gives malachite green (XIV) with ceric ion.[74] In the presence of cerium(III), carbinol

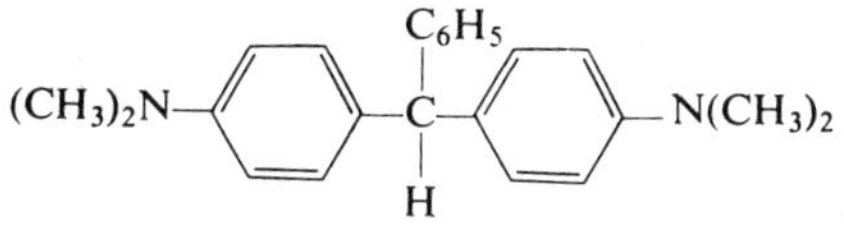

(XIII) 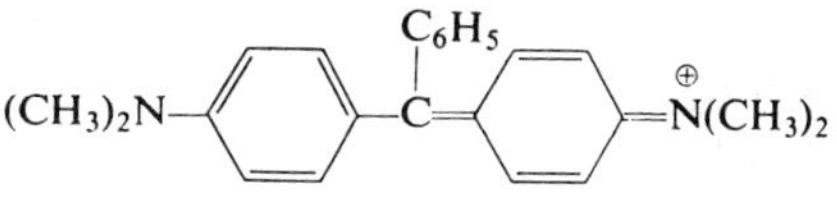   (XIV)

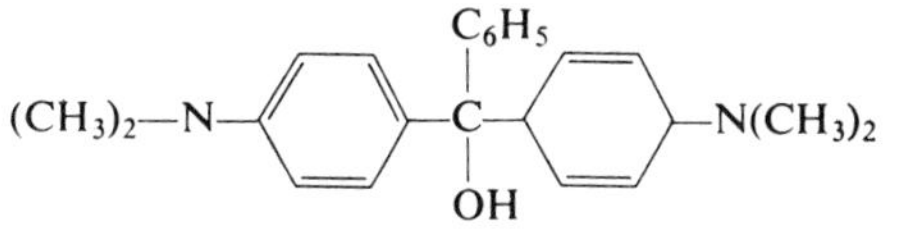

(XV)

(XV) is dehydrated more slowly than oxidation of XIII to XIV, which suggests that the carbinol is not an intermediate. It is not known whether 2 one-electron oxidations or 1 two-electron oxidation occurs. Also, the position of ceric ion attack, whether at nitrogen or the carbon–hydrogen bond, is unknown.

Oxidation of mesidine (XVI), a primary amine, gave the quinone-imine (XVII) in 70% yield[75]:

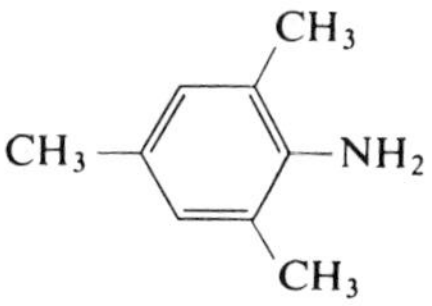

(XVI) 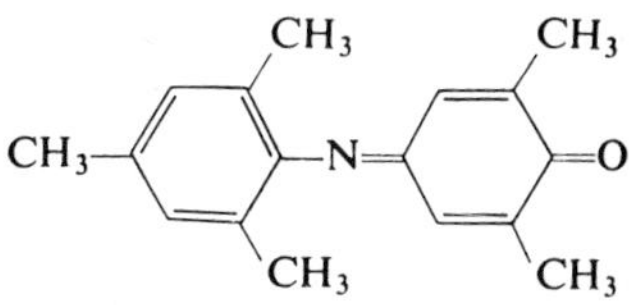   (XVII)

[72] F. P. Greenspan and D. G. MacKellar, *Anal. Chem.* **20**, 1061 (1948); F. E. Critchfield, "Organic Functional Group Analysis," p. 161. Macmillan (Pergamon), New York, 1963.

[73] E. Rabinowitch and J. Weiss, *Proc. Roy. Soc. Ser.* **A162**, 251 (1937).

[74] G. G. Swain and K. Hedberg, *J. Am. Chem. Soc.* **72**, 3373 (1950); R. G. R. Bacon, *Chem. & Ind. (London)* p. 19 (1962).

[75] A. G. Holmes-Siedle and B. C. Saunders, *Chem. & Ind. (London)* p. 164 (1959).

No mechanism was proposed; however, by analogy to the leuco malachite green oxidation, XVIII may be an intermediate.

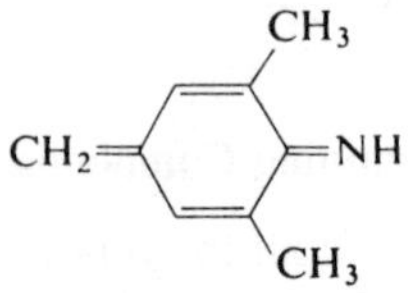

(XVIII) 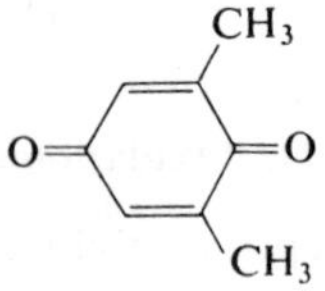   (XIX)

Further oxidation and hydrolysis of (XVIII) to 2,6-dimethylquinone (XIX), followed by condensation with mesidine, would give the product XVII. Steric effects may be responsible for preferential formation of only one isomer in the condensation reaction. An unidentified colored intermediate was noted, which could be the quinone XIX.

The aromatic azo-amine, N,N,N',N'-tetraethyl-4,4'-diaminoazobenzene (XX), has been reported to undergo an over-all two-electron oxidation.[76] According to potentiometric analysis, oxidation to XXI is apparently quantitative. At room temperature, XXI slowly yields acetaldehyde.

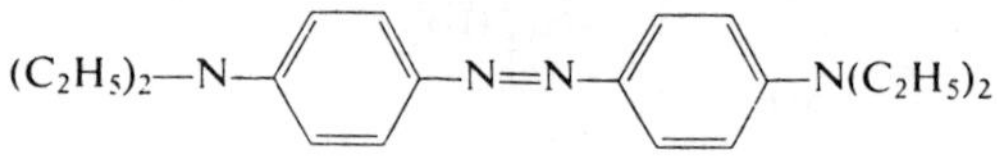

(XX)

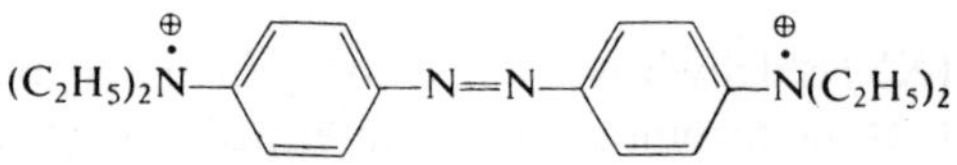

(XXI)

IX. Oxidation of Sulfur-Containing Compounds

Data for this type of reaction is extremely meager. In the only reported reaction, benzene sulfinic acid is oxidized by ceric sulfate to "compounds containing sexivalent sulfur."[77] Presumably, the sulfonic acid and sulfone are produced.

Stable cerium(IV) complexes of $HSCH_2CH_2OH$, $HSCH_2CH(SH)CH_2OH$, $CH_3CH(SH)CO_2Na$, and $HSCH(CO_2Na)_2$ in basic medium have been reported.[78] Under these conditions the thiol group is apparently resistant to

[76] M. Matrka, J. Poskočil, Z. Ságner, and Z. Stěrba, Collection Czech. Chem. Commun. **26**, 3177 (1961).

[77] S. P. Alimarin and D. I. Kuzenetsov, Vestn. Mosk. Univ. Ser. Mat. Mekh. Astron. Fiz. i Khim. **14** [3], 189 (1959); Chem. Abstr. **54**, 10466a (1960).

[78] F. Buscarons and E. Casassas, Anales Real Soc. Espan. Fis. Quim. (Madrid) Ser. **B55**, 663 (1959); Chem. Abstr. **54**, 4271a (1960).

oxidation. Under acidic conditions, oxidation of thiols may occur, since stable cerium(IV) alcoholate complexes are reported in basic medium; but in acidic solution, alcohols are readily oxidized (Section III).

X. Oxidation of Stable Free Radicals

The kinetics of the reaction between the α,α'-diphenyl-β-picrylhydrazyl radical and metal acetates were studied.[79] First-order dependence in each of the reactants was observed, and the rate constants (liters mole^{-1} sec^{-1}) in acetic acid at 25°C for the ions Co^{III}, Pb^{IV}, Ce^{IV}, and Fe^{III} are: 22, 35, 55, and 88. It is interesting to note that the rates do not parallel the oxidation potentials of the ions. On the basis of oxidation potentials,[80] reaction rate would be expected to increase in the order Fe^{III} < Pb^{IV} < Ce^{IV} < Co^{III}.

XI. Oxidation of Hydrocarbons

Ceric sulfate oxidation of *p*-xylene to *p*-tolualdehyde is reported to be first-order in each reactant and to have an activation energy (E_a) of 23.8 kcal/mole.[81] The aldehyde was obtained in about 50% yield. The following series of one-electron redox reactions was proposed to explain the data:

$$ArCH_3 + Ce^{IV} \rightarrow Ar\overset{.}{C}H_2 + Ce^{III} + H^{\oplus} \tag{79}$$

$$Ar\overset{.}{C}H_2 + Ce^{IV}(OH) \rightarrow ArCH_2OH + Ce^{III} \tag{80}$$

$$ArCH_2OH + Ce^{IV} \rightarrow Ar\overset{.}{C}HOH + Ce^{III} + H^{\oplus} \tag{81}$$

$$Ar\overset{.}{C}HOH + Ce^{IV}(OH) \rightarrow ArCH(OH)_2 + Ce^{III} \tag{82}$$

$$ArCH(OH)_2 \rightarrow ArCHO + H_2O \tag{83}$$

It is not known whether Ce^{IV}(OH) or Ce^{IV}(H$_2$O) is the oxidant in reactions (80) and (82).

Kinetics of the ceric sulfate oxidation of naphthalene in aqueous acetic-sulfuric acid medium has been surveyed.[82] First-order dependence in each reactant was reported with an activation energy of 14 kcal/mole. Products or

[79] L. H. Sutcliffe and J. Walkley, *Nature* **178**, 999 (1956).
[80] W. M. Latimer, "The Oxidation States of the Elements and Their Potentials in Aqueous Solutions." Prentice-Hall, Englewood Cliffs, New Jersey, 1952.
[81] R. Ramaswamy, M. S. Venkatachalapathy, and H. V. K. Udupa, *Bull. Chem. Soc. Japan* **35**, 1751 (1962).
[82] S. V. Gorbachev and Ya. I. Vabel, *Zh. Fiz. Khim.* **28**, 1782 (1954).

stoichiometry of the reaction were not specified. Although the data are sparse, it seems most reasonable that oxidation is initiated by hydroxylation of naphthalene (reactions 84 and 85):

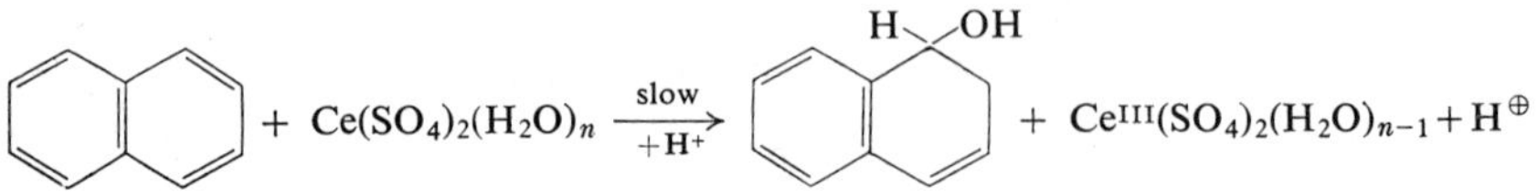

$$\text{(naphthalene)} + \text{Ce(SO}_4)_2(\text{H}_2\text{O})_n \xrightarrow[+\text{H}^+]{\text{slow}} \text{(hydroxylated)} + \text{Ce}^{\text{III}}(\text{SO}_4)_2(\text{H}_2\text{O})_{n-1} + \text{H}^{\oplus} \quad (84)$$

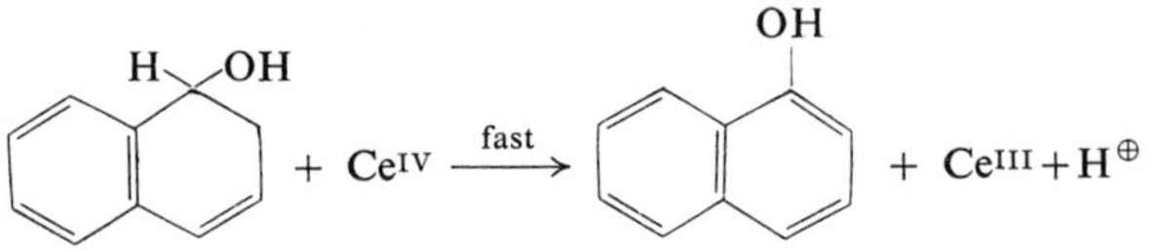

$$\text{(hydroxylated)} + \text{Ce}^{\text{IV}} \xrightarrow{\text{fast}} \text{(naphthol)} + \text{Ce}^{\text{III}} + \text{H}^{\oplus} \quad (85)$$

Oxidation at a carbon–hydrogen bond to give an aryl radical seems less likely.[83] Oxidation of anthracene by ceric sulfate has been reported[59]; however, no details were given.

XII. Indirect Oxidations with Ceric Ions

Reactions where cerium(IV) is not the primary oxidant, but instead is used to generate a reactive oxidant, are considered here.

A. CERIUM(IV) AND CHROMIUM IONS

Many organic compounds are oxidized by cerium(IV) to formic acid.[84] Although formic acid may be oxidized by ceric ion (Section VI,A), more severe conditions are usually required than in the preceding steps. It was found that catalytic amounts of chromium(III) salts, in the presence of cerium(IV), affect complete oxidation to carbon dioxide and water under mild conditions.[85] For example, ceric sulfate oxidation of glucose (an aldose) gives formic acid; oxidation of fructose (a ketose) yields formic acid, carbon dioxide, and water.[84a] If a catalytic amount of a chromium(III) salt is added, oxidation proceeds quantitatively to carbon dioxide and water in both instances.[85a] Complete oxidation of sucrose, lactose, and xylose was also accomplished by this method.

[83] For a discussion of aromatic free radical substitution, which is pertinent to this problem, see: C. Walling, "Free Radicals in Solution," p. 482. Wiley, New York, 1957.

[84] (a) N. N. Sharma, *Anal. Chim. Acta* **14**, 423 (1956); (b) N. N. Sharma and R. C. Mehrota, *ibid.* **13**, 419 (1955).

[85] (a) N. N. Sharma, *Z. Anal. Chem.* **154**, 340 (1957); (b) N. N. Sharma and R. C. Mehrota, *ibid.* **173**, 395 (1960).

Kinetics of formic acid oxidation by the cerium–chromium system have been studied and the rate law is given[85b]:

$$-\frac{d[\text{HCO}_2\text{H}]}{dt} = k[\text{HCO}_2\text{H}][\text{chromium ions}][\text{H}^\oplus]^2 \qquad (86)$$

This corresponds to a rapid reaction between chromium(III) and cerium(IV) followed by a rate-determining reaction between formic acid and chromium which is in a valence state greater than three. Most likely this is chromium(VI), but valence states of four and five cannot be ruled out. This system exemplifies the fact that oxidation potentials cannot be used as a reliable guide to rate of oxidation, since cerium(IV) has a higher oxidation potential than chromium(VI).[80]

B. CERIUM(IV) AND BROMIDE IONS

The reaction between cerium(IV) and bromide ions[86] in the presence of butadiene gave additive dimerization.[87] The mechanism below was suggested:

$$\text{Ce}^{\text{IV}} + \text{Br}^\ominus \longrightarrow \text{Ce}^{\text{III}} + \text{Br}^\bullet \qquad (87)$$

$$\text{Br}^\bullet + \overset{}{\diagdown\!\!\!=\!\!\!\diagup} \longrightarrow \text{BrC}_4\text{H}_6^\bullet \qquad (88)$$

$$2\ \text{BrC}_4\text{H}_6^\bullet \longrightarrow \text{Br—C}_4\text{H}_6\text{—C}_4\text{H}_6\text{—Br} \qquad (89)$$

Dibromide was obtained in 40–50% yield as a mixture of isomers, where 75% of the mixture was the 1,8-dibromide (XXII). The mechanism is written with bromine atoms; however, the radical anion ($\text{Br}_2^\ominus\cdot$) would be equally accept-

$$(\text{BrCH}_2\text{—CH}=\text{CH—CH}_2)_2$$
$$(\text{XXII})$$

able.[87] Similar reactions with other halides have not been reported. It seems that reaction with iodide and chloride ions would be possible. Oxidation of chloride ion by cerium(IV) is thought to give the $\text{Cl}_2^\ominus\cdot$ radical anion as a primary product.[88,89]

[86] E. L. King and M. L. Pandow, *J. Am. Chem. Soc.* **75**, 3063 (1953).
[87] C. M. Langkammerer, E. L. Jenner, D. D. Coffman, and B. W. Houk, *J. Am. Chem. Soc.* **82**, 1395 (1960).
[88] F. R. Duke and C. E. Borchers, *J. Am. Chem. Soc.* **75**, 5186 (1953).
[89] For the possible isolation of ceric chloride, see A. J. Grant and C. James, *J. Am. Chem. Soc.* **37**, 2652 (1915).

C. CERIUM(IV) AND RADIATION

Hydroxyl radicals have been suggested as intermediates when aqueous cerium(IV) solutions are exposed to ultraviolet radiation.[90-92] A limited number of organic compounds have been oxidized under these conditions. As yet, the reactions have not been studied in detail. Benzoic acid is apparently stable to refluxing aqueous cerium(IV) solutions, but in the presence of bright sunlight, oxidation to fumaric acid occurs.[58] Similarly, it was noted that ceric ion oxidation of methanol and formic acid was greatly enhanced by light.[60a] The mechanism in reactions (90)–(92) has been proposed for cerium(IV) photochemical oxidation of formic acid[90b]:

$$Ce^{IV}(H_2O) \xrightarrow{h\nu} Ce^{III} + OH + H^{\oplus} \tag{90}$$

$$\cdot OH + HCOOH \longrightarrow \cdot COOH + H_2O \tag{91}$$

$$Ce^{IV} + \cdot COOH \longrightarrow CO_2 + H^{\oplus} + Ce^{III} \tag{92}$$

Carbon–hydrogen bond cleavage is shown rather than oxygen–hydrogen cleavage as was originally suggested.[93-95] The mechanism is consistent with the finding that formic acid increases the rate of photoreduction of cerium(IV), since reaction (91) competes with (93):

$$Ce^{III} + \overset{\cdot}{O}H \rightarrow Ce^{IV} + \overset{\ominus}{O}H \tag{93}$$

Alternative reactions between light-activated cerium(IV) and organic compounds are also possible.

Formic acid oxidation in the presence of X-rays and cerium(IV) has been reported.[96] However, this reaction is initiated by hydroxyl radicals and hydrogen atoms produced from irradiation of water.[96, 97]

D. CERIUM ION CATALYSIS OF AUTOXIDATION

Neither an extensive discussion of the mechanism nor the literature of autoxidation is intended, since excellent reviews are available.[98] However, the utility of cerium salts as autoxidation catalysts should be noted.

[90] (a) T. J. Sworski, *J. Am. Chem. Soc.* **79**, 3655 (1957); (b) **77**, 1074 (1955); (c) J. Weiss and D. Porret, *Nature* **139**, 1019 (1937); (d) M. G. Evans and N. Uri, *ibid.* **166**, 602 (1950).

[91] It has been suggested that light-induced cerium(IV) oxidation of water proceeds directly to oxygen by a two-electron change involving cerium(IV) dimers.[92] This proposal was later contested.[90d]

[92] L. J. Heidt and M. E. Smith, *J. Am. Chem. Soc.* **70**, 2476 (1948).

[93] Oxygen–hydrogen cleavage from carboxylic acids by a free radical path is not favored,[94] whereas acyl carbon–hydrogen cleavage in formate esters proceeds readily.[95]

[94] M. Szwarc and J. Smid, *J. Chem. Phys.* **27**, 421 (1957).

[95] W. H. Urry and E. S. Huyser, *J. Am. Chem. Soc.* **75**, 4876 (1953).

[96] H. E. Spencer and G. K. Rollefson, *J. Am. Chem. Soc.* **77**, 1938 (1955).

[97] T. J. Sworski, *Radiation Science* **4**, 483 (1956).

[98] See, e.g., W. O. Lundberg, "Autoxidation and Antioxidants." Wiley (Interscience), New York, 1961.

Cyclic ethers, such as tetrahydrofuran, may be oxidized to lactones in 40% yield in the presence of cerium stearate, linoleate, naphthenate, or acetate catalysts.[99] With 2,6-dimethyl-3-tetrahydropyrancarboxaldehyde (XXIII), cerium-catalyzed autoxidation to carboxylic acid occurs, and oxidation at the 2-position is not reported.[100] Conversion of aldehydes to acids in over 60%

(XXIII)

yield by ceric sulfate-catalyzed oxidation has been reported with 2,2,3-trichlorobutanal, 2,2,3-trichloropropanal, and chloral.[101]

A study of metal ion-catalyzed oxidation of 2,5-dimethylhexane has revealed that the activity of the catalyst decreases with decreasing oxidation potential.[102] Similarly, the relative rates for cobalt, manganese, and cerium stearate-catalyzed oxidation of methyl linoleate in benzene solution are: 7, 5, and 4.[103] Ligands have a profound effect on catalytic activity. In the preceding reaction, none of the metal ions possessed catalytic activity in ethanol or ethyl acetate solvents. A ligand effect was noted in the oxidation of diamines with the general formula $(NH_2(CH_2)_n—NH_2)$. Cobalt, copper, palladium, osmium, and gold salts were found to have catalytic activity, but cerium was inactive.[104] Catalytic activity is usually associated with the ease of metal ion valence change. A strongly complexing ligand may preferentially stabilize one valence state.[35]

Ligand oxidation of metal chelates has been studied.[105] There is no correlation between the rate of ligand oxidation and the oxidation potential of the ions in aqueous solution.[80] The ease of acetylacetonate chelate oxidation decreases in the order: $V^{III} > Ce^{IV}$, $Ni^{II} > Mn^{III} > Fe^{III} > Co^{II} > Cu^{II} > Co^{III} > Th^{IV}$. It is felt that ease of oxidation is dependent on the facility of valence change. Again, the ligand effect is seen by comparison with autoxidation of methyl linoleate and 2,5-dimethylhexane (above).

[99] J. G. M. Bremmer and D. G. Jones (to Imperial Chem. Ind. Ltd.), British Patent 608,539 (September, 1948); *Chem. Abstr.* **43**, P2224e.

[100] B. T. Freure (to Carbide and Carbon Chem. Corp.), U.S. Patent 2,378,996 (June, 1945); *Chem. Abstr.* **40**, P98 (1946).

[101] R. E. Plump (to Penn. Salt Manuf. Co.), U.S. Patent 2,370,577 (February, 1945); *Chem. Abstr.* **39**, 4085⁴ (1945).

[102] J. P. Wibant and A. Strang, *Proc. Koninkl. Ned. Akad. Wetenschap.* **55B**, 207 (1952) [in English]; *Chem. Abstr.* **47**, 3230b (1953).

[103] N. Uri, *Nature* **177**, 1177 (1956).

[104] J. Nyilasi, *Magy. Kem. Folyoirat* **66**, 313 (1960); *Chem. Abstr.* **55**, 5222e (1961).

[105] M. A. Mendelsohn, E. M. Arnett, and H. Freiser, *J. Phys. Chem.* **64**, 660 (1960).

The mode of cerium-catalyzed autoxidation is not clear. Metal ion catalysis is generally thought to arise from the catalytic decomposition of hydroperoxides, which yield radicals for chain initiation.[70] However, it is reported that ceric ion does not effect *catalytic* decomposition of hydroperoxides (Section VII).

E. CERIUM(IV) AND HYDROGEN PEROXIDE

The use of this system[63] to oxidize organic compounds has been virtually ignored. A polarographic study of catechol oxidation by the hydrogen peroxide–ceric sulfate system has been reported.[106] On the basis of a comparison of half-wave potentials of other quinones, an intermediate (XXIV) was suggested. Unfortunately, no products were isolated from the reaction.

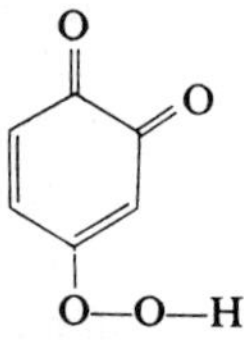

(XXIV)

ACKNOWLEDGMENT

The manuscript was prepared while the author was at the California Research Corporation, Richmond, California, and assistance in preparation is greatly appreciated. Thanks are also given to Dr. S. J. Lapporte for a profound criticism of the manuscript.

[106] J. Doskočil, *Collection Czech. Chem. Commun.* **15**, 780 (1950).

CHAPTER **V**

Oxidations with Lead Tetraacetate*

Rudolf Criegee

I. Introduction 278
  A. Brief History of Lead Tetraacetate 278
  B. Preparation of Lead(IV) Salts 279
  C. Physical Properties 280
  D. General Chemistry 281
  E. Experimental Procedure 283
II. Reactions with Hydroxyl Groups 284
  A. Alcohols 284
  B. Phenols 288
  C. Carboxylic Acids 293
  D. Hydroperoxides 302
III. Reactions with C—H Bonds 305
  A. Activated C—H Bonds 305
  B. Unactivated C—H Bonds 321
  C. Aromatic C—H Bonds 326
IV. Reactions with C—C Bonds in Saturated Systems 334
V. Reactions with Olefins and Acetylenes 335
  A. Addition of Two Acetoxy Groups to a Double Bond 335
  B. Substitution in Allylic Positions 337
  C. Oxidations with Rearrangement of the Carbon Skeleton 340
  D. Formation of Glycolic and Glyoxylic Esters 345
  E. Addition of Methyl Acetate 348
  F. Formation of γ-Lactones 348
  G. Other Reactions of Olefins 349
  H. Allenes and Acetylenes 350
VI. Reactions with Compounds of Sulfur, Nitrogen, and Phosphorus . . 351
  A. Sulfur Compounds 351
  B. Nitrogen Compounds 353
  C. Phosphorus Compounds 363
VII. Reactions with Organometallic Compounds 363
  Appendix: Oxidations by Thallic Acetate and Iodoso Acetates . . . 365

* This chapter has been translated by Professor Walter Lwowski, Department of Chemistry, Yale University, New Haven, Connecticut.

Since 1920 lead tetraacetate has been a tool of organic chemists. Depending on substrate and reaction conditions it acts in many different ways, thus becoming one of the most versatile oxidants. This versatility makes it difficult to organize a review on lead tetraacetate. One might treat its reactions according to the nature of the substrate: alkanes, olefins, alcohols, and so on, or one could use the type of reaction: substitution, addition, dehydrogenation, etc. The reaction mechanism also might serve to organize the wealth of facts. However, strict application of any one of these principles would separate facts that belong together. The compromise chosen here is reflected in the table of contents. Included are some reactions such as methylations and phenylations of aromatic compounds, which are not oxidations in the strict sense. The cleavage of glycols by lead tetraacetate will be treated in Chapter VI by C. A. Bunton in this volume together with the corresponding periodate oxidations.

Due to the lack of suitable methods, not all the products were found in all the investigations, especially the earlier ones. The products found were not always isolated in pure state; thus one has to be careful in using data on yields. In many cases it would be desirable to repeat the work using modern analytical methods.

The literature has been searched up to 1963, but inevitably some papers must have been overlooked. This is especially true for those dealing with natural products where the term "lead tetraacetate" is not mentioned in the subject indexes. The author would be indebted to all those who bring such papers to his attention. Some data are given without a literature reference. Most come from the experience of the author who has collected them during the 40 years he has been working with the oxidant. (Several papers from 1964 and 1965 are mentioned, but could not be discussed in detail.)

I. Introduction

A. BRIEF HISTORY OF LEAD TETRAACETATE

Berzelius, Dumas, and Schönbein (see Brückner[1]) found that red lead oxide dissolves in glacial acetic acid and they described the properties of the solution. Jacquelain[2] first isolated lead tetraacetate in 1851. The correct formula was proposed in 1896 by Hutchinson and Pollard[3] who also described the first practical preparation. Other lead(IV) salts were reported by Colson.[4] The

[1] The earlier history of lead tetraacetate is discussed in C. Brückner, *Chemiker Ztg.* **51**, 344 (1927).
[2] A. Jacquelain, *J. Prakt. Chem.* **53**, 151 (1851).
[3] A. Hutchinson and W. Pollard, *J. Chem. Soc.* **69**, 224 (1896).
[4] A. Colson, *Compt. Rend. Acad. Sci.* **136**, 675, 1664 (1903).

first practical use of lead tetraacetate was made by Dimroth and co-workers,[5] who oxidized quinizarine to quinizarine quinone. In 1923 a fundamental paper by Dimroth and Schweizer[6] outlined the scope of lead tetraacetate oxidations. The cleavage of glycols was found by Criegee[7] in 1931. Since then the use of lead tetraacetate as an oxidant has been increasing every year. Methylation by lead tetraacetate was found by Fieser and Chang[8] in 1942, and oxidation of unactivated C—H bonds in 1959 by a group of Swiss and Yugoslavian chemists.[9]

B. PREPARATION OF LEAD(IV) SALTS

1. LEAD TETRAACETATE

The only practical method for making lead tetraacetate is the reaction of red lead oxide with glacial acetic acid at $60°$ C. According to Eq. (1), only one-third of the lead is converted to lead tetraacetate. Lead dioxide ought to be converted completely to lead tetraacetate, but it is so insoluble in acetic acid that it does not react. As shown in Eq. (2), the addition of chlorine makes it possible to utilize a second lead atom in the red lead oxide.[4, 10] Lead tetraacetate and the lead chloride formed in this reaction can be separated by recrystallizing from hot acetic acid. However, the method is not advantageous in most cases because it is difficult to remove the last traces of lead chloride.

$$Pb_3O_4 + 8 \ AcOH \ \rightarrow \ Pb(OAc)_4 + 2 \ Pb(OAc)_2 + 4 \ H_2O \tag{1}$$

$$2 \ Pb(OAc)_2 + Cl_2 \ \rightarrow \ Pb(OAc)_4 + PbCl_2 \tag{2}$$

$$Pb(OAc)_4 + 2 \ H_2O \ \rightarrow \ PbO_2 + 4 \ AcOH \tag{3}$$

When lead tetraacetate is made from red lead oxide and acetic acid (Eq. 1), water is formed. It hydrolyzes lead tetraacetate according to Eq. (3). To avoid this hydrolysis, the calculated amount of acetic anhydride is added to the reaction mixture. To avoid oxidation of acetic anhydride, the temperature must be kept low. Bailar[11] reported a suitable laboratory preparation.

It has also been reported[12] that a 95% yield of lead tetraacetate can be obtained by the electrolysis of lead(II) acetate. The electrolyte was anhydrous acetic acid containing potassium acetate. Platinum anodes at a temperature of $80°$ C were employed.

[5] O. Dimroth, O. Friedemann, and H. Kämmerer, *Ber.* **53**, 481 (1920).
[6] O. Dimroth and R. Schweizer, *Ber.* **56**, 1375 (1923).
[7] R. Criegee, *Ber.* **64**, 260 (1931).
[8] L. F. Fieser and F. C. Chang, *J. Am. Chem. Soc.* **64**, 2043 (1942).
[9] G. Cainelli, M. L. Mihailović, D. Arigoni, and O. Jeger, *Helv. Chim. Acta* **42**, 1124 (1959).
[10] R. E. Oesper and C. L. Deasy, *J. Am. Chem. Soc.* **61**, 972 (1939).
[11] J. C. Bailar, *Inorg. Syn.* **1**, 47 (1939).
[12] M. J. Fiosin and J. J. Kazakova, *J. Gen. Chem.* **28** (90), 2005 (1958).

2. OTHER LEAD(IV) SALTS

Salts of liquid carboxylic acids can be prepared in the same way as lead tetraacetate. However, it often is sufficient to shake a suspension of red lead oxide in the anhydrous acid for 24 hours.[4, 13] Another method utilizes the reaction of lead tetraacetate with a higher boiling acid; acetic acid is distilled off as it is formed. Lead tetrabenzoate can be made this way using molten benzoic acid.[13] It is better, however, to use chlorobenzene as a solvent and to distill the azeotropic mixture of acetic acid and chlorobenzene.[14] Using this and similar procedures, many lead(IV) salts have been prepared.[4, 15, 16]

C. PHYSICAL PROPERTIES

1. GENERAL PROPERTIES

Lead tetraacetate crystallizes from hot glacial acetic acid in colorless monoclinic crystals. They are best stored wet with acetic acid. Dry crystals turn brown when in contact with traces of moisture. The lower the moisture content of the acetic acid used for recrystallization, the better is the storage stability of the product.

Lead tetraacetate is somewhat volatile at high vacuum, but vapor pressures have not been determined. In a melting point capillary, the decomposition begins at about 175° C. The density of the solid is $D_4^{16.9} = 2.228$.[3]

2. SOLUBILITY

A saturated solution of lead tetraacetate in anhydrous acetic acid is $0.072\,M$ at 25° C. A saturated solution of lead(II) acetate is $3.35\,M$ at the same temperature.[17] Lead tetraacetate solutions of $0.1\,N$ concentration are stable for a long time in the dark but rapidly lose their oxidizing power in quartz vessels in the sunlight.[18] There are many good inert solvents: benzene, chloroform, dichloromethane, trichloroethylene, nitrobenzene, and acetonitrile. To retard hydrolysis, addition of 1 % of acetic acid is recommended. The solubility is very low in ether, petroleum ether, and carbon tetrachloride. Alcohols cannot be used because of alcoholysis (see Section II,A). Lead tetraacetate is monomeric in boiling acetic acid and benzene.[19]

[13] R. Criegee, *Ann.* **481**, 263 (1930).
[14] R. Criegee, P. Dimroth, K. Noll, R. Simon, and C. Weis, *Ber.* **90**, 1070 (1957).
[15] C. D. Hurd and P. R. Austin, *J. Am. Chem. Soc.* **53**, 1543 (1931).
[16] Y. Yukawa and M. Sakai, *Bull. Chem. Soc. Japan* **36**, 761 (1963).
[17] A. W. Davidson, W. C. Lanning, and M. M. Zeller, *J. Am. Chem. Soc.* **64**, 1523 (1942).
[18] E. R. Cole, *Chem. & Ind. (London)* p. 544 (1959).
[19] G. Rudakoff, *Z. Naturforsch.* **17b**, 623 (1962).

3. OPTICAL AND ELECTRICAL PROPERTIES

Solutions of lead tetraacetate in glacial acetic acid and in methylene chloride containing 1 % acetic acid show strong ultraviolet absorption, but no absorption maximum in the accessible ultraviolet spectrum.[20] At 237 mμ log ϵ is 3.78. The absorption decreases at longer wavelengths.[21] In kinetic experiments, the concentration of lead tetraacetate can be monitored spectrometrically, even at high dilutions.[20, 22]

Since lead tetraacetate shows no carbonyl absorption in the infrared spectrum, Preuss and Janshen[23] conclude that it is not a mixed acid anhydride. On the other hand, the low molar conductivity in acetic acid solution shows that there is little salt character.[17] One might regard lead tetraacetate as a nonelectrolyte.

D. GENERAL CHEMISTRY

1. THERMAL DECOMPOSITION

For all practical purposes, lead tetraacetate is stable for indefinite periods if stored in a cold, dark place with exclusion of moisture. Decomposition with gas evolution starts only at 140° C. The gas consists of 62 % CO_2 and 29 % of an ethane–methane mixture in a ratio of 9:1. Methyl acetate also was found.[15, 24] The thermal and photochemical decomposition in solution is discussed in Sections II,C,1, III,A, and III,C.

2. LEAD TETRAACETATE AS AN OXIDANT

a. *For Inorganic Compounds.* Lead tetraacetate is one of the strongest oxidants known, the formal redox potential being about 1.6 volts in perchloric acid. It depends on the concentration of lead tetraacetate, lead diacetate, and acetic acid.[25] Lead tetraacetate oxidizes cobalt(II) to cobalt(III), manganese(II) to manganese(III), and cerium(III) to cerium(IV).[26] Surprisingly, and in contrast to an earlier paper of Hevesy,[27] lead(II) cannot be oxidized to lead(IV). According to Evans and co-workers,[28] the report of the exchange of radio-labeled lead between lead diacetate and lead tetraacetate at 80° C was due to an experimental error.

[20] D. Benson and L. H. Sutcliffe, *Trans. Faraday Soc.* **55**, 2107 (1959).
[21] J. Kalvoda and K. Heusler, *Chem. & Ind. (London)* p. 1431 (1963).
[22] A. S. Perlin and S. Suzuki, *Can. J. Chem.* **40**, 1225 (1962).
[23] F. R. Preuss and J. Janshen, *Arch. Pharm.* **295**, 284 (1962).
[24] C. Schall, *Z. Elektrochem.* **28**, 506 (1922).
[25] A. Berka, V. Dvorak, J. Nemec, and J. Zyka, *J. Electroanal. Chem.* **4**, 150 (1962); *Chem. Abstr.* **57**, 13167 c (1962); see J. R. Partington and J. W. Skeen, *Trans. Faraday Soc.* **32**, 975 (1936).
[26] D. Benson and L. H. Sutcliffe, *Trans. Faraday Soc.* **56**, 246 (1960).
[27] G. V. Hevesy and L. Zechmeister, *Ber.* **53**, 410 (1920).
[28] E. A. Evans, J. L. Huston, and T. H. Norris, *J. Am. Chem. Soc.* **74**, 4985 (1952).

Chloride, bromide, and iodide ions are oxidized to the three respective halogens. The oxidation of alkali iodides is instantaneous and is used to determine the lead tetraacetate content of solutions and solid samples.[6] To avoid the precipitation of lead iodide, large quantities of sodium acetate must be added.

b. *For Organic Compounds.* At first Dimroth[5] thought of lead tetraacetate as a soluble "lead dioxide" and used it for dehydrogenations. Later it was also regarded as a "mild halogen." Analogous to bromine, it substitutes activated CH groups and adds two acetoxy groups to double bonds. In both reactions, hydroxyl functions are introduced in protected form. Usually no further oxidation occurs, in contrast to reactions with permanganate or chromic acid. However, acetoxy groups can decompose or be oxidized during the reactions, which often leads to complications.

For the oxidation of organic compounds, many reaction mechanisms seem possible. Besides lead tetraacetate itself, acetoxy radicals, acetoxy cations, and $Pb(OAc)_3^+$ ions have been regarded as the oxidizing species.

Lead tetraacetate itself could react as an electrophile using empty orbitals of the lead. A transient increase in the coordination number of the lead is indicated by the rapid exchange of the acetoxy groups between lead tetraacetate and acetic acid or acetic anhydride,[28] but this can also be explained by a reversible dissociation of $Pb(OAc)_4$. However, the solubility of lead tetraacetate in acetic acid is decreased rather than increased by sodium or potassium acetate.[17, 28] Thus the complex anions $(Pb(OAc)_5^-$ or $Pb(OAc)_6^{2-}$ are not present in appreciable concentrations. Using empty orbitals of the lead, the unshared electron pair of an alcohol or phenol could initiate the oxidation of these substances, as could the formation of a π-complex with an olefin.[20]

Acetoxy radicals have been regarded as intermediates in many tetraacetate oxidations. They might be formed by dissociation, the lead tetraacetate losing one or two acetoxy radicals. In the first case, the trivalent lead formed would have to be very short lived and should itself have radical character.

Acetoxy cations have been postulated as an active species, particularly by Mosher and Kehr.[29] However, acetoxy cations certainly do not exist free. Moreover, the result of the reaction of lead tetraacetate with organomercury compounds (Section VII) makes it unlikely that acetoxy cations are produced at all.

On the other hand, many oxidations can be understood by assuming that lead tetraacetate loses an acetate ion, forming $Pb(OAc)_3^+$. An electrophilic attack of the latter forms an organolead compound with the substrate. Loss of lead diacetate completes the reaction, and an AcO^+ moiety has been transferred without ever existing as a species.

[29] W. A. Mosher and C. L. Kehr, *J. Am. Chem. Soc.* **75**, 3172 (1953).

In other cases the organolead compound R—Pb(OAc)$_3$ loses Pb(OAc)$_3^-$ which seems to be a good leaving group.[30] The electrophilic introduction of Pb(OAc)$_3^+$ followed by its loss as an anion corresponds to the loss of one electron pair—an example of Levitt's[31] general mechanism of oxidations.

Depending on substrate and reaction conditions, different mechanisms might be operative. The solvent is especially important as pointed out by Barron *et al.*[31a] The solvent used most frequently, acetic acid, has an intermediate dielectric constant and might equally favor ionic and radical mechanisms. Other small changes can then make one or the other mechanism prevail.

The following sections will show how far we are from fully understanding the oxidations by lead tetraacetate.

E. EXPERIMENTAL PROCEDURE

Acetic acid is used as a solvent in most lead tetraacetate oxidations. One can employ less solvent than required to dissolve the oxidant fully, stir well, and monitor the progress of the reaction by observing the disappearance of the solid. The reaction is complete when the spot test with leucomalachite green becomes negative. An excess of lead tetraacetate can be destroyed by adding a few drops of ethylene glycol or glycerol. The lead(II) acetate remains in solution.

The workup procedure depends on the nature of the reaction product. Usually the reaction mixture is poured into water and extracted with ether. Acetic acid is removed from the ether extract by shaking with sodium bicarbonate solution. Where anhydrous workup is required, the acetic acid is removed in vacuum. Treating the residue with ether induces crystallization of the lead(II) acetate. The solution is filtered and the lead salts are washed with ether. The whole operation is then repeated once more. When the reaction is run in benzene or other inert solvents, lead(II) acetate precipitates during the reaction. The precipitate is sticky at first and can occlude lead tetraacetate. This is avoided when crystallization is induced by seeding or scratching with a glass rod.

Occasionally the lead tetraacetate is generated *in situ*. The substrate is dissolved in acetic acid, sometimes with the addition of acetic anhydride. The oxidation is then carried out by adding portions of red lead oxide.

The temperature is kept as low as possible since the selectivity of the oxidation decreases rapidly with increasing temperature. Exothermic reactions should be run with cooling.

[30] N. Finch, C. W. Gemenden, J. H. Hsu, and W. J. Taylor, *J. Am. Chem. Soc.* **85**, 1520 (1963).
[31] L. S. Levitt, *J. Org. Chem.* **20**, 1297 (1955).
[31a] H. E. Barron, G. W. K. Cavill, E. R. Cole, P. T. Gilham, and D. H. Solomon, *Chem. & Ind. (London)* p. 76 (1954).

II. Reactions with Hydroxyl Groups

The hydrolysis of lead tetraacetate is a fast reaction, and exchange of acetate groups with other carboxylate groups is rapid. From this one can anticipate that equilibria will be established with all substances that contain acidic hydrogens such as ROH and RNH_2 (Eqs. 4 and 5). The positions of the

$$Pb(OAc)_4 + ROH \rightleftharpoons Pb(OAc)_3OR + AcOH \qquad (4)$$

$$Pb(OAc)_3OR + ROH \rightleftharpoons Pb(OAc)_2(OR)_2 + AcOH \qquad (5)$$

equilibria are determined by the acidity of ROH and by the mass law. The reaction rate is always very high. It is possible, therefore, that observed oxidations occur in species in equilibrium with lead tetraacetate.

A. ALCOHOLS

The alcoholysis of lead tetraacetate is demonstrated by the isolation of $Pb(OAc)_2(OCH_3)(OH)$. It crystallizes in yellow prisms from wet methanol.[32] Analogous products have been obtained from methanol and lead tetra-propionate and butyrate. No such products have been isolated from other alcohols, but solutions of lead tetraacetate in dry primary and secondary alcohols are likely to contain compounds such as $Pb(OAc)_3OR$ and $Pb(OAc)_2(OR)_2$. These solutions are very unstable, especially toward light. They decompose to give lead(II) acetate, acetic acid, and aldehydes or ketones.

The same species are present in solutions of equimolar amounts of alcohol and lead tetraacetate in inert solvents. When acetic acid is used as a solvent, the equilibria lie almost entirely on the side of lead tetraacetate plus alcohol. For this reason alcohols are stable in lead tetraacetate–acetic acid solutions, at least at low temperatures. In boiling benzene, however, alcohols can be oxidized to aldehydes or ketones in good yields, especially when these products are relatively stable toward further oxidations. Sometimes it is necessary to add some pyridine. Benzaldehyde[32] and the three isomeric formyl pyridines[33] can be prepared in 60–80% yield. In pyridine solution oxidation occurs even at room temperature in yields from 70–90%.[33a] Equation (6) represents a plausible mechanism:

$$R_2CHOH \longrightarrow R_2C\overset{O}{\underset{H}{\overbrace{}}}Pb(OAc)_2 \longrightarrow R_2C{=}O \begin{array}{l} + Pb(OAc)_2 \\ + HOAc \end{array} \qquad (6)$$

The great electron affinity of the lead causes heterolysis of the bond between the alcohol oxygen and the lead. This is possible only if the electron pair lost

[32] R. Criegee, L. Kraft, and B. Rank, *Ann.* **507**, 159 (1933).

[33] V. M. Mićović and M. L. Mihailović, *Rec. Trav. Chim.* **71**, 970 (1952); *Ber. Chem. Ges. Belgrad.* **18**, 105 (1953); *Chem. Zentr.* p. 580 (1955).

[33a] R. E. Partch, *Tetrahedron Letters* p. 3071 (1964).

by the oxygen is simultaneously replaced with the electron pair that had constituted the CH bond. The proton is captured by an acetate ion from the solution, or more probably from the $Pb(OAc)_3$ moiety. The use of the reaction in the steroid series is described in Section III,B.

This mechanism has not been proved[33b]. It agrees, however, with fragmentation which can occur in the oxidations of alcohols. Fragmentation was observed by Braude and Wheeler[34] in the oxidation of 1-allylcyclohexanol. At 20° C in benzene an 80% yield of cyclohexanone was formed. The hypothetical intermediate could decompose according to Eq. (7). The presumed second fragment, allyl acetate, was not isolated. The reaction has been reported to be generally applicable to tertiary and secondary β,γ-unsaturated alcohols.[35] β-Hydroxy aldehydes and ketones react analogously, diacetone alcohol giving acetone and acetoxy acetone.[35]

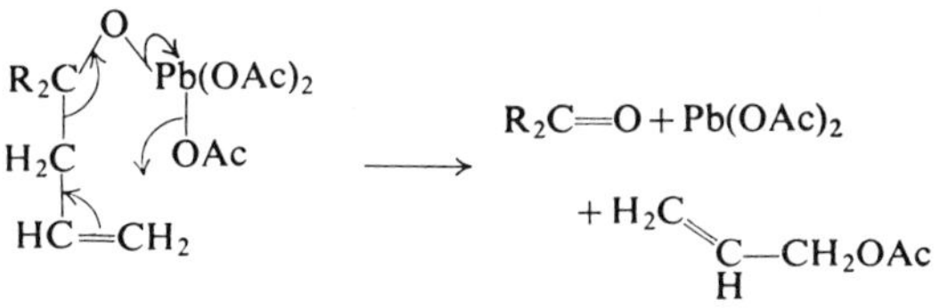

$$R_2C{=}O + Pb(OAc)_2 \qquad (7)$$

$$(H_3C)_2C{=}O + Pb(OAc)_2 \qquad (8)$$

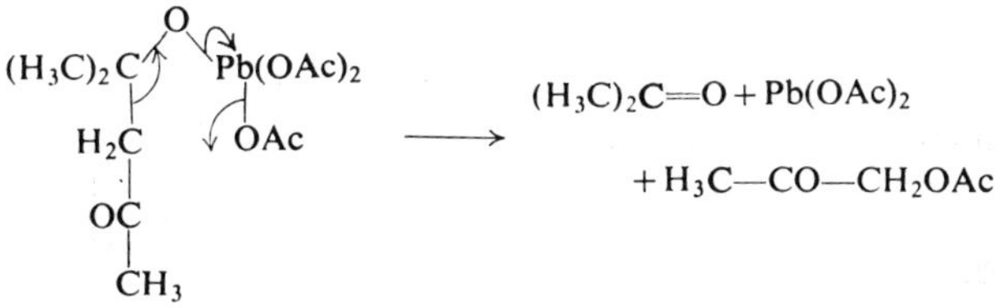

Amarosa et al.[36, 36a] observed oxidative fragmentation of primary and secondary steroid alcohols. In the second case allylic rearrangement occurs.

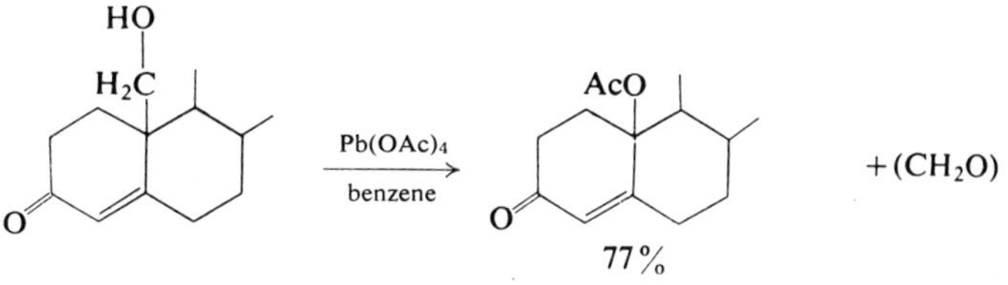

$$+ (CH_2O) \qquad (9)$$

[33b] Cf. M. L. Mihailović, Z. Maksimović, D. Jeremić, Ž. Čeković, A. Milovanović, and L. Lorenc, *Tetrahedron* **21**, 1395 (1965).

[34] E. A. Braude and O. H. Wheeler, *J. Chem. Soc.* p. 320 (1955).

[35] Baker Castor Oil Co., British Patent 759,416 (1956); *Chem. Zentr.* p. 1009 (1961).

[36] M. Amorosa, L. Caglioti, G. Cainelli, H. Immer, J. Keller, H. Wehrli, M. L. Mihailović, K. Schaffner, D. Arigoni, and O. Jeger; *Helv. Chim. Acta* **45**, 2674 (1962).

[36a] D. Hauser, K. Heusler, J. Kalvoda, K. Schaffner, and O. Jeger, *Helv. Chim. Acta* **47**, 1961 (1964).

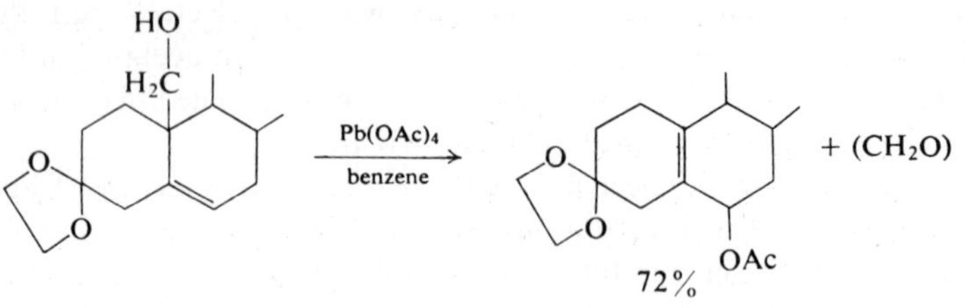

$$+ \ (CH_2O) \quad (10)$$

72%

Under the same conditions, an unsaturated aldehyde is obtained as the main product from the four stereoisomeric secondary alcohols with the hydroxy group in position 17 in ring D.[36] The authors give a number of reasons that make them assume, for these fragmentations, the radical mechanism discussed in Section III,B.

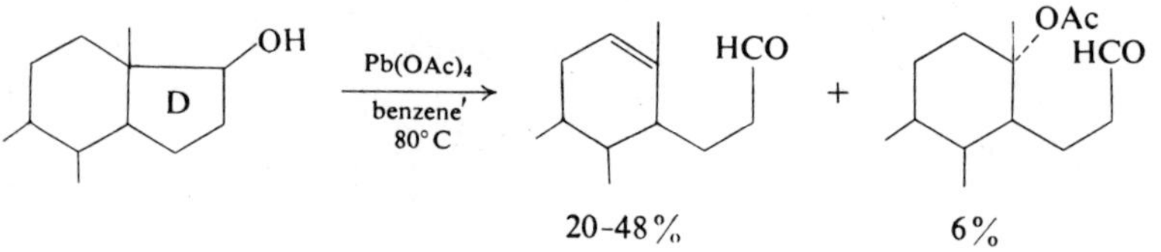

$$(11)$$

20–48%   6%

Related to this reaction is the opening of the 5-10 bond in certain steroid alcohols which occurs under the same conditions[36b]:

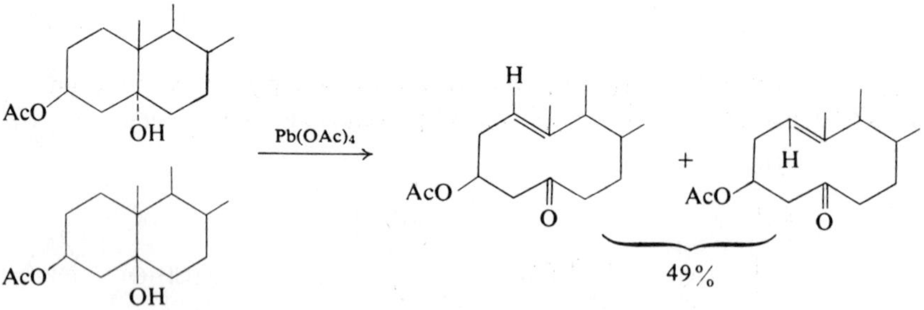

$$(11a)$$

49%

Mosher et al.[37] report the fragmentation of saturated alcohols that have a quaternary carbon next to the alcohol function. These pinacolyl alcohols

[36b] M. L. Mihailović, M. Stefanović, L. Lorenc, and M. Găsić, Tetrahedron Letters p. 1867 (1964); cf. M. Stefanović, M. Găsić, L. Lorenc, and M. L. Mihailović, Tetrahedron 20, 2289 (1964); V. M. Mićović, R, J. Mamuzić, D. Jeremić, and M. L. Mihailović, Tetrahedron 20, 2279 (1964).

[37] W. A. Mosher, C. L. Kehr, and L. W. Wright, J. Org. Chem. 26, 1044 (1961).

eliminate either a proton or the tertiary carbonium ion which then combines with acetate ion (Eq. 12):

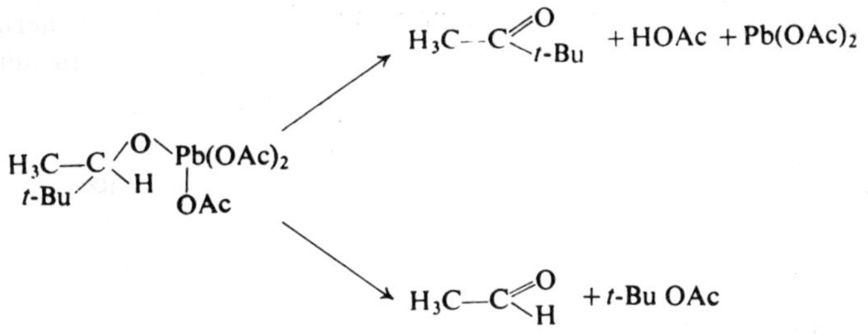

$$(12)$$

Pinacolyl acetate and isobutene are also formed, the latter by loss of a proton from the tertiary carbonium ion. The yields depend on the solvent and the temperatures. Fifty per cent fragmentation was found in acetic acid. At least in this case a radical mechanism is not probable. If tertiary butyl radicals were involved, one would expect to find the products of dimerization and disproportionation. However, neither hexamethylethane nor isobutane was found.

Benzpinacolyl alcohol yields triphenyl carbinol and benzaldehyde, together with tetraphenylethylene.[38] Wehrli et al.[39] oxidized the tertiary steroic alcohol I with lead tetraacetate in boiling benzene, and obtained the hydroxy ketone II. Here the relief of ring strain might have contributed to the high yield of 77%. A very interesting fragmentation of a dihemiacetal with lead tetraacetate in boiling benzene has been reported more recently.[39a]

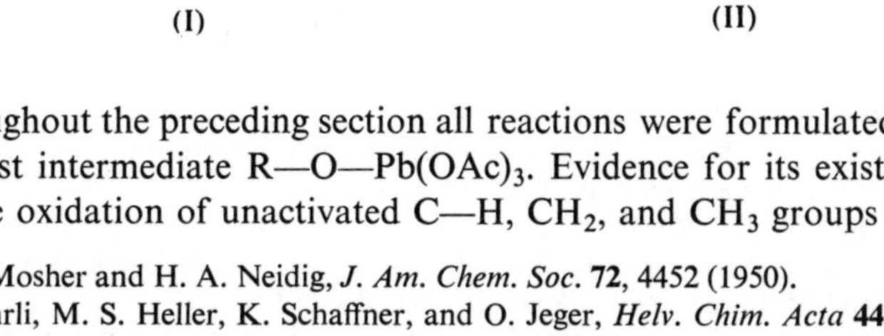

$$(13)$$

(I)   (II)

Throughout the preceding section all reactions were formulated as involving a first intermediate R—O—Pb(OAc)₃. Evidence for its existence comes from the oxidation of unactivated C—H, CH_2, and CH_3 groups of steroids.

[38] W. A. Mosher and H. A. Neidig, *J. Am. Chem. Soc.* **72**, 4452 (1950).
[39] H. Wehrli, M. S. Heller, K. Schaffner, and O. Jeger, *Helv. Chim. Acta* **44**, 2162 (1961).
[39a] R. B. Woodward, T. Fukunaga, and R. C. Kelly, *J. Am. Chem. Soc.* **86**, 3162 (1964).

This reaction is found only in cases where the oxidant can be bound by a hydroxyl group near the reaction site (see Section III,B). Furthermore, the glycol cleavage by lead tetraacetate is strongly retarded by acetic acid.[32] This can only be explained by assuming a preequilibrium (Eq. 14)[32]:

$$
\begin{array}{c}
\text{>C—OH} \\
| \qquad\qquad + \text{Pb(OAc)}_4 \\
\text{>C—OH}
\end{array}
\rightleftharpoons
\begin{array}{c}
\text{>C—O—Pb(OAc)}_3 \\
| \\
\text{>C—OH} + \text{HOAc}
\end{array}
$$

B. PHENOLS

1. MONOPHENOLS

Systematic studies especially by Wessely[40] and his group have brought order in the data on phenol oxidations. Depending on the number and position of substituents on the phenol, o- or p-quinol acetates, p-quinones and also quinone diacetates are formed. Tables I and II summarize the results.[40–58]

It is reasonable to assume that the first step of the reaction is the reversible formation of phenol derivatives of lead(IV). These derivatives, ArO—Pb(OAc)$_3$, are much less stable than the corresponding alkyl compounds. Most authors assume that these aryl intermediates dissociate into the radicals (AcO)$_3$ Pb· and ArO·. This view seemed to be supported by the work of Bogdanov, Postnikova, and Emanuel.[41] Using electron spin resonance (e.s.r.) spectrometry, these authors found radicals to be present during the oxidation

[40] F. Wessely and F. Sinwel, Monatsh. 81, 1055 (1950).
[41] G. N. Bogdanov, M. S. Postnikova, and N. M. Emanuel, Izv. Akad. Nauk SSSR p. 173 (1963).
[42] F. Wessely, J. Kotlan, and W. Metlesics, Monatsh. 85, 69 (1954).
[43] W. Metlesics, E. Schinzel, H. Vilcsek, and F. Wessely, Monatsh. 88, 1069 (1957).
[44] F. Wessely, J. Kotlan, and F. Sinwel, Monatsh. 83, 902 (1952); cf. F. Takacs, Monatsh. 95, 961 (1964).
[45] E. Zbiral, F. Wessely, and J. Jörg, Monatsh. 92, 654 (1961).
[46] F. Wessely, E. Zbiral, and J. Jörg, Monatsh. 94, 227 (1963).
[47] F. Wessely and J. Kotlan, Monatsh. 84, 291 (1953); cf. F. Wessely, J. Swoboda, and V. Guth, Monatsh. 95, 649 (1964).
[48] F. Wessely, E. Zbiral, and H. Sturm, Ber. 93, 2840 (1960).
[49] E. Zbiral, F. Wessely, and H. Sturm, Monatsh. 93, 15 (1962).
[50] L. J. Smith and H. H. Hoehn, J. Am. Chem. Soc. 61, 2619 (1939).
[51] E. Hecker, Ber. 92, 1386 (1959).
[52] E. Hecker and R. Lattrell, Ann. 662, 48 (1963).
[53] A. M. Gold and E. Schwenk, J. Am. Chem. Soc. 80, 5683 (1958).
[54] E. Hecker, Naturwissenschaften 46, 514 (1959).
[55] E. Hecker and E. Walk, Ber. 93. 2928 (1960).
[56] A. Ebnöther, T. M. Meijer, and H. Schmid, Helv. Chim. Acta 35, 910 (1952).
[57] H. Schmid and M. Burger, Helv. Chim. Acta 35, 928 (1952).
[58] R. R. Holmes, J. Conrady, J. Guthrie, and R. McKay, J. Am. Chem. Soc. 76, 2400 (1954).

TABLE I

OXIDATION OF SUBSTITUTED PHENOLS BY LEAD TETRAACETATE
IN ACETIC ACID AT 20° C

Substituents in position					Reaction products: yield in % of theoretical				
2	3	4	5	6	p-Quinol acetate	o-Quinol acetate	o-Quinone diacetate	Quinone	Reference
CH_3	—	CH_3	—	—	23	+		p:+	40
CH_3	—	CH_3	—	CH_3	42	+			40, 41
CH_3	CH_3	—	—	—	+	+		p:+	42
CH_3	—	—	CH_3	—	+			p:+	43
—	—	t-Bu	—	—	5–6	14			44
Allyl	—	—	—	—	34				45
Allyl	—	—	—	Allyl	34				45
CH_3	—	—	C_6H_5	—	+				43
C_6H_5	—	C_6H_5	—	C_6H_5	+				43
CH_3	—	CH_3	Br	—	32	6			46
CH_3	—	CH_3	—	Br	62				46
CH_3	—	—	Br	—	+			p:+	46
Br	—	Br	—	Br				p:+[a]	46
AcO	—	—	—	—			+		47
AcO	—	—	CH_3	—			+		47
CHO	—	—	—	CH_3	5–8[b]				48
CHO	—	CH_3	—	CH_3[c]	51				49
CO_2R	—	—	—	CH_3	40–50				48
CO_2R	—	CH_3	—	CH_3	50				49
$COCH_3$	—	CH_3	—	CH_3[c]	65				49
CN	—	CH_3	—	CH_3	20				49
—	CN	CH_3	—	CH_3	23				49
—	C_6H_5	C_6H_5	—	—[d]				o:+	50

[a] With elimination of the bromine in p-position and simultaneous formation of a dimer.
[b] A diphenoquinone derivative is also formed.
[c] In chloroform.
[d] In boiling acetic acid.

of phenols by lead tetraacetate. However, the work of Hecker and Lattrell[52] made it probable that the observed radicals were formed by air oxidation and are not involved in the main reaction. The authors regard the latter as ionic, because of its solvent dependence, catalysis by boron trifluoride, and its very high rate. (The maximum yield of quinol acetate was reached after 7 seconds.)

TABLE II

Oxidation of Phenols with Condensed Rings by Lead Tetraacetate in Acetic Acid at 20–30° C

	Reaction products: yield in % of theoretical					
Starting material	p-Quinol acetate	o-Quinol acetate	o-Quinone diacetate	p-Quinone	o-Quinone	Reference
α-Tetralol	—	+	—	+	—	42
β-Tetralol	18	—	—	—	—	51, 52
α-Hydrindenol	—	+	—	+	—	42
β-Hydrindenol	+	—	+	—	—	42
Oestrone	20	—	+	—	—	53–55
Oestradiol	19	—	—	—	—	53, 52
Naphthol-1	—	—	13	9	—	44
2-(3)-Methyl-	—	—	—	30–80	—	56
4-Methyl-	—	—	+	—	—	56
3-Methyl-5,7-dimethoxy-	—	—	—	78	—	57
2-Methyl-5,7-dimethoxy-	—	—	—	+	—	57
3,4-Diphenyl-	—	—	+	—	+	50
Naphthol-2	—	—	—	—	Trace	56
3-Methyl-	—	—	22	29	13	56
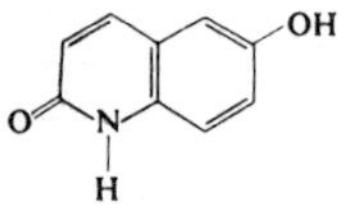	—	—	—	—	47	58
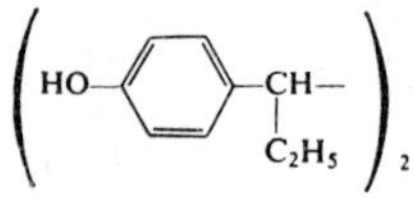 meso	—	—	30	—	—	44
racemic	—	—	10	—	—	44

This is in accord with earlier speculations by Criegee.[59] The reaction can be represented by Eq. (15):

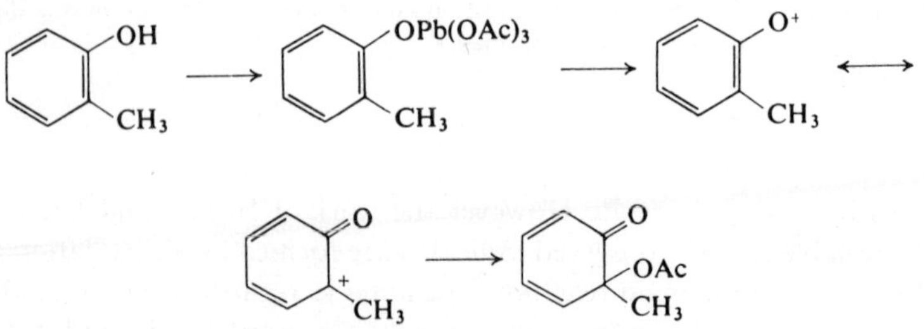

$$\tag{15}$$

[59] R. Criegee, *Angew. Chem.* **70**, 173 (1958).

For the formation of *o*-quinol acetates a concerted mechanism is also possible. Occasionally dimeric products are found. They are not necessarily formed by a radical reaction,[60] but could be the result of electrophilic substitution of the starting phenol by the intermediary carbonium ion. The type of solvent used seems to be of great importance.[31a, 60] The tables show that *ortho*-substituted phenols always give *o*-quinol acetate as the main products. *p*-Quinol acetates are formed in small yields only, even when a *para*-substituent is present. If the *ortho* or *para* positions are free, *o*- or *p*-quinones can be formed. The intermediates are *o*- and *p*-acetoxyphenols, respectively, as shown in Eq. (16):

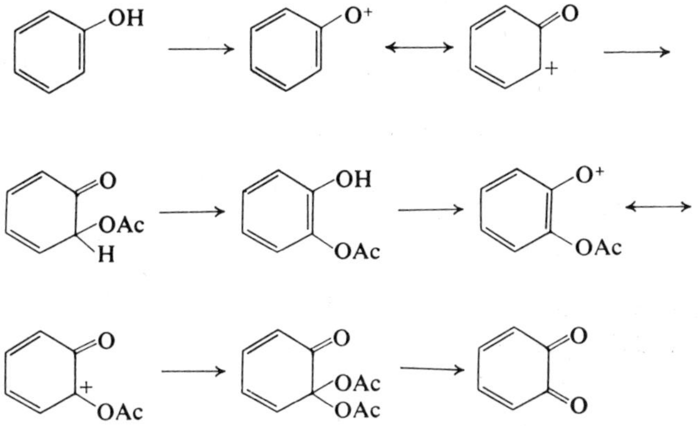

(16)

o-Quinone diacetates have been isolated in several cases. *p*-Quinone diacetates have never been found, probably because they are too unstable. Stephens and Bower[61] found that Schiff bases from *ortho* amino phenols give substituted benzoxazoles in 40–76% yield. Apparently the intermediate—be it an ion or a radical—attacks the C—N double bond:

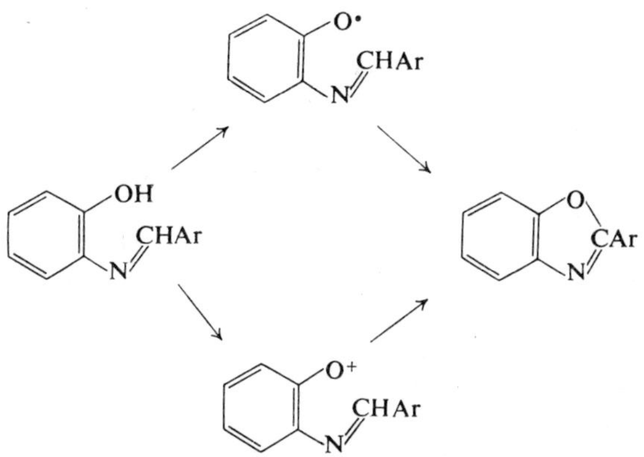

(17)

[60] G. W. K. Cavill, E. R. Cole, P. T. Gilham, and D. J. McHugh, *J. Chem. Soc.* p. 2785 (1954).
[61] F. F. Stephens and J. D. Bower, *J. Chem. Soc.* p. 2971 (1949).

Analogously, benzimidazoles are formed from Schiff bases having an *ortho* amino group instead of the *ortho* hydroxyl.[61]

Enols or enolizable ketones react like phenols (see Section III,A,1).

2. *Ortho* AND *Para* DIHYDRIC PHENOLS

The oxidation of monohydric phenols usually gives modest yields of a great variety of oxidation products. Catechol, hydroquinone, and their derivatives on the other hand are oxidized to *o*- or *p*-quinones rapidly and quantitatively. Simple hydroquinones can be titrated with lead tetraacetate in acetic acid, using dibromotolidine as an indicator.[62]

Even quinones with very high redox potentials can be prepared by lead tetraacetate oxidation. Examples are the di- and triquinones of anthracene,[5, 63–65] naphthodiquinones,[66] and diphenoquinones.[67] In these cases Dimroth and co-workers[5] found lead tetraacetate to be far superior to lead dioxide (cf. Section I).

The reactions can be run in acetic acid, benzene, or chloroform at room temperature. Where the solubility of the substrate is too low they are run at 50° C.

Intermediates of the type III might be involved, but a direct electron transfer from the hydroquinone dianion to the lead tetraacetate also seems possible:

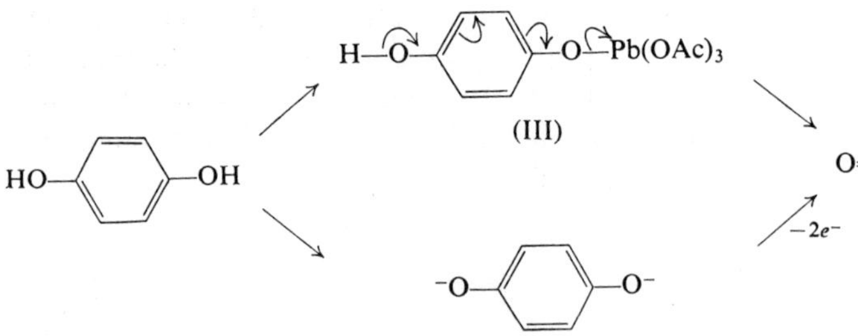

The high reaction rate makes it difficult to find evidence for the one or the other reaction path.

Amino groups in *ortho* or *para* position on benzene rings are dehydrogenated in the same manner as are hydroxyl groups (Section VI,B).

[62] W. Hecksteden, Dissertation, University of Würzburg, Germany, 1931.

[63] O. Dimroth and V. Hilcken, *Ber.* **54**, 3050 (1921).

[64] K. Brass and J. Stadler, *Ber.* **57**, 128 (1924).

[65] M. Tanaka, *Chem. News* **131**, 20 (1925).

[66] K. Zahn and P. Ochwat, *Ann.* **462**, 72 (1928); see R. Hellmuth, Dissertation, University of Würzburg, Germany, 1930.

[67] K. H. König, W. Schulze, and G. Möller, *Ber.* **93**, 554 (1960).

C. CARBOXYLIC ACIDS

1. MONOBASIC CARBOXYLIC ACIDS

Monocarboxylic acids are rather stable toward lead(IV) salts. They are oxidized only at elevated temperatures, except for formic acid, which is rapidly and quantitatively converted to carbon dioxide, even at room temperature.[29] This reaction can be used for the iodometric or manometric determination of formic acid.[68] The reaction is important in the glycol cleavage of 1,2,3-triols, such as carbohydrates. Periodate converts the central carbon atom to formic acid, but lead tetraacetate oxidizes it to carbon dioxide. The reaction must certainly be ionic and may be written as in Eq. (19):

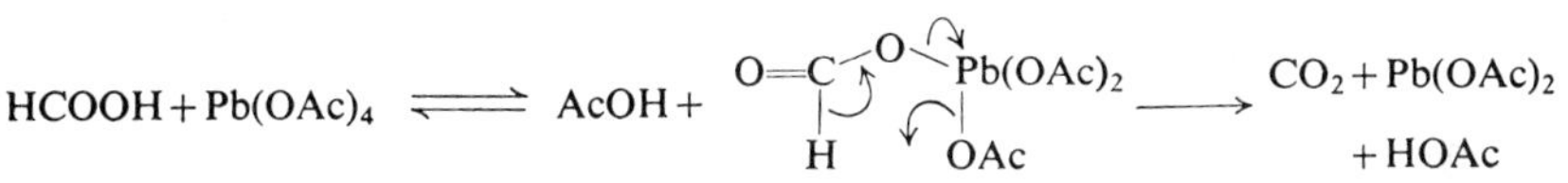

$$HCOOH + Pb(OAc)_4 \rightleftharpoons AcOH + \underset{H \quad OAc}{\overset{O=C\overset{O}{\diagup}\diagdown Pb(OAc)_2}{}} \longrightarrow \underset{+HOAc}{CO_2 + Pb(OAc)_2} \quad (19)$$

The homologs of formic acid require higher temperatures, most often 100° C. A radical mechanism[68a] has to be considered here. Kharasch and associates[69] compared the decomposition products with those obtained from diacetyl peroxide under the same conditions, as shown in Table III. The authors are

TABLE III

PRODUCTS OF THE DECOMPOSITION OF LEAD TETRAACETATE
AND DIACETYLPEROXIDE IN ACETIC ACID AT 90° C

Product	Moles per mole $(CH_3COO)_2$	Moles per mole $Pb(OAc)_4$
CO_2	1.5	0.3–0.4
CH_4	1.5	0.3
Methyl acetate	0.05	—
Acetoxyacetic acid	—	0.4–0.5
Succinic acid	0.5	Trace
$H_2C(OAc)_2$	—	0.06
Residue	—	Lead salts

clearly justified in assigning different mechanisms to the two reactions. There is no doubt that acetoxyl radicals start the reaction in the case of diacetyl peroxide. For lead tetraacetate, the authors postulate $\cdot CH_2COOH$ radicals

[68] A. S. Perlin, *Anal. Chem.* **26**, 1053 (1954).
[68a] Cf. J. K. Kochi, *J. Am. Chem. Soc.* **87**, 1811 (1965).
[69] M. S. Kharasch, H. N. Friedländer, and W. H. Urry, *J. Org. Chem.* **16**, 533 (1951).

initiating a radical chain reaction. The radicals are presumed to be formed from a acetoxy radical and solvent:

$$Pb(OAc)_4 + HOAc \rightarrow Pb(OAc)_3 \cdot + HOAc + \cdot CH_2COOH \qquad (20)$$

However, the scheme assumes that acetoxy radicals from lead tetraacetate will abstract a hydrogen atom from the methyl group of acetic acid. At the same time, acetoxy radicals from diacetyl peroxide, formed under the same conditions, are assumed to decompose to carbon dioxide and methyl radicals. A further argument against the occurrence of $\cdot CH_2COOH$ radicals in the thermal decomposition of lead tetraacetate are the results of Franzen and Edens.[70] These authors found (in addition to CO_2 and ethane) succinic acid to be the main product of the photolysis of $Pb(OAc)_4$ in acetic acid. This reaction must proceed via $\cdot CH_2COOH$ radicals.

The thermal decomposition of lead tetraacetate in acetic acid is strongly accelerated by sodium acetate.[71] Mosher and Kehr[29] assume a predominantly ionic decomposition, especially in cases where carbon dioxide is produced:

$$Pb(OAc)_4 + 4\,RCO_2H \rightleftharpoons Pb(OCOR)_4 + 4\,HOAc \qquad (21)$$

$$Pb(OCOR)_4 \rightarrow Pb(OCOR)_2 + RCO_2^- + RCO_2^+ \qquad (22)$$

$$RCO_2^+ \rightarrow CO_2 + R^+ \qquad (23)$$

Support for this mechanism comes from the observation that the more stable the carbonium ion produced by a given reaction, the lower the decomposition temperature required. Trimethylacetic acid reacts at 135° C, triphenylacetic acid at 100° C. In the first case *tert*-butyl acetate and isobutylene are produced, plus a little butene-2. The main product in the second case is triphenylmethyl acetate. No dimers are found, although they would be expected from a radical reaction. The oxidation of bicyclic tertiary carboxylic acid with lead tetraacetate in boiling benzene follows a similar course. Büchi et al.[72] found that olefin and carbon dioxide are formed, according to Eq. (24):

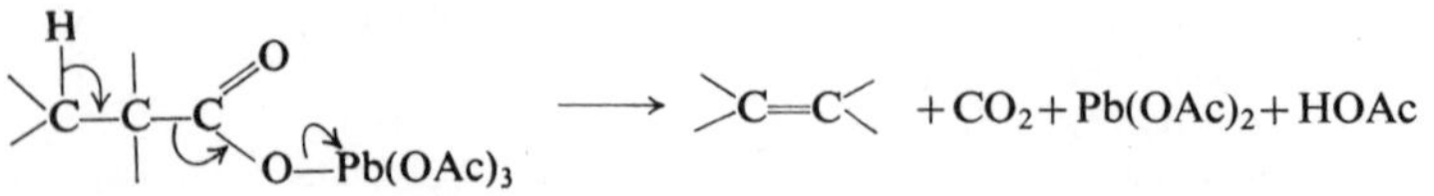

$$\longrightarrow\ \ >C=C< \ +CO_2 + Pb(OAc)_2 + HOAc \qquad (24)$$

Corey and Casanova[73] heated the acid (IV) to reflux with lead tetraacetate in pyridine. Since not only the acetate (V) but also phenyl benzhydryl ketone (VI) is formed, they also proposed an ionic mechanism. The intermediate car-

[70] V. Franzen and R. Edens, *Angew. Chem.* **73**, 579 (1961).
[71] D. Benson, L. H. Sutcliffe, and J. Walkley, *J. Am. Chem. Soc.* **81**, 4488 (1959).
[72] G. Büchi, R. E. Erickson, and N. Wakabayashi, *J. Am. Chem. Soc.* **83**, 927 (1961).
[73] E. J. Corey and J. Casanova, *J. Am. Chem. Soc.* **85**, 165 (1963).

bonium ion is stabilized either by the addition of an acetate ion or by Wagner-Meerwein rearrangement and loss of a proton.

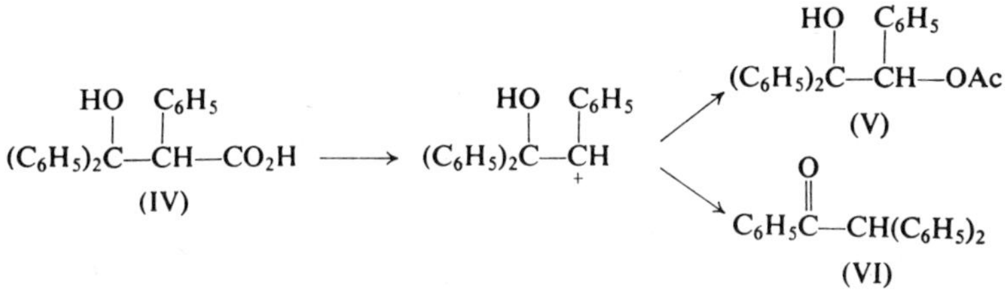

$$
\underset{(IV)}{(C_6H_5)_2\overset{\displaystyle HO}{C}-\overset{\displaystyle C_6H_5}{CH}-CO_2H} \longrightarrow \underset{+}{(C_6H_5)_2\overset{\displaystyle HO}{C}-\overset{\displaystyle C_6H_5}{CH}}
\begin{cases}
\underset{(V)}{(C_6H_5)_2\overset{\displaystyle HO}{C}-\overset{\displaystyle C_6H_5}{CH}-OAc} \\[2em]
\underset{(VI)}{C_6H_5\overset{\displaystyle O}{\overset{\|}{C}}-CH(C_6H_5)_2}
\end{cases} \quad (25)
$$

Under similar conditions *endo*- as well as *exo*-norbornane-2-carboxylic acid give CO_2 and exo-norbornyl acetate. The optically active acids give an exo-acetate of 43 % optical purity, that is, with 57 % racemization.

Probably the ionic mechanism also applies to the lead tetraacetate oxidation of *N*-benzylglycine, observed by Süs.[74] At 100° C in acetic acid CO_2 and a 20 % yield of a formaldehyde derivative are produced.

$$C_6H_5-CH_2-NH-CH_2-CO_2H \rightarrow C_6H_5-CH_2-NH-CH_2-OAc \quad (26)$$

Hippuric acid reacts analogously.

β,γ-Unsaturated acids are oxidized easily with loss of carbon dioxide. Jacques *et al.*[75] write an ionic mechanism, using Mosher's scheme. The reactions proceed with or without migration of the double bond, as illustrated in Eqs. (27) and (28):

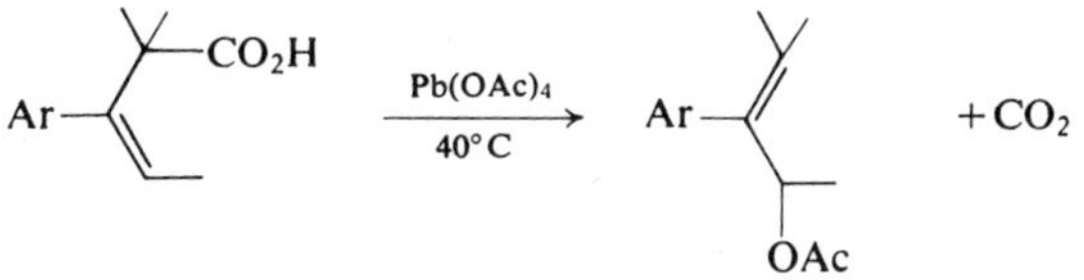

$$
Ar-\overset{\diagup}{\underset{\diagdown}{C}}-CO_2H \xrightarrow[40°C]{Pb(OAc)_4} Ar-\overset{\diagup}{C}\diagup \quad +CO_2 \quad (27)
$$
OAc

$$
Ar-\overset{\diagup}{\underset{\|}{C}}-CO_2H \xrightarrow[40°C]{Pb(OAc)_4} Ar-\overset{\diagup}{\underset{\|}{C}}-OAc \quad +CO_2 \quad (28)
$$

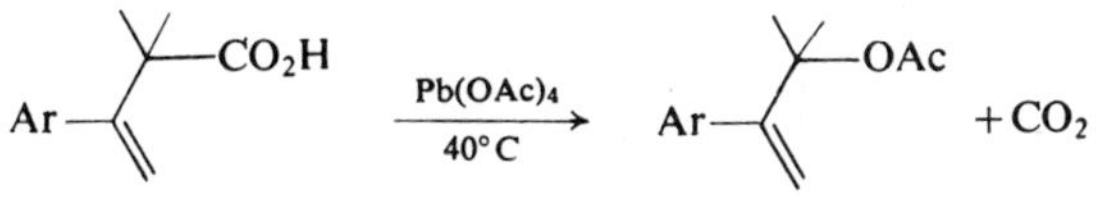

$$Ar = \quad H_3CO-\text{(naphthalene)}-$$

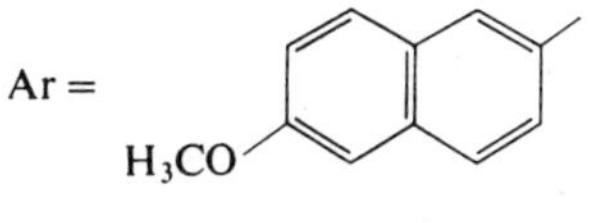

The oxidation of 3.3.3-triarylpropionic acids was studied by Starnes.[75a]

[74] O. Süs, *Ann.* **564**, 137 (1949).
[75] J. Jacques, C. Weidmann, and A. Horeau, *Bull. Soc. Chim. France* p. 424 (1959).
[75a] W. H. Starnes, *J. Am. Chem. Soc.* **86**, 5603 (1964).

According to Birch[76] and Plieninger and Ege,[77] benzene derivatives are obtained from cyclohexadiene carboxylic acids:

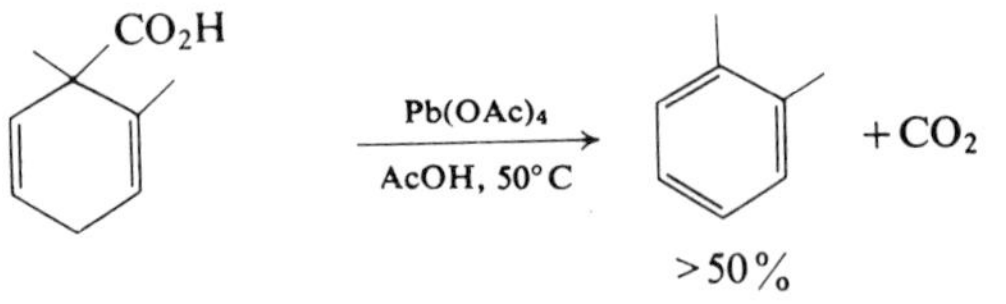

$$+ CO_2 \qquad (29)$$

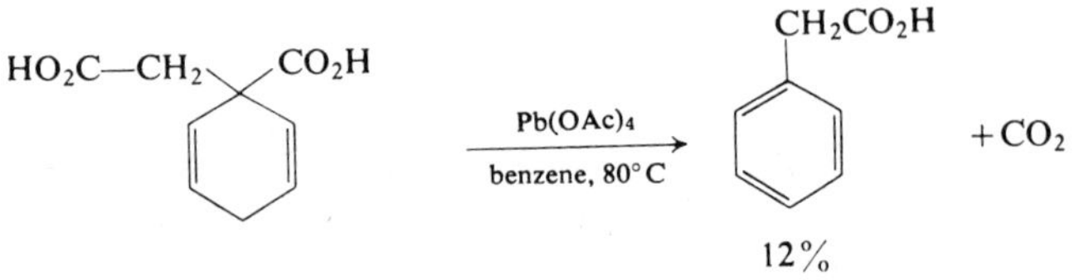

$$> 50\%$$

$$+ CO_2 \qquad (30)$$

$$12\%$$

The low yield in the second example is explained by the fact that lead tetraacetate oxidizes phenylacetic acid faster than o-xylene. LeBel and Huber[78] recently oxidized 5-carboxybicyclo[2.2.2]octene-2, a γ,δ-unsaturated acid. At 80–90° C in acetic acid containing potassium acetate, they obtained five isomeric acetates, all of which can be formed from the carbonium ion postulated by Mosher. Ganellin and Pettit[79] assume tropylium ions as intermediates in the oxidation of cycloheptatrienecarboxylic acid, at 70° C in acetic acid solution.

Another type of oxidative decarboxylation was found by Barton and Serebryakov.[80] The authors irradiated solutions of carboxylic acid and iodine in carbon tetrachloride at 80° C. The result was similar to a Hunsdiecker degradation since the carboxyl group was replaced by iodine:

$$2\ R\!-\!CO_2H + I_2 + Pb(OAc)_4 \ \rightarrow \ 2\ RI + 2\ CO_2 + 2\ AcOH + Pb(OAc)_2 \qquad (31)$$

Primary and secondary alkyl iodides are obtained in 63–91 % yield. Aromatic carboxylic acids give yields of 40–56 %, dicarboxylic acids 12–33 %, and pivalic acid only 10 %. Acyl hypoiodites are assumed as intermediates.

Under different conditions Bachman and Wittmann[81] obtained a reaction according to Eq. (32):

$$2\ Pb(OCOR)_4 + I_2 \ \rightarrow \ R\!-\!CO_2R + 2\ RI + 3\ CO_2 + 2\ Pb(OCOR)_2 \qquad (32)$$

[76] A. J. Birch, J. Chem. Soc. p. 1551 (1950).
[77] H. Plieninger and G. Ege, Ber. 94, 2095 (1961).
[78] N. A. LeBel and J. E. Huber, J. Am. Chem. Soc. 85, 3193 (1963).
[79] C. R. Ganellin and R. Pettit, J. Am. Chem. Soc. 79, 1767 (1957); M. J. S. Dewar, C. R. Ganellin, and R. Pettit, J. Chem. Soc. p. 55 (1958).
[80] D. H. R. Barton and E. P. Serebryakov, Proc. Chem. Soc. p. 309 (1962); D. H. R. Barton, H. P. Faro, E. P. Serebryakov, and N. F. Woolsey, J. Chem. Soc. p. 2438 (1965); B. Weinstein, A. H. Fenselau, and J. G. Thoene, ibid. p. 2281 (1965).
[81] G. B. Bachman and J. W. Wittmann, J. Org. Chem. 28, 65 (1963).

2. DICARBOXYLIC ACIDS

Just as permanganate, lead tetraacetate oxidizes oxalic acid to CO_2. However, the reaction does not go to completion since insoluble lead(II) oxalate precipitates. The reaction should become quantitative when the lead(II) salts are dissolved by adding a suitable stronger acid, such as perchloric acid. The oxidation of malonic acid has not been studied in detail. Because it is oxidized easily at 100° C, Fieser *et al.* used it as a promoter in methylations and phenylations (see Section III,C).

Much more important is the oxidation of succinic acids by lead tetraacetate, known as Grob degradation.[82] It is an improved form of a method of Doering[83] who used lead dioxide. The dicarboxylic acid is heated with lead tetraacetate and pyridine in a solvent, most often benzene or acetonitrile, sometimes acetic acid. Both carboxyl groups are lost as CO_2, and an olefin is formed in 20–70% yield. Good yields are obtained if the olefin is stable against lead tetraacetate or if it is volatile enough to be removed from the reaction mixture immediately after formation. Table IV summarizes the results.[73, 84–90a]

Other reactions sometimes supersede the desired degradation to olefin, for example when both carboxyl groups are in *endo*-position to a double bond.[91]

$$(33)$$

$$(34)$$

[82] C. A. Grob, M. Ohta, and A. Weiss, *Angew. Chem.* **70**, 343 (1958).

[83] W. v. E. Doering, M. Farber, and A. Sayigh, *J. Am. Chem. Soc.* **74**, 4370 (1952).

[84] M. Seki, quoted in H. Nohe, Dissertation, Technical University of Karlsruhe, Germany, 1960.

[85] E. E. van Tamelen and S. P. Pappas, *J. Am. Chem. Soc.* **85**, 3297 (1963).

[86] E. Grovenstein, D. V. Rao, and J. W. Taylor, *J. Am. Chem. Soc.* **83**, 1705 (1961).

[87] E. Vogel, W. Frass, and J. Wolpers, *Angew. Chem.* **75**, 979 (1963).

[88] C. A. Grob, M. Ohta, E. Renk, and A. Weiss, *Helv. Chim. Acta* **41**, 1191 (1958).

[89] K. Kitahonoki and Y. Takano, *Tetrahedron Letters* p. 1597 (1963).

[90] C. D. Nenitzescu, M. Avram, J. J. Pogany, G. D. Mateescu, and M. Fărcasin, *Acad. Rep. Populare Romine, Studii Cercetari Chem.* **11**, 7 (1963).

[90a] See also L. H. Zalkow and D. R. Brannon, *J. Chem. Soc.* Suppl. I, p. 5497 (1964); N. B. Chapman, S. Sotheeswaran, and K. J. Toyne, *Chem. Commun.* p. 214 (1965); S. Borćić and J. D. Roberts, *J. Am. Chem. Soc.* **87**, 1056 (1965).

[91] K. Alder and S. Schneider, *Ann.* **524**, 189 (1936).

TABLE IV

Degradation of Dicarboxylic Acids by Lead Tetraacetate

Dicarboxylic acid	Solvent	Temp. (°C)	Reaction products	Yield in % of theoretical	Reference
$C_6H_5-CH-CO_2H$ meso $\|$ $C_6H_5-CH-CO_2H$ rac.	Benzene, pyridine	120	Stilbene	41 44	73
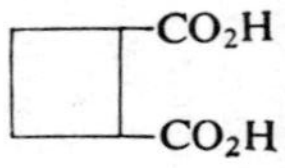 (cyclobutane-1,2-dicarboxylic acid structure)	Dimethylsulfoxide, pyridine	35	 (cyclobutene structure)	8.5	84
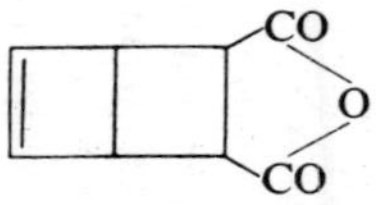 (bicyclic dicarboxylic anhydride structure)	Pyridine	43–45	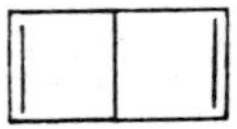 (bicyclic diene structure)	—	85
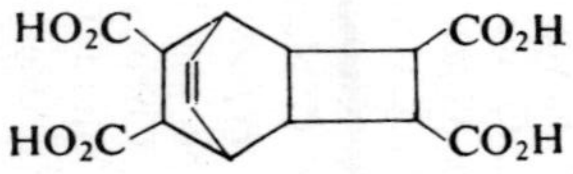 (diene diester HO_2C, HO_2C, CO_2H, CO_2H structure)	Pyridine	—	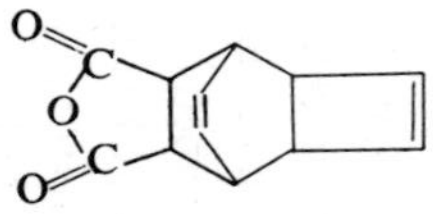 (tricyclic anhydride structure)	—	86

Substrate	Conditions	Temp	Product	Yield (%)	Ref.
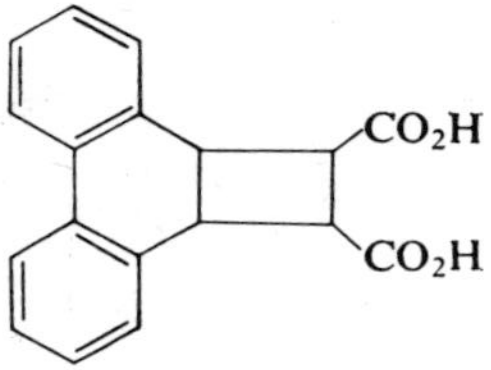 (structure, CO_2H, CO_2H)	—	—	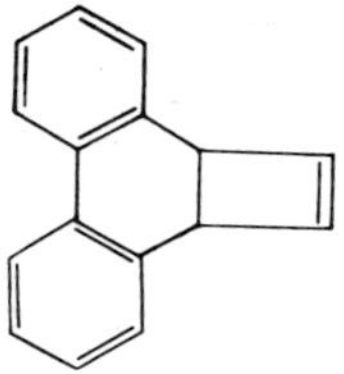 (structure)	—	87
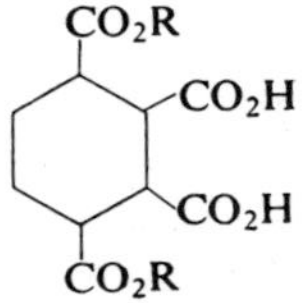 (structure, CO_2R, CO_2H, CO_2H, CO_2R)	AcOH, pyridine	120	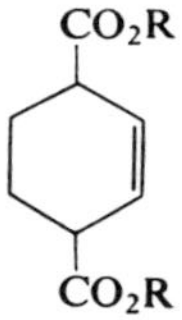 (structure, CO_2R, CO_2R)	73	88
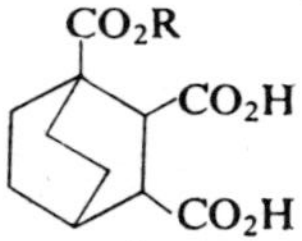 (structure, CO_2R, CO_2H, CO_2H)	Benzene, pyridine	—	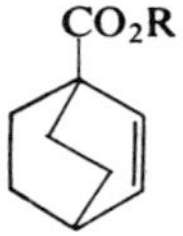 (structure, CO_2R)	—	82
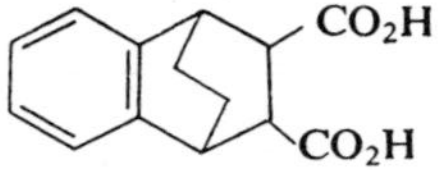 (structure, CO_2H, CO_2H)	Benzene, pyridine	60–70	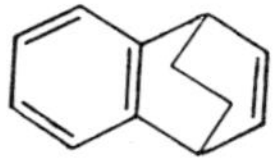 (structure)	24	89
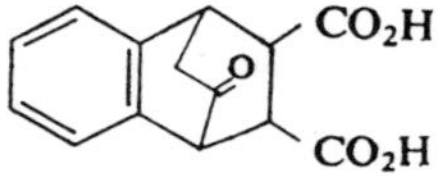 (structure, CO_2H, CO_2H)	Benzene, pyridine	40	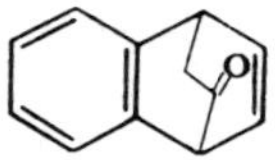 (structure)	10	89

TABLE IV—*continued*

DEGRADATION OF DICARBOXYLIC ACIDS BY LEAD TETRAACETATE

Dicarboxylic acid	Solvent	Temp. (°C)	Reaction products	Yield in % of theoretical	Reference
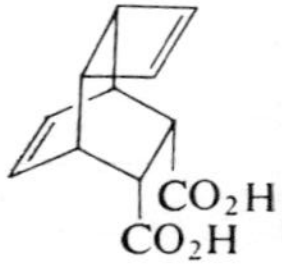	Benzene, pyridine	50-60	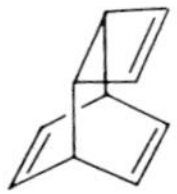	90	—
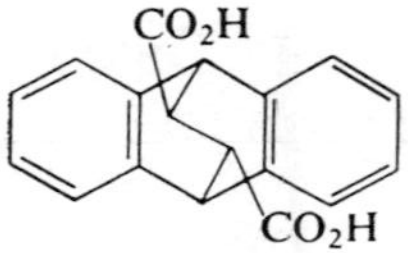	Benzene, pyridine	—	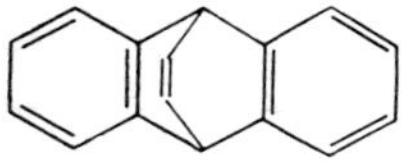	82	—
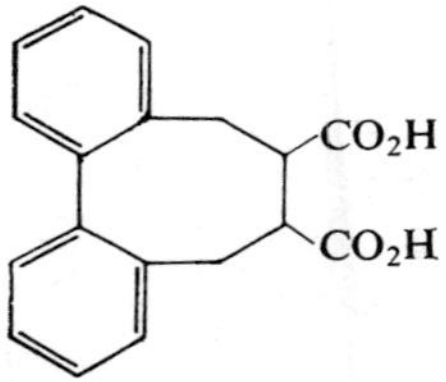	—	—	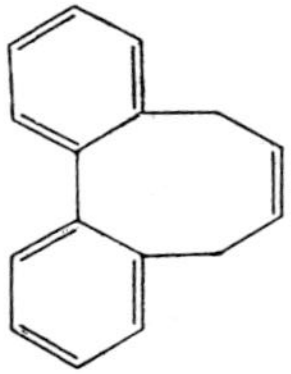	87	—

The Grob degradation could have a concerted mechanism:

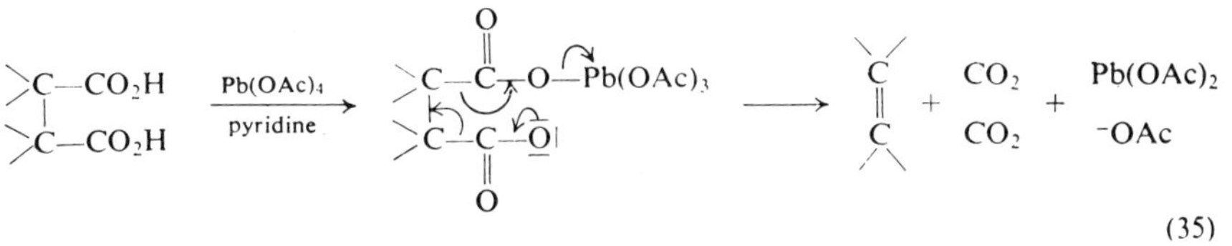

$$(35)$$

However, Corey and Casanova[73] found the reaction to be not stereospecific. The *racemic-* as well as the *meso-*diphenylsuccinic acids yield *trans-*stilbene in 44 and 41 % yield, respectively, excluding a concerted process.

Glutaric acid does not react under Grob's conditions. Substituted glutaric acids, in acetonitrile solution, give γ-lactones. McCoy and Zagalo[92] obtained the same β,γ-diphenylbutyrolactone from the two stereoisomers of α,β-diphenylbutyric acid. Again the reaction cannot be concerted but must involve a carbonium ion intermediate:

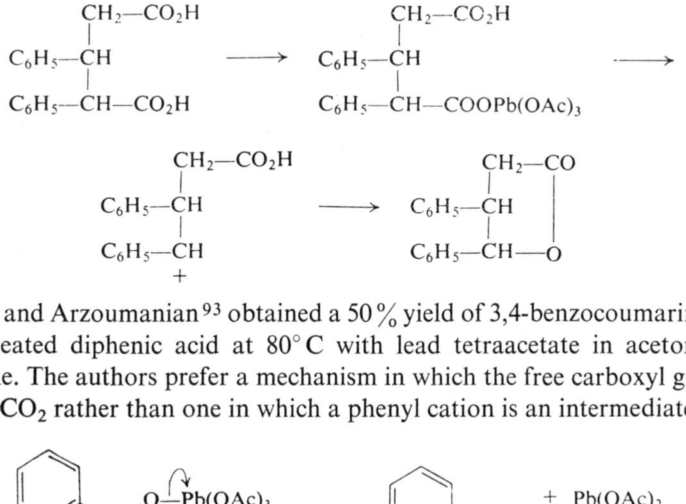

$$(36)$$

Moore and Arzoumanian[93] obtained a 50 % yield of 3,4-benzocoumarin when they treated diphenic acid at 80°C with lead tetraacetate in acetonitrile–pyridine. The authors prefer a mechanism in which the free carboxyl group is lost as CO_2 rather than one in which a phenyl cation is an intermediate.

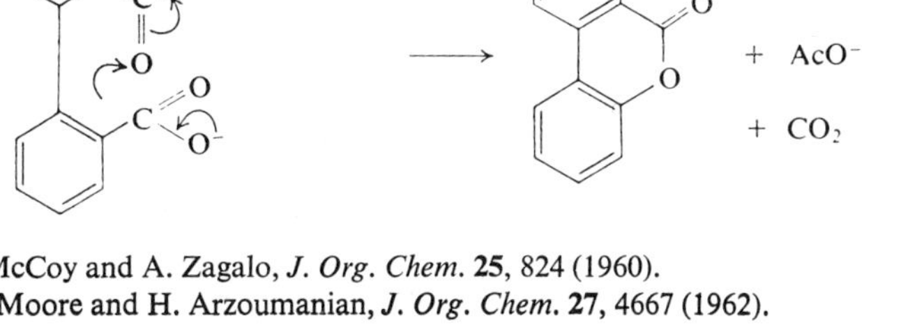

$$(37)$$

[92] L. L. McCoy and A. Zagalo, *J. Org. Chem.* **25**, 824 (1960).
[93] W. R. Moore and H. Arzoumanian, *J. Org. Chem.* **27**, 4667 (1962).

D. HYDROPEROXIDES

Alkyl and alkenyl hydroperoxides react vigorously with lead tetraacetate, even at low temperatures. Much oxygen is produced in almost all cases.[94] This reaction is one of the most important analytical tools for distinguishing hydroperoxides from peroxides, such as dialkyl peroxides, peracides, diacyl peroxides, ozonides, etc. Primary and secondary hydroperoxides[94,95] give aldehydes and ketones, respectively, in 80% yields, according to the summary Eq. (38):

$$\text{>CH—OOH} + \text{Pb(OAc)}_4 \longrightarrow \text{>C=O} + 2\,\text{AcOH} + \tfrac{1}{2}\text{O}_2 + \text{Pb(OAC)}_2 \qquad (38)$$

Actually, the reaction is more complicated. Less oxidant is consumed than Eq. (38) would predict from the amount of carbonyl compound formed. Products from C—C bond cleavages are found, and less oxygen is produced than corresponds to Eq. (38). It even has been reported that no oxygen is produced at all in the reaction of a few steroid hydroperoxides.[96,97]

Tertiary hydroperoxides[98] react by a far more complicated mechanism, since they have only one hydrogen atom that can be abstracted. The main product, formed in more than 50% yield, is the tertiary alcohol corresponding to the hydroperoxide. Ketones, dialkyl peroxides, and other products are also formed.

Ditertiary bishydroperoxides react cleanly and in a manner depending on the relative positions of the two OOH groups. Geminal bishydroperoxides, as far as studied, give esters or lactones.[99] The geminal bishydroperoxide from fluorenone (known only as molecular adduct with fluorenone) gives benzo-coumarin in 70% yield.

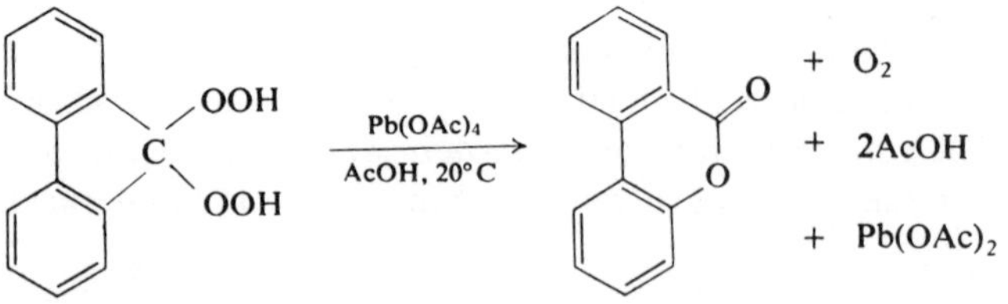

1,2-Bishydroperoxides are not known. 1,3- and 1,4-Bishydroperoxides are dehydrogenated by lead tetraacetate to 5- and 6-membered cyclic peroxides,

[94] R. Criegee, H. Pilz, and H. Flygare, *Ber.* **72**, 1799 (1939).

[95] H. Hock and S. Lang, *Ber.* **75**, 1051 (1942).

[96] G. O. Schenck and O. A. Neumüller, *Ann.* **618**, 194 (1958).

[97] G. O. Schenck, O. A. Neumüller, and W. Eisfeld, *Ann.* **618**, 202 (1958).

[98] R. Criegee, *Ber.* **77**, 22 (1944).

[99] R. Criegee, W. Schnorrenberg, and J. Becke, *Ann.* **565**, 7 (1949).

respectively.[99-101] The yields range from 40% to 70%, making the reaction attractive for the synthesis of these compounds difficult to obtain by other methods.

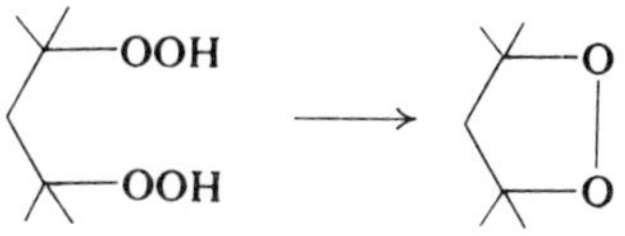

$$(40)$$

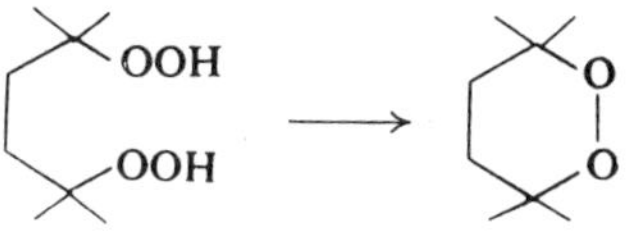

$$(41)$$

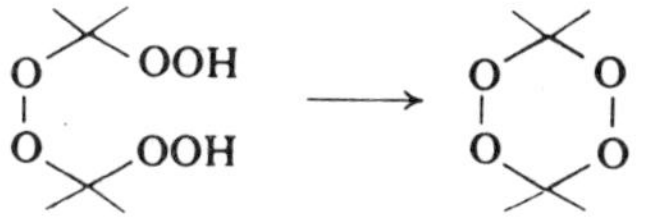

$$(42)$$

The so-called Kohler peroxides, such as

$$2,4,6\text{-trimethylphenyl-}CO-CH(OOH)-CH(C_6H_5)_2,$$

are oxidized with vigorous evolution of carbon monoxide.[102, 103] Isotopic labeling showed that it came from the keto group of the peroxide.

Only one thorough mechanistic study of a hydroperoxide–lead tetraacetate reaction has been reported. Hock and Kropf[104] investigated the oxidation of cumyl hydroperoxide, in particular the dependence of lead tetraacetate consumption and product composition on concentration and on additives. The consumption of lead tetraacetate and the evolution of oxygen decreased rapidly with increasing peroxide concentration. The main products were dimethylphenylcarbinol and acetophenone; a small quantity of dicumyl peroxide was also found. The authors propose a mechanism with a first step analogous to that in the reaction of alcohols. The —OOH function is dehydrogenated to the cation R—OO+ which can react in several ways:

$$C_6H_5C(CH_3)_2OOH + Pb(OAc)_4 \rightarrow C_6H_5C(CH_3)_2OO^+ + Pb(OAc)_2 + AcOH \quad (43)$$
$$+ AcO^-$$

[100] R. Criegee and G. Paulig, *Ber.* **88**, 712 (1955).
[101] R. Criegee and K. Metz, *Ber.* **89**, 1714 (1956).
[102] W. Pritzkow, *Ber.* **88**, 572 (1955).
[103] L. Rumberg, Dissertation, Technical University of Karlsruhe, Germany, 1958.
[104] H. Hock and H. Kropf, *Ber.* **91**, 1681 (1958).

$$C_6H_5C(CH_3)_2OO^+ + C_6H_5C(CH_3)_2OOH \rightarrow C_6H_5C(CH_3)_2OH \qquad (44)$$
$$+ C_6H_5C(CH_3)_2OO^+ + O$$

$$C_6H_5C(CH_3)_2OO^+ \rightarrow C_6H_5\overset{+}{C}(CH_3)_2 + O_2 \qquad (45)$$

$$C_6H_5C(CH_3)_2OO^+ \rightarrow C_6H_5COCH_3 + CH_3^+ + O \qquad (46)$$

$$C_6H_5\overset{+}{C}(CH_3)_2 + AcO^- \rightarrow C_6H_5C(CH_3){=}CH_2 + AcOH \qquad (47)$$

$$C_6H_5\overset{+}{C}(CH_3)_2 + C_6H_5C(CH_3)_2OOH \rightarrow C_6H_5C(CH_3)_2{-}O{-}O{-}C(CH_3)_2C_6H_5 \qquad (48)$$
$$+ H^+$$

$$C_6H_5C(CH_3){=}CH_2 + O_2 \rightarrow C_6H_5COCH_3 + CH_2O \qquad (49)$$

Step (44) is believed to proceed by the mechanism presented in Eq. (50):

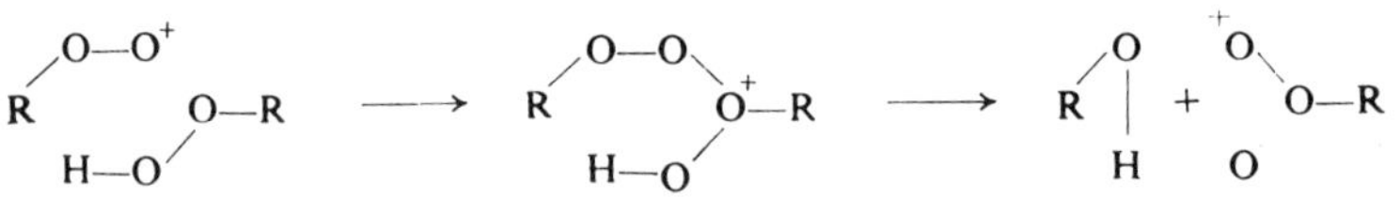

$$\qquad (50)$$

If α-methylstyrene is indeed the intermediate leading to acetophenone, then one must assume that it is very rapidly oxidized by oxygen—possibly by atomic oxygen. If this were not true it would be oxidized by lead tetraacetate to phenylacetone and phenylglycol diacetate[104] (see Section V,C). These two compounds are not found, however, even when α-methylstyrene is added to the reaction mixture.

The products of the oxidation of other hydroperoxides can also be explained by the assumption of a ROO$^+$ intermediate.[104] In the case of bishydroperoxides, it is not yet known whether the oxygen evolved comes from just one of the hydroperoxide groups or whether half of it comes from one and the other half from the other. In the latter case one would have to postulate a O$_4$-intermediate such as found by Bartlett[105] in chain termination reactions.

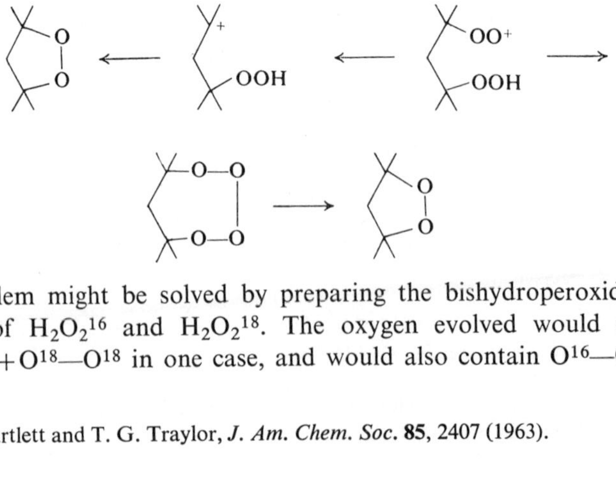

$$\qquad (51)$$

The problem might be solved by preparing the bishydroperoxides with a mixture of $H_2O_2^{16}$ and $H_2O_2^{18}$. The oxygen evolved would consist of $O^{16}{-}O^{16} + O^{18}{-}O^{18}$ in one case, and would also contain $O^{16}{-}O^{18}$ in the other.

[105] P. D. Bartlett and T. G. Traylor, *J. Am. Chem. Soc.* **85**, 2407 (1963).

The carbon monoxide evolution in the oxidation of Kohler peroxides must be caused by the intermediacy of 2,4,6-trimethylbenzoyl radicals or cations, which lose CO. The resulting mesityl radicals or cations are then oxidized by lead tetraacetate in a complex manner.

The reactions of hydroperoxides with lead tetraacetate invite further study.

III. Reactions with C—H Bonds

Reactions of lead tetraacetate with C—H bonds usually result in substitution by an acetoxy group, but dehydrogenation and other reactions are also known. Generally, only activated C—H bonds are attacked. Under special circumstances, however, nonactivated C—H bonds can react, as is discussed in Section III,B. Certain aromatic compounds are substituted in the nucleus, with the introduction of an acetoxy or of a methyl group (Section III,C).

A. ACTIVATED C—H BONDS

C—H bonds are activated toward lead tetraacetate by adjacent carbonyl groups of all types (Section III,A,1), aromatic rings (Section III,A,2), or C=C double bonds. The last case is not discussed here because olefins are attacked at the double bond as well as at the position *alpha* to it. Furthermore, products substituted in the allyl position sometimes do not arise from direct attack at this position. For these reasons, the oxidation of olefins and acetylenes is discussed separately in Section V.

1. CARBONYL COMPOUNDS

Lead tetraacetate converts carbonyl compounds to α-acetoxy derivatives. The reactivity increases in the sequence: acid anhydride < ester < ketone. It is especially high when two activating groups are adjacent to the C—H bond. The tendency to enolize increases in the same sequence, so that one is tempted to assume that the enols are the species that are actually attacked. This assumption is supported by a number of observations. The first comes from Fuson's[106] studies of compounds which can exist only as enols. In acetic acid at 40°C they are oxidized almost quantitatively to α-acetoxy aldehydes:

$$\left(H_3C-\underset{CH_3}{\overset{CH_3}{\bigcirc}}-\right)_2 C=CH-OH \xrightarrow{Pb(OAc)_4} \left(H_3C-\underset{CH_3}{\overset{CH_3}{\bigcirc}}-\right)_2 C\overset{OAc}{\underset{H}{\overset{|}{\diagdown}}}C=O \tag{52}$$

[106] R. C. Fuson, E. W. Maynert, T. Tan, R. E. Trumbull, and F. W. Wassmundt, *J. Am. Chem. Soc.* **79**, 1938 (1957).

The mechanism should be entirely analogous to that for the oxidation of monohydric phenols[107] (Section II,B):

$$
\text{\textbackslash C=CH—OH} \longrightarrow \quad \overset{O}{\underset{C}{HC}} \; Pb(OAc)_2 \quad \longrightarrow \quad \overset{O}{HC} \underset{C—OAc}{\overset{||}{}} \; + \; Pb(OAc)_2 \qquad (53)
$$

Second, Ichikawa and Yanaguchi[108] found that the rate of oxidation of ketones depends only on the concentration of ketones, not on that of lead tetraacetate. As with the bromination of ketones, the rate-determining step is the enolization.

Third, Henbest and associates[109] observed that the oxidation of ketones is strongly accelerated by boron trifluoride, so much that it can be accomplished in benzene at room temperature. The authors explain the catalysis as an acceleration of enol formation due to the boron trifluoride. In addition, however, boron trifluoride could increase the dissociation of lead tetraacetate and thus the formation of the cation $Pb(OAc)_3^+$.

If a radical mechanism were operative, one would expect the formation of dehydrodimers R—CO—CHR′—CHR′—CO—R. Simple ketones do not give such products in the lead tetraacetate oxidation, but they do when treated with diacylperoxides, according to Kharasch. Only acetoacetic ester and acetylacetone give 20 and 7.5%, respectively, of these dimers.[110, 111] These reactions however, proceed at temperatures so low as to be unfavorable to radical reactions. Therefore, just as in the case of phenols, the possibility that a molecule of starting material is attacked by a cation

$$CH_3—CO—C^+II—CO—CH_3$$

to form the dimer has to be considered.

Table V summarizes the oxidations of simple monoketones.[111–118] The lead tetraacetate oxidation is a general method for the preparation of α-acetoxy-ketones. Two acetoxy functions can be introduced where there are two α-CH groups. Geminal diacetoxy compounds may be formed in small yields. On hydrolysis, they give ketoaldehydes or α-diketones.[112] The reactions are faster in acetic acid but give better yields in benzene.[111]

[107] E. J. Corey and J. P. Schaefer, *J. Am. Chem. Soc.* **82**, 918 (1960).
[108] K. Ichikawa and Y. Yamaguchi, *Nippon Kagaku Zassi* **73**, 415 (1952); *Chem. Zentr.* p. 4095 (1956).
[109] H. B. Henbest, D. N. Jones, and G. P. Slater, *J. Chem. Soc.* p. 4472 (1961).
[110] W. Cocker and J. C. P. Schwarz, *Chem. & Ind.* (*London*) p. 390 (1951).
[111] G. W. K. Cavill and D. H. Solomon, *J. Chem. Soc.* p. 4426 (1955).

TABLE V

Oxidation of Monoketones by Lead Tetraacetate in Acetic Acid to α-Acetoxy-
and α,α′-Diacetoxyketones

Ketone	Temp. (°C)	Reaction products: yield in % of the theoretical		Reference
		Acetoxyketone	Diacetoxyketone	
Acetone	70–80	+	+	6
Methyl ethyl ketone	75	31	—	112
Diethyl ketone	80	32	+	111
Mesityloxide	80	35	—	112
$CH_3COCH_2CH(OC_2H_5)_2$		40	—	113
Acetophenone				
in acetic acid	85	32	—	112
in benzene	80	75	—	111
Deoxybenzoin[a]	100	20–50	—	112, 114
Cyclopentanone	110	+	—	115
Cyclohexanone (in benzene)	80	61	2	111
α-Acetoxycyclohexanone	80	—	40	111
Cycloheptanone	115	58	15	116
α-Hydrindone[b]	80	35	—	115
β-Hydrindone	70	+	—	115
α-Tetralone	90	14	—	115
Benzsuberone	77	43	—	117
Acenaphthenone	80	18	—	115

[a] Also many methoxy derivatives of deoxybenzoin.
[b] Also 3,3-dimethyl- and 2,3,3-trimethylhydrindone.

A special case is represented by the flavanones investigated by Cavill.[118]
Reaction occurs in acetic acid at 80–90° C and generally gives three products,
VII, VIII, and IX; IX must be formed by phenyl migration. The chromones
having a methyl instead of the phenyl substituent do not rearrange but give

[112] E. Detilleux and J. Jadot, *Bull. Soc. Roy. Sci. Liege* **29**, 208 (1960); *Chem. Abstr.* p. 7275 (1961).
[113] H. Plieninger and R. Müller, *Angew. Chem.* **68**, 618 (1956).
[114] G. G. Badcock, G. W. K. Cavill, A. Robertson, and W. B. Whalley, *J. Chem. Soc.* p. 2961 (1950).
[115] R. Criegee and K. Klonk, *Ann.* **564**, 1 (1949).
[116] W. Treibs and P. Grossmann, *Ber.* **90**, 103 (1957).
[117] P. D. Gardner, *J. Am. Chem. Soc.* **78**, 3421 (1956).
[118] G. W. K. Cavill, F. M. Dean, A. McGookin, B. M. Marshall, and A. Robertson, *J. Chem. Soc.* p. 4573 (1954).

only the normal substitution by acetoxy groups. The authors explain this by assuming a radical mechanism, but the ionic mechanism outlined above seems to be more probable. The ratio in which VII, VIII, and IX are formed depends

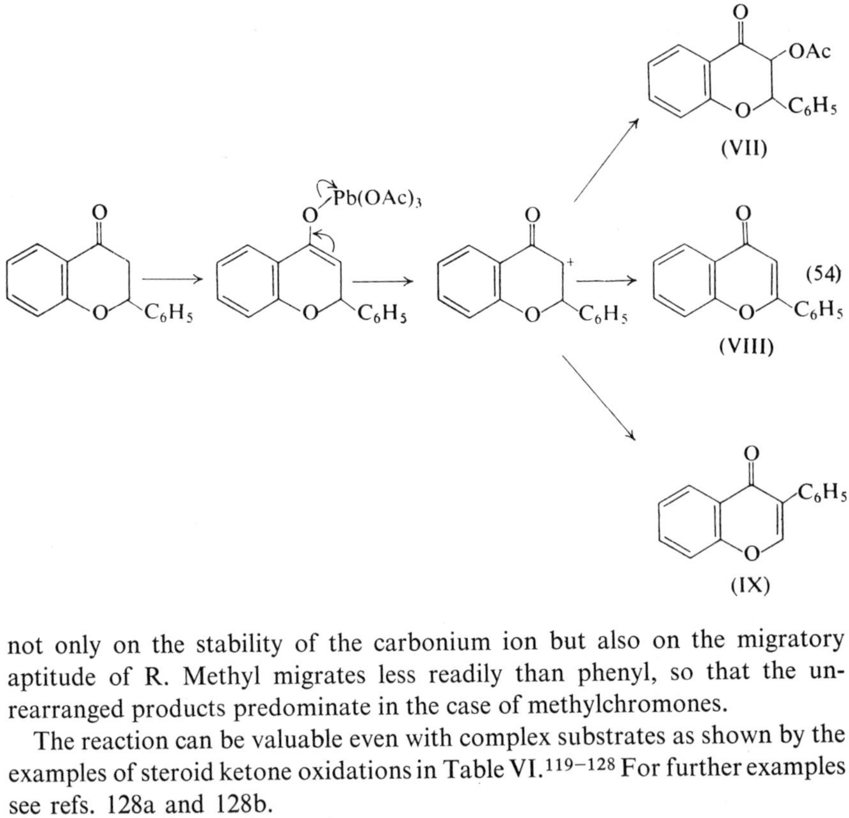

not only on the stability of the carbonium ion but also on the migratory aptitude of R. Methyl migrates less readily than phenyl, so that the un-rearranged products predominate in the case of methylchromones.

The reaction can be valuable even with complex substrates as shown by the examples of steroid ketone oxidations in Table VI.[119-128] For further examples see refs. 128a and 128b.

[119] L. F. Fieser and R. Stevenson, *J. Am. Chem. Soc.* **76**, 1728 (1954).

[120] H. B. Henbest, D. N. Jones, and G. P. Slater, *J. Chem. Soc.* p. 4472 (1961).

[121] D. Lavie, E. Glotter, and Y. Shoo, *Tetrahedron* **19**, 1377 (1963).

[122] E. Seebeck and T. Reichstein, *Helv. Chim. Acta* **27**, 948 (1944).

[123] L. F. Fieser and M. A. Romero, *J. Am. Chem. Soc.* **75**, 4716 (1953).

[124] R. L. Clarke, K. Dobriner, A. Mooradian, and C. M. Martini, *J. Am. Chem. Soc.* **77**, 661 (1955).

[125] F. Sondheimer, S. Kaufmann, J. Romo, H. Martinez, and G. Rosenkranz, *J. Am. Chem. Soc.* **75**, 4712 (1953).

[126] G. Ehrhart, H. Ruschig, and W. Aumüller, *Ber.* **72**, 2035 (1939).

[127] T. Reichstein and C. Montigel, *Helv. Chim. Acta* **22**, 1212 (1939).

[128] O. Mancera, *J. Am. Chem. Soc.* **72**, 5752 (1950).

[128a] J. Fishman, *J. Org. Chem.* **28**, 1528 (1963).

[128b] S. Kaufmann, *J. Org. Chem.* **29**, 1348 (1964).

TABLE VI

OXIDATION OF STEROID KETONES BY LEAD TETRAACETATE

Ketone partial structure	Solvent and catalyst	Temp. (°C)	Reaction product (partial structure)	Yield (% of theoretical)	Reference
(structure A)	AcOH	20	(structure, OAc)	30–40	119
(structure)	C_6H_6, BF_3	20–25	(structure, AcO)	50	120
(structure)	C_6H_6, BF_3	20–25	(structure, AcO)		120
(structure)	C_6H_6, BF_3	20	(structure, AcO)	50	121

TABLE VI—*continued*

Oxidation of Steroid Ketones by Lead Tetraacetate

Ketone partial structure	Solvent and catalyst	Temp. (°C)	Reaction product (partial structure)	Yield (% of theoretical)	Reference
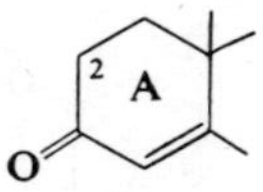 Δ⁴-Cholestenone	AcOH	70	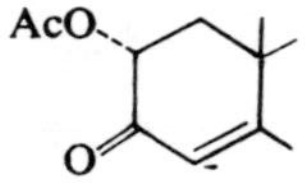 [AcO structure]	10	122, 123
Testosterone	AcOH	85–90	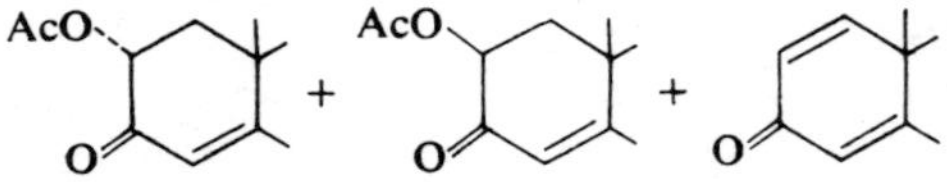 [AcO structure] + [AcO structure] + [structure]		124, 125
Progesterone	AcOH	85–90	2-α-Acetoxy- 2-α,21-Diacetoxy- 21-Acetoxy-progesterone	7	126, 127 124, 125
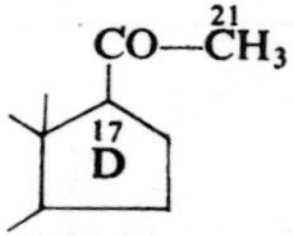 Pregnenolone acetate	AcOH	115	21-Acetoxy and 17,21-Diacetoxy compound		127
benzoate	AcOH	115	21-Acetoxy compound	39	128
Allopregnanolone acetate	AcOH	115	21-Acetoxy and 17,21-Diacetoxy compound	50 2	127

As mentioned above, β-dicarbonyl compounds react very easily, commonly even at room temperature.[6] Surprisingly, the yields of α-acetoxy compounds are not always good. The yields were found to be 80% for malonic ester,[111] 53% for acetoacetic ester,[111] 45% for benzoylacetic ester,[6] and 25% acetylacetone.[111] α-Methylacetoacetic ester also was oxidized successfully.[129] The yields of dimers account for only a part of the deficit, so that products of further oxidation must be formed. From the reaction of acetylacetone with an excess of lead tetraacetate, Detilleux and Jadot[112] obtained a 54% yield of diacetoxy-acetylacetone, H_3C—CO—$C(OAc)_2$—CO—CH_3. A smaller yield of the diacetoxy compound was formed from acetoacetic ester. Other oxidations beyond the first stage have been demonstrated by Janculev.[130] Substituted diketo esters gave 46–67% yields of degraded carboxylic acids:

$$\begin{array}{c} \text{OAc} \\ | \\ \text{R—CO—CH}_2\text{—CO—CO}_2\text{R} \longrightarrow \text{R—CO—C—CO—CO}_2\text{R} \longrightarrow \\ | \\ \text{OAc} \end{array}$$

$$\text{R—CO—CO—CO—CO}_2\text{R} \longrightarrow \text{R—CO}_2\text{H} \qquad (55)$$

In the case of acetoacetic ester, lead oxalate was found.

Cyclic α-hydroxy-β-keto esters are of interest in the pyrethrolone field. LaForge and co-workers[131] were able to prepare them in 50% yield from the corresponding cyclic β-keto esters by lead tetraacetate oxidation at 50°C in acetic acid.

Decarboxylation occurs when half esters of substituted malonic acids are oxidized at 50°C in benzene. Esters of substituted acetylglycolic acids are formed.

$$\text{R—CH(CO}_2\text{R)CO}_2\text{H} \rightarrow \text{R—CH(CO}_2\text{R)OAc} \qquad (56)$$

Vilkas and Rouhi-Laridjani[132] assumed that a substitution is effected by a $Pb(OAc)_3$ group bound by the carboxyl function, and that decarboxylation occurs later. It seems more likely, however, that decarboxylation is concerted with substitution, as is true for many other monocarboxylic acids (see Section II,C,1).

Acid anhydrides are represented only by the example of Dimroth and Schweizer.[6] Acetic anhydride when heated to reflux with lead tetraacetate was converted to the anhydride of acetylglycolic acid in 40% yield.

$$\text{H}_3\text{C—CO—O—CO—CH}_3 \rightarrow \text{AcO—CH}_2\text{—CO—O—CO—CH}_2\text{—OAc} \qquad (57)$$

Acetic anhydride was present in large excess, making it improbable that both

[129] L. O. Krampitz, *Arch. Biochem.* **17**, 81 (1948).
[130] J. Janculev and B. Podolesov, *Croat. Chem. Acta* **33**, 59 (1961).
[131] F. B. LaForge, N. Green, and W. A. Gersdorff, *J. Am. Chem. Soc.* **70**, 3707 (1948).
[132] M. Vilkas and M. Rouhi-Laridjani, *Compt. Rend. Acad. Sci.* **251**, 2544 (1960).

methyl groups of one substrate molecule are attacked by the oxidant. The product perhaps results from the disproportionation, during workup, of the expected primary product, the mixed anhydride

$$CH_3—CO—O—CO—CH_2OAc.$$

Very few examples of oxidation of esters at the *alpha* position are known. Simple esters such as cyclohexyl acetate are hardly attacked by lead tetraacetate even in boiling acetic acid. Azalactones and esters of hippuric acid,[133] however, are converted to the acetoxy derivatives. The yields are 25–30% and 65%, respectively, in benzene at 80° C. Section V,D describes the coupled lead tetraacetate oxidations of carboxylic acids and cyclopentadiene.

2. SIDE CHAINS ON AROMATIC COMPOUNDS

Dimroth and Schweizer[6] observed that lead tetraacetate converts toluene to benzyl acetate. The reaction has been extended to many analogous systems, as shown in Table VII.[134–144a] Usually the oxidation is run in acetic acid at 80° C, but room temperature is sufficient in some cases. Yields are moderate to good. Geminal diacetoxy compounds are formed as side products, but usually only in small yields. Hydrolysis of these diacetoxy compounds gives aldehydes or ketones.

The reaction mechanism has not been clearly established. Dewar[145] proposes a radical chain reaction involving acetoxy and benzyl radicals as chain carriers. This is supported by the observation that oxidations of tetralin and of ethyl benzene are accelerated by the addition of 5% of dibenzoyl peroxide. Cavill and Solomon[134] found pronounced electronic influence of substitutents on rates and yields of the benzyl substitution. Electron-donating

133 M. M. Schemjakin and W. K. Antonow, *Izv. Akad. Nauk SSSR* **129**, 349 (1959); *Chem. Zentr.* p. 16071 (1960).

134 G. W. K. Cavill and D. H. Solomon, *J. Chem. Soc.* p. 3943 (1954).

135 E. Detilleux and J. Jadot, *Bull. Soc. Roy. Sci. Liege* **24**, 366 (1955).

136 L. Kraft, Dissertation, University of Würzburg, Germany, 1932.

137 M. M. Bokadia, B. R. Brown, and W. Cummings, *J. Chem. Soc.* p. 3308 (1960).

138 W. S. Johnson, J. M. Anderson, and W. E. Shelberg, *J. Am. Chem. Soc.* **66**, 218 (1944).

139 W. S. Johnson, A. D. Kemp, R. Pappo, J. Ackerman, and W. F. Johns, *J. Am. Chem. Soc.* **78**, 6312 (1956).

140 G. Dupont, R. Dulon, G. Ourisson, and C. Thibault, *Bull. Soc. Chim. France* p. 708 (1955).

141 L. F. Fieser and E. B. Hershberg, *J. Am. Chem. Soc.* **60**, 1893 (1938).

142 G. M. Badger and J. W. Cook, *J. Chem. Soc.* p. 802 (1939).

143 L. F. Fieser and E. B. Hershberg, *J. Am. Chem. Soc.* **60**, 2542 (1938).

144 G. A. R. Kon and E. M. F. Roe, *J. Chem. Soc.* p. 143 (1945).

144a G. W. K. Cavill, A. Robertson, and W. B. Whalley, *J. Chem. Soc.* p. 1567 (1949).

145 M. J. S. Dewar, "The Electronic Theory of Organic Chemistry," p. 276. Oxford Univ. Press, London and New York, 1949.

TABLE VII

LEAD TETRAACETATE OXIDATION OF AROMATIC COMPOUNDS BEARING SIDE CHAIN, IN ACETIC ACID SOLUTION

Starting material		Temp. (°C)	Reaction product	Yield (% of theoretical)	Reference
p-R—C$_6$H$_4$—CH$_3$	R = H		Benzyl acetate	10–38	6, 134, 135
	R = CH$_3$		p-Xylyl acetate	47	134
	R = OCH$_3$		p-Methoxybenzyl acetate	50–60	134
	R = NO$_2$		p-Nitrobenzyl acetate	0–7	134, 136
Ethylbenzene[a]		83	Acetate of methylphenyl carbinol	32–34[a]	135
Diphenylmethane		80	Benzhydryl acetate	71	6, 135, 136
p-Methoxydiphenylmethane		80	p-Methoxybenzhydryl acetate	80	137
Triphenylmethane			Triphenylmethyl acetate	50	6, 135, 136
p-Methoxytriphenylmethane			p-Methoxymethyl acetate	76	136
p-Nitrotriphenylmethane			p-Nitromethyl acetate	25	136
Tetralin		80–100	α-Acetoxytetralin	37	13
			1,4-Diacetoxytetralin	12	
α-Acetoxytetralin		85	1,4-Diacetoxytetralin	38	
6-Methoxytetralin		20	1-Acetoxy-6-methoxytetralin	62	138
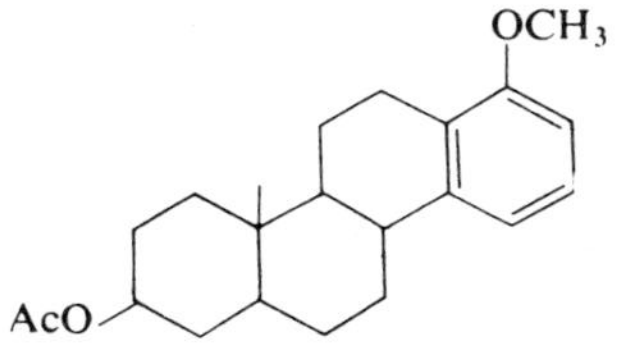 Several isomers		90	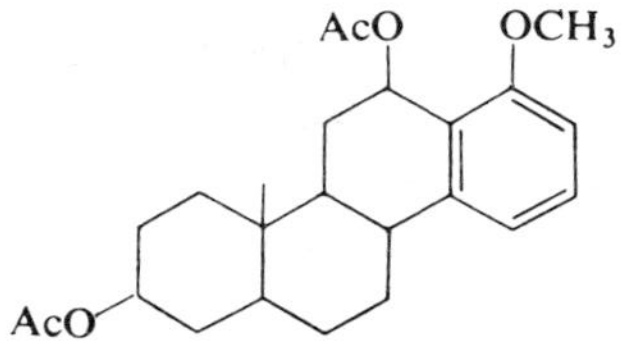	60–80	139

TABLE VII—continued

LEAD TETRAACETATE OXIDATION OF AROMATIC COMPOUNDS BEARING SIDE CHAIN, IN ACETIC ACID SOLUTION

Starting material	Temp. (°C)	Reaction product	Yield (% of theoretical)	Reference
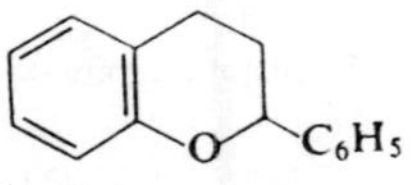	80	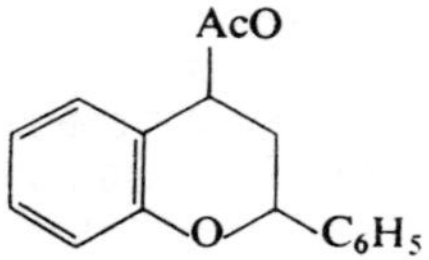	60	137
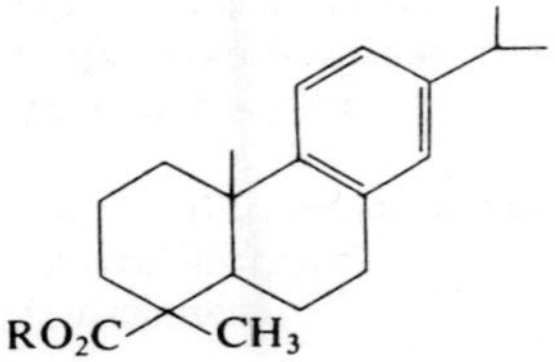	80	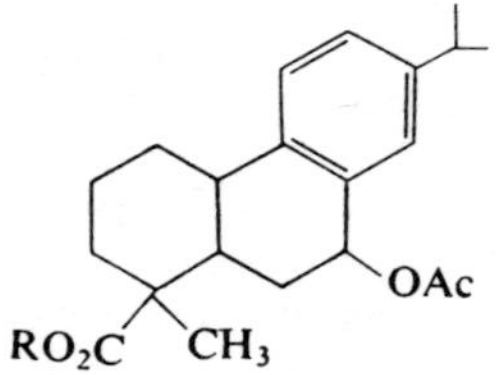	45	140
9,10-Dimethylanthracene R = H R = CH₃	100 100 100	9,10-Bis(acetoxymethyl)anthracene R = H R = CH₂OAc	50 17 50	142 141 142

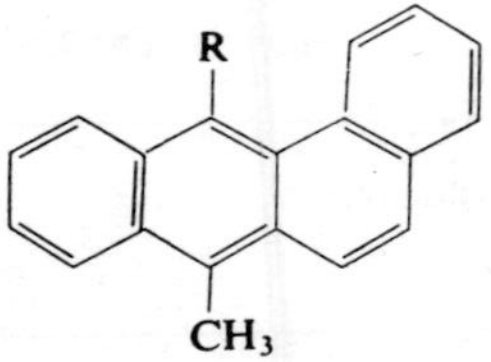

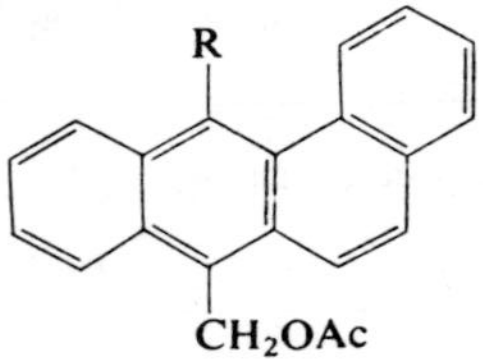

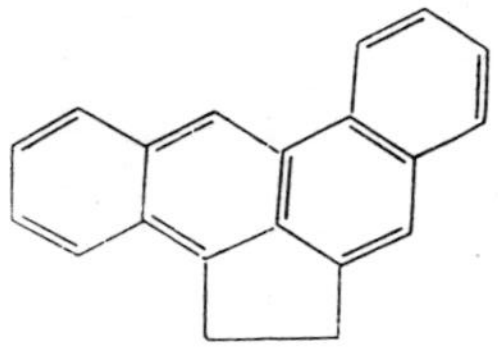

+7% ketone 46   143

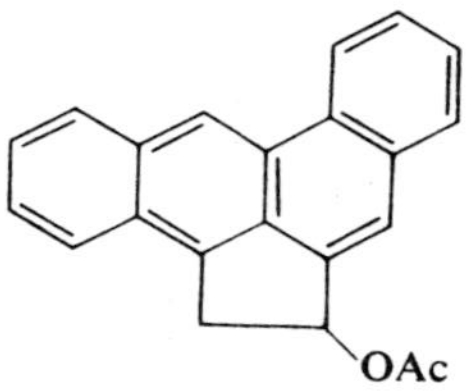

20

+   144

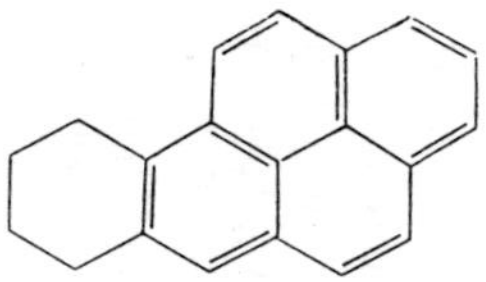

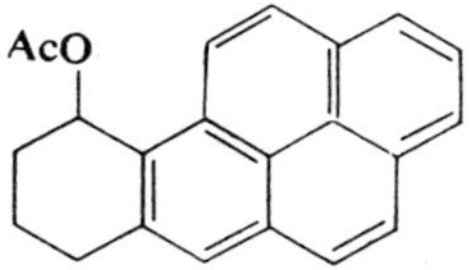

20

R = H   (2 days)   20   60   144a

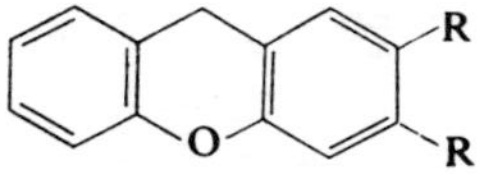

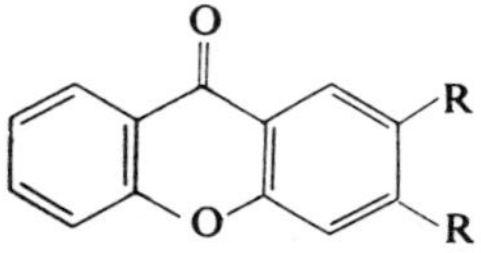

R = OCH₃   (1 hour)   20   75   144a

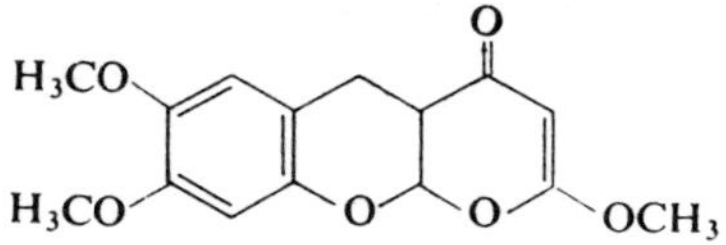

80–90   144a

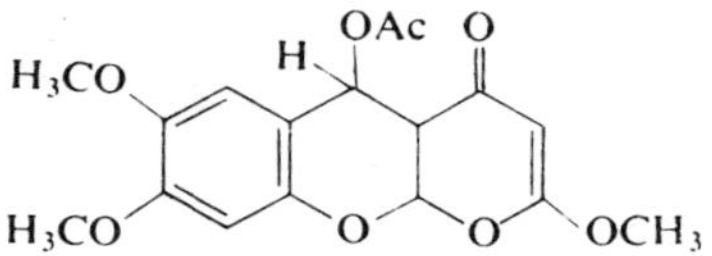

30–40

a Same with propylbenzene and isopropylbenzene (yields 30%).[135]

b 63% in ethyl benzene as solvent.[134]

groups favor, while electron-withdrawing groups hinder, the reaction. The results of many other authors agree with this rule.

Dimerization products, such as dibenzyl, have never been reported in these oxidations but are always formed when diacetyl peroxide is the oxidant. Also, the British authors did not find attack on the solvent, carbon tetrachloride. Such attack is the rule in radical chain reactions and leads to halogenated by-products. Thus there is evidence both for and against a radical chain mechanism. This dilemma is not solved by assuming a lead tetraacetate hydrocarbon complex that then decomposes specifically to the reaction products.

Compounds of the type C_6H_5—CH_2—$Pb(OAc)_3$ could be intermediates. As will be discussed in Section VII, they ought to decompose spontaneously to benzyl acetate and lead diacetate. However, there is little likelihood for a normal electrophilic substitution at the benzyl carbon, which would lead to the organolead intermediate.

Davies[146] proposes a concerted mechanism:

$$\begin{array}{ccc}
H_3C-C\overset{O}{\diagdown}Pb(OAc)_3 & & H_3C-C\overset{\nearrow O}{} \qquad Pb(OAc)_3 \\
\overset{\parallel}{O}\diagdown CH_2-C_6H_5 & \longrightarrow & O \qquad + \quad CH_2-C_6H_5 \\
\overset{|}{H} & & \diagdown H
\end{array} \qquad (58)$$

However, the intermediacy of benzyl radicals has not altogether been excluded. If involved, the radicals would have to be short-lived enough to exclude dimerization. Each collision with a lead tetraacetate molecule would have to give benzyl acetate and a $\dot{Pb}(OAc)_3$ radical. The latter would start a new chain, or disproportionate to lead tetraacetate and lead diacetate. In the oxidation by diacetyl peroxide, collision of a benzyl radical and a peroxide molecule would not always lead to a reaction, thus permitting dimerization to dibenzyl.

3. DEHYDROGENATION OF H-ATOMS BOUND TO CARBON

Substitution by an acetoxy group is not the only path for the lead tetra-acetate oxidation of activated CH groups. Dehydrogenation may occur in cases where it leads to the formation of an aromatic system, most readily with six-membered rings already containing two double bonds in 1,4-position. With 1,3-cyclohexadienes, dehydrogenation is the exception; in this case addition reactions are usually observed (see Section V). 1,4-Dihydronaphthalenes and 9,10-dihydroanthracenes are readily aromatized. The reaction of lead tetra-acetate with 2-methoxy-1,4,5,8-tetrahydronaphthalene, in benzene at 20°C, yields not only 2-methoxynaphthalene but also 20% of the theoretical yield of

146 D. I. Davies, *J. Chem. Soc.* p. 2351 (1963).

the partially dehydrogenated compound, in which only the ring bearing the methoxy group has been aromatized.[147] This demonstrates that electron-donating groups accelerate the dehydrogenation by lead tetraacetate, as well as substitution and addition reactions (see Section V).

Dehydrogenation requires further activating groups where the ring contains only one double bond or is condensed with only one aromatic ring. Aromatization of carboxylic esters, lactones, or acid anhydrides of this type has been reported. Table VIII summarizes dehydrogenations by lead tetraacetate.[13, 147–157] The last entry in Table VIII shows a case in which no aromatic system is formed. Surprisingly, lead tetraacetate does not introduce

TABLE VIII

DEHYDROGENATIONS BY LEAD TETRAACETATE

Starting material	Solvent	Temp. (°C)	Reaction product	Yield (% of the theoretical)	Reference
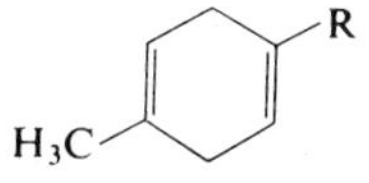 H_3C — (ring) — R	AcOH		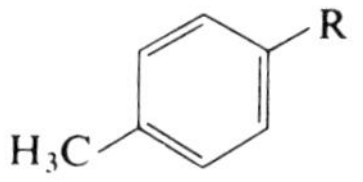 H_3C — (ring) — R		148
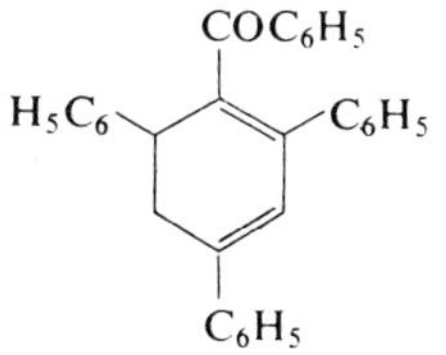 H_5C_6 — (ring, COC$_6$H$_5$, C$_6$H$_5$, C$_6$H$_5$)	AcOH	70	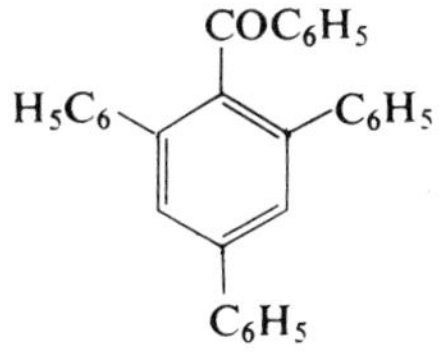 H_5C_6 — (ring, COC$_6$H$_5$, C$_6$H$_5$, C$_6$H$_5$)	82	149
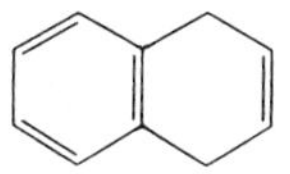 (tetrahydronaphthalene)	AcOH	20	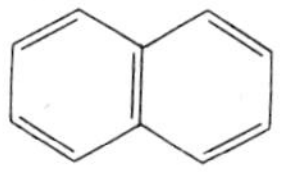 (dihydronaphthalene)		13

[147] A. J. Birch, A. R. Murray, and H. Smith, *J. Chem. Soc.* p. 1945 (1951).

[148] A. J. Birch and S. M. Mukherji, *J. Chem. Soc.* p. 2531 (1949).

[149] H. Meerwein, *Ber.* **77**, 227 (1944).

[150] C. Weizmann, E. Bergmann, and T. Berlin, *J. Am. Chem. Soc.* **60**, 1331 (1938).

[151] M. S. Newman, *J. Am. Chem. Soc.* **62**, 1683 (1940).

[152] E. Bergmann and F. Bergmann, *J. Am. Chem. Soc.* **60**, 1805 (1938).

[153] H. Erdtman, *Ann.* **513**, 229 (1934).

[154] M. L. Tamayo and A. D'Ocón, *Ann. Fis. Quim.* **42**, 809 (1946); *Chem. Abstr.* p. 6540b (1947).

[155] R. D. Haworth and G. Sheldrick, *J. Chem. Soc.* p. 636 (1935).

[156] R. D. Haworth and T. Richardson, *J. Chem. Soc.* p. 348 (1936).

[157] P. D. Gardner and R. J. Thompson, *J. Org. Chem.* **22**, 36 (1957).

TABLE VIII—*continued*

Starting material	Solvent	Temp. (°C)	Reaction product	Yield (% of the theoretical)	Reference
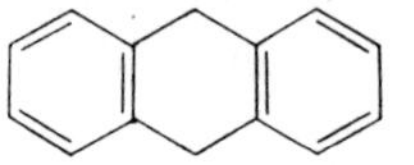	C₆H₆	80	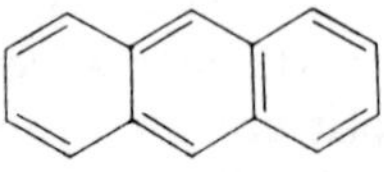	25[a]	13
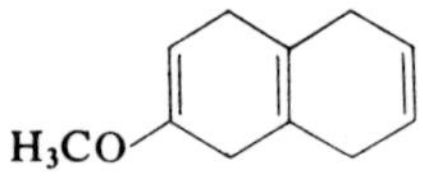	C₆H₆	20	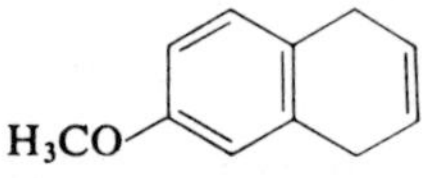	20	147
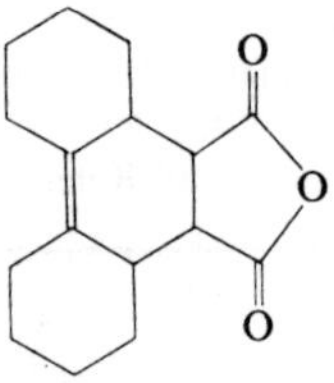	AcOH	70	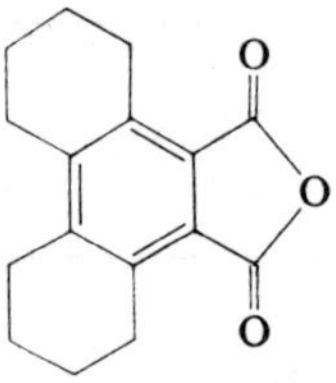	25	150
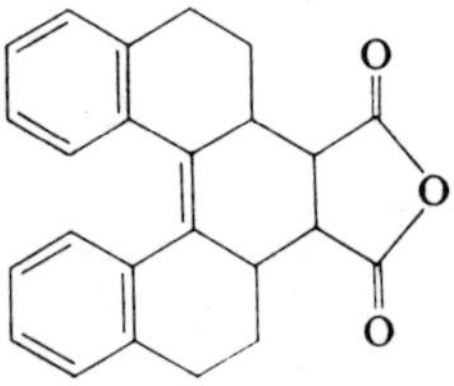	AcOH	100	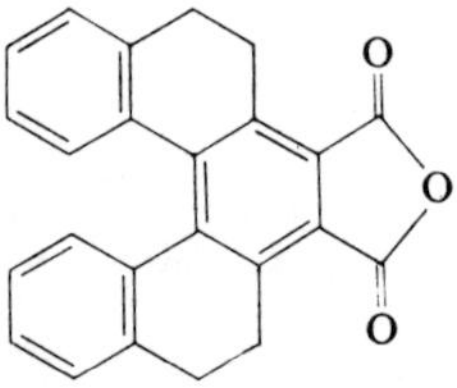	73[b]	151
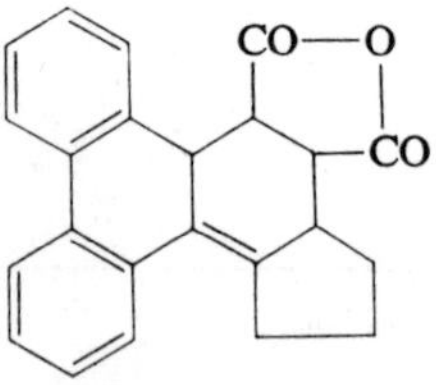	AcOH	100	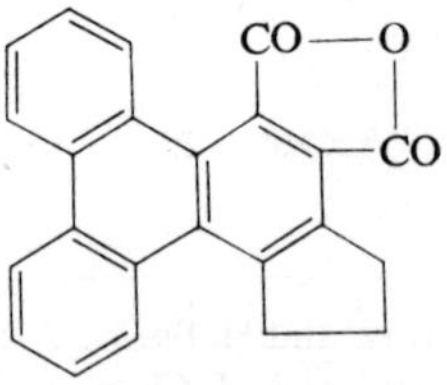	50	152[c]
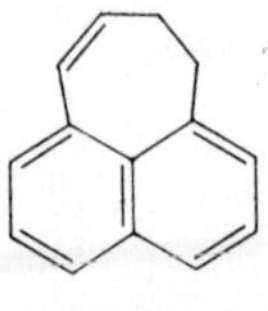	AcOH	100	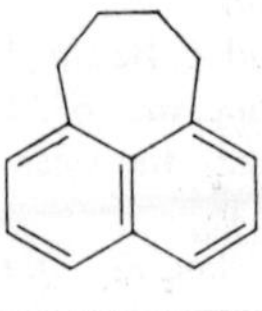	51	157

[a] Small yield due to further oxidation.
[b] Plus some totally dehydrogenated product.
[c] Other examples of the same type are found in references 153–156.

a second double bond into the seven-membered ring, although this can be accomplished readily by chloranil.

Nothing is known about the mechanisms of these dehydrogenations. Some reactions, especially those proceeding only at elevated temperatures, might involve acetoxylation followed by elimination of acetic acid. It seems more probable, however, that an intermediate ion or radical loses a hydrogen atom or a proton.

A remarkable cyclodehydrogenation of a α,δ-diarylbutane was found by Haworth and Kelly[158]:

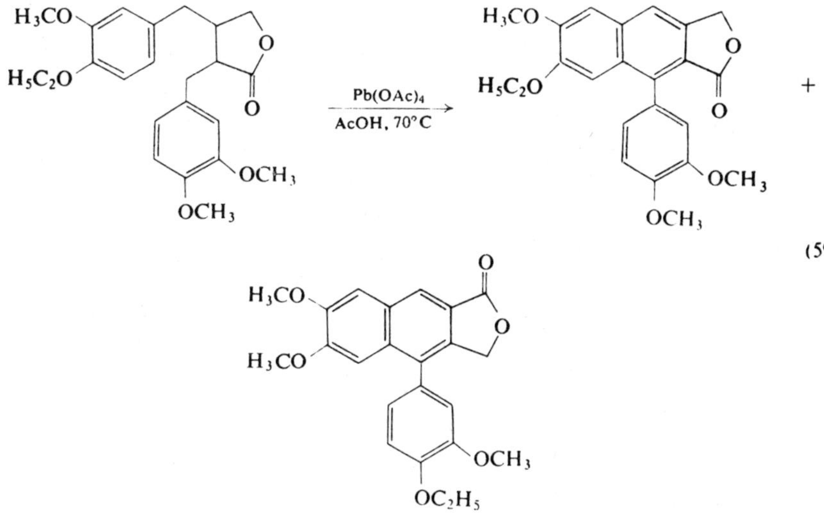

(59)

Presumably a carbonium ion or a radical is first formed at the benzyl position next to one of the aromatic rings. This then leads to electrophilic or radical substitution on the other aromatic nucleus, followed by dehydrogenation.

Dehydrogenations involving participation of CH_2–NH groups are discussed in Section VI,B.

4. ACTIVATION BY ETHER OXYGENS

The attack of radicals on C—H bonds next to ether oxygen is well known. Correspondingly, lead tetraacetate reacts as summarized in Eq. (60):

$$R—CH_2—OR' + Pb(OAc)_4 \longrightarrow R—\underset{\underset{OAc}{|}}{CH}—OR' + Pb(OAc_2) + HOAc \qquad (60)$$

The products are acylals which, upon hydrolysis, give an aldehyde, an alcohol, and an acid. Table IX records the products obtained by heating lead tetraacetate

[158] R. D. Haworth and W. Kelly, *J. Chem. Soc.* p. 998 (1936).

TABLE IX

OXIDATION OF ETHERS BY LEAD TETRAACETATE[159]

Ether	Temp. (°C)	Reaction time (days)	Products	Yield based on Pb(OAc)[4]
Diethyl	reflux	7	$CH_3CH(OAc)OC_2H_5$	10
Di-*n*-butyl	70	9	$C_3H_7CH(OAc)OC_4H_9$	67
Tetrahydrofuran	55–60	4	α-Acetoxytetrahydrofuran	45

in ethers.[159] Since the products are analogs of those formed by dibenzoyl peroxide, a radical chain mechanism is indicated. $C_6H_5CH(OAc)OC_6H_5$ is one of the products formed from phenylbenzyl ether under similar conditions.[160]

Methyl ethers of phenols not only undergo substitution in the ring (see Section III,C), but are attacked at the methyl groups as well. The oxidation of phloroglucinol trimethyl ether in boiling benzene gave a 32% yield of $3,5\text{-}(CH_3O)_2C_6H_3\text{—}OCH_2OAc$.[137] Preuss and Tan[161] made similar observations in the oxidation of the dimethyl ethers of hydroquinone and resorcinol. They discussed an ionic mechanism, the first step of which is a coordination of the $Pb(OAc)_3^+$ cation with a free electron pair of the ether oxygen.

Remarkably, the lead tetraacetate oxidation of diisopropyl ether gives a 36% yield of an α,β-diacetoxy derivative[69, 159]: Isopropyl isopropenyl

$$(H_3C)_2CH—O—CH(CH_3)_2 \longrightarrow (H_3C)_2CH—O—\overset{\displaystyle CH_3}{\underset{\displaystyle OAc}{C}}—CH_2OAc \qquad (61)$$

ether is a probable intermediate. We do not know whether it is formed by disproportionation of a radical, as assumed by Kharasch,[69] or from the carbonium ion postulated by Preuss.[161]

Little is known about the oxidation of acetals. At elevated temperatures, lead tetraacetate attacks the $O—CH_2—O$ function of safrole, the cyclic formal of catechol. Presumably a derivative of orthoformic acid is formed.

As shown by Mosher and Kehr,[162] heating butyl butyrate to reflux with lead tetraacetate leads to attack on the position next to the ether oxygen, rather than on that next to the carbonyl group, and $C_3H_7COOCH(OAc)C_3H_7$ is formed.

[159] W. Frass, Dissertation, Technical University of Karlsruhe, Germany, 1960.
[160] J. Jadot, A. David, and J. Kasperczyck, *Bull. Roy. Sci. Liege* **29**, 196 (1960); *Chem. Abstr.* p. 11348 g (1961).
[161] F. R. Preuss and L. Tan, *Arch. Pharm.* **293**, 505 (1960).
[162] W. A. Mosher and C. L. Kehr, *J. Am. Chem. Soc.* **82**, 5342 (1960).

B. UNACTIVATED C—H BONDS

In 1959, a Swiss and Yugoslavian group[9] discovered the oxidation of CH_3, CH_2, and CH groups not adjacent to an activating function. Lead tetraacetate oxidation of steroid alcohols in boiling benzene gave 5- and sometimes 6-membered cyclic ethers[162a]:

The reaction occurs only when a free hydroxyl group is present. Apparently the OH group binds the lead tetraacetate, forming a —O—Pb(OAc)₃ group. Heterolysis or homolysis of the O—Pb bond then gives a R—O⁺ or R—O· function which attacks C—H bonds in suitable spatial positions. The cyclic ethers are often formed in good yields. Since they can be converted further in many ways, the reaction opens a route to oxygen-substituted steroids which could not be obtained before.

A modification of the reaction discussed above was published 2 years later.[163] The steroid alcohol is treated with lead tetraacetate in refluxing cyclohexane in the presence of 1 mole of iodine, usually under irradiation. A labile iodo ether is formed. Sodium acetate converts this to an acetoxy ether in which the former CH_3 or CH_2 group is now on the oxidation level of an aldehyde or a ketone. In the first case oxidation with chromium trioxide yields a lactone. Equation (63) gives a schematic picture of the reaction:

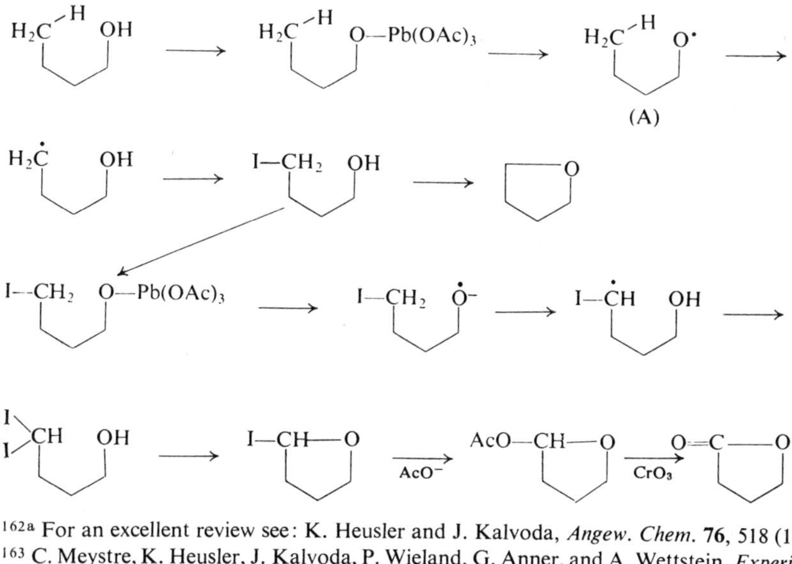

(63)

[162a] For an excellent review see: K. Heusler and J. Kalvoda, *Angew. Chem.* **76**, 518 (1964).
[163] C. Meystre, K. Heusler, J. Kalvoda, P. Wieland, G. Anner, and A. Wettstein, *Experientia* **17**, 475 (1961); *Helv. Chim. Acta* **45**, 1317 (1962).

An alternative mechanism involves reaction of (A) with iodine, to form a hypoiodite. This, in an intramolecular redox reaction, could exchange I for an H at a group in suitable spatial position. (A), or the corresponding cation, is also the intermediate in two common side reactions: the oxidation of the alcohol to the ketone and the fragmentation of the alcohol (see Section II,A). Table X gives details on the oxidation of unactivated C—H groups in steroid alcohols.[163-184]

TABLE X
OXIDATIONS OF UNACTIVATED GROUPS IN STEROIDS

Position of OH group	Reaction conditions (temp. in °C; c. = cyclo)	Type of reaction product, Yield in % of theory	Position of the C atom attacked	Remarks	Reference
2β	C_6H_6, 80	Ether, 60	19	+ 14% Ketone	164
	C_6H_6, 80	Ether, 0.7	19	+ 31% Ketone	164
	c. C_6H_{12}, I_2, hv	Half-acetal	19	—	168

164 P. N. Rao and J. C. Uroda, *Naturwissenschaften* **50**, 548 (1963).
165 A. Bowers and E. Denot, *J. Am. Chem. Soc.* **82**, 4956 (1960).
166 H. Immer, M. L. Mihailović, K. Schaffner, D. Arigoni, and O. Jeger, *Experientia* **16**, 530 (1960); *Helv. Chim. Acta* **45**, 753 (1962).
167 K. Heusler and J. Kalvoda, *Helv. Chim. Acta* **46**, 2020 (1963).
168 K. Heusler, J. Kalvoda, P. Wieland, G. Anner, and A. Wettstein, *Helv. Chim. Acta* **45** 2575 (1962).
169 A. Bowers, L. C. Ibánez, M. E. Cabezas, and H. J. Ringold, *Chem. & Ind. (London)* p. 1299 (1960).
170 A. Bowers, E. Denot, L. C. Ibánez, E. Cabezas, and H. J. Ringold, *J. Org. Chem.* **27**, 1862 (1962).
171 J. Kalvoda and K. Heusler, *Chem. & Ind. (London)* p. 1431 (1963).
172 H. Ueberwasser, K. Heusler, J. Kalvoda, C. Meystre, P. Wieland, G. Anner, and A. Wettstein, *Helv. Chim. Acta* **46**, 344 (1963).
173 A. Bowers, R. Villotti, J. A. Edwards, E. Denot, and O. Halpern, *J. Am. Chem. Soc.* **84**, 3204 (1962).
174 J. Tadanier, *J. Org. Chem.* **28**, 1744 (1963).
175 P. B. Sollman, *J. Org. Chem.* **28**, 3559 (1963).
176 K. Heusler and J. Kalvoda, *Helv. Chim. Acta* **46**, 2732 (1963).
177 K. Heusler, J. Kalvoda, C. Meystre, G. Anner, and A. Wettstein, *Helv. Chim. Acta* **45**, 2161 (1962).
178 J. Kalvoda, G. Anner, D. Arigoni, K. Heusler, H. Immer, O. Jeger, M. L. Mihailović, K. Schaffner, and A. Wettstein, *Helv. Chim. Acta* **44**, 186 (1961).
179 G. B. Spero, J. L. Thompson, W. P. Schneider, and F. Kagan, *J. Org. Chem.* **28**, 2225 (1963).
180 K. Heusler, J. Kalvoda, G. Anner, and A. Wettstein, *Helv. Chim. Acta* **46**, 352 (1963).
181 J. Kalvoda, K. Heusler, G. Anner, and A. Wettstein, *Helv. Chim. Acta* **46**, 618 (1963).
182 C. Meystre, J. Kalvoda, G. Anner, and A. Wettstein, *Helv. Chim. Acta* **46**, 2844 (1963).
183 P. F. Beal and J. E. Pike, *Chem. & Ind. (London)* p. 1505 (1960).
184 L. Velluz, G. Muller, R. Bardoneschi, and A. Poittevin, *Compt. Rend. Acad. Sci.* **250**, 725 (1960).

TABLE X—*continued*

Position of OH group	Reaction conditions (temp. in °C; c. =cyclo)	Type of reaction product, Yield in % of theory	Position of the C atom attacked	Remarks	Reference
3α	C_6H_6, 80	Ether	9α	—	165
	c. C_6H_{12}, DBP	Ether, 4	9α	—	166
	C_6H_6	Ether, 71	9α	Keto group on C-11	166
	C_6H_6	Ether, 18	9α	Double bond, C-11–C-12	166
4α	c. C_6H_{12}, I_2, $h\nu$	Ether	9α	—	167
4β	c. C_6H_{12}, I_2, $h\nu$	Half-acetal	$19+9\alpha$	Partial inversion at C-4	168, 180
6β	C_6H_6, 80	Ether, 68	19	$+7.5\%$ Ketone	169, 170
	C_6H_6, Py, $h\nu$, 18	Ether, 53	19	Cl in 5α	171
	c. C_6H_{12}, I_2, $h\nu$, 80	Ether, > 80	19	Cl in 5α	172
	C_6H_6	Ether	19	Br in 5α	173
	C_6H_6	Ether, 22	19	Cyclo 3–5	174, 175
	c. C_6H_{12}, I_2, $h\nu$	Ether	3β	CH_3 in 6α Inversion at C-10	176
	c. C_6H_{12}, I_2, $h\nu$	Ether, 60–85	19	—	177
	c. C_6H_{12}, I_2, $h\nu$	Ether + half-acetal	19	Keto group at C-11	177
11α	c. C_6H_{12}, 80	Ether, 50	1α	Double bond 5–6	178
	c. C_6H_{12}, 80	Ether, 85	1α	—	178, 179, 180
11β	c. C_6H_{12}, 80	Ether, 7.5	19	—	180
		Ether, 4	18	—	
	c. C_6H_{12}, I_2, $h\nu$	Ether + half-acetal	18, 19	—	181
	c. C_6H_{12}, I_2, $h\nu$	Enol ether	1	Keto group at C-3	182
20α	C_6H_6, 80	Ether, 80	18	—	184
20β	C_6H_6, 80	Ether, 31	18	—	9, 183
20	c. C_6H_{12}, I_2, $h\nu$ 80	Half-acetal, 70	18	Isolated as the lactone	163

Epimerizations are sometimes observed,[180] either at the carbon bearing the hydroxyl group or even at carbons further removed. Both can be explained by assuming a reversible fragmentation:

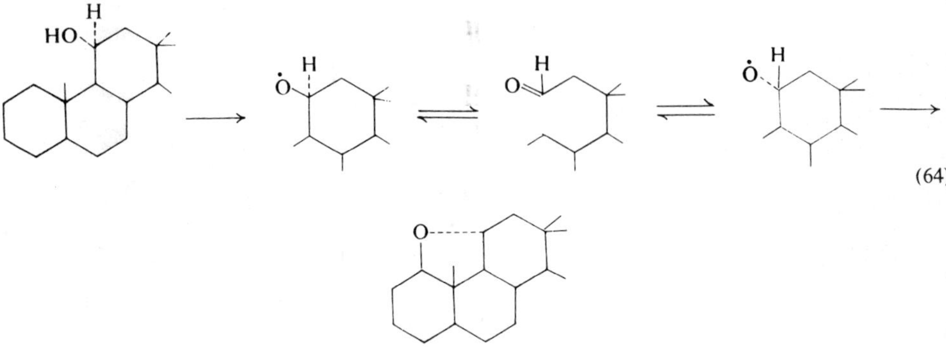

(64)

Another example[168, 180] is given in Eq. (65):

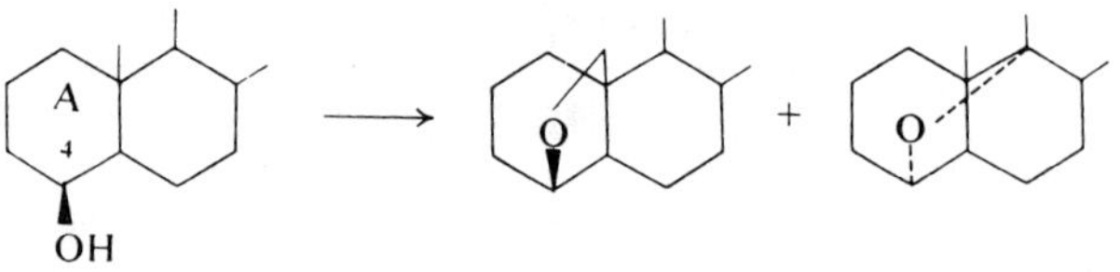

(65)

Most interesting is an epimerization of the methyl group at C-10[176]:

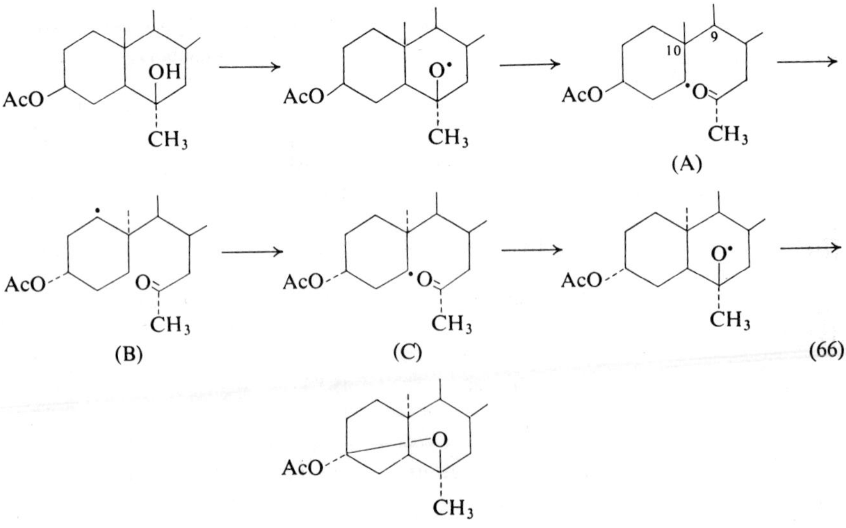

(66)

The conversion of (A) to (B) requires rotation around the 9–10 axis, and conversion of (B) to (C) a 1,5-hydride shift. This is followed by a recyclization of ring (B). The authors suspect a similar epimerization to be the first step in the glycol cleavage of diols that cannot form cyclic lead esters, such as *trans*-decalin-9,10-diols.

Obviously, oxidations of the type discussed are also possible with systems other than steroids. Such reactions were reported with diterpenes[185] and bridged bicyclic alcohols.[185a] Unexpected, however, was the formation of ethers from saturated aliphatic alcohols, discovered by Mićović *et al.*[186] Here the reaction is not facilitated by a rigid conformation. Nevertheless, almost 50% yields of 2-propyl- and 2-butyl-tetrahydrofuran were obtained from 1-heptanol and 1-octanol, respectively, when these alcohols were heated to reflux in benzene with lead tetraacetate for 1 hour. Small quantities of the corresponding tetrahydropyrans were also formed.

$$R-(CH_2)_5-OH \longrightarrow R-CH_2-\overset{\frown}{\underset{O}{\bigsqcup}} + R-\overset{\frown}{\underset{O}{\bigcirc}} \qquad (67)$$

Secondary alcohols react analogously, but more slowly. Stereoisomeric tetrahydrofurans are formed in 30–40% yields:

$$R-(CH_2)_3-\underset{OH}{\overset{|}{C}H}-R' \longrightarrow \overset{R}{\underset{R'}{\bigsqcup}}_O + \overset{R}{\underset{R'}{\bigsqcup}}_O \qquad (68)$$

In all cases, only small yields of aldehydes or ketones are produced, together with the acetates of the starting alcohols. The same is true for the oxidation of cyclooctanol.[186a]

Stoll *et al.*[187] refluxed the dibromide of citronellol with lead tetraacetate in heptane. A tetrahydrofuran derivative was formed in 15% yield, apparently without the expected attack of lead tetraacetate on the bromine atoms.

Hydroxy groups are not the only functions which can play the role of a "mooring group" for lead tetraacetate. Barton and Beckwith[188] showed that

[185] U. Scheidegger, K. Schaffner, and O. Jeger, *Helv. Chim. Acta* **45**, 400 (1962).

[185a] K. Kitahonoki and A. Matsuura, *Tetrahedron Letters* p. 2263 (1964).

[186] V. M. Mićović, R. J. Mamuzić, D. Jeremic, and M. L. Mihailović, *Tetrahedron Letters* p. 2091 (1963); V. M. Mićović, S. Stojčić, S. Mladenović, and M. Stefanović, *ibid.* p. 1559 (1965).

[186a] R. M. Moriarty and H. G. Walsh, *Tetrahedron Letters* p. 465 (1965).

[187] C. F. Seidel, D. Felix, A. Eschenmoser, K. Biemann, E. Palluy, and M. Stoll, *Helv. Chim. Acta* **44**, 598 (1961).

[188] D. H. R. Barton and A. J. L. Beckwith, *Proc. Chem. Soc.* p. 335 (1963).

the NH group of a carboxamide can also serve. Treatment of carboxamides with lead tetraacetate and iodine in chloroform under irradiation, followed by alkaline hydrolysis and reacidification, gave γ-lactones:

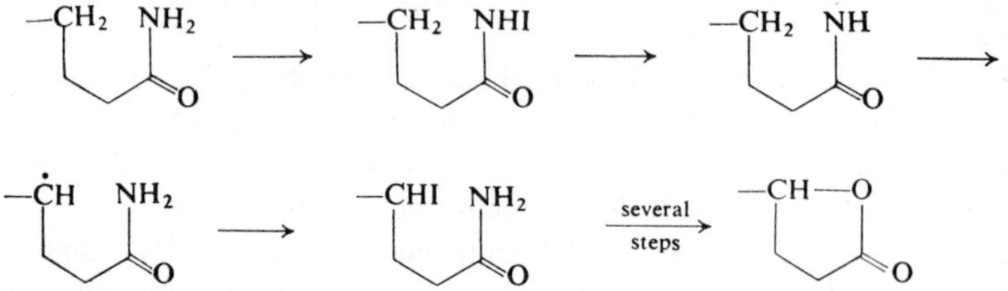

(69)

Stearyl amide gave γ-stearolactone in 60% yield, plus a little of the δ-lactone. o-Toluic amide produced phthalide in 25% yield, and a steroid bearing a CO—NH$_2$ group on C-20 gave 14% of the theoretical yield of a γ-lactone from attack on C-16.

C. AROMATIC C—H BONDS

Benzene is rather stable toward lead tetraacetate, but this is not true for condensed aromatic compounds such as anthracene, for benzene derivatives bearing electron-donating groups, and for heterocyclic compounds, such as furan. Aromatic nitro compounds can also be oxidized under certain conditions. In these oxidations, a variety of very different reactions occur, often simultaneously or one after the other. These are:
  (1) substitution of a hydrogen on the nucleus by
      (a) —OAc,
      (b) —CH$_3$ (or other alkyl or aryl groups),
      (c) —Pb(OAc)$_3$;
  (2) addition of two AcO— groups;
  (3) formation of dimers;
  (4) further oxidation of a group introduced according to (1,b);
  (5) formation of quinones;
  (6) replacement of —OCH$_3$ groups by —OAc groups.

Pure benzene can be heated to reflux with lead tetraacetate for several hours without change. In refluxing acetic acid solution, vigorous CO$_2$ evolution indicates the beginning of oxidation after an induction period of 4–5 hours. Fieser and co-workers[189] isolated benzyl acetate in 18% yield. It must come from toluene produced by methylation of the benzene. Under irradiation, the reaction proceeds at lower temperatures.[71] Nitro-, dinitro-, and trinitro-benzene react in the same manner but the methylation products are more stable toward lead tetraacetate and could be isolated or at least detected.

[189] L. F. Fieser, R. C. Clapp, and W. H. Daudt, *J. Am. Chem. Soc.* **64**, 2052 (1942).

Trinitrotoluene gave the highest yields; heating with 3 moles of lead tetra-acetate to 100° C in acetic acid gave a 32% yield of trinitroxylene. Recently, Davies[146] carefully studied the reaction with chlorobenzene and with ethyl-benzoate. Chlorobenzene gave chlorotoluenes and chlorobenzyl acetates in the isomer ratios of $o:m:p$ equal to 63:13:19 and 59:15:26, respectively. Ethylbenzoate gave only toluic acid esters in the isomer ratio of $o:m:p = 68:10:22$.

Ortho-para substitution is predominant in most examples, thus indicating a radical type substitution rather than electrophilic substitution, especially for the last example. The author doubts, however, that truly free methyl radicals are involved. Such free methyl radicals ought to react with the chlorotoluenes, giving chlorobenzyl radicals which should dimerize to dichlorodiphenyl-ethanes. It was shown that none of the latter were formed. The author therefore assumes that the methyl radicals remain loosely bound to the lead atom of the lead tetraacetate molecule from which they were generated. The preference for *ortho* substitution could be caused by a loose coordination of the oxidant with the chlorine atom or the carbethoxy group in the starting material. A new interpretation of these reactions was given by Harvey and Norman.[189a]

Methylations of pyridine, quinoline,[190] and 2-phenyl-oxazole-4-carboxylic ester[191] have been reported.

Fieser and Chang[8] discovered the methylation ability of lead tetraacetate when they oxidized naphthoquinone derivatives. The hydroquinone, X, and the dihydronaphthoquinone, XI, gave a 25% yield of dimethyl naphtho-quinone (XII) when treated at 100° C with 4 or 3 moles, respectively, of lead tetraacetate:

(70)

(X)   (XI)   (XII)

Methyl naphthoquinone, which one might insert between XI and XII in the reaction sequence, does not by itself react with lead tetraacetate at 100° C, but when the reaction mixture is overheated locally, or when malonic acid or methanol is added as a "promoter," a 49% yield of XII is obtained. Such promotion is not necessary with X or XI, where the dihydrobenzene rings act as promoters. They serve to start a radical chain, which then is sustained by

[189a] D. R. Harvey and R. O. C. Norman, *J. Chem. Soc.* p. 4860 (1964).
[190] Reilly Tar and Chem. Corp. (W. H. Rieger), U.S. Patent 2,502,174 (1947); *Chem. Zentr.* II, p. 2970 (1950).
[191] J. W. Cornforth and E. Cookson, *J. Chem. Soc.* p. 1085 (1952).

(71)

acetoxy radicals and by the methyl radicals produced from the former by loss of CO_2.

Other alkyl groups can be introduced into methylnaphthoquinone via the lead(IV) salts of higher carboxylic acids.[8] These salts can be made *in situ* from red lead oxide and the corresponding acids. Propionic, butyric, and phenylacetic acids give ethyl-, propyl-, and benzylmethylnaphthoquinone, respectively.

Lead tetrabenzoate leads to phenylation. Hey *et al.*[192] converted chlorobenzene to a mixture of isomeric chlorobiphenyls, nitrobenzene to a mixture of nitrobiphenyls, and pyridine to a mixture 2-, 3-, and 4-phenylpyridines in the ratio of 52:32.5:15.5. The assumption of a radical chain mechanism is supported by the fact that a similar isomer distribution is found in other radical substitutions on pyridine.

Naphthalene[189] reacts in a different manner. Heating it with lead tetraacetate in acetic acid produced 1-acetoxynaphthalene in 26% yield, but neither methylnaphthalenes nor products of their further conversion were detected.

Anthracene is acetoxylated in the *meso* positions. Fieser and Putnam[193] explained the products by assuming a sequence of additions and eliminations as shown in Eq. (71), on page 328. The yields are poor in some of the steps and resulting mixtures could not all be separated. It seems desirable, therefore, to repeat the experiments, employing modern methods of separation.

Water and methanol strongly accelerate the oxidation of anthracene, especially the addition reactions. Such an acceleration is also observed in the glycol cleavage. The interesting effect remains unexplained.

As discussed in Section III,A,2, lead tetraacetate oxidation of 9,10-dimethylanthracene gives 9,10-diacetoxymethylanthracene. Fieser assumes a primary addition of two AcO groups to the 9,10 positions followed by elimination and acyl migration (see page 330).

Fieser and Hershberg[141, 143, 194] studied the lead tetraacetate oxidation of benzanthracene, benzpyrene, and some of their derivatives. Substitution on the aromatic ring was again observed. However, in contrast to anthracene, the investigated compounds do not readily undergo addition reactions, for example with maleic anhydride. This makes it less likely that the first step of the reaction is the addition of two acetoxy groups. As shown in Table XI, benzpyrene in particular reacts rapidly even at room temperature. The rate of oxidation at 25° C in acetic acid was measured for 23 derivatives of polycyclic hydrocarbons.[195] In most cases the reaction products were not determined.

[192] D. H. Hey, C. J. M. Stirling, and G. H. Williams, *J. Chem. Soc.* p. 2747 (1954); p. 3963 (1955).
[193] L. F. Fieser and S. T. Putnam, *J. Am. Chem. Soc.* **69**, 1038 (1947).
[194] L. F. Fieser and E. B. Hershberg, *J. Am. Chem. Soc.* **61**, 1565 (1939).
[195] L. F. Fieser and S. T. Putnam, *J. Am. Chem. Soc.* **69**, 1041 (1947).

An expected correlation of the oxidation rate with the cancerogenic activity
was not found.

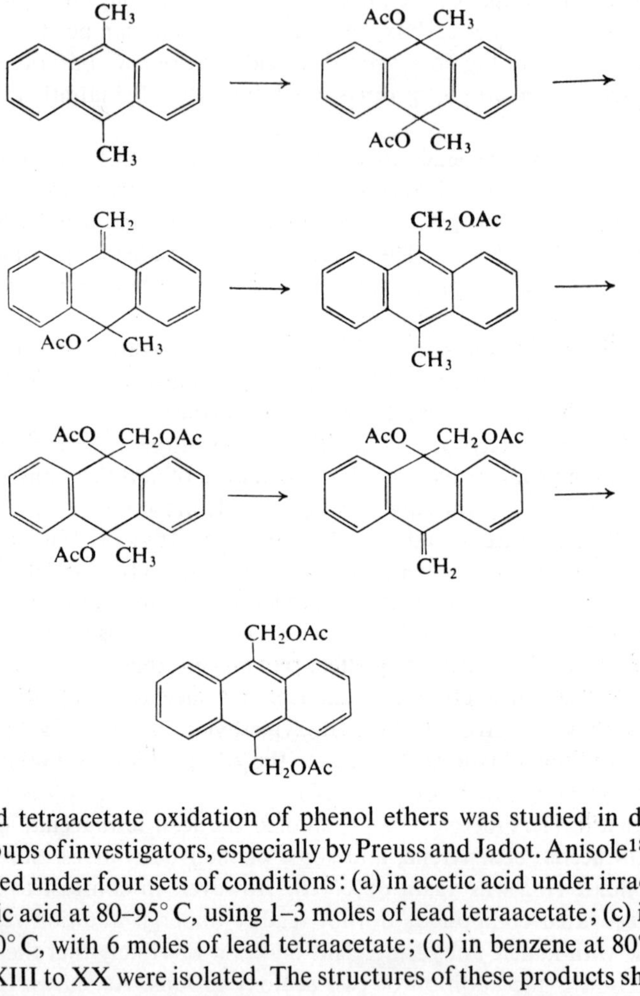

(72)

The lead tetraacetate oxidation of phenol ethers was studied in detail by
several groups of investigators, especially by Preuss and Jadot. Anisole[18, 196, 197]
was oxidized under four sets of conditions: (a) in acetic acid under irradiation;
(b) in acetic acid at 80–95° C, using 1–3 moles of lead tetraacetate; (c) in acetic
acid at 120° C, with 6 moles of lead tetraacetate; (d) in benzene at 80° C. The
products XIII to XX were isolated. The structures of these products show that
several reactions occur: substitution by AcO— in *ortho* and in *para* positions,
methylation in *para* position, oxidation of the *p*-methyl group, and dimerization to diphenyl derivatives. Attack on the OCH_3 group produces formaldehyde, which was identified in some cases and which might be the source of the
CO— group in compound XX. Under reaction conditions (c), XVI is formed
in 87% yield.

[196] G. W. K. Cavill and D. H. Solomon, *J. Chem. Soc.* p. 1404 (1955).
[197] J. Jadot and M. Neuray, *Bull. Soc. Roy. Sci. Liege* **29**, 138 (1960).

TABLE XI

<small>Oxidation of Some Aromatic Compounds by Lead Tetraacetate in Acetic Acid</small>

Starting material	Temp. (°C)	Reaction time (minutes)	Reaction product	Yield (% of theoretical)	Reference
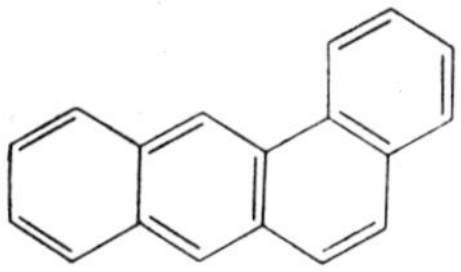	100		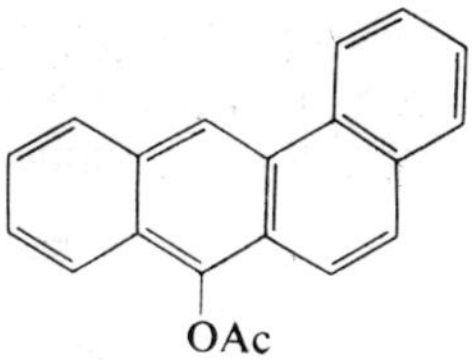	52	141
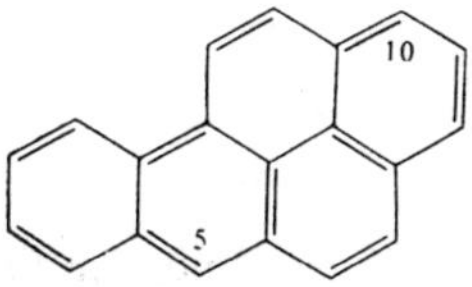	20	30	5-Acetoxybenzpyrene	94	143
5-Acetylaminobenz-pyrene	20	60	5-Acetylamino-10-acetoxybenzpyrene		194
10-Acetylaminobenz-pyrene	20	2	5-Acetoxy-10-acetyl-aminobenzpyrene		194

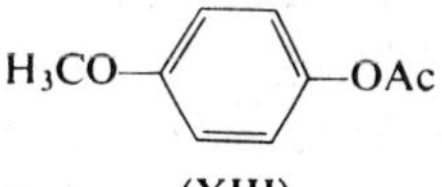

H_3CO—⟨⟩—OAc (a, b, c, d); H_3CO—⟨AcO⟩ (a);

(XIII)   (XIV)

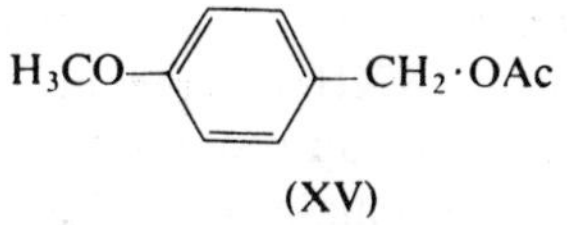

H_3CO—⟨⟩—$CH_2 \cdot OAc$ (b); H_3CO—⟨⟩—$CH(OAc)_2$ (b, c);

(XV)   (XVI)

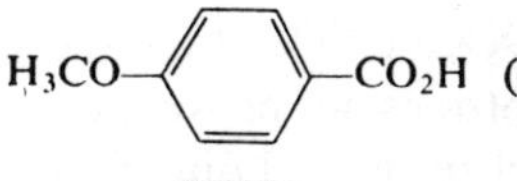

H_3CO—⟨⟩—CO_2H (c); H_3CO—⟨⟩—⟨⟩ (d);

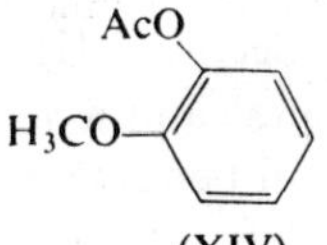

(XVII)   (XVIII)

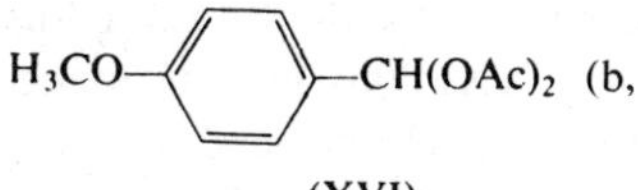

H_3CO—⟨⟩—⟨⟩—OCH_3 (b); H_3CO—⟨⟩—CO—⟨⟩—OCH_3 (b)

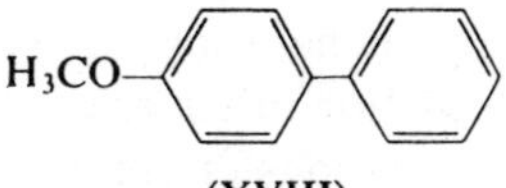

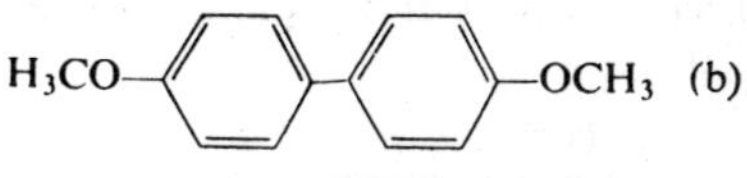

(XIX)   (XX)

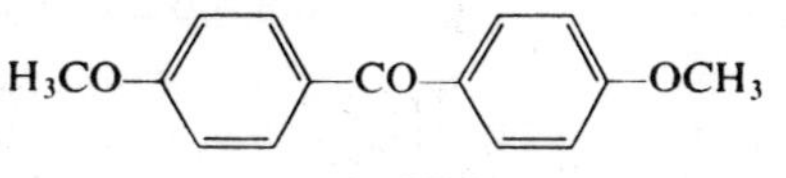

The dimethyl ethers of catechol,[161] resorcinol,[23, 197, 198] and hydroquinone[197, 199] as well as α- and β-methoxynaphthalene[42] react in the same manner as does anisole. To a small extent, CH_3O— groups are replaced by OAc groups. Presumably this is not a direct substitution, but involves first the oxidation of Ar—OCH_3 to ArO—CH_2OAc. The latter decomposes to Ar—OAc and formaldehyde under the reaction conditions (see also Section III,A,3).

2,5-Dimethoxyquinone is one of the by-products in the oxidation of hydroquinone dimethyl ether. 2,5-Diacetoxyhydroquinone methyl ether seems to be the intermediate because its treatment with lead tetraacetate at 90° C gives a 72 % yield of the 2,5-dimethoxyquinone:

(73)

Phloroglucinol trimethyl ether,[137] when treated with lead tetraacetate in benzene, yields 17 % of the theoretical yield of 2,6-dimethoxyquinone, presumably by a similar route.

Of the greatest interest is the isolation of an organic $Pb(OAc)_3$— compound by Preuss and Janshen.[23] Oxidation of resorcinol dimethyl ether gave an 18–19 % yield of the orange-yellow compound XXII, a member of a class of compounds otherwise accessible only by reacting organomercury compounds with lead tetraacetate (see Section VII). Only thiophene could be "plumbated" in a similar manner by Panov and Kotscheschkov,[200] who treated it with lead tetraisobutyrate at 20° C in benzene and obtained $(C_4H_3S)_2Pb[OCOCH(CH_3)_2]_2$. The reactions seem to be electrophilic substitutions [see Eq. (74), page 333]. Such lead organic compounds might or might not be intermediates in lead tetraacetate oxidations. Heating XXII in acetic acid gives some of the products obtained from XXI and lead tetraacetate. However, XXII is probably in equilibrium with XXI and lead tetraacetate, since anisyl lead triacetate gives a 70 % yield of anisole when heated with acetic acid. It remains for a careful kinetic study to decide whether the reaction products such as XXIII are formed from XXII or by an independent reaction of XXI with lead tetraacetate.

The observed formation of dimeric products does not prove the presence of free radicals. The oxidations of anisole and of resorcinol dimethyl ether give p,p'-dimethoxybiphenyl in 30 % yield and tetramethoxybiphenyl in 12 % yield, respectively. But the first compound is also obtained from anisole and lead

[198] F. R. Preuss and J. Janshen, *Arch. Pharm.* **293**, 933 (1960).
[199] F. R. Preuss and R. Menzel, *Arch. Pharm.* **291**, 350, 377 (1958).
[200] E. M. Panov and K. A. Kocheshkov, *Dokl. Akad. Nauk SSSR* **123**, 295 (1958).

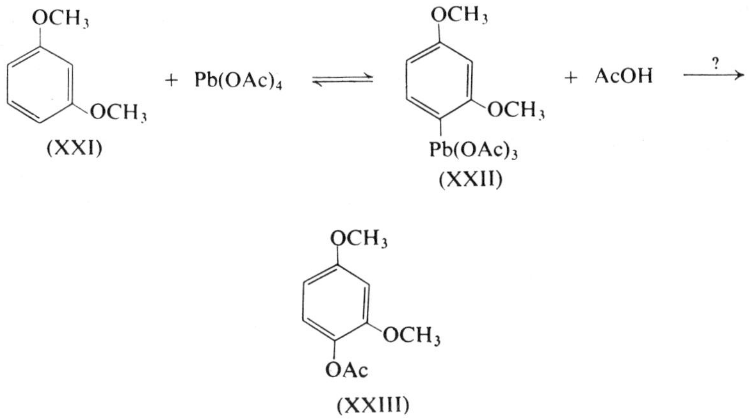

$$(74)$$

(XXIII)

tetraacetate in dichloromethane at $-40°$ C, if one adds some borontrifluoride etherate and carefully works up the blue compound which is formed first.[159] The yield is modest, but the reaction conditions indicate an electrophilic substitution mechanism. Dimethylaniline and mesitylene also give dimers under these conditions. The reaction ought to be studied further.

Of the heteroaromatic compounds, furan has been investigated more closely. Elming and Clausson-Kaas[201] oxidized it at $60°$ C and obtained, in 69% yield, a mixture of the two stereoisomeric 2,5-diacetoxy-2,5-dihydro-furans, in the ratio 2:1. The lead(IV) salts of propionic, butyric, and benzoic acids give analogous results. α-Disubstituted furans are reported not to give 2,5-addition products: α-acetoxyfuran at $20–45°$ C yields 88% of 5-acetoxy-furanone-2.[202] β-Isopropylfuran, however, when oxidized in acetic acid at $55–60°$ C, gives the corresponding 2,5-diacetoxy-compound in 54% yield.[203]

2,5-Diarylfurans have been studied carefully by Dien and Lutz.[204] A, B, and C are the main reactions:

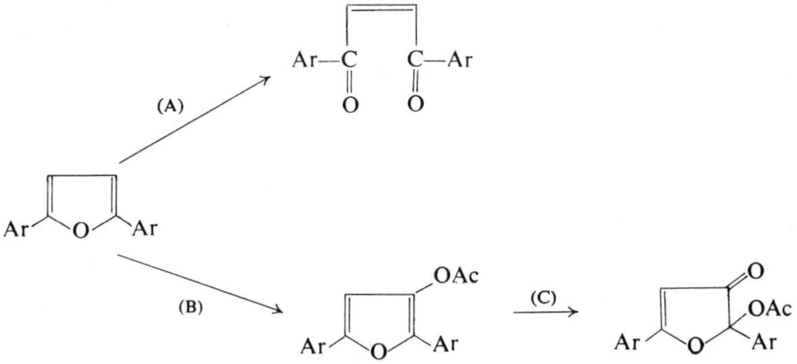

$$(75)$$

[201] N. Elming and N. Clausson-Kaas, *Acta Chem. Scand.* **6**, 535 (1952).
[202] N. Elming and N. Clausson-Kaas, *Acta. Chem. Scand.* **6**, 565 (1952).
[203] N. Elming, *Acta Chem. Scand.* **6**, 578 (1952).
[204] C. K. Dien and R. E. Lutz, *J. Org. Chem.* **22**, 1355 (1957).

Reaction A opens the furan ring to a *cis*-diaroylethylene, and proceeds best in chloroform solution. Reaction B is, in most cases, observed in acetic acid solution and results in acetoxylation of one of the two β-positions. Subsequent formation of an α-acetoxyfuranone (reaction C) may occur. All these reactions can be interpreted as involving attack on the α- or β-position of the furan ring by an AcO$^+$— cation or, more likely, attack by the $^+$Pb(OAc)$_3$ cation followed by loss of Pb(OAc)$_2$. Equations (76)–(78) show the probable reaction paths:

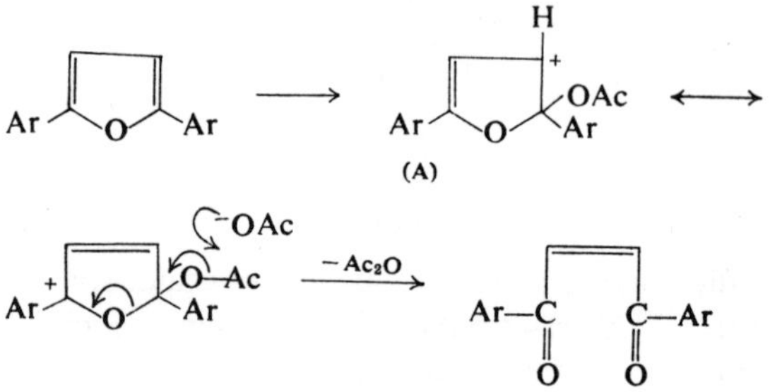

$$(76)$$

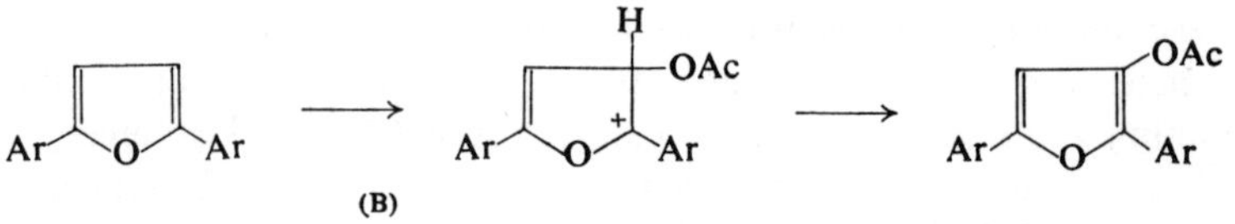

$$(77)$$

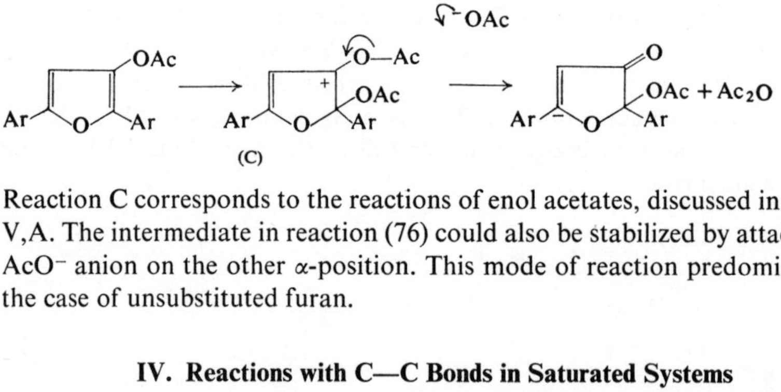

$$(78)$$

Reaction C corresponds to the reactions of enol acetates, discussed in Section V,A. The intermediate in reaction (76) could also be stabilized by attack of an AcO$^-$ anion on the other α-position. This mode of reaction predominates in the case of unsubstituted furan.

IV. Reactions with C—C Bonds in Saturated Systems

In the absence of activating atoms, C—C bonds in saturated systems react with lead tetraacetate only when they are strained heavily. Bicyclo[2.1.0]-pentane was the first known example.[205] The hydrocarbon reacts exothermically at temperatures as low as 29° C in acetic acid. A mixture of 43% 3-acetoxycyclopentene and 33% *trans*-1,3-diacetoxycyclopentane is produced:

[205] R. Criegee and A. Rimmelin, *Ber.* **90**, 414 (1957); A. Ludwig, Dissertation, Technical University of Karlsruhe, Germany, 1958.

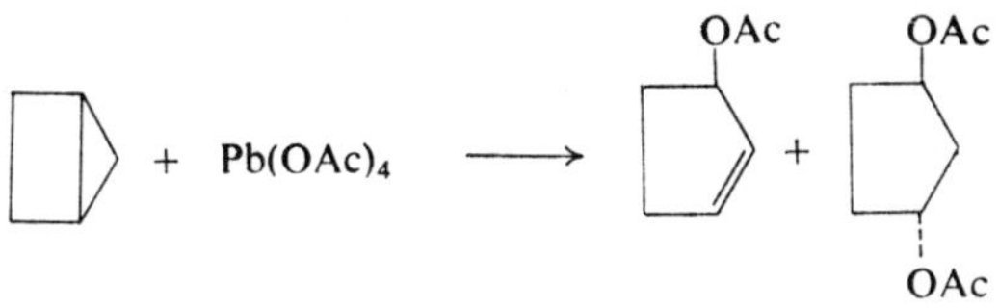

$$
\text{[structure]} + \text{Pb(OAc)}_4 \longrightarrow \text{[structure]} + \text{[structure]} \tag{79}
$$

Oulette and Shaw[205a] have recently found that monocyclic cyclopropanes are attacked by lead tetraacetate at 75° C, especially aryl-substituted ones. The products are 1,3-dioldiacetates together with unsaturated monoacetates. The oxidation of bicyclo[3.1.0]hexane and bicyclo[4.1.0]heptane is described by Moon.[205b]

V. Reactions with Olefins and Acetylenes

Unsaturated compounds react with lead tetraacetate in a confusing variety of ways. The addition of two acetoxy groups to the double bond, and the substitution of allylic hydrogens by OAc groups were discovered first; many other reaction paths were found later. Seemingly small changes in the structure of the olefin or in the reaction conditions can utterly change the type of reaction. Parallel and consecutive reactions occur in many cases. This section will discuss typical examples of these reactions, but will not be exhaustive.

A. ADDITION OF TWO ACETOXY GROUPS TO A DOUBLE BOND

The reaction

$$
{>}C{=}C{<} + \text{Pb(OAc)}_4 \longrightarrow {>}\underset{\text{OAc}}{C}{-}\underset{\text{OAc}}{C}{<} + \text{Pb(OAc)}_2 \tag{80}
$$

occurs with simple aliphatic or cyclic olefins, but as a side reaction only. 20% is a typical yield.[13] It can be higher where no allylic hydrogens are present.[112] Electron-withdrawing groups at the double bond make the addition more difficult; stilbene gives none and mesityl oxide only a little of the corresponding diacetoxy derivative. Electron donors have the opposite effect. Enols (see Section III,A,1) and enol ethers[14, 16, 206–208] react under mild conditions. The latter give derivatives of 2-hydroxyaldehydes or -ketones:

$$
\text{H}_2\text{C}{=}\text{CH}{-}\text{OR} + \text{Pb(OAc)}_4 \longrightarrow \text{AcO}{-}\text{CH}_2{-}\text{CH}{<}^{\text{OR}}_{\text{OAc}} \tag{81}
$$

[205a] R. J. Ouelette and D. L. Shaw, *J. Am. Chem. Soc.* **86**, 1651 (1964).
[205b] S. Moon, *J. Org. Chem.* **29**, 3456 (1964).
[206] M. Lavas, *Ann. Chim. (Paris)* [12] **7**, 697 (1952).
[207] R. Müller and H. Plieninger, *Ber.* **92**, 3009 (1959).
[208] H. O. L. Fischer, E. Baer, and L. Feldmann, *Ber.* **63**, 1732 (1930).

The cyclic enol ether dioxene[14] reacts analogously. The reactions are carried out at room temperature in acetic acid or in benzene. Yields range from 50–90%. When methanol is used as a solvent, acetals are produced instead of acylals.[207]

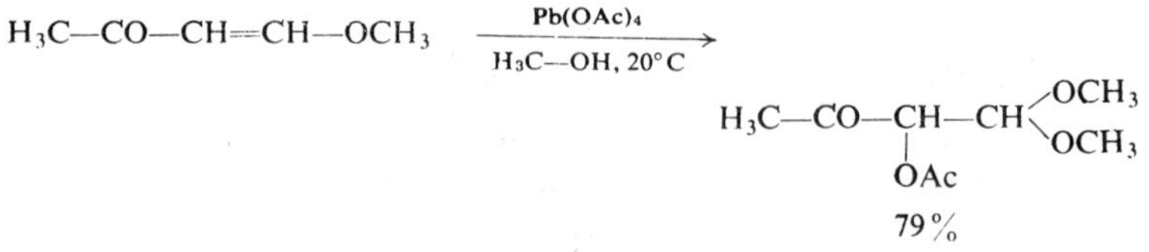

$$H_3C—CO—CH{=}CH—OCH_3 \xrightarrow[\text{H}_3\text{C—OH, 20°C}]{\text{Pb(OAc)}_4}$$

$$H_3C—CO—\underset{\underset{\text{OAc}}{|}}{CH}—CH\overset{OCH_3}{\underset{OCH_3}{<}} \qquad (82)$$

$$79\%$$

Enol esters usually do not give the expected triacetoxy compounds but acetoxy ketones and acetic anhydride[59, 209]:

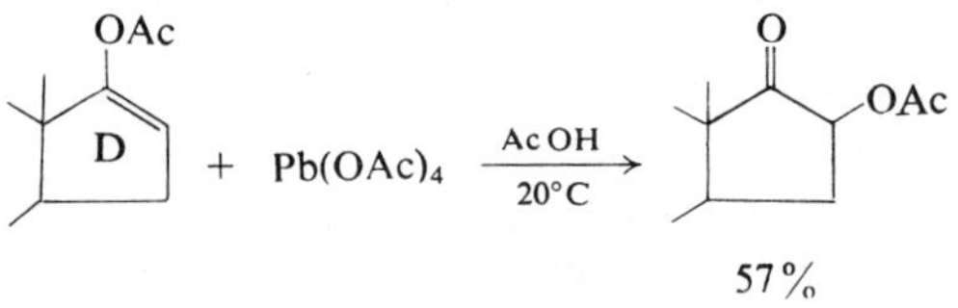

$$\qquad (83)$$

$$57\%$$

The activating effect of an electron-donating group can be transmitted through a benzene ring. Anethole and isoeugenole methyl ether give the diacetoxy derivatives at 20–30° C and in fair yields.[6, 13] p-Methoxystyrene differs from anethole only by the lack of the methyl group on the double bond but, surprisingly, reacts in an entirely different manner (see Section V,C).

Most cyclic dienes can be oxidized at room temperature.[13] Addition of two AcO groups occurs in the 1,2- as well as in the 1,4-position. These reactions are discussed in more detail in Section V,D.

The addition to double bonds seems not to be stereoselective. In most of the known examples, both possible isomers were found. More or less pure trans addition was observed in the lead tetraacetate oxidation of indene, 1,2-dihydronaphthalene, dioxene, and in the lead tetrabenzoate oxidation of cyclopentadiene.[13] Ergosterol gave pure cis addition.[210] Conclusions as to the reaction mechanism cannot be drawn, however, since there are no investigations using modern analytical methods. A study of the dependence of stereoselectivity on the solvent should be carried out, since the water content of the acetic acid used can play a decisive role, as is discussed in Section V,D.

The reaction of mercuric acetate with olefins involves electrophilic attack by the AcOHg+ cation. One might suspect that lead tetraacetate analogously adds a (AcO)3Pb+ cation to the double bond, perhaps via a π-complex intermediate. The lead organic cation could be stabilized by the addition of an AcO⁻ anion

[209] W. S. Johnson, B. Gastambide, and R. Pappo, J. Am. Chem. Soc. 79, 1991 (1957).
[210] A. Windaus and U. Riemann, Z. Physiol. Chem. 274, 206 (1942).

to give an organolead adduct as shown in Eq. (84). Such an adduct would be less long-lived than the corresponding mercury analog since the electron affinity of Pb is higher than that of Hg. The $(AcO)_3Pb^-$ group may be displaced by an AcO^- anion, carrying with it the electron pair that had been associated with the double bond (Eq. 85). Another possibility is an intramolecular transfer of AcO^- by a cyclic mechanism (Eq. 86):

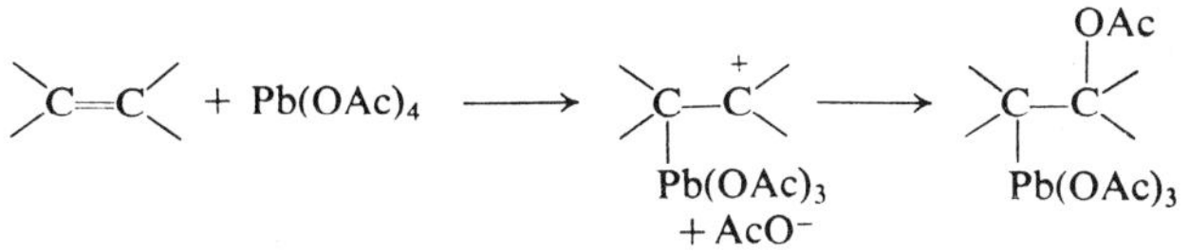

$$\text{(84)}$$

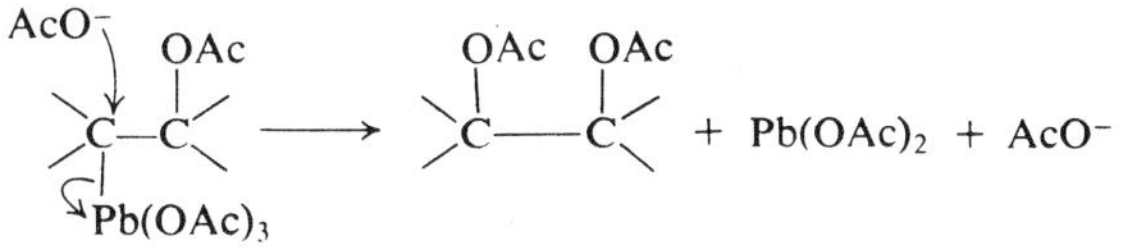

$$\text{(85)}$$

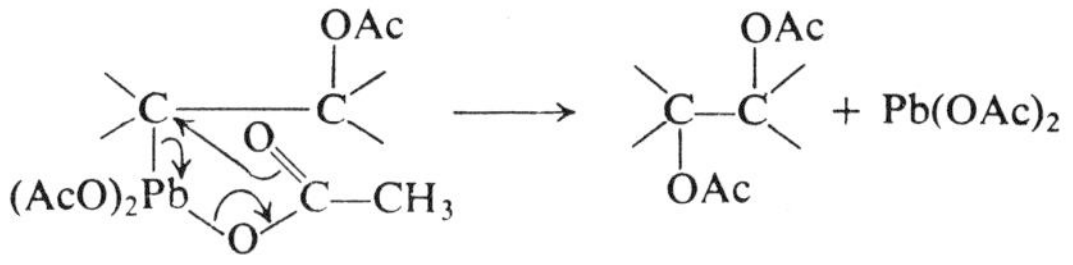

$$\text{(86)}$$

The observations discussed in Sections V,C and V,D are in agreement with such a mechanism,[59] as are some of those described in Section V,B (also see Section VII).

B. SUBSTITUTION IN ALLYLIC POSITIONS

Hydrogen atoms in allyl positions can be replaced by OAc^- groups to give allyl acetates. Formally, the C=C double bonds act as activating groups, like keto groups or aromatic rings.

Cyclohexene[13] is the earliest and most typical example. At 80°C a 35% yield of 3-cyclohexenyl acetate was obtained in acetic acid solution, and 40–50% in benzene.[211]

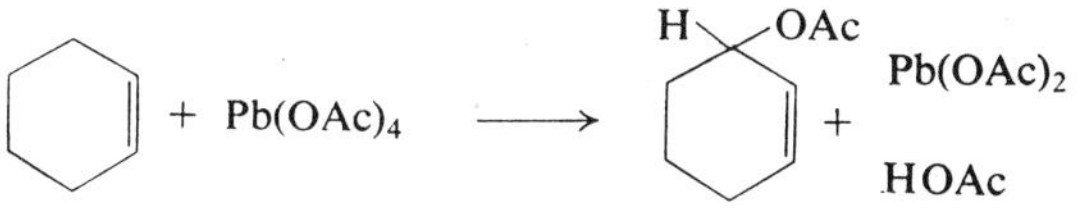

$$\text{(87)}$$

In principle, the allylic substitution might involve the rearrangement of the double bond. As yet, too few data are available to conclude whether such a

[211] C. Weis, Dissertation, Technical University of Karlsruhe, Germany, 1953.

rearrangement occurs always or only sometimes. Witham[212] showed for the case of α-pinene that the workup procedure determines the nature of the product isolated. The primary product, XXVI, is formed with double bond migration, but easily rearranges to *trans*-verbenol acetate (XXIX), which has the double bond in the original position and was isolated in 74% yield.[211] Witham's mechanism explains this and the stereoselectivity of the reaction.

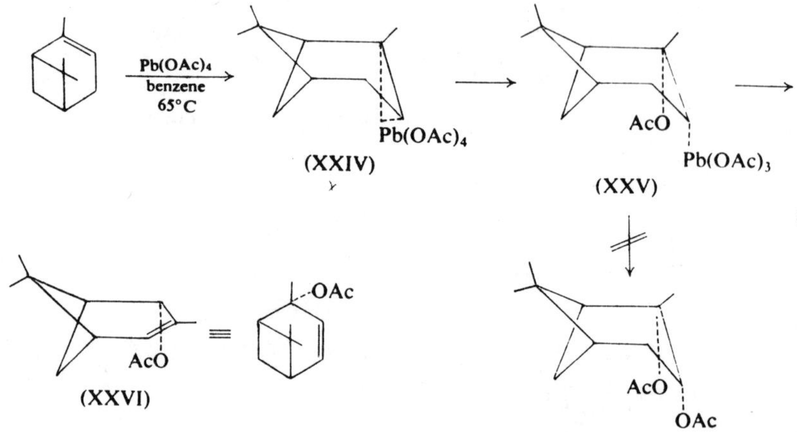

(XXIV) (XXV) (XXVI) (XXVII) (88)

The flagpole interaction of the 4-acetoxy group with the CH_2 group in the bridge in XXV explains the formation of XXVI rather than the otherwise expected diacetoxy compound XXVII. To a small extent, opening of the 4-membered ring in the π-complex XXIV gives sorbrerole diacetate (XXVIII):

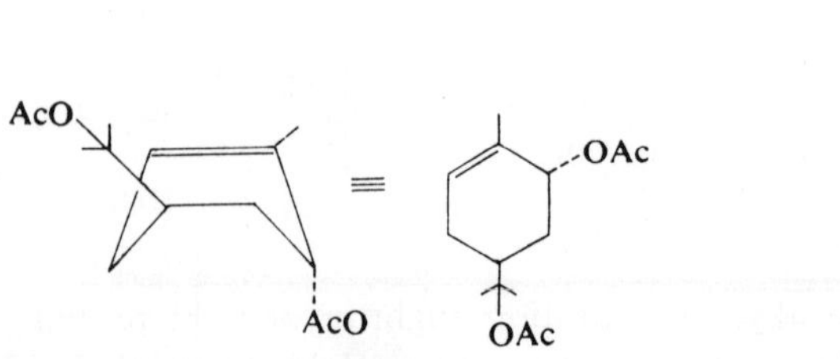

(XXIV) (89)

(XXVIII)

[212] G. H. Witham, *J. Chem. Soc.* p. 2232 (1961).

XXVI rearranges to *trans*-verbenol acetate (**XXIX**) when distilled in the presence of acetic acid and some lead diacetate. An ion pair intermediate is assumed:

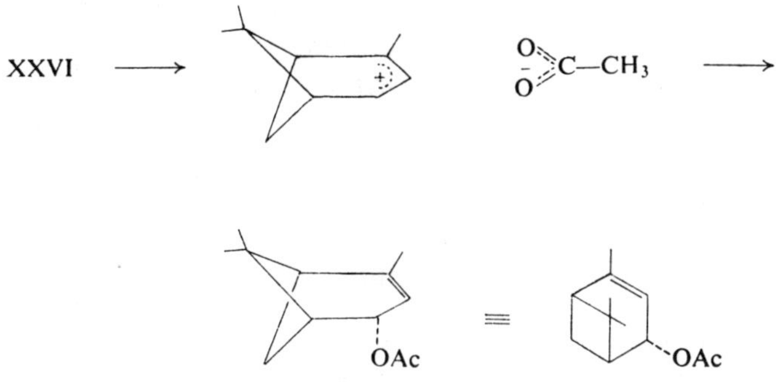

$$\text{(90)}$$

(XXIX)

TABLE XII

ALLYL SUBSTITUTION IN LEAD TETRAACETATE OXIDATIONS OF OLEFINS

Olefin	Solvent	Temp. (°C)	Double bond migration Yes	No	Yield (% of theoretical)	Reference
Hexene-2	AcOH	70	—	+	7	135
3-Methylpentene-(2)	AcOH	70	—	+	6	135
cis-Octene-(4)	AcOH	80	—	+	27	213
Cyclopentene	AcOH	50	—	—	20	214
Cyclohexene	AcOH	80	—	—	27	13
	C_6H_6	80	—	—	44	211
	AcOH/ AcONa	80	—	—	59	211
	Ac_2O	90–95	—	—	55	211
$\varDelta^1$-Menthene	C_6H_6	—	—	+	—	215, 215a
$\varDelta^2$-Menthene	AcOH	85–90	—	+	—	216
α-Pinene	C_6H_6	—	+	—	—	59, 212, 217
β-Pinene	AcOH	45	+	—	—	218
α-Cyclogeraniolene	AcOH	65–70	+	—	—	219
	C_6H_6	65	—	+	—	219
trans-$\varDelta^2$-Octalin	AcOH	70	—	+	22	220
9-Methyl-$\varDelta^2$+$\varDelta^3$-*cis*-octalin	AcOH	70	+	+	46	220
Indene	AcOH	70	—	—	14	13
$\varDelta^2$-Dihydropyrane	C_6H_6	30	+	+	31	221
Pulegone	C_6H_6	80	+	—	—	221a

Table XII summarizes the allyl substitutions reported. Not all of the data are equally reliable.[13, 59, 135, 211–221a]

Just as in other lead tetraacetate oxidations, the reactions are faster in acetic acid than in benzene. In benzene, however, the yields of allyl-substituted products are higher. The yields of cyclohexenyl acetate from cyclohexene are especially high in acetic anhydride and in acetic acid in the presence of sodium acetate.[211] It has been reported[219] that the allyl substitution of cyclogeraniol proceeds with migration of the double bond in acetic acid, but without migration in benzene.

C. OXIDATIONS WITH REARRANGEMENT OF THE CARBON SKELETON

When olefins are oxidized with lead tetraacetate, rearrangements occur frequently. Their nature indicates the intermediacy of carbonium ions.

All the reactions can be explained by assuming as the first step the addition of AcO^- and $^+Pb(OAc)_3$ to the double bond, as postulated in Sections V,A and V,B. Loss of an $(AcO)_3Pb^-$ anion gives a carbonium ion. Where the rate of rearrangement is small, an AcO^- anion is added or a proton is lost. Where rearrangement is fast, Wagner-Meerwein rearrangement occurs before an AcO^- is added. Equation (91) (page 341) demonstrates the three possibilities, using cyclohexene as an example.

With cyclohexene, all three reactions actually do occur. XXXII, the diacetate of cyclopentylformaldehyde, had been overlooked in earlier investigations, but is present to 44% in the diacetate fraction, which also contains the diacetate XXXI.[222]

The diacetate of tetrahydrofurfural constitutes 23% of the total oxidation products of 2,3-dihydropyran.[221]

The results reported on the oxidation of camphene differ to some extent

[213] E. Hahl, Diplomarbeit, Technical University of Karlsruhe, Germany, 1956.

[214] E. Dane and K. Eder, *Ann.* **539**, 207 (1939).

[215] T. Aratani, *J. Chem. Soc. Japan Pure Chem. Sect.* **78**, 1534 (1957).

[215a] K. B. Wiberg and S. D. Nielsen, *J. Org. Chem.* **29**, 3353 (1964).

[216] W. Hückel and K. Kümmerle, *J. Prakt. Chem.* [2] **160**, 74 (1942).

[217] Y. Matsubara, *Nippon Kaguku Zasshi* **78**, 907, 909 (1957); *Chem. Zentr.* pp. 13244, 13245 (1958).

[218] Y. Matsubara, *Nippon Kaguku Zasshi* **75**, 809, 894 (1954); *Chem. Zentr.* pp. 3927 S, 4640 S (1950–1954); T. Sato, *Nippon Kaguku Zasshi* **86**, 252 (1965); L. E. Grunewald and D. C. Johnson, *J. Org. Chem.* **30**, 1673 (1965).

[219] J. Alkonyi, *Ber.* **96**, 1873 (1963).

[220] V. C. E. Burnop and R. P. Linstead, *J. Chem. Soc.* p. 720 (1940).

[221] C. D. Hurd and O. E. Edwards, *J. Chem. Org.* **19**, 1319 (1954).

[221a] L. H. Zalkow and J. W, Ellis, *J. Org. Chem.* **29**, 2626 (1964).

[222] H. J. Kabbe, *Ann.* **656**, 204 (1962).

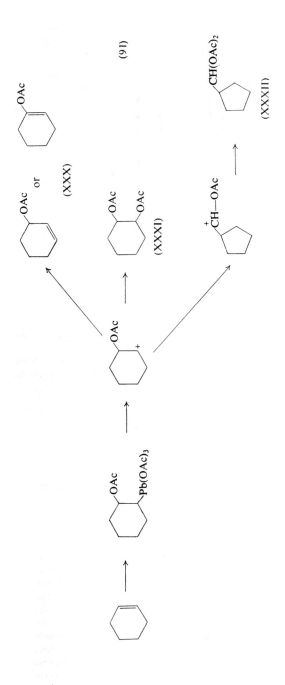

(91)

from each other.[223-226] This could be caused by different reaction conditions and workup procedures. In all cases, the main product is the enol acetate of homocamphenilone, XXXIII, formed in 61–85% yield. Ring expansion is also

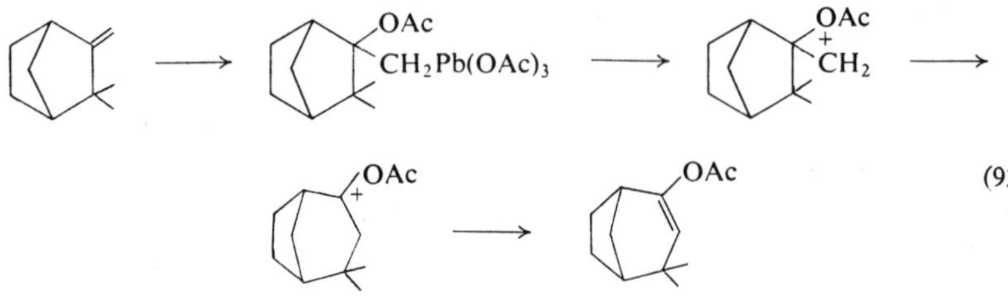

$$(92)$$

(XXXIII)

observed with longifolene[227] which gives a 50% yield of an enol acetate when oxidized at 70°C in acetic acid. It is remarkable that rapid further oxidation of the enol acetate is not observed (compare Section V,A).

The lead tetraacetate oxidation of norbornene, norbornadiene, and dicyclopentadiene has been studied carefully by Alder et al.[228] All their observations agree with the assumption of initial electrophilic attack of a $^+Pb(OAc)_3$ cation on the strained double bond. Equations (93)–(95) summarized the more important reaction products. The importance of the nature of the solvent is remarkable.

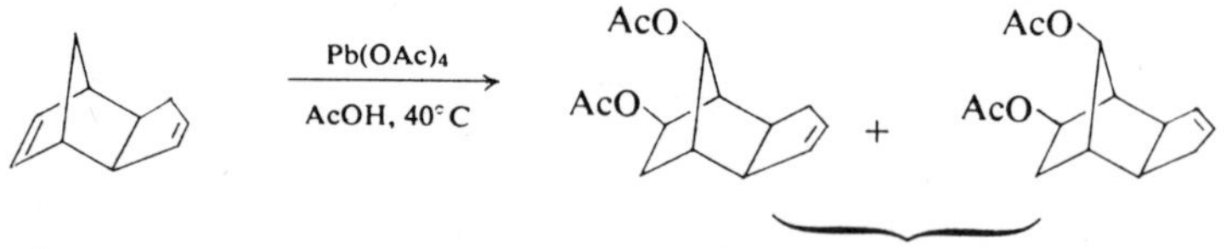

$$(93)$$

85%

[223] W. Hückel and K. Hartmann, Ber. **70**, 959 (1937).

[224] W. Hückel and H. G. Kirschner, Ber. **80**, 41 (1947).

[225] Y. Matsubara, Nippon Kaguku Zasshi **76**, 1088 (1955); **78**, 726, 730 (1957); Chem. Zentr. p. 5493 (1960); p. 4494 (1958).

[226] S. Wakabayashi, J. Chem. Soc. Japan **63**, 627 (1960); Chem. Abstr. **56**, 7165d (1962).

[227] P. Naffa and G. Ourisson, Bull. Soc. Chim. France p. 1115 (1954).

[228] K. Alder, H. F. Flock, and H. Wirtz, Ber. **91**, 609 (1958).

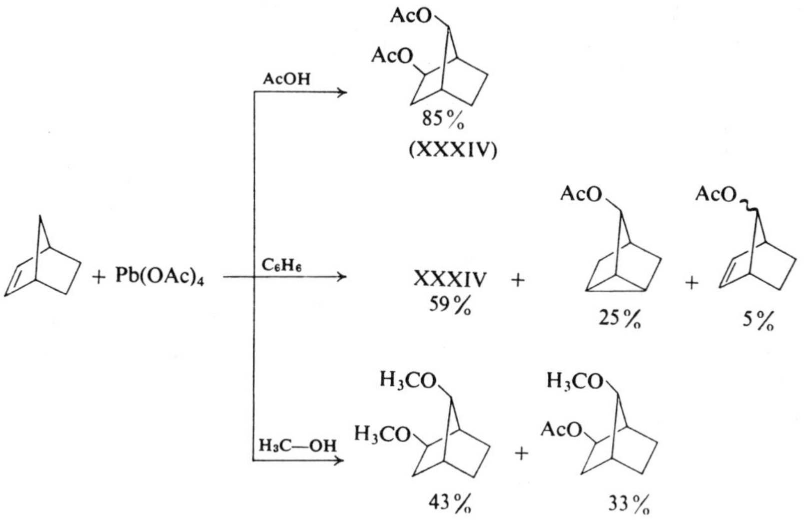

$$\text{(XXXIV)} \quad 85\%$$

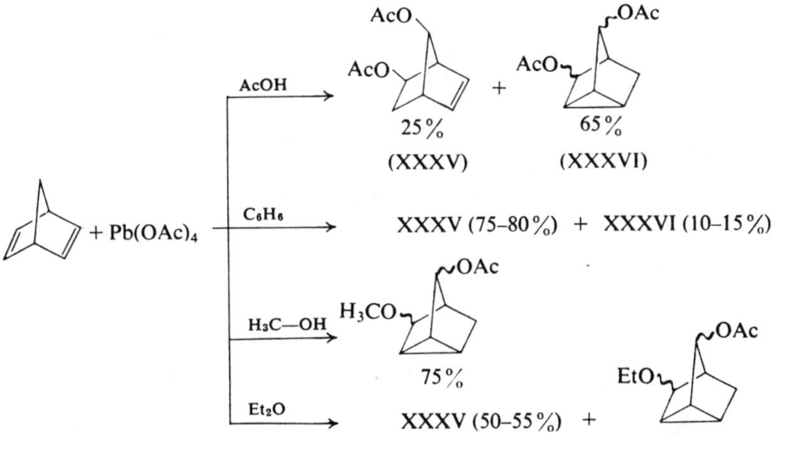

$$\text{XXXIV} + \quad + \quad \quad (94)$$
$$59\% \quad\quad 25\% \quad\quad 5\%$$

$$43\% \quad\quad 33\%$$

$$25\% \quad\quad 65\%$$
$$\text{(XXXV)} \quad\quad \text{(XXXVI)}$$

$$\text{XXXV (75–80\%)} + \text{XXXVI (10–15\%)} \quad (95)$$

$$75\%$$

$$\text{XXXV (50–55\%)} +$$

Under favorable steric conditions, a double bond can add an AcO^- group and an oxy function contained in the molecule[228a]:

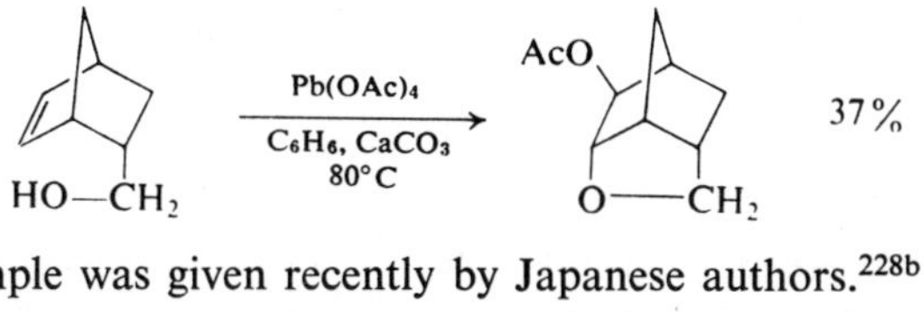

$$37\% \quad (95a)$$

Another example was given recently by Japanese authors.[228b]

[228a] R. M. Moriarty and K. Kapadia, *Tetrahedron Letters* p. 1165 (1964).
[228b] T. Okuda and T. Yoshida, *Chem. Ind.* (*London*) p. 37 (1965).

Cyclooctatetraene gives the "normal" bicyclic diacetate. The yield is 32% in benzene solution and 38% in acetic acid. In the presence of borontrifluoride etherate, ring contraction occurs[229]:

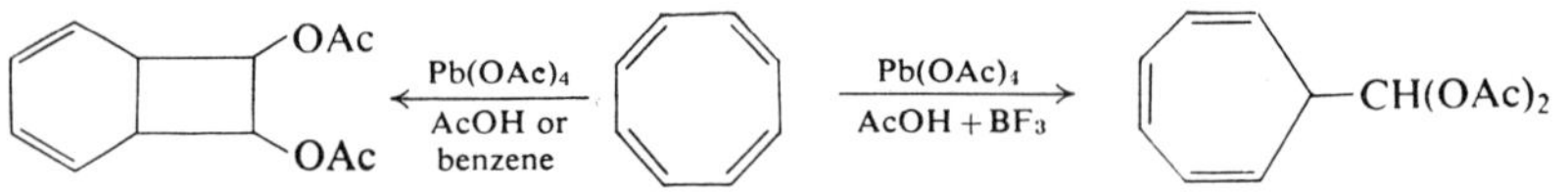

$$
\underset{\substack{\text{AcOH or}\\ \text{benzene}}}{\overset{\text{Pb(OAc)}_4}{\longleftarrow}} \qquad \underset{\substack{\text{AcOH + BF}_3}}{\overset{\text{Pb(OAc)}_4}{\longrightarrow}} \qquad -\text{CH(OAc)}_2 \quad (96)
$$

Smooth rearrangement is observed with many styrene derivatives (for styrene itself, see Section V,E). *p*-Methoxystyrene[14] reacts at a temperature as low as 20° C to give a 90% yield of the diacetate of *p*-methoxyphenylacetaldehyde:

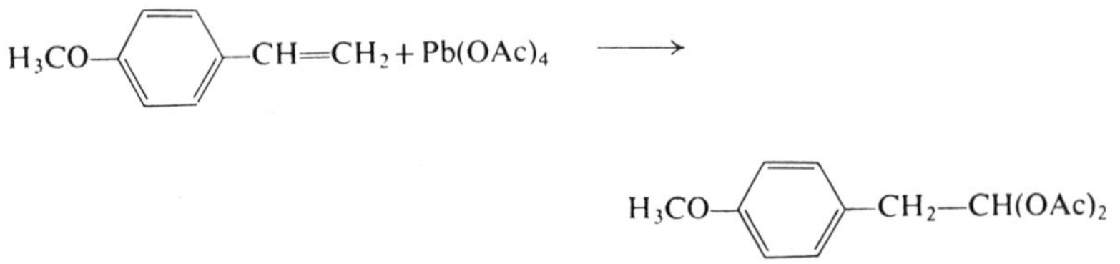

$$
\text{H}_3\text{CO}-\!\!\!\bigcirc\!\!\!-\text{CH}=\text{CH}_2 + \text{Pb(OAc)}_4 \longrightarrow
$$

$$
\text{H}_3\text{CO}-\!\!\!\bigcirc\!\!\!-\text{CH}_2-\text{CH(OAc)}_2 \quad (97)
$$

The *ortho* compound reacts analogously in 64% yield.

It is the phenyl group which migrates in these reactions, as demonstrated by the lead tetraacetate oxidation of *p*-methoxy-α-methylstyrene. The only product other than "normal" diacetate (XXXVII) is *p*-methoxyphenyl acetone (XXXVIII), formed in 48% yield:

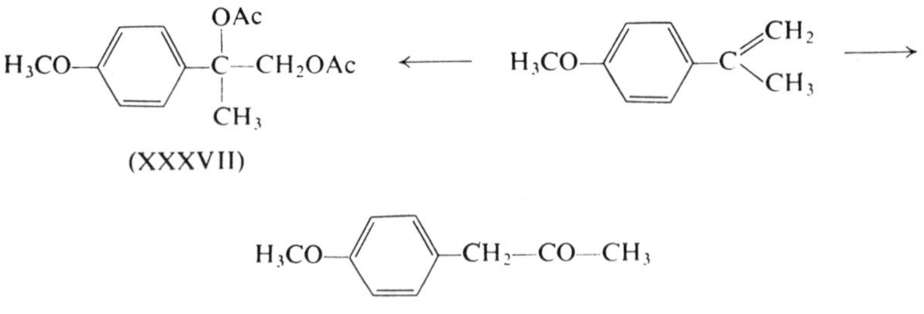

$$
\underset{(\text{XXXVII})}{\text{H}_3\text{CO}-\!\!\!\bigcirc\!\!\!-\underset{\underset{\text{CH}_3}{|}}{\overset{\overset{\text{OAc}}{|}}{\text{C}}}-\text{CH}_2\text{OAc}} \longleftarrow \text{H}_3\text{CO}-\!\!\!\bigcirc\!\!\!-\text{C}\overset{\text{CH}_2}{\underset{\text{CH}_3}{\diagdown}} \longrightarrow
$$

$$
(98)
$$

$$
\underset{(\text{XXXVIII})}{\text{H}_3\text{CO}-\!\!\!\bigcirc\!\!\!-\text{CH}_2-\text{CO}-\text{CH}_3}
$$

Analogously, α-methylstyrene gives 40% phenyl acetone,[104] and 1,1-bis-*p*-methoxyphenylethylene (XXXIX) is oxidized to deoxyanisoin (XL):

229 M. Finkelstein, *Ber.* **90**, 2097 (1957).

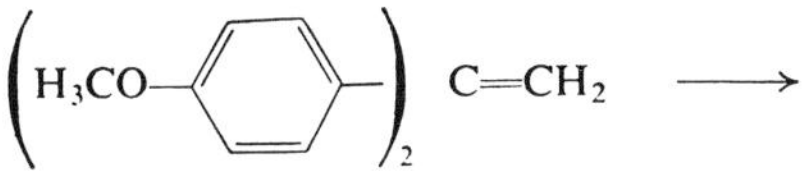

$$\left(H_3CO-\bigcirc\hspace{-0.3em}\right)_2 C{=}CH_2 \longrightarrow$$

(XXXIX)

(99)

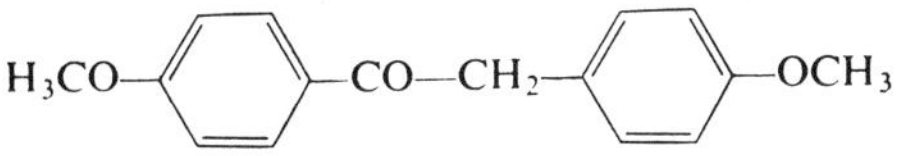

$$H_3CO-\bigcirc-CO-CH_2-\bigcirc-OCH_3$$

(XL)

Equation (100) gives a plausible mechanism for the reaction of *p*-methoxy-styrene:

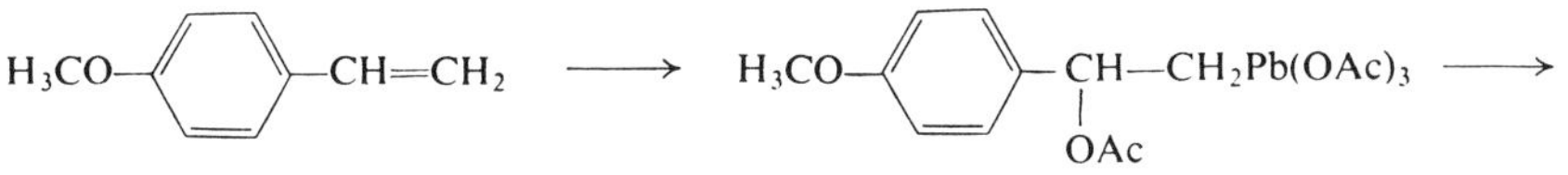

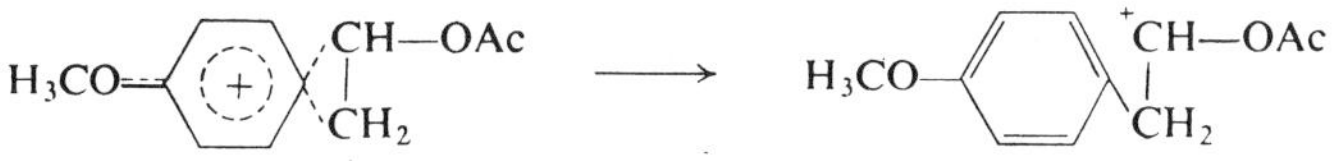

$$H_3CO-\bigcirc-CH{=}CH_2 \longrightarrow H_3CO-\bigcirc-\underset{\underset{OAc}{|}}{CH}-CH_2Pb(OAc)_3 \longrightarrow$$

$$H_3CO{=}\bigcirc\hspace{-1.5em}(+)\hspace{-0.5em}\underset{CH_2}{\overset{CH-OAc}{<}} \longrightarrow H_3CO-\bigcirc\overset{\overset{+}{C}H-OAc}{\underset{CH_2}{<}} \qquad (100)$$

$$\longrightarrow H_3CO-\bigcirc-CH_2-CH(OAc)_2$$

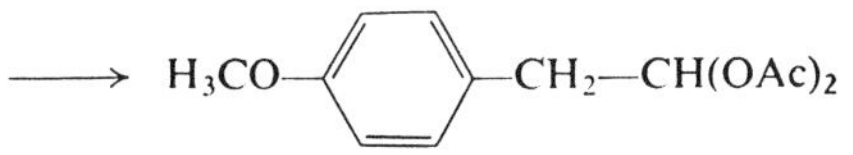

D. FORMATION OF GLYCOLIC AND GLYOXYLIC ESTERS

When cyclopentadiene[13] is oxidized at 20° C in dry acetic acid or in benzene, relatively little 1,2- and 1,4-diacetoxy compounds are formed. The main products are the mixed esters of the cyclopentenediols with acetic acid and acetylglycolic acid. Hydrolysis gives the free glycolic acid. Despite the very mild reaction conditions, one of the acetic acid groups is oxidized to a glycolic acid group. Similar reactions have been observed in the oxidation of cyclo-hexadiene-1,3, anethole, isoeugenol methyl ether, menthene-2,[216] styrene, α,α-diphenylethylene,[211] acetone–enol acetate,[230] and especially isobutylene.[231]

[230] R. Simon, Dissertation, Technical University of Karlsruhe, Germany, 1951.
[231] E. Hahl, Dissertation, Technical University of Karlsruhe, Germany, 1958.

Two hydrogens of one acetic acid group were replaced by AcO— groups in the oxidations of methylene cyclopentane, methylene cyclohexane,[211] and iso-butylene, forming derivatives of glyoxylic acid. Analogously, derivatives of lactic and α-hydroxybutyric acid are formed in oxidations with lead(IV) propionate and butyrate, respectively. Lead(IV) benzoate, of course, cannot give such "anomalous" products.[13]

Since esters of carboxylic acids are completely stable toward lead tetra-acetate under the reaction conditions, the nature of the reactive intermediate remained unexplained for a long time, until Brutcher and Vara[232] found the solution. According to these authors a AcO$^+$ cation [or, more probably, a (AcO)$_3$Pb$^+$ cation] attacks the double bond to form a Winstein type bridge ion XLI. This can react with water to the *ortho* ester derivative XLII and further to a mixture of the two *cis*-diol monoacetates XLIII. Potassium

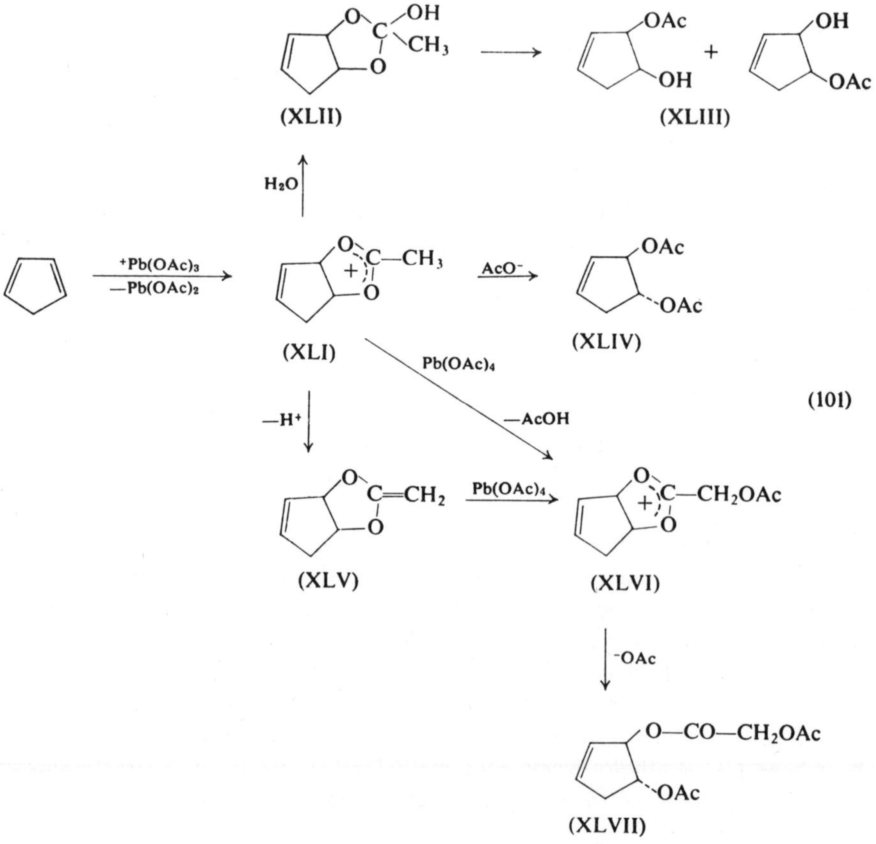

$$(101)$$

[232] F. V. Brutcher and F. J. Vara, *J. Am. Chem. Soc.* **78**, 5695 (1956).

acetate converts XLI to the *trans*-diol acetate and excess lead tetraacetate converts it to the glycol ester XLVII. Cyclopentadiene can thus be converted in 75–80% yield to *cis*-cyclopentene-1,2-diol of 93% purity by oxidizing it in acetic acid containing water. Using dry acetic acid containing potassium acetate, a 40–50% yield of *trans*-cyclopentene-1,2-diol of 97% purity was obtained. Whether such stereoselective hydroxylations also occur with other olefins remains to be investigated.

The spontaneous oxidation of XLI to XLVII can be explained by a strong activation of the CH_3 group by the positive charge in the dioxolenium cation. Another possibility is loss of a proton from XLI to give the cyclic ketene acetal XLV, which would be expected to be oxidized even more easily than an enol ether (see Section V,A).

Isobutylene[231] reacts about as easily as does cyclopentadiene. Little of the normal diacetoxy compound is formed; the glyoxylic acid derivative XLVIII

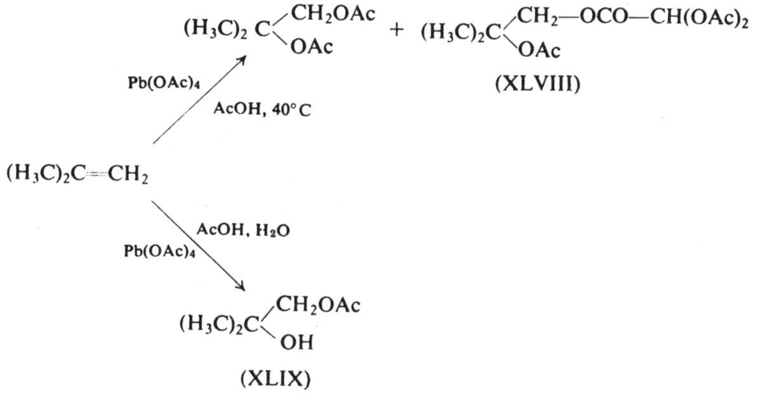

$$(H_3C)_2 C \begin{array}{l} CH_2OAc \\ OAc \end{array} \quad + \quad (H_3C)_2 C \begin{array}{l} CH_2-OCO-CH(OAc)_2 \\ OAc \end{array}$$

(XLVIII)

Pb(OAc)$_4$ / AcOH, 40°C

$$(H_3C)_2C = CH_2$$

(102)

AcOH, H$_2$O / Pb(OAc)$_4$

$$(H_3C)_2 C \begin{array}{l} CH_2OAc \\ OH \end{array}$$

(XLIX)

is the main product. Two acetoxy groups are introduced into the methyl group of the dioxolenium cation. This might, in part, be due to the experimental conditions: gaseous isobutylene is bubbled into a suspension of lead tetra-acetate in acetic acid, so that a large excess of the oxidant is present at all times. When the acetic acid contains water, an 82% yield of the monoacetate of isobutylene glycol (XLIX) is obtained. In agreement with Brutcher's mechanism, 2,4,4-trimethyl dioxolenium fluorborate, prepared by the method of Meerwein,[233] is oxidized to the same products as is isobutylene.

Not yet understood are the structural factors in the starting olefin which determine the formation of glycol and glyoxyl esters. The lifetime of the dioxolenium cation must certainly play a decisive role.

[233] H. Meerwein and K. Wunderlich, *Angew. Chem.* **69**, 481 (1957).

E. ADDITION OF METHYL ACETATE

When styrene and 1,1-diphenylethylene are treated with lead tetraacetate in benzene at 75–80° C, a remarkable reaction occurs.[211] It has few analogies and leads in 80–90 % yield to the addition of a methyl and an acetoxy group to the double bond:

$$C_6H_5-CH=CH_2+Pb(OAc)_4 \longrightarrow$$

$$\underset{\overset{|}{OAc}}{C_6H_5-CH}-CH_2-CH_3+Pb(OAc)_2+CO_2 \qquad (103)$$

$$(C_6H_5)_2C=CH_2+Pb(OAc)_4 \longrightarrow$$

$$\underset{\overset{|}{OAc}}{(C_6H_5)_2C}-CH_2-CH_3+Pb(OAc)_2+CO_2 \qquad (104)$$

The reaction is much more complex in acetic acid solution. Lead tetrapropionate and benzoate introduced an ethyl and a phenyl group, respectively.[16] The styrene is not polymerized during the reaction, but a radical chain mechanism of the kind represented in Eq. (105) cannot be excluded:

$$C_6H_5-CH=CH_2+\overset{\bullet}{C}H_3 \longrightarrow C_6H_5-\overset{\bullet}{C}H-CH_2-CH_3$$

$$(105)$$

$$C_6H_5-\overset{\bullet}{C}H-CH_2-CH_3+Pb(OAc)_4 \longrightarrow$$

$$\underset{\overset{|}{OAc}}{C_6H_5-CH}-CH_2-CH_3+CO_2+\overset{\bullet}{C}H_3+Pb(OAc)_2$$

It is not understood why the reaction seems to be limited to styrene and 1,1-diphenylethylene.

F. FORMATION OF γ-LACTONES

No less remarkable than the addition of methyl acetate is a side reaction observed during the oxidation of octene-4 by lead tetraacetate in acetic acid.[213, 231] Apart from the addition of two AcO groups to the double bond and substitution in the allylic positions, the group —OCO—CH$_2$— is added to the double bond:

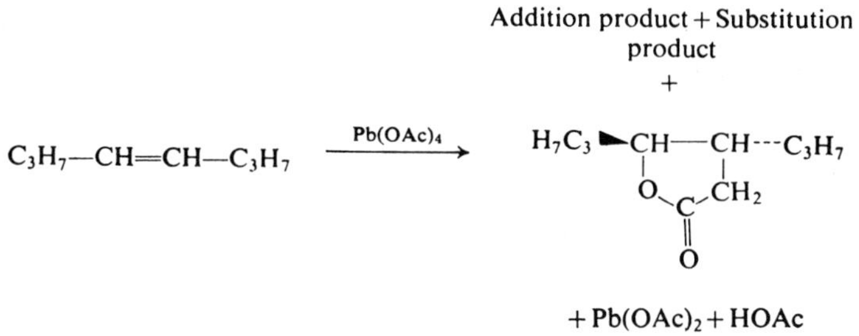

$$
\text{C}_3\text{H}_7-\text{CH}=\text{CH}-\text{C}_3\text{H}_7 \xrightarrow{\text{Pb(OAc)}_4}
$$

Addition product + Substitution product
+

$$
\text{H}_7\text{C}_3\text{—CH—CH---C}_3\text{H}_7 \quad (106)
$$

+ Pb(OAc)$_2$ + HOAc

The same lactone is formed from *cis*- and from *trans*-octene-4 in about 20% yield. The propyl groups are *trans* to each other as shown by independent synthesis from *cis*-octene epoxide and sodiomalonic ester. The reaction was not observed with other olefins and its mechanism remains unknown.

G. OTHER REACTIONS OF OLEFINS

Enol acetates are not formed exclusively by rearrangements (see Section V,C). They are also side products in the oxidation of olefins with exocyclic double bonds, such as methylene cyclopentane, methylene cyclohexane,[211] and 4-*tert*-butyl-1-methylenecyclohexane.[234] Equation (91) indicated the possibility of formation of enol acetates from a carbonium ion intermediate which also leads to the formation of other products. However, the enol acetate formation is retarded by iodine, so that Cross and Witham[234] assume a direct radical-type substitution at the double bond.

The formation of dihydrofurans was observed in the carotinoid series by Bodea *et al.*[235] The net result of the reaction is the 1,4-addition of an oxygen atom across a 1,3-diene system:

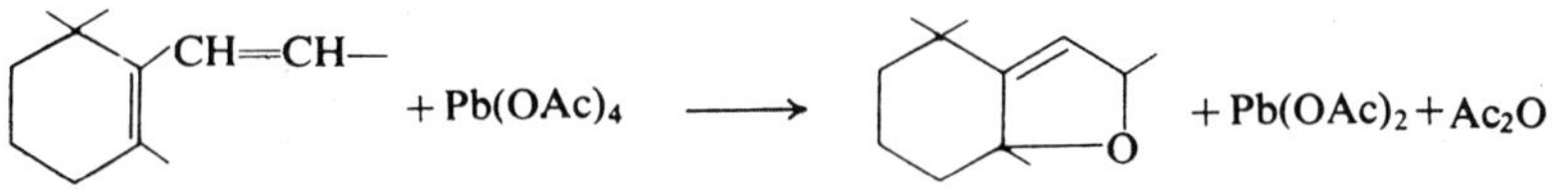

$$
\text{+ Pb(OAc)}_4 \longrightarrow \text{+ Pb(OAc)}_2 + \text{Ac}_2\text{O} \quad (107)
$$

In chloroform or benzene solution the reaction is complete after a few seconds at room temperature. Yields up to 22% were observed. Like most of the reactions of lead tetraacetate with double bonds, it can be understood by assuming primary attack of an AcO$^+$ or (AcO)$_3$Pb$^+$ cation.

The dehydrogenation of olefins has already been mentioned in Section III,A,3. Dehydrogenations also occur in the steroid and the carotinoid series.[235]

---

[234] B. Cross and G. H. Witham, *J. Chem. Soc.* p. 3895 (1960).
[235] C. Bodea, E. Nicoara, and R. Salontai, *Ann.* **648**, 147 (1961); C. Bodea and V. Tamas, *ibid.* **671**, 57 (1964).

Windaus *et al.*[236] observed dehydrogenation of steroids which have two double bonds in positions 6 and 8 in ring B:

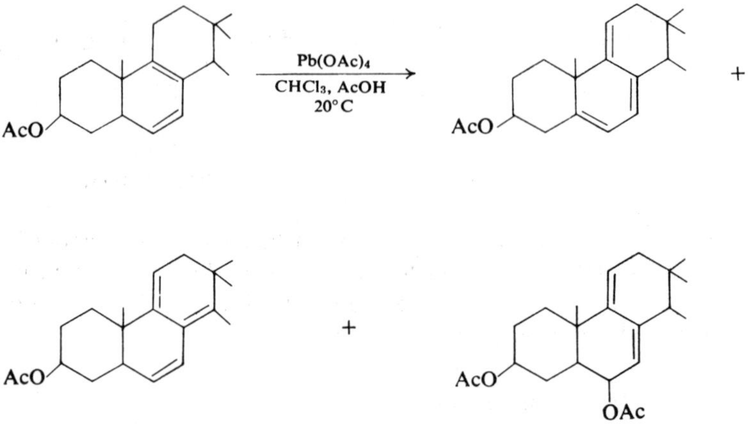

(108)

H. ALLENES AND ACETYLENES

The oxidation of some allenes is described in an earlier paper by LaForge and Acree.[237] At 20° C in acetic acid solution, addition to one of the double bonds gives diacetoxy compounds. One of the acetoxy groups is of the enol acetate type:

$$R-CH=C=CH-R + Pb(OAc)_4 \longrightarrow R-CH-C=CH-R$$

$$\underset{\displaystyle OAc \quad OAc}{\vert \qquad \vert} \tag{109}$$

It remains to be established which of the two double bonds in unsymmetric allenes is attacked first. Also it is not yet known whether a second mole of oxidant can be consumed by the enol acetate formed first.

In general, electrophilic reagents react with acetylenes more slowly than with olefins. With lead tetraacetate in acetic acid, acetylenes react only above 80° C, and slowly even then. Gas evolution often accompanies the oxidations and complex mixtures are usually produced. Substitution in α-position to the triple bond occurs with octyne-4[238] and with decyne-5.[239] In these two cases the α-acetoxy compounds were isolated in about 20% yield and were characterized by conversion to the saturated alcohols. Phenylbenzylacetylene[240]

[236] A. Windaus and U. Riemann, *Z. Physiol. Chem.* **274**, 206 (1942).

[237] F. B. LaForge and F. Acree, *J. Org. Chem.* **6**, 208 (1941).

[238] F. Marktscheffel, Diplomarbeit, Technical University of Karlsruhe, Germany, 1952.

[239] V. Franzen, *Ber.* **87**, 1478 (1954).

[240] J. Jadot and M. Neuray, *Bull. Soc. Roy. Sci. Liege* **30**, 34, 52, 431 (1961); **31**, 247 (1962).

even gave a 61 % yield of the allylic substitution product. This might be due to the activation of the α-position by both the triple bond and the phenyl group. Lead tetraacetate in excess gave phenylbenzoylacetylene. No pure compounds could be isolated from the higher boiling fractions of this and other acetylene oxidations. Jadot and Neuray[240] subjected these fractions to alkaline hydrolysis. Their results indicated that the triple bond had added two and four acetoxy groups. Propargyl alcohol reacts more cleanly. At 80° C lead tetraacetate in acetic acid gave a diacetoxy compound which, upon hydrolysis with NaHCO₃, gave dihydroxyacetone in 78 % yield:

$$HO-CH_2-C\equiv CH \longrightarrow HO-CH_2-\underset{\underset{OAc}{|}}{C}=CH-OAc \longrightarrow$$

$$HO-CH_2-\underset{\underset{O}{\|}}{C}-CH_2OH \qquad (110)$$

Considerable quantities of polymers are often formed. Tolane is quite stable towards lead tetraacetate.

VI. Reactions with Compounds of Sulfur, Nitrogen, and Phosphorus

This section deals only with reactions in which the hetero atom participates decisively. Much fewer systematic investigations have been performed here than on hydrocarbons and oxygen compounds.

A. SULFUR COMPOUNDS

Lead tetraacetate is among the many oxidants that convert mercaptans to disulfides even at low temperatures.[241] The reaction is faster than the glycol cleavage of pinacol. Accordingly, thioglycol is not cleaved but converted to the disulfide:

$$\underset{H_2C-SH}{\overset{H_2C=OH}{|}} \overset{\nleftrightarrow}{\underset{\searrow}{}} \begin{array}{l} H_2C=O+H_2C=S \\ HO-CH_2-CH_2-S-S-CH_2-CH_2-OH \end{array} \qquad (111)$$

It is uncertain whether the preference for disulfide formation holds also for small ring *cis*-1,2-thioglycols. Simple —SH compounds, however, can be titrated with lead tetraacetate.[242] Field and Lawson[241] formulate the reaction according to Eq. (112):

$$R-SH \longrightarrow R-S-Pb(OAc)_3 \longrightarrow R-S^+ \xrightarrow[-H^+]{R-SH} R-S-S-R \qquad (112)$$

[241] L. Field and J. E. Lawson, *J. Am. Chem. Soc.* **80**, 838 (1958).
[242] L. Suchomelova and J. Zyka, *J. Electroanal. Chem.* **5**, 57 (1963); *Chem. Abstr.* **59**, 1482b (1963).

Sulfur compounds without S—H bonds can be attacked by lead tetraacetate, usually with formation of sulfoxides.[74] Depending on the nature of the solvent, different sites are oxidized in sulfide molecules and the rates of oxidation are quite different. According to Böhme, Fischer, and Frank,[243] dibenzylsulfide is converted to the sulfoxide by lead tetraacetate in acetic acid solution, but to α-acetoxydibenzylsulfide when it is allowed to react for 24 hours at 20°C in benzene. Cavill *et al.*[31a] determined the yields of dibutylsulfoxide from

$$C_6H_5CH-S-CH_2C_6H_5 \quad \xleftarrow{C_6H_6} \quad C_6H_5CH_2-S-CH_2C_6H_5 \quad \xrightarrow{AcOH}$$
$$\overset{|}{OAc}$$

$$C_6H_5CH_2-SO-CH_2C_6H_5 \quad (113)$$

dibutylsulfide in various solvents. The yield in benzene was 6%; in carbon tetrachloride, 11%; in nitrobenzene, 21%; in acetic acid, 36%; and in acetonitrile, 55%. This argues for an ionic mechanism in which AcO^+-cation is transferred to sulfur:

$$R-S-R \quad \xrightarrow[-Pb(OAc)_2]{(AcO)_3Pb^+} \quad \underset{\overset{|}{OAc}}{R-S^{\pm}-R} \quad \xrightarrow[-Ac_2O]{AcO^-} \quad \underset{\overset{||}{O}}{R-S-R} \quad (114)$$

Still another reaction path is open to mercaptals. Oxidation of benzaldehyde dibenzyl mercaptal in acetic acid gave an acylal and a disulfide[244]:

$$C_6H_5-HC\overset{S-CH_2C_6H_5}{\underset{S-CH_2C_6H_5}{\diagup\diagdown}} \quad \longrightarrow \quad C_6H_5-CH(OAc)_2 \; + \; \overset{S-CH_2C_6H_5}{\underset{S-CH_2C_6H_5}{|}} \quad (115)$$

According to the authors, this is not an oxidation of the mercaptal itself. Rather the mercaptal and acetic acid are in equilibrium with the acylal and mercaptan. The latter is oxidized to the disulfide and thus removed from the equilibrium mixture.

$$C_6H_5CH(SCH_2C_6H_5)_2 + AcOH$$

$$C_6H_5-\overset{\overset{OAc}{|}}{CH}-SCH_2C_6H_5 + C_6H_5CH_2SH \quad (116)$$

$$C_6H_5CH(OAc)_2 + 2\,C_6H_5CH_2SH$$

No oxidation is observed in benzene, where the initial equilibrium is not possible.

[243] H. Böhme, H. Fischer, and R. Frank, *Ann.* **563**, 54 (1949).
[244] E. J. Bourne, W. M. Corbett, M. Stacey, and R. W. Stephens, *Chem. & Ind.* (*London*) p. 106 (1954).

The reaction can be quite fast, as demonstrated by the lead tetraacetate reaction of carbohydrate mercaptals.[245-247] Here, the thioether groups successfully compete for the oxidant with the glycol groups, if the reaction is run in acetic acid solution. In benzene, however, glycol cleavage becomes the main reaction. Field *et al.*[248] found that disulfides can be converted to sulfinic esters by heating them to reflux with lead tetraacetate in chloroform–methanol for extended periods of time. The yields obtained were 30–87%.

$$R—S—S—R + 3\ Pb(OAc)_4 + 4\ H_3C—OH \rightarrow$$
$$2\ R—SO—OCH_3 + 3\ Pb(OAc)_2 + 4\ AcOH + 2\ AcOCH_3 \quad (117)$$

B. NITROGEN COMPOUNDS

Many classes of nitrogen compounds behave in a similar manner to the corresponding oxygen compounds. Like alcohols, aliphatic amines are relatively inert toward lead tetraacetate. Primary, secondary, and tertiary amines are not attacked by lead tetraacetate in acetic acid solution, at least not at moderate temperatures. Refluxing in benzene solution, however, gives nitriles from primary amines up to 60% yield.[248a]

Carboxamides, analogous to carboxylic acids, also are not attacked under these conditions. Only in dichloroethane at 120–130° C is acetamide dehydrogenated and rearranged to methylisocyanate.[249]

Like phenols, primary and secondary aromatic amines are rapidly oxidized even at low temperatures. As with phenols, quinones can be formed from suitable systems. α-Naphthylamine gives a 16% yield of 1,4-naphthoquinone; from β-naphthylamine, 25% of the theoretical yield of 2-aminonaphthoquinone-1,4 is formed.[250] In the latter case the main product is a naphthoquinonimine (60%). A small yield of phenazine derivative is also formed. When the NH_2 group in α-naphthylamine is protected by a benzenesulfonyl group, the α-naphthoquinonimine derivative is formed. With benzoyl as the protecting group, the reaction proceeds only to the stage of 1-benzamino-4-acetoxynaphthalene. Acyl derivatives of β-naphthylamine, however, are converted to substituted α-naphthoquinones in good yields (Eq. 118).[251]

[245] C. F. Huebner, R. A. Pankratz, and K. P. Link, *J. Am. Chem. Soc.* **72**, 4811 (1950).

[246] S. B. Baker, *J. Am. Chem. Soc.* **74**, 827 (1952).

[247] H. Zinner, W. Bock, and H. P. Klöcking, *Ber.* **92**, 1307 (1959).

[248] L. Field, C. B. Hoelzel, J. M. Locke, and J. E. Lawson, *J. Am. Chem. Soc.* **83**, 1256 (1961); L. Field, J. M. Locke, C. B. Hoelzel, and J. E. Lawson, *J. Org. Chem.* **27**, 3313 (1962).

[248a] M. L. Mihailović, A. Stojiljković, and V. Andrejević, *Tetrahedron Letters* p. 461 (1965).

[249] J. Bollinger, Thesis, University of Marburg, Germany, 1937; cf. H. E. Baumgarten and A. Staklis, *J. Am. Chem. Soc.* **87**, 1141 (1965); B. Acott and A. L. J. Beckwith, *Chem. Commun.* p. 161 (1965).

[250] K. H. Pausacker and J. G. Scroggie, *J. Chem. Soc.* p. 4003 (1954).

[251] H. J. Richter and R. L. Dressler, *J. Org. Chem.* **27**, 4066 (1962).

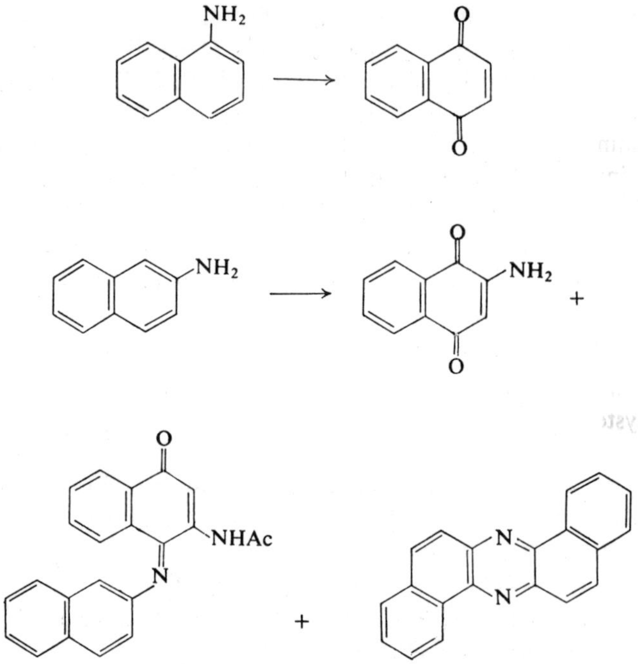

(118)

Phenetidine and acetanisidide give the substituted benzoquinones in 59%
and 80% yields, respectively[250]:

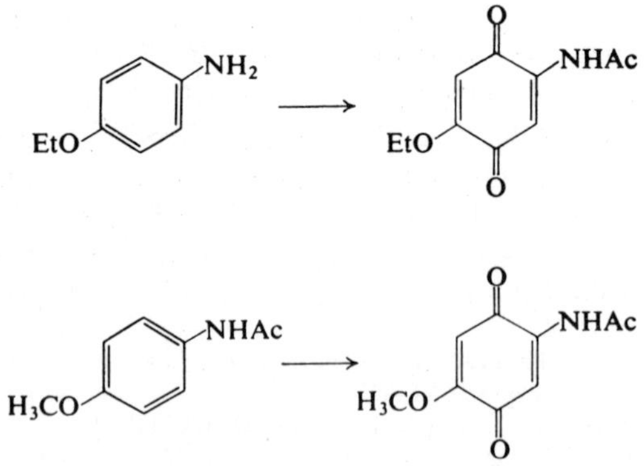

(119)

Here the aromatic C—H bonds might be the site attacked in the primary
reaction step.

The oxidation of aromatic amines to azo compounds[250, 252] has no parallel
in the phenol series. Hydrazo compounds must be intermediates. They could

252 E. Baer and A. L. Tosoni, *J. Am. Chem. Soc.* **78**, 2857 (1956).

be formed by the dimerization of Ar—NH radicals or by attack of Ar—NH$^+$ cations on the amino group of another molecule of amine. In benzene solution the reaction proceeds at temperatures as low as 20° C and gives yields up to 56%.

Dimroth et al.[252a] showed that *N*-radicals actually can be formed from primary amines and lead tetraacetate. The authors oxidized the 2,4,6-triphenyl-aniline to a stable radical. Analogously, α,α-diphenyl-β-picryl hydrazine gave the corresponding hydrazyl.

Horner et al.[253] found that tertiary aromatic amines are oxidized as easily as are primary and secondary ones. One alkyl group is lost as the aldehyde and the acetyl derivative of the secondary amine is formed:

$$\text{Ar—N}\genfrac{}{}{0pt}{}{\text{CH}_2\text{R}'}{\text{R}} + \text{Pb(OAc)}_4 \xrightarrow[\text{20°C}]{\text{HCCl}_3/\text{Ac}_2\text{O}} \text{Ar—N}\genfrac{}{}{0pt}{}{\text{Ac}}{\text{R}} + \text{R}'\text{CHO} \qquad (120)$$

The yields of aldehyde and acetyl amine are usually between 50% and 90%. The mechanism is not known in detail, but the reaction resembles a side reaction in the lead tetraacetate oxidation of phenol ethers (Section III,C), in which a methoxy group is replaced by an acetoxy group.

The lead tetraacetate oxidation of *o*- and *p*-dihydric phenols has a parallel in the reaction of *o*- and *p*-diamino compounds. Systematic investigations by Adams et al.[254] showed that the sulfonyl derivatives of such amino compounds can be oxidized almost quantitatively to quinone diimides by lead tetra-acetate in acetic acid, by red lead oxide, and by activated lead dioxide:

$$\underset{\text{NHSO}_2\text{C}_6\text{H}_5}{\overset{\text{NHSO}_2\text{C}_6\text{H}_5}{\bigcirc}} \longrightarrow \underset{\text{NSO}_2\text{C}_6\text{H}_5}{\overset{\text{NSO}_2\text{C}_6\text{H}_5}{\bigcirc}} \qquad (121)$$

The reaction gave *o*- and *p*-quinone mono- and diimides of the benzene and naphthalene series, amphinaphthaquinone diimide,[254] and diphenoquinone diimides.[255] Carboxamides can be employed in the place of sulfonamides.[256]

252a K. Dimroth, F. Kalk, and G. Neubauer, *Ber.* **90**, 2058 (1957).

253 L. Horner, E. Winkelmann, K. H. Knapp, and W. Ludwig, *Ber.* **92**, 288 (1959).

254 R. Adams and A. S. Nagarkatti, *J. Am. Chem. Soc.* **72**, 4601 (1950); R. Adams and J. L. Anderson, *ibid.* **72**, 5154 (1950); R. Adams and R. A. Wankel, *ibid.* **73**, 131 (1951); R. Adams and J. H. Looker, *ibid.* **73**, 1145 (1951); R. Adams and K. R. Eilar, *ibid.* **73**, 1149 (1951); R. Adams and R. A. Wankel, *ibid.* **73**, 2219 (1951); R. Adams and C. N. Winnick, *ibid.* **73**, 5687 (1951).

255 R. Adams and R. R. Holmes, *J. Am. Chem. Soc.* **74**, 3033 (1952); R. Adams, R. R. Holmes, and J. W. Way, *ibid.* **75**, 5901 (1953).

256 R. Adams and J. W. Way. *J. Am. Chem. Soc.* **76**, 2763 (1954).

Imines bearing one hydrogen on each of the N and the C atoms are dehydrogenated to nitriles with great ease: $R-CH=NH \rightarrow R-C\equiv N$.[249] Such imines are usually very unstable, but are intermediates in the lead tetraacetate cleavage of α-diamines and of α-amino acids. Thus, the amino analog of the glycol cleavage leads to nitriles rather than to imines:

$$\begin{array}{ll} H_5C_6-CH-NH_2 \\ \quad\quad | \quad\quad\quad\quad +3\ Pb(OAc)_4 \xrightarrow[20°]{AcOH} 2\ H_5C_6-C\equiv N & \quad +3\ Pb(OAc)_2 \\ H_5C_6-CH-NH_2 & \quad\quad\quad 85\% \quad\quad +6\ AcOH \end{array} \qquad (122)$$

$$\begin{array}{ll} H_5C_6-CH-NH_2 \\ \quad\quad | \quad\quad\quad\quad +2\ Pb(OAc)_4 \xrightarrow[20°C]{AcOH} H_5C_6-CN+CO_2+2\ Pb(OAc)_2 \\ \quad CO_2H & \quad\quad\quad 78\% \quad\quad\quad +4\ AcOH \end{array} \qquad (123)$$

Oximes are derivatives of imines and at the same time the nitrogen analogs of enols. Iffland and Criner[257] found that the oxidation is analogous to enols:

$$>C=N-OH \xrightarrow[CH_2Cl_2,\ 5°C]{Pb(OAc)_4} >C=N-O-Pb(OAc)_3 \longrightarrow >\!\!\overset{OAc}{\underset{|}{C}}-NO \qquad (124)$$

The blue acetoxynitroso compounds formed are unstable, and are easily oxidized further to stable colorless acetoxynitro compounds.[257a]

   Ketohydrazones with a hydrogen on N_β behave like oximes. Iffland et al.[258] reported 14 examples of formation of α-acetoxy azo compounds in 55–90% yield:

$$>C=N-NHR \longrightarrow >\!\!\overset{OAc}{\underset{|}{C}}-N=N-R \qquad (125)$$

At 0–10°C the reactions are complete after a few seconds. The authors write a radical mechanism, but it seems to be more likely that an ionic process is operative, like that given for the oxime reaction. Surprisingly, acetoxy azo compounds are formed also from hydrazones not possessing a hydrogen on N. The reaction conditions are the same and the yields are similar to the systems monosubstituted at N_β, but 2 moles of lead tetraacetate are required.[259]

$$(C_6H_5)_2C=N-N\!\!<\!\!\overset{R}{\underset{R'}{}} \xrightarrow[CH_2Cl_2,\ 5°C]{Pb(OAc)_4} (C_6H_5)_2\overset{OAc}{\underset{|}{C}}-N=N-R \qquad (126)$$

[257] D. C. Iffland and G. X. Criner, *Chem. & Ind. (London)* p. 176 (1956).
[257a] H. E. Baumgarten. A. Staklis, and E. M. Miller, *J. Org. Chem.* **30**, 1203 (1965).
[258] D. C. Iffland, L. Salisbury, and W. R. Schafer, *J. Am. Chem. Soc.* **83**, 747 (1961); W. A. F. Gladstone and R. O. C. Norman, *J. Chem. Soc.* p. 3048 (1965).
[259] D. C. Iffland and E. Cerda, *J. Org. Chem.* **28**, 2769 (1963).

Presumably, the first step of the reaction is a dealkylation at N_β, similar to that observed with tertiary amines, with loss of the alkyl group as an aldehyde or a ketone.

A special hydrazone, $(F_3C)_2C{=}N{-}NH_2$, is oxidized in benzonitril solution to the stable yellow diazo compound $(F_3C)_2CN_2$.[259a] In the same manner, however, in benzene solution at 20°C, 1-aminobenztriazol loses two hydrogen atoms. The reaction product spontaneously decomposes to nitrogen and dehydrobenzene.[259b]

The oxidation of formazanes to tetrazolium salts, discovered by Kuhn and Jerchel,[260] can also be explained by assuming an ionic mechanism. The reaction gives excellent yields in chloroform solution at room temperature:

$$R{-}C\underset{N=N-R''}{\overset{N-NHR'}{\Big\langle}} \longrightarrow R{-}C\underset{N=NR''}{\overset{N-NR'}{\Big\langle}} \longrightarrow R{-}C\underset{N=NR''}{\overset{N-NR'}{\Big\langle}} \quad (127)$$

When R is an acyl group, it is replaced by H during the reaction.[261]

Among the aliphatic diazo compounds,[262] diazoketones are stable toward lead tetraacetate. Diazomethane and other diazoalkanes, however, are oxidized readily with loss of nitrogen and formation of geminal diacetoxy compounds.

$$H_2CN_2 + Pb(OAc)_4 \xrightarrow[\text{2°C}]{\text{benzene}} N_2 + H_2C(OAc)_2 + Pb(OAc)_2 \quad (128)$$

Diazodiphenylmethane and diazofluorene react analogously.[263] Hydrazones with two hydrogens at N_β are easily oxidized to diazo compounds. Consequently they consume 2 moles of oxidant and give directly geminal diacetoxy compounds.[263]

$$R_2C{=}N{-}NH_2 + 2\,Pb(OAc)_4 \rightarrow R_2C(OAc)_2 + N_2 + 2\,Pb(OAc)_2 + 2\,AcOH \quad (129)$$

The work of Hünig and Fritsch[264] has to be mentioned in this context. The

[259a] D. M. Gale, W. J. Middleton, and C. G. Krespan, *J. Am. Chem. Soc.* **87**, 657 (1965).

[259b] C. D. Campbell and C. W. Rees, *Proc. Chem. Soc.* p. 296 (1964); C. D. Campbell and C. W. Rees, *Chem. Commun.* p. 192 (1965); C. W. Rees and R. C. Storr, *ibid.* p. 193 (1965).

[260] R. Kuhn and D. Jerchel, *Ber.* **74**, 941 (1941); D. Jerchel and H. Fischer, *Ann.* **563**, 208 (1949).

[261] B. Hirsch, *Ann.* **648**, 151 (1961).

[262] A. J. Jakubowitsch, S. P. Makarow, W. A. Ginsburg, G. J. Gawrilow, and J. N. Merkulowa, *Izv. Akad. Nauk SSSR* **72**, 69 (1950); *Chem. Zentr.* I, 2419 (1951); A. J. Jakubowitsch, J. N. Merkulowa, S. P. Makarow, and G. J. Gawrilow, *J. Gen. Chem.* **22** (84), 2060 (1952); *Chem. Zentr.* p. 6861 (1953).

[263] R. H. Hensel, *Ber.* **88**, 527 (1955).

[264] S. Hünig and K. H. Fritsch, *Ann.* **609**, 143 (1957).

authors oxidized thiazolidone–hydrazones together with suitably substituted ethylenes and obtained dyes similar to the cyanine type:

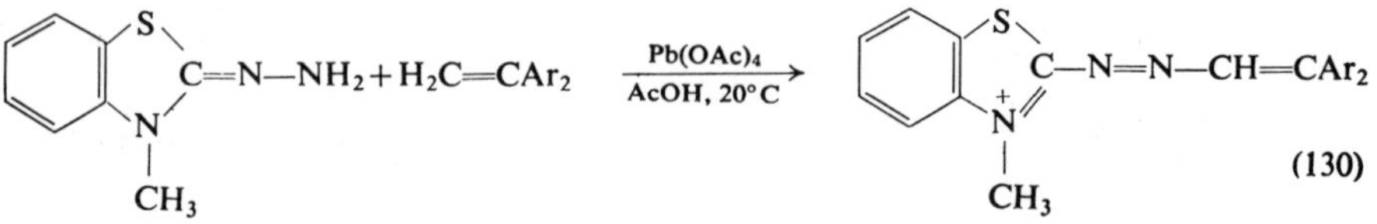

$$\underset{\substack{|\\CH_3}}{\text{[benzothiazoline]}}C{=}N{-}NH_2 + H_2C{=}CAr_2 \xrightarrow[\text{AcOH, 20°C}]{Pb(OAc)_4} \underset{\substack{|\\CH_3}}{\text{[benzothiazolium]}}C{-}N{=}N{-}CH{=}CAr_2 \qquad (130)$$

Hydrazides are oxidized only with difficulty by most of the common reagents. Lead tetraacetate, however, dehydrogenates them smoothly. Wittig and Hoffmann[265] used the reaction to prepare a cyclic azosulfone which they used as a source of benzyne:

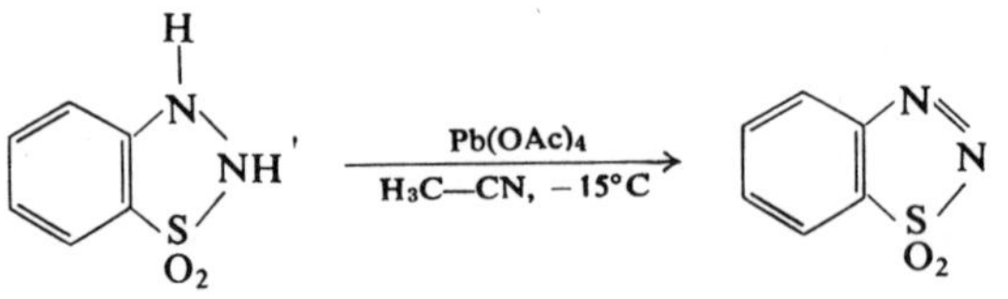

$$\xrightarrow[\text{H}_3\text{C—CN, }-15°C]{Pb(OAc)_4} \qquad (131)$$

At about the same time, Clement[266] dehydrogenated cyclic dicarboxylic hydrazides with lead tetraacetate. He could not isolate the azo compounds, but used them *in situ* as highly effective dienophiles. The dehydrogenation is almost instantaneous in methylene chloride solution containing 2% acetic acid:

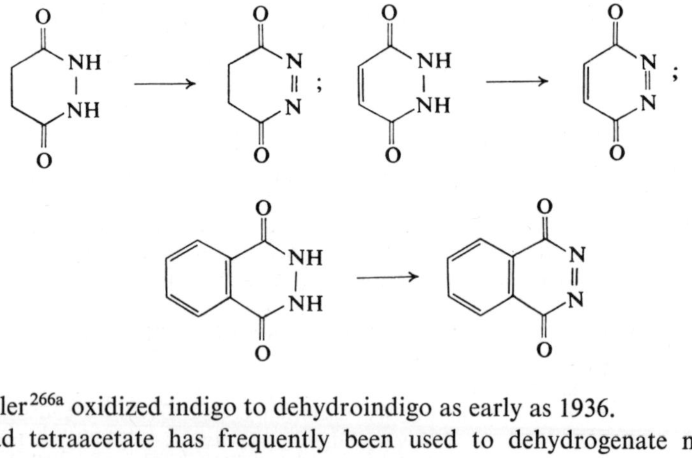

$$\longrightarrow \quad ; \qquad \longrightarrow \quad ; \qquad (132)$$

$$\longrightarrow$$

Heller[266a] oxidized indigo to dehydroindigo as early as 1936.

Lead tetraacetate has frequently been used to dehydrogenate nitrogen

[265] G. Wittig and R. W. Hoffmann, *Ber.* 95, 2718 (1962).
[266] R. A. Clement, *J. Org. Chem.* 27, 1115 (1962).
[266a] G. Heller, *Ber.* 69, 563 (1936).

heterocyclic compounds. Ring C in yohimbine can be aromatized by this method.[267, 268]

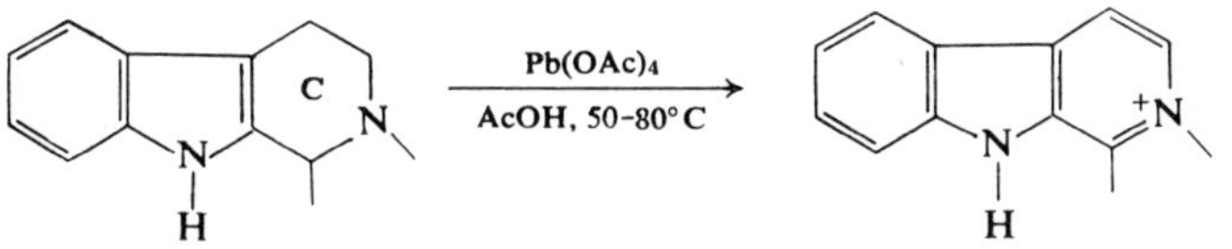

$$(133)$$

According to Taylor *et al.*,[30] the first step of the reaction is attack by the $^+Pb(OAc)_3$ cation on the 7-position. A 7-acetoxy- or, in methanol solution, a 7-methoxyindolenine is formed:

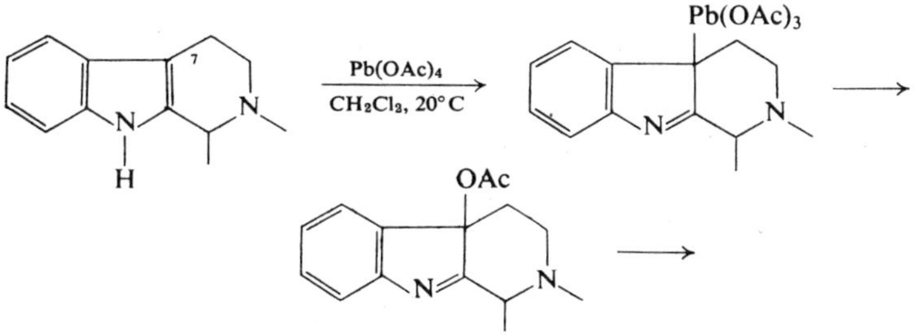

$$(134)$$

The subsequent steps leading to the aromatized product are believed to be those of Eq. (135):

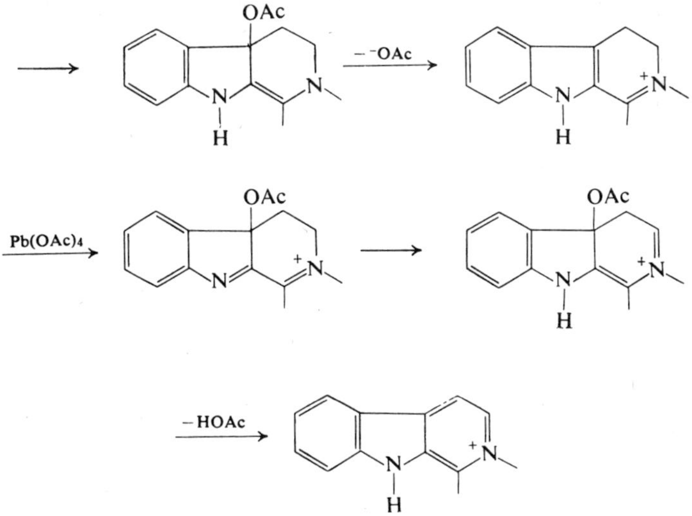

$$(135)$$

[267] G. Hahn, E. Kappes, and H. Ludewig, *Ber.* **67**, 686 (1934).
[268] N. Finch, C. W. Gemenden, J. H. Hsu, and W. J. Taylor, *J. Am. Chem. Soc.* **85**, 1520 (1963).

Chen and Leete[269] oxidized the benzyl group in α-benzylindoles. The first steps might be analogous to those in the oxidation of yohimbine:

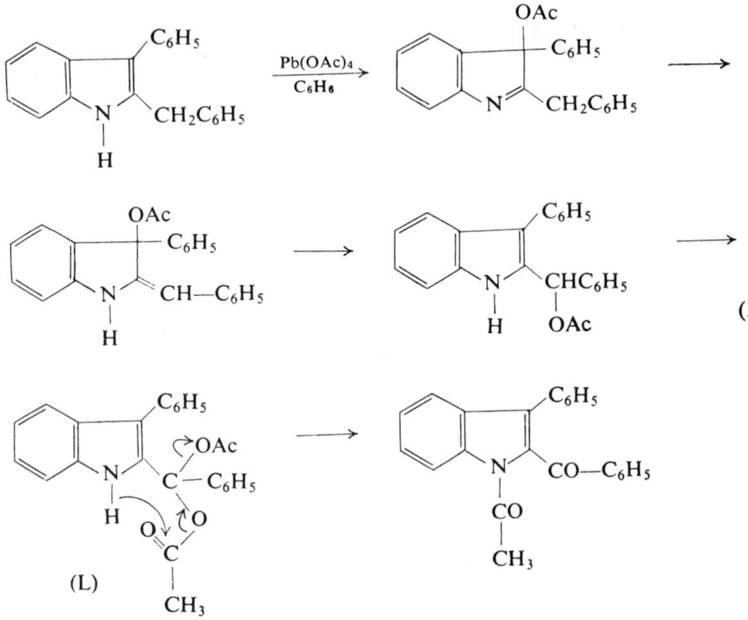

$$\text{(136)}$$

From 2,3-dimethylindole and lead tetraacetate, Taylor[270] obtained an α-diacetoxy compound corresponding to L in Eq. (136). No further oxidation occurred in this case.

Methyl groups in the α-position of pyrrole rings are acetoxylated very easily. The mechanism seems to be indirect and similar to that operating in the oxidation of α-substituted indoles. Siedel and Winkler[271] isolated the reaction products after hydrolysis, obtaining carbinols or aldehydes:

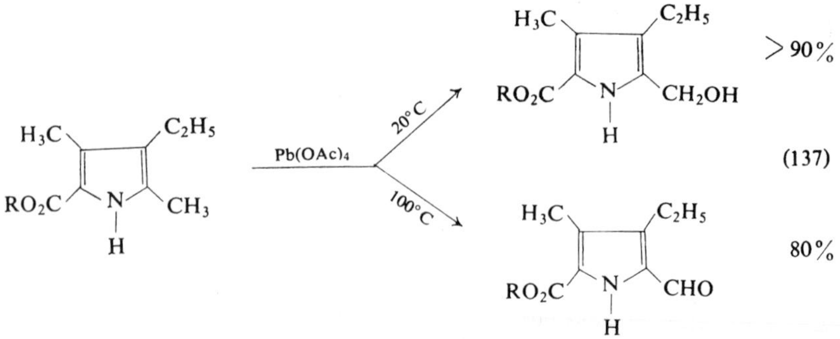

$$\text{(137)}$$

[269] F. Y. Chen and E. Leete, *Tetrahedron Letters* p. 2013 (1963).
[270] W. J. Taylor, *Abstr. 144th Meeting Am. Chem. Soc., Los Angeles,* 1963.
[271] W. Siedel and F. Winkler, *Ann.* **554**, 162, 201 (1943).

(138)

The original papers should be consulted on the oxidation of dipyrryl-methenes and of bile pigments.[272]

9,10-Dihydroacridines[273] are oxidized in a different manner. Acridines are formed but, depending on the solvent, substituents in the 9-position may or may not be lost [Eq. (138), page 361].
Analogous reactions occur with compounds having a 9-substituent other than the acetoacetic ester group or lacking the methyl groups on the aromatic rings.

N,N-Diacetyltetrahydro-γ,γ-dipyridyl[274] is instantly dehydrogenated to pyridine by lead tetraacetate at room temperature. The corresponding dihydro compound, however, gives γ,γ-dipyridyl.

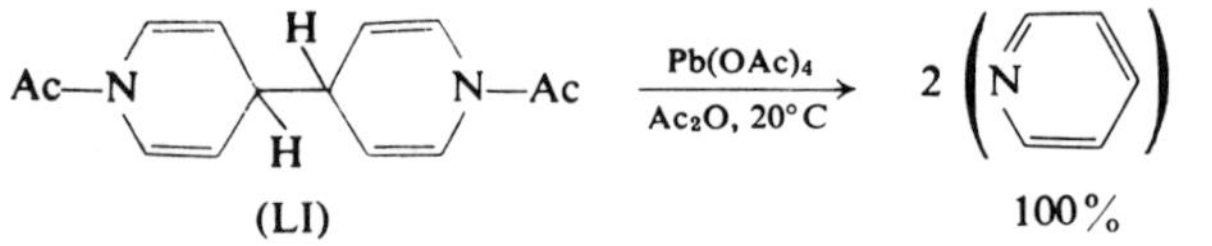

$$\text{(139)}$$

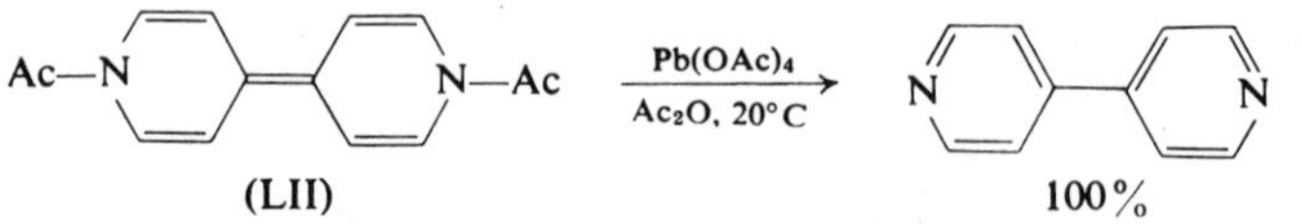

$$\text{(140)}$$

Thus, LII cannot be an intermediate in the oxidation of LI. Rather, an electron pair from one of the nitrogens is transferred to the oxidant, and reorganization of the bonds leads to fragmentation of the molecule:

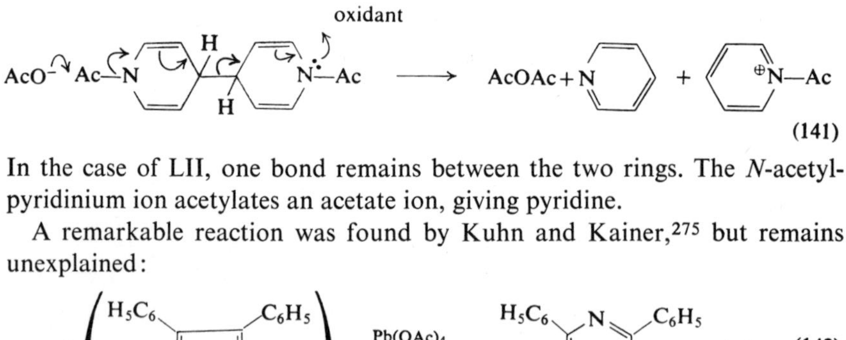

$$\text{(141)}$$

In the case of LII, one bond remains between the two rings. The N-acetyl-pyridinium ion acetylates an acetate ion, giving pyridine.

A remarkable reaction was found by Kuhn and Kainer,[275] but remains unexplained:

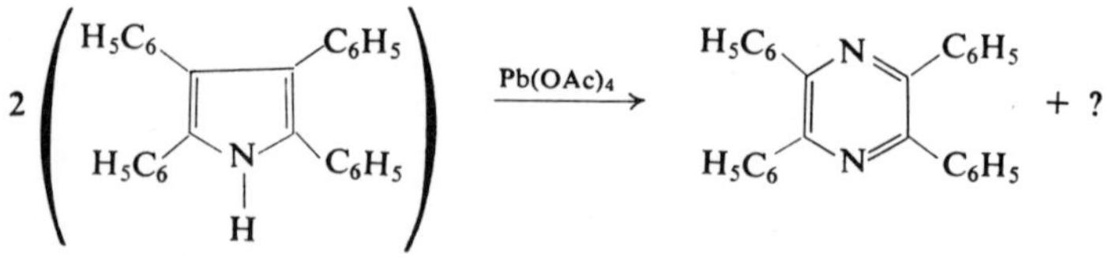

$$\text{(142)}$$

[272] W. Siedel and H. Möller, Z. Physiol. Chem. **259**, 113 (1939); W. Siedel and E. Grams, ibid. **267**, 49 (1941).

[273] O. Dimroth and R. Criegee, Ber. **90**, 2207 (1957); F. Kröhnke and H. L. Honig, Ann. **624**, 97 (1959).

[274] O. Dimroth and F. Frister, Ber. **55**, 1223 (1922).

[275] R. Kuhn and H. Kainer, Ann. **578**, 226 (1952).

C. PHOSPHORUS COMPOUNDS

Dimroth and Lerch[276] found that lead tetraacetate converts trialkylphosphites to trialkylphosphates. The reaction is almost instantaneous at 20° C in benzene solution and gives yields between 70 and 80%:

$$(RO)_3P + Pb(OAc)_4 \rightarrow (RO)_3PO + Pb(OAc)_2 + Ac_2O \qquad (143)$$

The method can be applied to the preparation of cyclic glycol esters of phosphoric acid, which are exceedingly sensitive to hydrolysis.

Dialkylphosphites are oxidized much more slowly. It is necessary to heat the benzene solution to reflux to obtain 77–99% yields. Monoalkylphosphites are usually oxidized as ammonium salts. Heating with an excess of lead tetraacetate for extended periods of time gives very good yields of monoalkylphosphates.

The intermediates in these oxidations might be quasi-phosphonium salts $[(OR)_3^+P\text{—}OAc]^-OAc$, akin to the intermediate in the oxidation of thioethers to sulfoxides.

VII. Reactions with Organometallic Compounds

Since 1943 Nessmejanow and his collaborators have studied the reactions of lead tetraacetate with mercury organic compounds[277–280]:

$$Ar_2Hg + Pb(OAc)_4 \xrightarrow[20° C]{HCCl_3} ArHgOAc + ArPb(OAc)_3 \qquad (144)$$

$$Ar_2Hg + ArPb(OAc)_3 \longrightarrow ArHgOAc + Ar_2Pb(OAc)_2 \qquad (145)$$

Depending on the proportions used, good yields of either aryl lead triacetates or diaryl lead diacetates are obtained. The reaction will proceed with widely different aryl groups, and even with a chlorovinyl group instead of Ar.[281, 282] Other lead(IV) salts can be used in the place of lead tetraacetate.[283]

[276] K. Dimroth and B. Lerch, *Angew. Chem.* **72**, 751 (1960).

[277] M. M. Nad' and K. A. Kotscheschkow, *J. Gen. Chem.* **12**, 409 (1942); *Chem. Abstr.* **37**, 3068 (1943).

[278] E. M. Panow and K. A. Kotscheschkow, *Dokl. Akad. Nauk SSSR* **85**, 1037 (1952); *Chem. Zentr.* p. 1798 (1953).

[279] E. M. Panow, V. J. Lodochnikowa, and K. A. Kotscheschkow, *Dokl. Akad. Nauk SSSR* **111**, 1042 (1956).

[280] R. Criegee, P. Dimroth, and R. Schempf, *Ber.* **90**, 1337 (1957).

[281] A. N. Nessmejanow, R. C. Freidlina, and K. A. Kotscheschkow, *Izv. Akad. Nauk SSSR* p. 127 (1948); *Chem. Abstr.* **43**, 1716 i (1949).

[282] A. N. Nessmejanow and A. E. Borisow, *Dokl. Akad. Nauk SSSR* **60**, 67 (1948); *Chem. Abstr.* **43**, 560 e (1949).

[283] V. J. Lodochnikowa, E. M. Ranow, and K. A. Kotscheschkow, *J. Gen. Chem.* **33** (4), 1199 (1963).

Aliphatic mercury organic compounds give alkyl acetate and lead diacetate.[280] Presumably, alkyl lead triacetates are formed first, but decompose spontaneously:

$$R-Pb(OAc)_3 \rightarrow ROAc + Pb(OAc)_2 \qquad (146)$$

The alkyl group can rearrange during this process. Dineopentyl mercury did not give neopentyl acetate, but tertiary amylacetate. Dineophyl mercury reacts analogously. Apparently the alkyl cation is not stable in the transition state.

When unsymmetrical organomercury compounds are employed, the more negative group combines with the lead, and an acetoxy group takes its place at the mercury atom.[280]

$$Pb(OAc)_4 + C_6H_5CH_2-Hg-C_6H_5 \xrightarrow{\quad\quad} \begin{array}{l} C_6H_5CH_2-Hg-OAc + C_6H_5Pb(OAc)_3 \\[1em] C_6H_5-Hg-OAc + (C_6H_5CH_2-Pb(OAc)_3) \\ \qquad\qquad\qquad\qquad\qquad\qquad \downarrow \\ \qquad\qquad C_6H_5CH_2OAc + Pb(OAc)_2 \end{array}$$

$$(147)$$

Thus the lead tetraacetate reacts as $AcO^-(OAc)_3Pb^+$, rather than as $AcO^+Pb(OAc)_3^-$. It seems reasonable to generalize this observation and to assume that other ionic lead tetraacetate oxidations also involve a $^+Pb(OAc)_3$ cation as the active species. It remains open to discussion whether the dissociation $Pb(OAc)_4 \rightarrow Pb(OAc)_3^+ + AcO^-$ takes place before, during, or after the reactive collision with the substrate molecule.

Lead organic compounds also react with lead tetraacetate,[284] the aliphatic ones at room temperature, the aromatic ones in boiling chloroform:

$$Pb(C_2H_5)_4 + Pb(OAc)_4 \rightarrow Pb(C_2H_5)_3OAc + H_5C_2Pb(OAc)_3 \qquad (148)$$

Only the first product was isolated. The second one should decompose to lead diacetate and ethyl acetate. Diphenyl lead diacetate was isolated in the case of lead tetraphenyl.

According to Frey and Cook,[285] aluminum organic compounds react with lead(IV) salts according to Eq. (149):

$$3\ PbX_4 + 4\ AlR_3 \rightarrow 3\ PbR_4 + 4\ AlX_3 \qquad (149)$$

X represents the acid residue, R the alkyl or aryl. The yields can exceed 90%. The conversion of $Pb(OAc)_4$ to $Pb(C_2H_5)_4$ must involve the intermediacy of

[284] K. A. Kocheshkov and R. C. Freidlina, *Izv. Akad. Nauk SSSR* p. 203 (1950); *Chem. Abstr.* **44**, 9342 (1950).
[285] F. W. Frey and S. E. Cook, *J. Am. Chem. Soc.* **82**, 530 (1960).

the unstable $C_2H_5Pb(OAc)_3$. Thus the reaction of the latter with triethyl aluminum has to be very rapid.

Appendix: Oxidations with Thallic Acetate and Iodoso Acetates

It would be beyond the scope of this article to discuss oxidants other than lead tetraacetate. However, it seems appropriate to point out the similarities between oxidations by lead tetraacetate and by mercuric acetate, thallium(III) acetate, and the iodoso acetates. Many analogies as well as many differences have been found. Mercuric acetate oxidations are discussed in this book in a separate article, which should be consulted.

Thallium(III) acetate exhibits properties in between those of lead tetra- acetate and mercuric acetate. Kabbe[222] conducted a detailed comparative investigation. Other reactions that have been reported are the oxidation of phenols,[52] the "thallation" of aromatic compounds,[286] the reaction with olefins,[222, 287–289a] and reactions with organomercury compounds.[290] Because of its relatively low redox potential, thallic acetate does not cleave glycols.[222]

The oxidizing power of iodoso acetates depends on the nature of the sub- stituent. This is an advantage in their use as oxidants, but there are very few systematic studies of this point.[291] Many of the oxidations possible with lead tetraacetate can also be accomplished with iodoso acetates. Substrates on which information is available are phenols,[292, 293] β-diketones and β-keto acid esters,[294] aromatic and nitroaromatic compounds,[295–297] olefins,[291] sulfur

[286] V. P. Glushkova and K. A. Kocheshkov, *Dokl. Akad. Nauk SSSR* **103**, 615 (1955); *Izv. Akad. Nauk SSSR* pp. 1186, 1391 (1957).

[287] R. R. Grinstead, *J. Org. Chem.* **26**, 238 (1961).

[288] J. B. Lee and M. J. Price, *Tetrahedron Letters* p. 1155 (1962); 936 (1963).

[289] C. B. Anderson and S. Winstein, *J. Org. Chem.* **28**, 605 (1963).

[289a] K. C. Paude and S. Winstein, *Tetrahedron Letters* p. 3393 (1964).

[290] V. P. Glushkova and K. A. Kocheshkov, *Izv. Akad. Nauk SSSR* p 1193 (1957); *Chem. Abstr.* **52**, 6239d (1958).

[291] R. Criegee and H. Beucker, *Ann.* **541**, 218 (1939).

[292] A. Siegel and F. Antony, *Monatsh. Chem.* **86**, 292 (1955).

[293] A. R. Fox and K. H. Pausacker, *J. Chem. Soc.* p. 295 (1957).

[294] O. J. Neiland and G. J. Wanag, *Dokl. Akad. Nauk SSSR* **131**, 1351 (1960); *Chem. Zentr.* p. 13713 (1962).

[295] R. S. Sandin and W. B. McCormack, *J. Am. Chem. Soc.* **67**, 2051 (1945).

[296] D. H. Hey, C. J. M. Stirling, and G. H. Williams, *J. Chem. Soc.* p. 3963 (1955); p. 1475 (1956).

[297] B. M. Lynch and K. H. Pausacker, *Australian J. Chem.* **10**, 329 (1957).

compounds,[74, 298] and aromatic amines.[299-304] Glycols are cleaved quantitatively by iodoso acetates,[291, 305, 306] just as by lead tetraacetate.

[298] L. Hellerman, F. P. Chinard, and P. A. Ramsdell, *J. Am. Chem. Soc.* **63**, 2551 (1941).

[299] K. H. Pausacker, *J. Chem. Soc.* p. 1989 (1953).

[300] G. B. Barlin, K. H. Pausacker, and N. V. Riggs, *J. Chem. Soc.* p. 3122 (1954).

[301] K. H. Pausacker and J. G. Scroggie, *J. Chem. Soc.* p. 4499 (1954).

[302] J. Mitchell and K. H. Pausacker, *J. Chem. Soc.* p. 4502 (1954).

[303] G. B. Barlin and N. V. Riggs, *J. Chem. Soc.* p. 3125 (1954).

[304] H. H. Szmant and R. L. Lapinski, *J. Am. Chem. Soc.* **78**, 458 (1956).

[305] K. H. Pausacker, *J. Chem. Soc.* p. 107 (1953).

[306] L. K. Dyall and K. H. Pausacker, *J. Chem. Soc.* p. 3950 (1958).

CHAPTER **VI**

Glycol Cleavage and Related Reactions

C. A. Bunton

I. Introduction 367
II. Periodic Acid 368
   A. Periodic Acid and Its Salts 369
   B. General Chemical Application 371
   C. Non-Malapradian Oxidation 388
   D. Experimental Applications 393
III. Lead Tetraacetate 398
   A. Diol Cleavage 398
   B. α-Hydroxy Acids 403
   C. 1,2-Dicarbonyl and 1,2-Hydroxycarbonyl Compounds 403
   D. Experimental Methods 404
IV. Iodoso Compounds 405
V. Sodium Bismuthate 406
VI. Xenic Acid 406

I. Introduction

This chapter discusses the carbon–carbon bond fission of 1,2-diols and related compounds. Two reagents, periodic acid and its salts, and lead tetraacetate, are particularly effective for this purpose because their reactions are generally clean and quantitative. These two reagents complement each other, in that periodate is most effective in water and has therefore been used especially for the quantitative oxidation of low molecular weight compounds and water-soluble carbohydrates, whereas lead tetraacetate is generally used in acetic acid, which may contain some water, or in aprotic solvents. The use of iodoso compounds and sodium bismuthate is also discussed, but compounds of silver, chromium, manganese, and vanadium are not considered because they are discussed elsewhere. The use of periodate as a general oxidant is considered briefly, but such uses of lead tetraacetate are not included here; they are discussed in Chapter V by Criegee, in this volume.

In the oxidative cleavage of 1,2-diols and related compounds, periodic acid, lead tetraacetate, phenyliodosoacetate, and sodium bismuthate probably act as two-electron oxidants, with transfer of two electrons to the outer shell of the central atom. The less specific oxidants are generally compounds of the transition metals, and can act as single electron acceptors, the electron being transferred to the available d-orbitals in the penultimate shell. Several authors have pointed out the difference in the behavior of these two types of oxidants toward diols.[1a, b] (The suggestion that free radicals are the reactive species in the cleavage of 1,2-diols by lead tetraacetate or periodic acid was based on preconception rather than experiment,[2a] and it has been shown that acetoxy radicals do not cleave 1,2-diols rapidly.[2b]) A further requirement for diol cleavage is that the radius of the central atom of the oxidant must be within a range which permits the diol to complex to the oxidant.[1b]

II. Periodic Acid

In 1928 Malaprade found that periodic acid and its salts quantitatively cleaved the carbon–carbon bond of 1,2-diols[3]:

$$R_2C(OH)CR_2OH + H_5IO_6 \rightarrow 2\ R_2C{=}O + HIO_3 + 2\ H_2O$$

Fleury then showed that the hydroxyl groups had to be on adjacent carbon atoms, and established periodic acid as a useful analytical reagent.[4] The method was soon extended to the cleavage of 1,2-hydroxycarbonyl and 1,2-dicarbonyl compounds,[3, 5] and then to the oxidation of 1,2-amino alcohols,[6] e.g.,

$$CH_3CO \cdot CHO + H_5IO_6 \rightarrow CH_3CO_2H + HCO_2H + HIO_3 + H_2O$$

$$C_6H_5CO \cdot CH(OH)C_6H_5 + H_5IO_6 \rightarrow C_6H_5CO_2H + C_6H_5CHO + HIO_3 + 2\ H_2O$$

$$CH_2(OH)CH_2(NH_2)CO_2H + H_5IO_6 \rightarrow CH_2O + CHO \cdot CO_2H + NH_3 + HIO_3 + 2\ H_2O$$

These so called "Malapradian" oxidations were quantitative, and reasonably fast at room temperature. They could be carried out over a wide range of pH, an important consideration when reactants or products are sensitive to acids and bases. Periodate ion could easily be analyzed in the presence of

1a J. Rocek and F. H. Westheimer, *J. Am. Chem. Soc.* **84**, 2241 (1962).

1b L. J. Heidt, E. K. Gladding, and C. B. Purves, *Paper Trade J.* **121**, 81 (1945); *Chem. Abstr.* **40**, 546 (1946).

2a W. A. Waters, *Trans. Faraday Soc.* **42**, 185 (1946); *Ann. Rept. Progr. Chem.* (*Chem. Soc. London*) **42**, 143 (1945).

2b M. S. Kharasch, H. N. Friedlander, and W. H. Urry, *J. Org. Chem.* **14**, 91 (1949).

3 L. Malaprade, *Compt. Rend, Acad. Sci.* **186**, 382 (1928); *Bull. Soc. Chim. France* [4] **43**, 683 (1928); [5] **1**, 833 (1934).

4 P. Fleury and J. Lange, *Compt. Rend. Acad. Sci.* **195**, 1395 (1932); P. Fleury and R. Paris, *ibid.* **196**, 1416 (1933).

5 P. W. Clutterbuck and F. Reuter, *J. Chem. Soc.* p. 1467 (1935).

6 B. M. Nicolet and L. A. Shinn, *J. Am. Chem. Soc.* **61**, 1615 (1939).

iodate ion and the other reaction products, because it oxidized iodide ion to iodine in neutral or mildly alkaline solution. A general discussion of the use of periodate as a reagent in organic chemistry is given by Jackson.[7]

These rapid oxidations by periodate are specific—e.g., monofunctional alcohols, aldehydes, and ketones are either inert or react only very slowly with it—and therefore it is one of the most useful reagents in qualitative and quantitative organic analysis. However, it does oxidize some other organic compounds readily (even though they do not have 1,2-hydroxyl, carbonyl, or amino groups), e.g., active methylene compounds, some aromatic phenols, and some organic sulfur compounds. These so-called "non-Malapradian" oxidations are discussed in Section II,C.

The generality of the oxidation of 1,2-diols by periodate, and the known ability of these diols to form cyclic complexes with boric acid or with cuprammonium ions, led to the suggestion that cyclic periodate esters, e.g., I or its anions, were probable reaction intermediates.[3, 8]

$$\begin{array}{c} R_2C\!-\!O \\ | \qquad\quad \diagdown \\ \qquad\qquad IO_4H_3 \\ | \qquad\quad \diagup \\ R_2C\!-\!O \end{array}$$

(I)

Similar cyclic intermediates were also postulated for diol cleavage by lead tetraacetate.[8] Study of the stereochemical requirements for diol cleavage by periodate has given very powerful support to this hypothesis (cf. Angyal and Young[9] and Section II,B,2), and mechanistic work on diol cleavage has shown, with a fair degree of certainty, that diol–periodate complexes are indeed reaction intermediates (Section II,B,2). Very stable complexes are formed between periodate and some triols (Section II,B,2,a), and there is some nonconclusive evidence that cyclic esters are reaction intermediates in the oxidation of 1,2-diketones and of reactive methylene compounds (Sections II,B,3 and II,C).

A. PERIODIC ACID AND ITS SALTS

Periodic acid in water is polybasic, and exists as H_5IO_6, orthoperiodic acid.[7, 10] Orthoperiodic acid is not strong, and the dehydrated periodic acid, HIO_4, does not exist as such in aqueous solution; it reacts violently with

[7] E. L. Jackson, "Organic Reactions" (R. Adam, ed.), Vol. II, Chapter 8. Wiley, New York, 1944.

[8] R. Criegee, L. Kraft, and B. Rank, *Ann.* **507**, 159 (1933); R. Criegee, *Sitzber. Ges. Befoerder. Ges. Naturw. Marburg* **69**, 25 (1934); *Chem. Abstr.* **29**, 6820 (1935).

[9] S. J. Angyal and R. J. Young, *J. Am. Chem. Soc.* **81**, 5251, 5467 (1959).

[10] K. J. Morgan, *Quart. Rev.* **8**, 123 (1954).

water.[11] Salts of both HIO_4 and H_5IO_6 are known. The dimeric acid $H_4I_2O_9$ has been reported,[11] and its salts have been isolated but, except in alkali, only monomeric species exist in aqueous solution.

X-ray crystallography has shown that the periodate monoanion, IO_4^-, is tetrahedral,[12] and the orthoperiodate dianion, $H_3IO_6^{2-}$, is octahedral.[13]

Equilibrium between periodic acid and its various anions is set up rapidly, e.g., they give the same ultraviolet spectra in a given solution,[14] and there is a rapid oxygen exchange between periodate ions and water.[15] Reagent solutions can be made up with either periodic acid or its salts, and the general term periodate will be applied to the reagent.

There is some uncertainty as to the state of the periodate monoanion in water. Considering only monomers, the main equilibria are thought to be[14]:

$$H_5IO_6 \rightleftharpoons H_4IO_6^- \rightleftharpoons H_3IO_6^{2-} \rightleftharpoons H_2IO_6^{3-}$$

$$\updownarrow$$

$$I\bar{O}_4 + 2 H_2O$$

The directly determined acid dissociation constants may therefore be "apparent" ones, in that they include the hydration equilibrium constant relating $H_4IO_6^-$ to IO_4^-. These various equilibrium constants have been separated, and ultraviolet spectroscopic evidence suggests that IO_4^- is the predominant monoanionic species,[14] and this conclusion is supported by Raman spectroscopy.[16] However, it has been claimed that infrared spectroscopy excludes the existence of IO_4^- as an important species in water, and that $H_4IO_6^-$ is the predominant monoanion.[17] Fortunately this uncertainty as to the state of the reagent does not impair its utility, although it complicates the detailed analysis of the reaction mechanism. All the various workers agree that the monohydrates, e.g., $H_2IO_5^-$, are not present in aqueous solution. The "apparent" pK_a values of the acid at $25°$ C are[14,17a]: first dissociation, 1.64;

[11] J. R. Partington and R. K. Bahl, *J. Chem. Soc.* p. 1086 (1934).

[12] E. A. Hazlewood, *Z. Krist.* **98**, 439 (1938).

[13] L. Helmholz, *J. Am. Chem. Soc.* **59**, 2036 (1937).

[14] C. E. Crouthamel, H. V. Meek, D. S. Martin, and C. V. Banks, *J. Am. Chem. Soc.* **71**, 3031 (1949); C. E. Crouthamel, A. M. Hayes, and D. S. Martin, *ibid.* **73**, 82 (1951).

[15] M. Anbar and S. Guttmann, *J. Am. Chem. Soc.* **83**, 781 (1961); A. I. Brodskii and N. A. Vysotskaya, *Zh. Fiz. Khim.* **32**, 1521 (1958); *Chem. Abstr.* **53**, 1901 (1959).

[16] H. Siebert, *Z. Anorg. Allgem. Chem.* **273**, 21 (1953).

[17] N. Keen and M. C. R. Symons, *Proc. Chem. Soc.* p. 383 (1960).

[17a] G. J. Buist and J. D. Lewis [*Chem. Commun.* p. 66 (1965)] have shown that the dimesoperiodate anion $I_2O_9^{2-}$ (or probably its hydrate) is present in aqueous solutions of periodate at high pH. The second dissociation constant is independent of temperature, provided that allowance is made for this dimerization.

second, 8.36; third, 15. These pK_a values are said to vary markedly with temperature, and the variation of pK with temperature is consistent with the suggestion that both hydrated and dehydrated forms of the anion exist in water. There are other pK_a values in the literature which agree with those given.[18] However, Ivanova and Neimann report that temperature has little effect upon these dissociation constants.[19]

The general term "periodate" will be applied to all the species which have the same stoichiometry as HIO_4. They will oxidize iodide ions to iodine in neutral solution, and can therefore be estimated in the presence of iodate ion, which reacts rapidly with iodide ion only in acid solution.

B. GENERAL CHEMICAL APPLICATIONS

1. MALAPRADIAN OXIDATIONS

Periodate is the best reagent for the quantitative determination of 1,2-diols, hydroxycarbonyl and dicarbonyl compounds, and 1,2-amino alcohols. It is also a simple reagent for distinguishing between vicinal and other diols, e.g., for distinguishing between α- and β-derivatives of glycerol.[4]

$$\alpha\text{-}\quad \begin{array}{c} CH_2OPO_3H_2 \\ | \\ CHOH \\ | \\ CH_2OH \end{array} \;+\; H_5IO_6 \;\longrightarrow\; \begin{array}{c} CH_2OPO_3H_2 \\ | \\ CHO \\ \\ CH_2O \end{array} \;+\; HIO_3$$

$$\beta\text{-}\quad \begin{array}{c} CH_2OH \\ | \\ CHOPO_3H_2 \\ | \\ CH_2OH \end{array} \;+\; H_5IO_6 \qquad\qquad \text{no reaction}$$

These methods are not completely general, because certain *trans*-diols are inert; even these unreactive 1,2-diols react quantitatively, although slowly, with lead tetraacetate (Section III,A). Another complication arises when the initial oxidation products react further with periodate: this is the phenomenon of "overconsumption" (Section II,C), and usually manifests itself as a slow reaction of periodate with the products, following an initial rapid uptake.[20, 21]

[18] P. Souchay and A. Hessaby, *Bull. Soc. Chim. France* p. 614 (1953); R. Nasanen, *Acta Chem. Scand.* **8**, 1587 (1954).

[19] M. F. Ivanova and M. B. Neiman, *Dokl. Akad. Nauk SSSR* **60**, 1005 (1948); *Chem. Abstr.* **42**, 8583 (1948).

[20] D. H. Bell, *J. Chem. Soc.* p. 992 (1948); G. D. Greville and D. H. Northcote, *ibid.* p. 1945 (1952); F. S. H. Head and G. Hughes, *ibid.* p. 603 (1954); M. L. Wolfrom, A. Thompson, A. N. O'Neill, and T. T. Galkowsi, *J. Am. Chem. Soc.* **74**, 1062 (1952).

[21] P. Fleury, *Bull. Soc. Chim. France* p. 1126 (1955).

An excess of periodate is usually added to the substrate, and after oxidation is complete the excess is determined by addition of iodide ion and titration of the liberated iodine with either sodium arsenite or thiosulfate.[7] The carbonyl products may react with iodine, and then a mixture of potassium iodide and a known excess of sodium arsenite is added, so that no iodine is liberated; the excess sodium arsenite is titrated rapidly with standard iodine. Examples of these methods, and some variants of them, are given in Section II,D.

Solubility is not usually a limitation, because low molecular weight diols are usually water soluble, and very low concentrations can be used, e.g., $10^{-4}M$ if starch is used as an indicator. (For the lower concentrations, it is better to use amperometric methods for determination of iodine.[22]) Polarography[23] and ultraviolet spectrophotometry[14] can also be used for the quantitative detection of periodate and for rate measurements with very low concentrations of reagent. For optically active diols, reaction can be followed polarimetrically, a particularly useful technique in carbohydrate chemistry[24] (Section II,D,2). Organic solvents can be added to the water to increase the solubility of the organic compound,[7] but unfortunately many of them decrease both the solubility of periodate and the reaction rate.[25]

These general methods can also be applied to the determination of the structures of carbohydrates and polyols, but because it is often necessary to isolate and identify the reaction products, the scale of the experiment has to be larger than that required for analysis.

Many of the classic applications of periodate in structural determination have been in carbohydrate chemistry, although some of this early evidence was misleading, largely because the possibility of reaction between the products and periodate was not at first appreciated. The uses of periodate oxidation for the determination of carbohydrate structures are discussed in refs. 24, 26–28. It is necessary to follow not only the uptake of periodate, but also the formation of formaldehyde and formic acid. Some examples of structural studies on carbohydrates are given in Section II,D,2.

[22] D. C. Davis, *in* "Handbook of Analytical Chemistry" (L. Meites, ed.), Sec. 5-164. McGraw-Hill, New York, 1963.

[23] P. Zuman, J. Sicher, J. Krupicka, and M. Svoboda, *Nature* **178**, 1407 (1956); P. Zuman and J. Krupicka, *Collection Czech. Chem. Commun.* **23**, 598 (1958).

[24] J. M. Bobbitt, *Advan. Carbohydrate Chem.* **2**, 1 (1956).

[25a] J. Honeyman and C. J. G. Shaw, *J. Chem. Soc.* p. 2455 (1959).

[25b] R. D. Guthrie, *Chem. & Ind.* (*London*) p. 691 (1960).

[26] R. J. Dimler, *Advan. Carbohydrate Chem.* **7**, 37 (1952).

[27] A. S. Perlin, *in* "Methods in Carbohydrate Chemistry" (R. L. Whister and M. L. Wolfrom, eds.), Vol. 1, p. 427. Academic Press, New York, 1962.

[28] R. D. Guthrie, *in* "Methods in Carbohydrate Chemistry" (R. L. Whister and M. L. Wolfrom, eds.), Vol. 1, p. 432. Academic Press, New York, 1962.

Periodate can be used to distinguish between *erythro-* and *threo-*isomeric diols, provided that both isomers are available, and their rates of reaction with periodate can be measured. The *threo-*isomers are the more reactive[23, 29, 30] (Sections II,B,2 and II,D,2). Somewhat similarly, *cis-*carbocyclic diols are generally more reactive than *trans-* (Sections II,B and II,D,2). However, these tests should be used circumspectly, because the cleavage of diols by periodate is a multistage reaction, and the nature of the rate-limiting step depends upon the structure of the diol and upon the reaction conditions. Also, there are oxidations of diols by various reagents in which the *trans-*diol is more reactive than the *cis-*[31, 32] (cf., Section III,A).

Periodate is more useful in analysis than as a preparative oxidant. Its high molecular weight requires its use in large amounts, and moreover many high molecular weight organic compounds are only sparingly soluble in water. It is probably better in general to use lead tetraacetate, in an organic solvent, in preference to periodate as a preparative oxidant. However, for certain preparative applications, periodate possesses unique features in that: (i) it can be used in neutral solution; (ii) it is highly specific; and (iii) isolation of the reaction products from the aqueous solution is usually simple.[7, 33]

2. MECHANISMS OF OXIDATION OF 1,2-DIOLS

The first extensive kinetic study of the oxidative cleavage of 1,2-diols by periodate was made by Price and co-workers, who found a marked effect of acidity upon reaction rates for pinacol, ethane diol, and *cis-* and *trans-*cyclohexane-1,2-diol.[34, 35a] For the oxidation of pinacol, rate maxima were observed in acid and at pH about 8; these general observations have been confirmed by other workers,[35b] but complete explanations are lacking. The *cis* isomer of cyclohexane-1,2-diol was approximately 30 times more reactive than the *trans*, and Price explained this difference in terms of a cyclic diol–periodate complex, similar to that postulated by Criegee for the oxidative cleavage of 1,2-diols by lead tetraacetate.[8] (Malaprade had inferred that periodate and a 1,2-diol formed a complex, because the pH of a periodate solution changed rapidly on addition of a diol.[3]) The unreactivity of some 1,2-diols to periodate strongly

[29] F. R. Duke and V. C. Bulgrin, *J. Am. Chem. Soc.* **76**, 3803 (1954).
[30] G. J. Buist, C. A. Bunton, and J. H. Miles, *J. Chem. Soc.* p. 4567 (1957).
[31] P. Levesley, W. A. Waters, and A. N. Wright, *J. Chem. Soc.* p. 840 (1956).
[32] R. Criegee, E. Hoger, G. Huber, P. Kruck, F. Marktscheffel, and H. Schellenberger, *Ann.* **599**, 81 (1956).
[33] R. D. Guthrie and J. Honeyman, *J. Chem. Soc.* p. 2441 (1959).
[34] C. C. Price and T. J. Kroll, *J. Am. Chem. Soc.* **60**, 2727 (1938).
[35a] C. C. Price and M. J. Knell, *J. Am. Chem. Soc.* **64**, 552 (1942).
[35b] S. Sevent-Perez and P. Escudero, *Anales Real. Soc. Espan. Fis. Quim. (Madrid) Ser.* **B57**, 153 (1961).

supports formation of a cyclic, rather than an open-chain, intermediate,[9, 36] because most of these unreactive diols have geometries which prevent their forming a cyclic periodate ester, as in *trans*-decalin-9,10-diol (II):

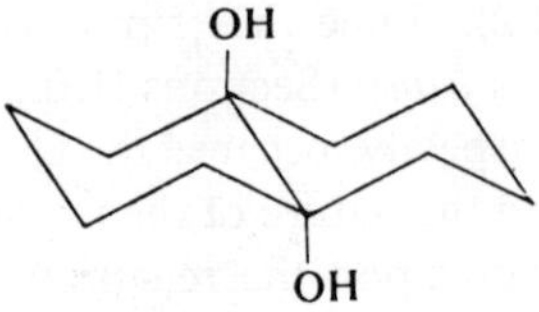

OH

OH

(II)

Although *trans*-cyclopentane-1,2-diol (III) is split by periodate,[37] the corresponding 1,2-dimethyl compound (IV) is inert,[38] because formation of a cyclic intermediate would involve not only considerable distortion of the cyclopentane ring but also compressions between nearby atoms and groups.

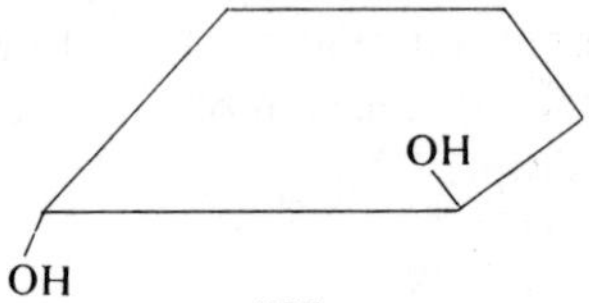

OH

OH
(III)

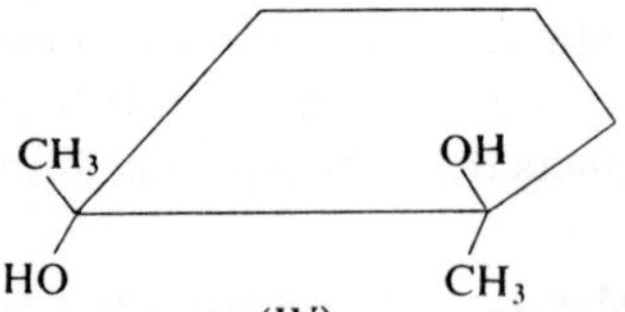

CH_3 OH

HO CH_3
(IV)

Somewhat similarly the rigidity of their fused ring systems makes D-glucosan[39] (V) and D-galactosan[40] (VI) inert to periodate, and relatively so to lead tetraacetate, although the more flexible L-threitan (VII) is readily oxidized.[41]

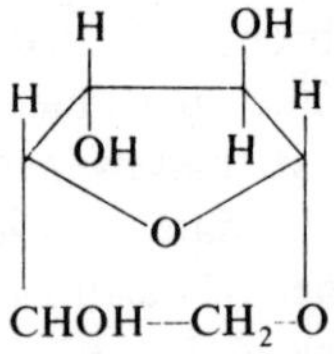

H   OH

H   H

OH   H

O

$CHOH$—CH_2–O

(V)

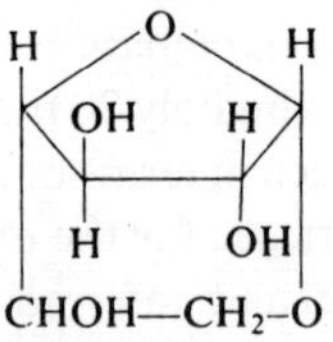

H   O   H

OH   H

H   OH

$CHOH$—CH_2–O

(VI)

OH   H

H   H

H   HO

H   O   H

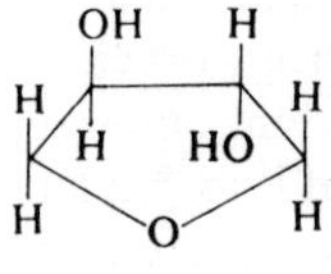

(VII)

Honeyman and his co-workers have investigated several other inert fused ring sugar derivatives, whose configuration prevents their forming cyclic complexes.[25a]

[36] R. Criegee, E. Büchner, and W. Walther, *Ber.* **73**, 571 (1940).

[37] V. C. Bulgrin, *J. Phys. Chem.* **61**, 702 (1957); V. C. Bulgrin and G. Dahlgren, *J. Am. Chem. Soc.* **80**, 3883 (1958).

[38] C. A. Bunton and M. D. Carr, *J. Chem. Soc.* p. 770 (1963).

[39] R. J. Dimler, H. A. Davis, and G. E. Hilbert, *J. Am. Chem. Soc.* **68**, 1377 (1946).

[40] B. H. Alexander, R. J. Dimler, and C. L. Mehltretter, *J. Am. Chem. Soc.* **73**, 4658 (1951).

[41] H. Klosterman and F. Smith, *J. Am. Chem. Soc.* **74**, 5336 (1952).

Rigidity of a ring is not the only factor which can hinder oxidation of a diol by periodate.

In the cyclohexane series the hydroxyl groups of 1,2-*trans*-dimethylcyclohexane-1,2-diol (VIIIa,b) can take up the diequatorial diol conformation (VIIIa) required for formation of a cyclic periodate ester. Nevertheless, this diol is almost completely inert to periodate because the nonbonding repulsions would be very great in a periodate ester and in the cyclic transition state leading to it[38] [*trans*-cyclohexane-1,2-diol is not particularly unreactive (Section II,B,2)].

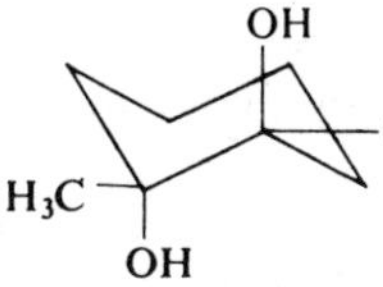

(VIIIb)

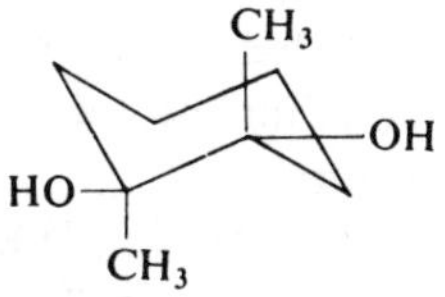

(VIIIa)

All this evidence suggests that a cyclic periodate ester is the key reaction intermediate, and Duke showed that the kinetic form of oxidation of ethane diol by periodate could be interpreted in terms of such an intermediate (I), present in appreciable concentration, and decomposing slowly to product[42]:

$$\begin{array}{l} R_2COH \\ \;| \\ R_2COH \end{array} + HIO_4 \underset{}{\overset{K}{\rightleftarrows}} \begin{array}{l} R_2C{-}O \\ \;| \qquad\quad IO_4H_3 \\ R_2C{-}O \end{array} \xrightarrow{k} 2\,R_2CO + HIO_3 \qquad (1)$$

(The equation is written to indicate only the stoichiometry with respect to periodate and diol. Periodic acid, HIO_4, is almost certainly not the reactive form of the oxidant.)

This reaction sequence leads to the following rate equation:

$$k' = \frac{kK[D]}{1+K[D]} \qquad (2a)$$

or

$$\frac{1}{k'} = \frac{1}{kK[D]} + \frac{1}{k} \qquad (2b)$$

where k' is the observed first-order rate constant with respect to periodate (P) and D is the diol.

A value was calculated for the equilibrium constant (K) and the rate constant (k) for oxidation of ethane diol,[42] and subsequently for other diols; both these constants depend on acidity.[43]

[42] F. R. Duke, *J. Am. Chem. Soc.* **69**, 3054 (1947).
[43] G. J. Buist and C. A. Bunton, *J. Chem. Soc.* p. 1406 (1954).

There is direct evidence for an intermediate, e.g., addition of a simple 1,2-diol to periodate in initially neutral or acid solution gives a rapid decrease in pH [3, 43] and a rapid change in the ultraviolet spectrum.[44] Also, the uptake of periodate during the oxidation of glucose is faster than the over-all reaction, as measured by formation of formic acid, suggesting that an intermediate can build up in concentration.[45] However, in this reaction the intermediate may not be a periodate ester, but merely an unstable oxidation product of glucose. These results do not prove that this complex of diol and periodate is a reaction intermediate, e.g., the reagents might react directly, and irreversibly, to give products, and reversibly to give an otherwise inert complex.[46] But this hypothesis is excluded by the analysis of the induction period which occurs during the oxidation of 2-methylbutane-2,3-diol by periodate, and will not be considered further.[47]

The effect of changes in pH upon the rate of oxidation of a simple diol can be explained quantitatively.[30, 43] The rate constant, k, increases with increasing pH to a maximum value at pH 4–5, where the concentration of the singly negatively charged complex, which is the reactive form of the intermediate, is at a maximum. It then decreases sharply, whereas the equilibrium constant, K, is independent of a limited change of acidity at low pH, then increases sharply to a plateau at pH 4–5, and then increases again at higher pH (Table I).

TABLE I

EFFECT OF pH ON THE RATE AND EQUILIBRIUM CONSTANTS k AND K^a

pH	0.96	1.15	1.61	1.98	3.05	4.34
$10^4 k$ (sec^{-1})	20.3	27.9	36.8	41.7	45.1	45.5
K (liters mole^{-1})	17.7	18.7	40	68	141	189

pH	5.25	6.76	7.07	7.68	9.58
$10^4 k$ (sec^{-1})	44.0	18.5	16.5	2.73	0.03
K (liters mole^{-1})	188	345	540	ca. 1000	ca. 2500

^{a} Ethane diol at 0° C in water.

44 G. J. Buist, C. A. Bunton, and J. H. Miles, *J. Chem. Soc.* p. 4575 (1957).

45 G. Hughes and T. P. Nevell, *Trans. Faraday Soc.* **44**, 941 (1948).

46 J. E. Taylor, *J. Am. Chem. Soc.* **75**, 3912 (1953); J. E. Taylor, B. Soldano, and G. A. Hall, *ibid.* **77**, 2656 (1955).

47 G. J. Buist and C. A. Bunton, *J. Chem. Soc.* p. 4580 (1957).

Both periodic acid and its ester (I) are polybasic acids, and the equilibrium constant K can be expressed in terms of the acid dissociation constants of periodic acid and the periodate ester, and the acidity of the solution; from the variation of K with pH one can calculate these dissociation constants, as well as those between the reactants and the periodate ester. The dissociation constants for periodic acid determined in this way agree well with those determined conventionally.[43] As expected, the periodate esters are stronger acids than periodic acid.

For the simple open chain diols the equilibria are:

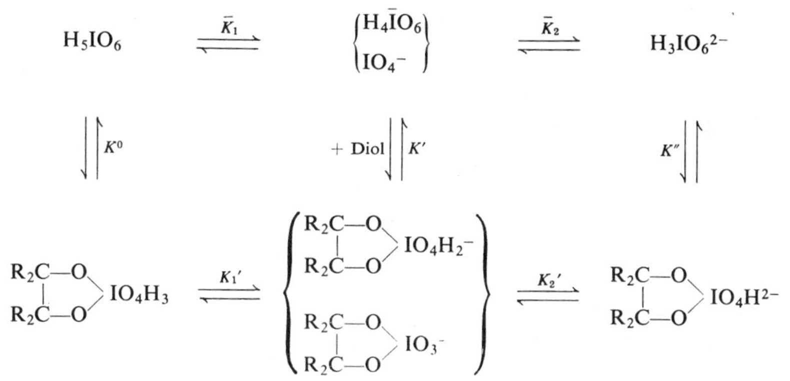

$$H_5IO_6 \quad \underset{\overline{K}_1}{\rightleftharpoons} \quad \begin{cases} H_4\bar{I}O_6 \\ IO_4^- \end{cases} \quad \underset{\overline{K}_2}{\rightleftharpoons} \quad H_3IO_6{}^{2-}$$

$$\Big\downarrow K^0 \qquad\qquad + \text{Diol} \,\Big\downarrow K' \qquad\qquad K'' \,\Big\uparrow$$

$$\begin{array}{c} R_2C-O \\ | \quad\quad\; \diagup IO_4H_3 \\ R_2C-O \end{array} \;\; \underset{K_1'}{\rightleftharpoons} \;\; \left\{ \begin{array}{c} R_2C-O \\ | \quad\quad\; \diagup IO_4H_2{}^- \\ R_2C-O \\[8pt] R_2C-O \\ | \quad\quad\; \diagup IO_3{}^- \\ R_2C-O \end{array} \right\} \;\; \underset{K_2'}{\rightleftharpoons} \;\; \begin{array}{c} R_2C-O \\ | \quad\quad\; \diagup IO_4H^{2-} \\ R_2C-O \end{array}$$

Some of these equilibrium constants should depend upon the state of hydration of the various species, e.g., the acid dissociation constants $\overline{K}_1$ and $\overline{K}_2$ for periodic acid, and K_1' and K_2' for the intermediate are all apparent.

a. *Equilibrium Constants.* Because the intermediates are stronger acids than periodic acid (Table II), increasing the pH changes the equilibrium in their favor, and in alkaline solution it is very much toward the dianionic form of the intermediate.

The equilibrium constants depend upon alkyl substituents as well as upon the stereochemistry of the diol.[29, 30] In general the states of hydration of the cyclic esters are not known, but there is no ambiguity with regard to the equilibrium constant, K'', which relates the periodate dianion, $H_3IO_6{}^{2-}$, to the dinegatively charged periodate ester, because neither of these ions can exist in dehydrated forms [except as penta-coordinated structures for which there is no evidence (Section II,A)]. The neutral species also probably exists predominantly as the hydrated structure shown, just as does periodic acid, because the dehydrated form should be a very strong acid.[43] Only the variation of K'' will be discussed, although as can be seen from Table II, the constants K^0 and K' vary similarly to K'' with changes in structure of the diol.

TABLE II

EQUILIBRIUM, DISSOCIATION, AND RATE CONSTANTS FOR THE
INTERMEDIATE COMPLEXES [30, 43, 49] [a]

	Complex equilibria			Acid dissociation[b]		Decomposition[c]
Diol	K^0	K'	K''	$10^2 K'_1$	$10^7 K'_2$	$10^4 k$
Ethane	10	189	1800	17.4	1.1	45.7
Propane-1,2-	39	500	2800	5.0	0.65	120
meso-Butane-2,3-	19	68	373	2.6	0.50	182
(−)-Butane-2,3-	270	—	8000	3.4	0.42	302
2-Methylpropane-1,2-	16	101	360	2.6	0.28	607
2-Methylbutane-2,3-	60	—	940	1.4	0.19	244
cis-Cyclohexane	—	—	400	0.83	0.48	3300
trans-Cyclohexane	—	—	1000	3.11	0.85	165

[a] Temperature, 0° C. Equilibrium and dissociation constants are given in mole^{-1} liter. Rate constants are given in sec^{-1}.

[b] For periodic acid,[14, 43] $10^2 \bar{K}_1 = 0.36$; $10^7 \bar{K}_2 = 0.12$.

[c] First-order rate constant for decomposition of the mononegative anion of the intermediate.

Inductive electron release by alkyl groups should stabilize the intermediate, relative to the reactants, by increasing the electron density of the oxygen atoms of the hydroxyl group. But there is also a steric hindrance to formation of the intermediate, as evidenced by the values of K'' for oxidations of the *meso-* and *dl*-butane-2,3-diols. (These have *erythro* and *threo* configurations, respectively.) The electronic effects of the substituents should be the same, but the steric effects different, because they depend upon geometry.[29, 30] The equilibrium constants for the *dl*-diol are considerably greater than for the *meso*-diol (Table II). Two different nonbonding repulsions must be considered. (i) There may be methyl–methyl repulsions caused by partial eclipsing of these groups in a cyclic periodate ester. Eclipsing will not be complete in an octahedral complex, because the ring in it should be slightly puckered rather than planar.[30] [Although the dinegatively charged intermediate is probably not planar, the transition state for decomposition of intermediate to products may be, particularly if it is formed from a dehydrated species (Section II,B,2,b).] (ii) There may be repulsions between the methyl groups and one of the oxygen atoms attached to the octahedral iodine atom. Figure 1 shows the octahedral complex formed between a diol and periodate. If the complex is formed from the *meso*-diol, one of the groups attached to each carbon atom must be in a hindered position, marked with an asterisk, which is close to one of the shaded oxygen atoms attached to the iodine atom, and the other will be in a free position away from the oxygen atoms.

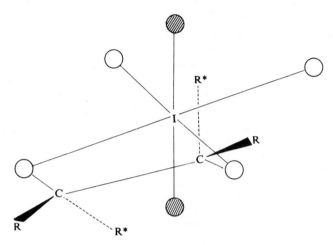

FIG. 1. Cyclic periodate ester.

Interference between the shaded oxygen atoms and the hindered groups may be relieved by decreasing the puckering of the ring, but at the cost of increasing eclipsing strain between the methyl groups.

In the cyclic ester formed from *dl*-butane-2,3-diol the two methyl groups are not eclipsed, and they do not interfere with any of the oxygen atoms attached to the octahedral iodine atom, i.e., they can both go into the free positions. With the *meso*-diol they can be eclipsed to a greater or lesser extent, and one of them must go into a "hindered" position and interfere with a "periodate" oxygen atom; if the conformation of the five-membered ring is changed, so that the interference between this methyl group and an oxygen atom is decreased, then methyl–methyl eclipsing will increase, and vice versa. Steric hindrance, between a methyl group and an oxygen atom, or between eclipsed methyl groups, will also occur in the cyclic esters formed from periodate and 2-methylpropane-2,3-diol or 2-methylbutane-2,3-diol, and the equilibrium constants for formation of periodate esters from these diols are low (Table II). For pinacol the internal repulsions are large enough to prevent detection of a cyclic ester, except perhaps in strongly alkaline solution where equilibrium constants are generally high.[29, 30, 48]

[48] G. J. Buist, Ph.D. Thesis, University of London, 1954; J. H. Miles, Ph.D. Thesis, University of London, 1956.

Except for the cyclohexane-1,2-diols,[49] intermediates are not detected between periodate and cyclic diols.[37, 38, 50] The cyclohexane case is interesting because the equilibrium constants for formation of the dinegatively charged intermediate are greater for the *trans*- than for the *cis*-diol (Table II). It is not possible to measure these constants for the uncharged and single negatively charged intermediates, because reactants and intermediate are not in equilibrium. Qualitative measurements suggest, however, that in acid solution the equilibrium constant is larger for the *cis*-diol.[49] Two steric factors are at work. (i) Formation of an intermediate between the diols and the octahedral periodate dianion requires a slight decrease in the interoxygen distance of the hydroxyl groups of the diol, which will flatten the cyclohexane ring for *cis*-diol (in the *ax-eq* configuration), but pucker it more for the *trans*-diol, (in the *eq-eq* conformation). These distortions of the cyclohexane ring will be energetically more costly for the *trans*- than for the *cis*-diol.[25a, 51] (ii) Opposing factor (i) is the interference which exists between one of the periodate oxygen atoms and the carbon and hydrogen atoms of the *cis*-diol. The cyclic ester of *cis*-cyclohexane-1,2-diol has a similar configuration to that of an *erythro*-diol, whereas *trans*-cyclohexane diol and a *threo*-diol give cyclic esters of similar configuration[49]; to this extent we can compare *cis*-cyclohexane-1,2-diol with *meso*-butane-2,3-diol, and the *trans*-diol with *dl*-butane-2,3-diol.

The situation for these octahedral periodate complexes therefore differs from that for cyclic borates or ketals,[51] where generally $K_{cis} > K_{trans}$.[51a] For these compounds, factor (i) is more important, and this should be true also for dehydrated forms of the periodate complexes, which must have a penta-coordinated iodine atom. This difference in behavior between the periodate complexes which have a penta- and a hexa-coordinated iodine atom probably has important kinetic consequences (Section II,B,2,b).

Long-lived tridentate complexes are formed between some *cis-cis* triols and periodate; the stereochemistry of the triol is critical,[54] and it is suggested that two axial and one equatorial hydroxyl groups are complexing with the iodine atom (Fig. 2). These complexes apparently do not decompose to the products,

[49] G. J. Buist, C. A. Bunton, and J. H. Miles, *J. Chem. Soc.* p. 743 (1959).

[50] J. Honeyman and C. J. G. Shaw, *J. Chem. Soc.* p. 2451 (1959).

[51] S. J. Angyal and C. G. MacDonald, *J. Chem. Soc.* p. 686 (1952); S. J. Angyal and D. J. McHugh, *ibid.* p. 1423 (1957).

[51a] The use of borate esters as model compounds for the formation of periodate esters is complicated by the variety of borate–diol complexes which may form,[51, 52] and in some cases their stability does not correlate with the dihedral angle of the 1,2-hydroxyl groups of the diol.[53]

[52] A. Boeseken, *Advan. Carbohydrate Chem.* 4, 189 (1949); A. B. Foster, *ibid.* 12, 81 (1957).

[53] M. Mazurek and A. S. Perlin, *Can. J. Chem.* 41, 2403 (1963).

[54] G. R. Barker and D. F. Shaw, *J. Chem. Soc.* p. 584 (1959); T. P. Nevell, *Chem. & Ind. (London)* p. 567 (1959).

and the chemical reaction occurs through formation and decomposition of the normal cyclic intermediate. Formation of these inert complexes is good evidence for configuration of a triol.

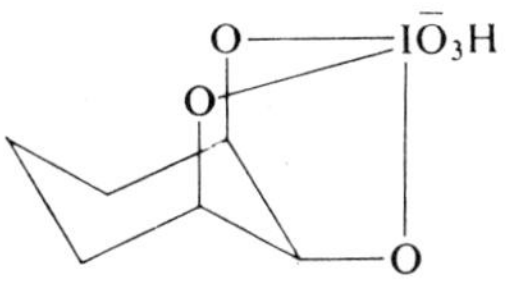

FIG. 2. Inert tridentate periodate ester.

b. *Decomposition of the Intermediate to Products.* In Table I, it was shown that the rate constant, k, for decomposition of the intermediate products, increased with increasing pH, to a maximum at pH 4–5, and then decreased. A more detailed analysis of the rate measurements shows that only the mono-negatively charged intermediate decomposes to products, and that the un-dissociated or dinegatively charged intermediates are inert.[30, 43] It was suggested that the mononegatively charged intermediate could fragment easily, provided that it was in its dehydrated form (IX).

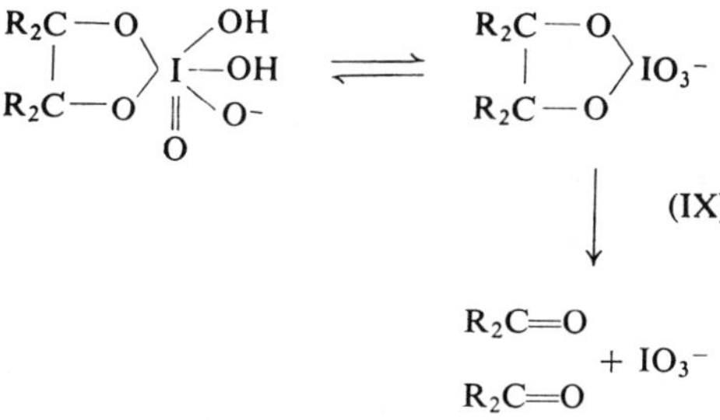

The dinegatively charged intermediate cannot exist in a dehydrated form, and the dehydrated form of the uncharged intermediate should be a strong acid, and therefore fully ionized at the pH of the reaction solutions. Increasing methylation of the diol generally speeds decomposition of the cyclic inter-mediate to products.[29, 30] Release of eclipsing strains is apparently not of overwhelming importance, as can be seen by a comparison of k for *meso-* and *dl*-butane-2,3-diol (Table II), because the least strained ester decomposes faster. *gem*-Dimethyl groups assist decomposition, possibly because hyper-conjugative electron release stabilizes the forming carbonyl group, or because repulsion between these methyl groups makes it easier for the carbon atom to change its bond angles from those of a tetrahedral to those of a trigonal carbon atom. A further point is that bulky alkyl groups may increase the amount of periodate ester present in the dehydrated form, and so indirectly assist its decomposition. One might expect the hydrated ester to have a more congested structure than the more reactive dehydrated ester (IX). It is therefore difficult to disentangle these various structural effects with any certainty.

The only cyclic diols for which the rates of breakdown of the cyclic intermediate monoanions are known are the *cis*- and *trans*-cyclohexane-1,2-diols,[49] where $k_{cis}/k_{trans} \approx 20$. This difference in rates of decomposition overcomes the effect of the equilibrium constants, which are less favorable for the *cis*-diol (Section II,B,2,a). Several factors speed the decomposition of the *cis*-diol to products. (i) An octahedral complex of the *cis*-diol is strained by interference between nearby groups, and this interference should be smaller in a dehydrated complex, which contains a penta-coordinated iodine atom, and any factor which increases the relative amount of the intermediate monoanion which is in the dehydrated form, IX, should speed reaction. (ii) These internal steric strains will also be relieved by decomposition of the intermediate, either to reactants or products, i.e., decomposition of the *cis*-diol to both reactants and products could be sterically accelerated (relative to that of the *trans*-diol). This second effect will increase the rate constant for decomposition of the intermediate monoanion, and at the same time decrease the equilibrium constant for formation of the intermediate from the *cis*-diol. (iii) It is likely that decomposition of the cyclic ester involves concerted bond breaking, and therefore concerted electron transfers, which will occur most readily if the heterocyclic system of the periodate ester is planar. As has been noted, it is difficult for this ring to be planar without increasing the puckering, and hence the internal strains, in the cyclic ester of the *trans*-cyclohexane-1,2-diol (Section II,B,2,a).

However, the second-order rate constant for decomposition of the cyclohexane-1,2-diols, which is the product, kK, of rate and equilibrium constants (provided that the concentration of an intermediate is low), is always greater for the *cis*-diol, i.e., the effects upon the rate of decomposition of the intermediate are more important than those upon the equilibrium constant.[49]

c. *Formation of the Cyclic Intermediate.* Kinetic forms indicative of intermediate formation are observed only with a few simple diols; more generally there is no evidence for an intermediate,[55] and the reaction has a second-order kinetic form:

$$v = k_2'[D][P]$$

Such kinetic forms can be singularly uninformative. For the reaction scheme:

$$D + P \underset{k_b}{\overset{k_f}{\rightleftharpoons}} I \overset{k}{\longrightarrow} \text{products} \tag{1a}$$

[55] C. A. Bunton, *Ann. Rept. Progr. Chem. (Chem. Soc. London)* **56**, 186 (1959).

(where I is an intermediate and $k_f/k_b = K$), they can arise (i) because $K[D] \ll 1$ in Eq. (2a,b) (Section II,B,2), or (ii) because $k \gg k_b$, i.e., the rate-limiting step of the reaction is the formation of the intermediate. Both situations are met experimentally.

Situation (i) can arise because K is very small, but $k_b \gg k$, and then there is a small standing concentration of intermediate in equilibrium with the reactants, and the intermediate decomposes slowly to products. Even for those simple acyclic diols which can form intermediates in high concentration, a second-order rate law is followed when the reactant concentrations became so small that $K[D] \ll 1$. In either case Eq. (2a,b) reduces to [29, 30, 46]:

$$k' = kK[D] \tag{3a}$$

or

$$k'_2 = kK[D][P] \tag{3b}$$

The value of the second-order rate constant k'_2, determined at very low concentration, should equal the product kK of the rate and equilibrium constants determined at higher reactant concentrations by the use of Eq. (2b), provided that the reactants and intermediate are in equilibrium.[30, 43]

Situation (ii) is much more interesting, and it occurs with the more complex diols, and the carbohydrates. It is important that experiment should differentiate between the two situations, because reasoning based purely on structural considerations is of little help. Increased alkyl substituent upon the diol could change the kinetic form by retarding the formation of the intermediate (decreasing k_f), by increasing both k_b and k, and by decreasing the equilibrium constant, K. The evidence which relates to the oxidation of pinacol will be discussed, because for this reaction it seems certain that formation of the cyclic intermediates is rate limiting, i.e., situation (ii) holds (except perhaps at high pH).

A plot of the second-order rate constant, k'_2, for the oxidation of pinacol against pH shows two maxima,[29, 34, 35, 48] at pH ca. 2 and 8, but between these regions the rate varies little with pH. If the intermediate were in equilibrium with the reactants, the rate of reaction should follow the concentration of the monoanion intermediate,[43] and increase with increasing pH to a plateau at pH ca. 4, and then decrease. This behavior is observed with the simple diols, provided that reactant concentrations are so low that $k_b \gg k$ (cf., Refs. 30 and 46). Therefore pinacol must be behaving differently from the less substituted diols, in that the rate-limiting step of its oxidation is formation of the cyclic intermediate. This hypothesis is confirmed by the observation of general acid–base catalysis in the oxidation of some ditertiary diols.[23, 29, 35b]

General acids and bases have little effect upon either the equilibrium constant, K, for formation of the intermediate, or the rate constant, k, for its breakdown, in the oxidation of ethane diol. Therefore they must speed the oxidation of, for example, pinacol by catalyzing the formation of an unstable intermediate, which breaks down very rapidly to products, and whose formation is probably the two-stage reaction:

$$
\begin{array}{c}
\text{R}_2\text{C—OH} \\
| \qquad\quad + \text{ I}\bar{\text{O}}_4 \rightleftharpoons \\
\text{R}_2\text{C—OH}
\end{array}
\qquad
\begin{array}{c}
\text{R}_2\text{C—O—I}\bar{\text{O}}_4\text{H} \\
| \\
\text{R}_2\text{C—OH}
\end{array}
$$

$$\downarrow \quad (\text{X})$$

$$
2\,\text{R}_2\text{CO} + \text{I}\bar{\text{O}}_3 \xleftarrow{\text{fast}}
\begin{array}{c}
\text{R}_2\text{C—O} \\
| \qquad\rangle\ \text{I}\bar{\text{O}}_3 \\
\text{R}_2\text{C—O}
\end{array}
$$

In this formulation the various periodate species are written, for convenience, in their least hydrated forms. The reaction could be written equally well as proceeding through hydrated forms of X, and involving concerted loss of water and ring closure.

A base, B, could catalyze the ring closure of the mono-coordinated intermediate X just as it catalyzes the interconversion of the open-chain and cyclic forms of glucose.[56] The mechanism of cyclization can be written as:

$$
\begin{array}{c}
\quad\ \ \text{O} \\
\quad\ \ \parallel\ \diagup\text{O} \\
\text{R}_2\text{C—O—I —}\bar{\text{O}} \\
| \qquad\quad \diagdown\text{OH} \\
\text{R}_2\text{C—O}\nwarrow \\
\qquad\quad \diagup\text{H}\cdots\bar{\text{B}}
\end{array}
\longrightarrow
\begin{array}{c}
\text{R}_2\text{C—O} \\
| \qquad\rangle\ \text{I}\bar{\text{O}}_3 + \text{HB} + \text{O}\bar{\text{H}} \\
\text{R}_2\text{C—O}
\end{array}
$$

Experiments by G. J. Buist, J. Lomas, and the writer, on the general acid–base catalyzed oxidation of pinacol, show that in the pH range 3–6, weak bases, e.g., carboxylate ions, give a good Brönsted catalysis law relation between rate and dissociation constant of the base. However, a stronger base, e.g., ammonia, is a much more effective catalyst than would be predicted by such a simple relation.

This is understandable if in these buffers the intermediate X is in equilibrium with the reactants, and decomposes slowly to the cyclic intermediate, which then itself decomposes rapidly to the products. However, a stronger base, such as ammonia, is a more effective catalyst than would have been predicted from a comparison with the catalytic power of carboxylate ions. It is suggested that, in ammonia buffers, decomposition of the intermediate X is so speeded

56 R. P. Bell, "Acid-Base Catalysis." Oxford Univ. Press, London and New York, 1941.

that it is no longer in equilibrium with the reactants. This hypothesis requires that the forward reaction of X, but not its reversion to reactants, is general acid–base catalyzed; it also requires that mono-coordinated periodate esters may, in some cases, be sufficiently stable to exist in the presence of reactants, and, for ditertiary diols, they may be more stable than the cyclic esters. With the open chain primary and secondary 1,2-diols, it is clear that the cyclic ester intermediates are more stable than their open-chain counterparts, but it is reasonable that the steric effects of bulky groups should destabilize the cyclic more than the open-chain intermediate ester X.

The oxidation of pinacol is acid catalyzed, and there appeared to be a rate maximum in dilute acid.[29, 35b] Experiments by Buist, Lomas, and the writer have shown that there is indeed a well-defined rate maximum at pH 1.

An explanation of this kinetic form is that the diol adds to the periodate monoanion (probably to $I\bar{O}_4$) to form the intermediate X, whose cyclization can be catalyzed by general acids, e.g.,

$$(X) \underset{}{\overset{\overset{+}{H}}{\rightleftharpoons}} \begin{array}{c} \\ R_2C-O-I\overset{\displaystyle O}{\underset{\displaystyle \overset{+}{O}H_2}{\diagdown}}\\ | \\ R_2C-O \\ \diagdown\diagup H \cdots \bar{B} \end{array}$$

$$\downarrow$$

$$\begin{array}{c} R_2C-O \\ | \quad \rangle \; I\bar{O}_3 + HB + H_2O \\ R_2C-O \end{array}$$

The base $\bar{B}$ can be H_2O or the conjugate base of the acid HB.

In dilute acid it is assumed that the reactants and X are in equilibrium, and the rate-limiting step, the cyclization and decomposition of X, should be catalyzed by general acids. In more concentrated acid, the cyclization of X should become fast and its formation slow, because the concentration of IO_4^- will be low; the rate should then decrease with increasing acid concentration. Again, this general scheme could be formulated in terms of intermediates whose hydration is different from that shown.

There is a second maximum at pH ca. 8 in the rate constant for the oxidation of pinacol, and the rate decreases sharply in more alkaline solution.[34, 35, 48] There is no certain explanation of this second rate maximum, although evidence obtained by G. J. Buist suggests that it is associated with a change in mechanism. At high pH the rate of decomposition of the cyclic intermediate decreases, and whereas at pH < 8 the decomposition of the cyclic intermediate is probably fast, compared with its formation, it seems that at pH > 8 both formation and decomposition of the intermediate are kinetically significant. Study of the kinetic form of reaction in this alkaline region is complicated by dimerization of periodate.[17a]

There is need for more work on the oxidation of pinacol, and of other diols for which formation of the intermediate is rate limiting, especially because the oxidations of cis- and trans-cyclopentane-1,2-diol do not show the rate maximum at pH 8 which is so characteristic of the oxidation of pinacol.[37]

3. 1,2-DIKETONES AND HYDROXYCARBONYL COMPOUNDS

Although the oxidation of 1,2-diketones by periodate was observed many years ago, it is only recently that mechanistic evidence has been obtained on this reaction. The rate of oxidation of biacetyl by periodate increases rapidly with increasing pH, but at all times is first order with respect to each reactant.[57] It was therefore suggested that reaction occurred by nucleophilic attack of the periodate dianion upon the diketone, to give a cyclic intermediate XI, which decomposes rapidly to products:

$$CH_3 \cdot CO \cdot CO \cdot CH_3 + H_3IO_6^{2-} \longrightarrow \begin{matrix} OH \\ | \\ CH_3C-O \\ | \quad \quad \rangle IO_4^{2-} \\ CH_3C-O \\ | \\ OH \end{matrix} \longrightarrow 2\,CH_3CO_2H + IO_3^- + OH^-$$

(XI)

This mechanism suggests that the hydrate of, e.g., biacetyl is not particularly reactive to periodate, although there is spectral evidence that biacetyl is extensively hydrated in water.[58] The proposed reaction scheme is supported by tracer work with $[O^{18}]$–water.[59] If isotopically normal periodate is added to isotopically labeled biacetyl in alkaline H_2O^{18}, the isolated acetic acid is not fully isotopically enriched, which it would have been had the hydrate been the key intermediate. On the other hand, a mechanism involving nucleophilic attack by periodate on the diketone requires that some of the oxygen atoms of the acetic acid come from the periodate. (This tracer work was done at high pH, and it is of course possible that another mechanism applies at low pH.) The observation that aromatic 1,2-diketones are relatively unreactive to periodate is consistent with either direct nucleophilic attack by periodate, or oxidation of a preformed hydrate.

[57] V. J. Shiner and C. R. Wassmuth, J. Am. Chem. Soc. 81, 37 (1959).
[58] R. P. Bell and A. O. McDougall, Trans. Faraday Soc. 56, 1281 (1960).
[59] C. A. Bunton and V. J. Shiner, J. Chem. Soc. p. 1593 (1960).

There is little mechanistic evidence on the oxidation of 1,2-hydroxyketones. The rapid oxidation of methylacetoin is first order with respect to each reagent,[57] and has a maximum rate at pH 8. Oxidation in [O^{18}]–water with isotopically enriched periodate gives isotopically normal acetone and 50% enriched acetic acid.[59] These results can be explained in terms of a nucleophilic attack by periodate upon the carbonyl group, and coordination of the hydroxyl group to the periodate, but the timing of these steps is unknown.

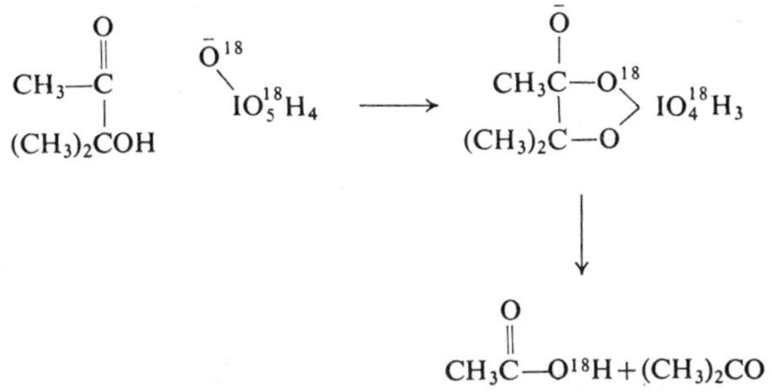

$$
\begin{array}{c}
\underset{\substack{|\\(CH_3)_2COH}}{\overset{\overset{O}{\|}}{CH_3-C}} \quad \overset{\bar{O}^{18}}{\underset{IO_5^{18}H_4}{\diagdown}}
\end{array}
\longrightarrow
\begin{array}{c}
\overset{\bar{O}}{\underset{\substack{|\\(CH_3)_2C-O}}{\overset{|}{CH_3C-O^{18}}}} \overset{}{\diagup} IO_4^{18}H_3
\end{array}
$$

$$
\downarrow
$$

$$
\overset{O}{\overset{\|}{CH_3C}}-O^{18}H + (CH_3)_2CO
$$

4. 1,2-AMINO ALCOHOLS

Periodate will oxidize α-amino alcohols quantitatively, with elimination of the nitrogen atom as ammonia.[6] The amino group may be primary or secondary, e.g., as in serine, ethanolamine, or diethanolamine[6]:

$$
\underset{\substack{|\quad\;\;|\\ OH\;\;NH_2}}{CH_2-CH-CO_2H} + H_5IO_6 \longrightarrow CH_2O + CHO\cdot CO_2H + NH_3 + HIO_3
$$

$$
\underset{\substack{|\quad\;|\\ OH\;\;NH_2}}{CH_2-CH_2} + H_5IO_6 \longrightarrow 2\,CH_2O + NH_3 + HIO_3
$$

$$
\underset{\substack{|\\ OH}}{CH_2-CH_2}\diagdown\underset{NH}{}\diagup\underset{\substack{|\\ OH}}{CH_2-CH_2} + 2\,H_5IO_6 \longrightarrow 4\,CH_2O + NH_3 + 2\,HIO_3
$$

If the amino group is tertiary, reaction is very slow:

$$
N(CH_2CH_2OH)_3 + 3\,HIO_4 \rightarrow 6\,CH_2O + NH_3 + 3\,HIO_3
$$

Diamines are oxidized by periodate, but again only slowly:

$$
\underset{\substack{|\quad\;\;|\\ NH_2\;\;NH_2}}{CH_2-CH_2} + HIO_4 \longrightarrow 2\,CH_2O + 2\,NH_3 + HIO_3
$$

There is little mechanistic evidence on these reactions, but the relative unreactivity of tertiary amines and diamines suggests that formation of an intermediate by coordination of the hydroxyl group with the iodine atom of periodate is important, and that carbon–carbon bond cleavage then gives an imine, or its conjugate acid:

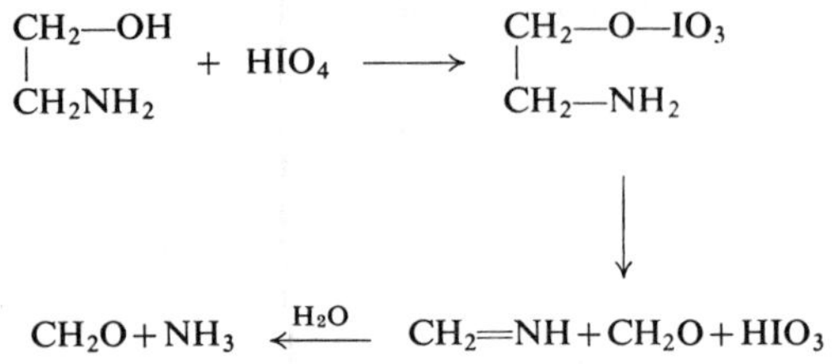

$$
\begin{array}{c}
\text{CH}_2\text{—OH} \\
| \qquad\qquad + \text{ HIO}_4 \longrightarrow \\
\text{CH}_2\text{NH}_2
\end{array}
\qquad
\begin{array}{c}
\text{CH}_2\text{—O—IO}_3 \\
| \\
\text{CH}_2\text{—NH}_2
\end{array}
$$

$$
\text{CH}_2\text{O} + \text{NH}_3 \xleftarrow{\text{H}_2\text{O}} \text{CH}_2{=}\text{NH} + \text{CH}_2\text{O} + \text{HIO}_3
$$

C. NON-MALAPRADIAN OXIDATIONS

The early work of Fleury and others showed that periodate would oxidize many organic compounds very slowly in cold, and more rapidly in hot, solutions,[7, 21] and it has been shown that light will assist these oxidations,[60] suggesting that periodate is decomposing either thermochemically or photochemically to a more reactive oxidant. However, many of the so-called non-Malapradian oxidations occur rapidly, even in the dark, at rates comparable with those of the normal Malapradian oxidations,[21, 61–63] and these oxidations complicate the use of periodate as a specific analytical reagent.

1. ACTIVE METHYLENE COMPOUNDS

A factor which restricts the applicability of periodate for the general determination of carbohydrate structures is overconsumption, i.e., the amount of periodate consumed is greater than would be expected if the only reaction was the carbon–carbon bond cleavage of 1,2-diols, 1,2-hydroxycarbonyl, or 1,2-dicarbonyl compounds.[20, 21, 61–63] Many active methylene compounds react readily with periodate, and also a compound, which may itself be inert to periodate, may be hydrolyzed to products which are themselves reactive to periodate.[64]

[60] F. S. H. Head and G. Hughes, *J. Chem. Soc.* p. 2046 (1952).

[61] C. F. Huebner, S. R. Ames, and E. C. Bubl, *J. Am. Chem. Soc.* **68**, 1621 (1946).

[62] D. B. Sprinson and E. Chargaff, *J. Biol. Chem.* **164**, 433 (1946).

[63] F. S. H. Head and G. Hughes, *J. Chem. Soc.* p. 603 (1954).

[64] M. Cantley, L. Hough, and A. O. Pittet, *J. Chem. Soc.* p. 2527 (1963) and references cited therein.

The reaction between benzyloxymalondialdehyde and periodate illustrates these sources of overconsumption[65]:

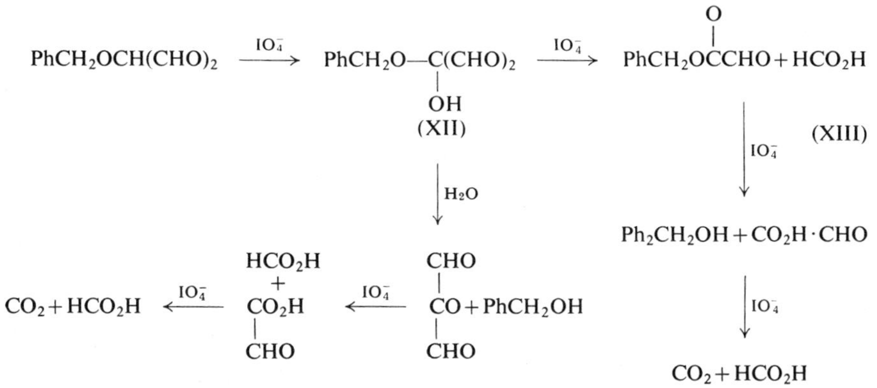

$$PhCH_2OCH(CHO)_2 \xrightarrow{IO_4^-} \underset{\substack{| \\ OH \\ (XII)}}{PhCH_2O-C(CHO)_2} \xrightarrow{IO_4^-} \underset{}{PhCH_2O\overset{O}{\overset{||}{C}}CHO + HCO_2H}$$

$$\downarrow H_2O \qquad\qquad\qquad\qquad \Big| IO_4^- \quad (XIII)$$

$$Ph_2CH_2OH + CO_2H\cdot CHO$$

$$CO_2 + HCO_2H \xleftarrow{IO_4^-} \underset{\substack{| \\ CHO}}{\overset{\substack{HCO_2H \\ + }}{CO_2H}} \xleftarrow{IO_4^-} \underset{\substack{| \\ CHO}}{\overset{CHO}{CO}} + PhCH_2OH$$

$$\Big| IO_4^-$$

$$CO_2 + HCO_2H$$

In this reaction the amount of periodate consumed depends upon the ease of hydrolysis of XII and XIII, and it is often possible to control the amount of periodate consumed by varying the pH and temperature, and so varying the relative rates of hydrolysis and oxidation. Overconsumption can be reduced by lowering the temperature, and can be recognized, and to some extent controlled, by following the uptake of periodate with time.

The first step in these reactions of activated methylene compounds is hydroxylation. A mechanism has been suggested involving a cyclic intermediate, formed between periodate and enols, e.g., for malondialdehyde, a cyclic intermediate is first formed, and is then hydroxylated by water[66]:

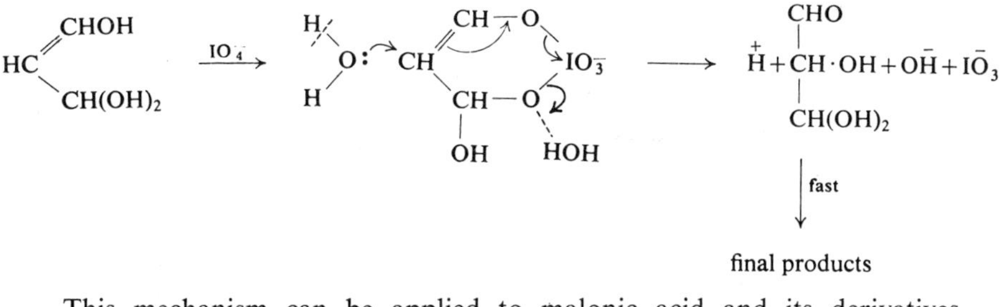

$$HC\underset{\substack{\diagdown \\ CH(OH)_2}}{\overset{\substack{CHOH \\ \diagup}}{}} \xrightarrow{IO_4^-} \cdots \longrightarrow \underset{\substack{| \\ CH(OH)_2}}{\overset{\substack{CHO \\ \overset{+}{H}+CH\cdot OH+O\bar{H}+I\bar{O}_3}}{}}$$

$$\Big| \text{fast}$$

final products

This mechanism can be applied to malonic acid and its derivatives, XCH_2CO_2H, and explains the rate sequence,[61]

$$X = CO_2H > CH_3CO > CO_2Et > CN,$$

in terms of ease of forming the cyclic intermediate. It also explains the readier oxidation of cyclic, as opposed to open-chain, 1,3-diketones in terms

[65] J. C. P. Schwarz and M. MacDougall, *J. Chem. Soc.* p. 3065 (1956).
[66] J. L. Bose, A. B. Foster, and R. W. Stephens, *J. Chem. Soc.* p. 3314 (1959).

of their readier enolization.[67] In the following reaction scheme the first formed oxidation product is assumed to be oxidized rapidly in reactions which could also involve cyclic periodate esters:

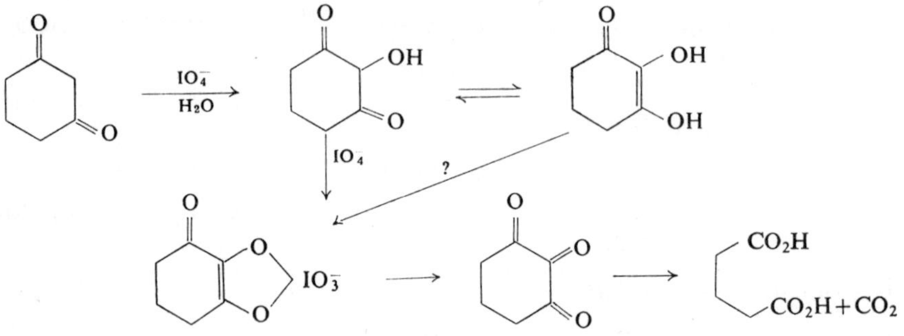

The rate of these reactions is generally greatest at pH 4–5 where the periodate monoanion is the predominant species, and it could well be this reagent that forms a cyclic intermediate with the enolic form of the substrate (compare, however, Section II,C,2).

2. OXIDATION OF SULFIDES

Periodate has been used very successfully for the oxidation of organic sulfides to sulfoxides.[68] Reaction occurs in mild conditions, e.g., in water or in aqueous methanol at $0°C$; at higher temperatures, e.g., $> 60°C$, there is a further slow oxidation to sulfones.

There is no mechanistic evidence on this reaction, but analogy with the mechanism of the oxidation of sulfides by peroxyacids suggests:

$$R_2S: + O{=}IO_3^- \rightarrow R_2\overset{+}{S}{-}O{-}IO_3^{2-} \rightarrow R_2SO + IO_3^-$$

A similar mechanism can be applied to the reaction between iodide and periodate ions[10]:

$$\bar{I} + O{=}IO_3^- \longrightarrow I{-}O{-}IO_3^{2-} \longrightarrow I\bar{O} + IO_3^-$$

$$\downarrow \bar{I}$$

$$I_2$$

On this mechanistic picture periodate is acting as an electrophilic oxidant, transferring oxygen to such nucleophiles as an iodide ion, or an organic sulfide. A similar mechanism could be applied to the hydroxylation of active

[67] M. L. Wolfrom and J. M. Bobbitt, *J. Am. Chem. Soc.* **78**, 2489 (1956).
[68] N. J. Leonard and C. R. Johnson, *J. Org. Chem.* **27**, 282 (1962).

methylene compounds, as an alternative to that discussed in Section II,C,1, e.g., the first step of reaction could be written as a direct hydroxylation by periodate, instead of involving a cyclic intermediate. If the most powerful electrophilic oxidant in the solution was the unhydrated monoanion, IO_4^-, this alternative mechanism would explain the rate maximum at pH 4.

$$\begin{array}{c} CHO \\ | \\ CH_2 \\ | \\ CHO \end{array} + O{=}\bar{I}O_3 \longrightarrow \begin{array}{c} CHO \\ | \\ CH{\cdot}OH \\ | \\ CHO \end{array} + \bar{I}O_3$$

3. Oxidation of Phenols and Phenolic Ethers

Adler and his collaborators have shown that periodate is an excellent reagent for the preparation of *o*-quinones[69]:

(XIV)

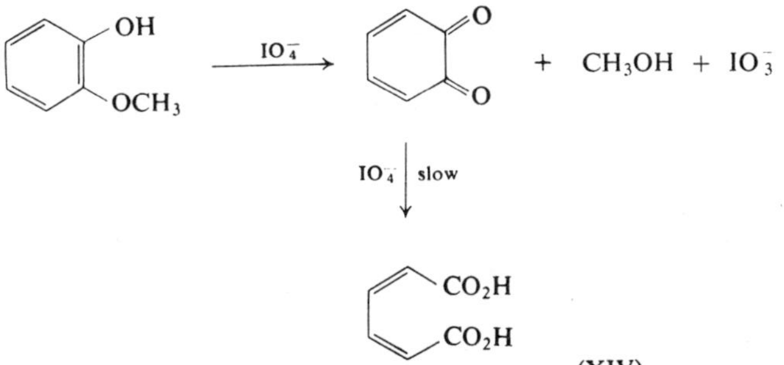

The quinone can be isolated, but is itself slowly oxidized to *cis-cis*-muconic acid (XIV).

Sodium bismuthate ($NaBiO_3$) behaves like periodate, but *p*-quinones are formed by reaction of lead tetraacetate or Fremy's salt (potassium nitrosodisulfonate), e.g.,

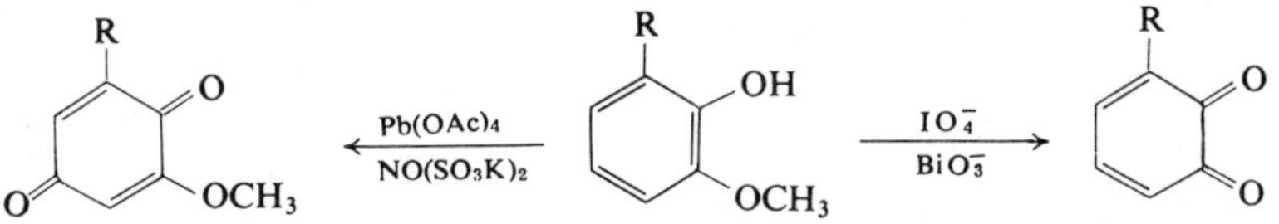

$R = H, OCH_3$

[69] E. Adler and S. Hemestarn, *Acta Chem. Scand.* **9**, 319 (1955); E. Adler and R. Magnusson, *ibid.* **13**, 505 (1959); E. Adler, J. Dahlen, and G. Westin, *ibid.* **14**, 1580 (1960) and references cited therein.

Quinol and its monoethers are oxidized rapidly to *p*-quinone:

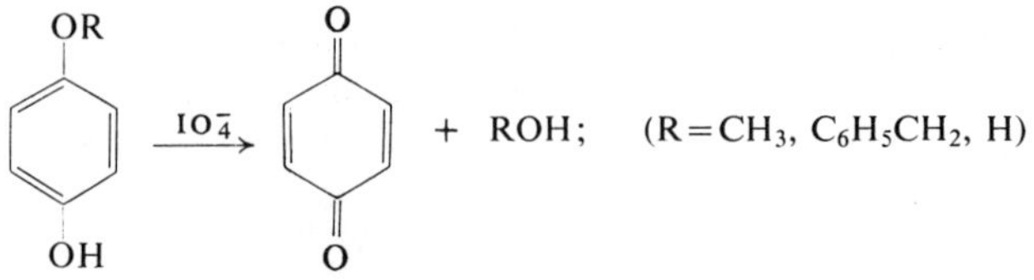

$$+ ROH; \quad (R = CH_3, C_6H_5CH_2, H)$$

Resorcinol and its monoethers are relatively inert to periodate, as is phenol itself. However, alkyl-substituted phenols are oxidized by periodate to give largely dimeric products.

The periodate oxidation of mono- and di-ethers of pyrogallol gives a variety of quinonoid products, depending upon the reaction conditions, and is a particularly useful method for the preparation of quinones.

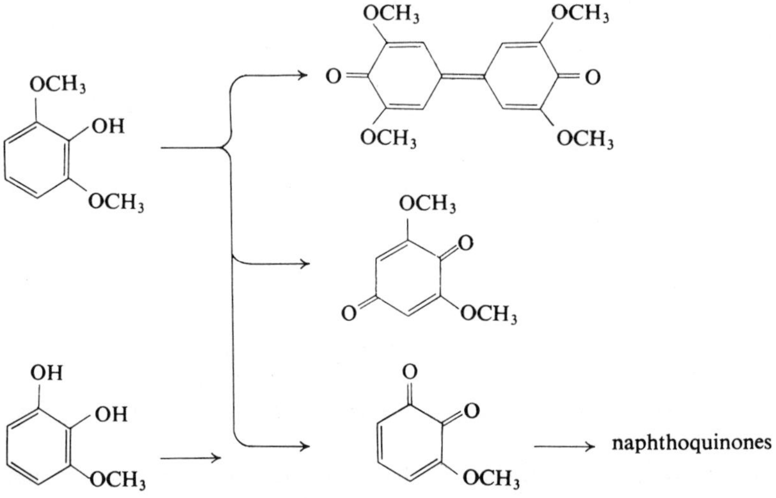

Adler has suggested that phenolic esters of periodic acid are intermediates, and writes the reaction scheme as [70]:

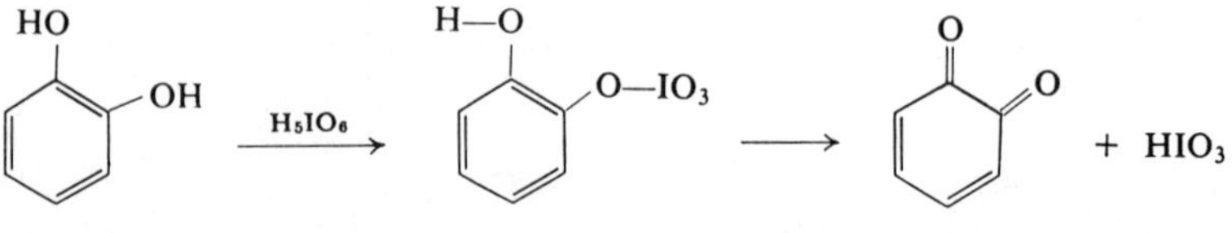

$$+ HIO_3$$

Similar mechanisms can be written for the oxidation of the monoethers, and are supported by experiments with oxygen-18. However, the timing of the reaction and the precise nature of the intermediates are not known.

[70] E. Adler, I. Falkehag, and B. Smith, *Acta Chem. Scand.* **16**, 529 (1962).

Recent kinetic work has shown that the rate limiting step of the oxidation of these phenols and their monoethers is probably formation of an aryl periodate, by attack of periodic acid, or its monoanion, upon the phenolic hydroxyl group.[70a]

D. EXPERIMENTAL APPLICATIONS

Orthoperiodic acid, H_5IO_6, can be used as the source of periodate, but it is very hygroscopic, and it is often more convenient to use sodium periodate, $NaIO_4$; up to ca. $M/2$, solutions of this salt can be prepared in water. Sodium periodate is available commercially, or can be prepared by acidification of the sparingly soluble $Na_3H_2IO_6$ with dilute nitric acid. Periodate solutions can be purified by precipitation as the barium salt, and acidification with sulfuric acid. Because sodium periodate is only slightly soluble in aqueous organic solvents, it is often useful to use amine or tetraalkylammonium salts. They can be prepared by neutralization of the acid.

1. QUANTITATIVE ANALYSIS

The conventional method for the analysis of a 1,2-diol, hydroxycarbonyl, or dicarbonyl compound is to add an excess of aqueous standard periodate solution to a solution or suspension of the organic compound, and then, after complete oxidation, to determine the amount of residual periodate. The conditions are not in general critical. The periodate can be added in any convenient form, and because it can be determined in very low concentration, the relatively low solubility of some of its salts is no great problem. The pH of the solution is generally not critical, except that the rate of oxidation of 1,2-diols becomes very slow at high pH. (The rate of oxidation of 1,2-diketones increases with increasing alkali concentration.[57])

High concentrations of mineral acid are undesirable on several counts. The rate of oxidation usually decreases at low pH (Section II,B,2), pinacolic rearrangements of highly substituted 1,2-diols may become a complicating side reaction, and acids may decompose the products of oxidation. Because the oxidation of some 1,2-diols is general base catalyzed, it is often useful to do the reaction in a mildly alkaline buffer, e.g., ammonia or amines are very useful for this purpose. Periodate is light sensitive[60] and reactions should be done in the dark or in dark bottles, and the solutions stored in the dark.

It is always desirable to follow the uptake of periodate with time whenever an unknown compound is first examined; one can then often detect the presence of impurities which will be oxidized at a rate different from that of the major component, and one also can recognize overconsumption, if it occurs, and correct for it. Variation of the reaction conditions, e.g., pH and temperature, will also give information on the existence of side reactions.

[70a] E. T. Kaiser and S. W. Weidman, *J. Am. Chem. Soc.* **86**, 4354 (1964).

Overconsumption can be reduced by working at the lowest possible temperature.

The residual periodate can be estimated in various ways. The simplest method is reduction by iodide ion.[7] In neutral solution periodate is reduced by iodide ion only to iodate, which is itself reduced only in acid.[71] It is therefore easy to analyze for periodate in the presence of iodate:

$$\text{Neutral} \qquad IO_4^- + 2\,\overset{+}{I} + 2\,\overset{+}{H} \;\rightarrow\; I\bar{O}_3 + I_2 + H_2O$$

$$\text{Acid} \qquad IO_3^- + 5\,\overset{+}{I} + 6\,\overset{+}{H} \;\rightarrow\; 3\,I_2 + 3\,H_2O$$

The pH of the solution can be controlled by excess sodium hydrogen carbonate or borax; excess potassium iodide is then added, and the liberated iodine titrated with sodium arsenite or thiosulfate. Alternatively, potassium iodide and an excess of standard sodium arsenite are added, and the excess sodium arsenite is back titrated with standard iodine. This second procedure is desirable if there is any possibility of the iodine reacting with, e.g., the carbonyl compounds produced by oxidation of the 1,2-diol.

Another procedure is to allow iodide ion to react with both periodate and iodate in acid.[3] A disadvantage of this method is that large amounts of iodine are then liberated, and the titration requires large volumes of reagent.

Either freshly prepared starch or sodium starch glycolate can be used as the indicator, and if very dilute solutions are used it is desirable to deoxygenate them. Periodate can then easily be determined in concentrations down to ca. $10^{-4}\,M$, and the sensitivity can be increased by using electrochemical methods for titration of the iodide.[22]

The sensitivity of the determination can be increased still further by determining periodate either spectrophotometrically[14] (from the absorption of the periodate anion at 2225 Å) or polarographically.[23] For optically active organic compounds, the reaction can be followed polarimetrically,[24,25a] although this method is relatively insensitive.

Any of these methods can also be used for measuring the rate of reaction, except that the high sensitivity of periodate to light makes spectrophotometry unsuitable for slow reactions.

For organic compounds which are only very slightly soluble in water, it is possible to use some organic diluent.[7,25] However, the low solubility of periodate salts in organic solvents restricts the quantity of organic diluent which can be added, and oxidation by periodate is slower in aqueous organic solutions than in water.[25] It is often worthwhile varying the nature of the cation; e.g., tetraethylammonium periodate is soluble in concentrated tetraethylammonium hydroxide, whereas the alkali metal periodates are salted out by the corresponding hydroxides.[59]

[71] P. Fleury and J. Lange, *J. Pharm. Chim.* [8] **17**, 107, 196 (1933).

2. QUALITATIVE ANALYSIS AND PREPARATIVE APPLICATIONS

Periodate is used for identifying compounds which have hydroxyl or carbonyl groups on adjacent carbon atoms, and it is a clean and relatively selective reagent for their oxidative carbon–carbon cleavage. Carbohydrate chemistry has been one major field of application, and periodate oxidation is one of the general methods used for determination of carbohydrate structure.[7] For this purpose it is necessary to follow not only the uptake of periodate, but also the appearance of formic acid and formaldehyde, and to guard against overconsumption of periodate in a non-Malapradian oxidation of, e.g., an active methylene compound.

A classical example of the use of periodate in the determination of carbohydrate structures is the study of the oxidation of the α- and β-methyl-D-aldohexopyranosides (XV and XVI) by Hudson and his co-workers.[24] Two molecules of periodate are consumed, and one carbon atom of the carbohydrate is lost as formic acid. The α-series all give a product XVIIa, which is shown for convenience as a dialdehyde, although it exists preferentially as a cyclic hemiacetal.[72] Its rotation is different from that of the product XVIIb obtained from the β-series. Oxidation removes the asymmetry associated with C-2, C-3, and C-4, but leaves that of C-1 and C-5 intact; therefore the α- and β-series differ only in the configuration of C-1. The oxidations of α-D-manno- and gluco-pyranoside (XVa and XVIa) and the corresponding β-glycosides (XVb and XVIb) are shown below, and illustrate the power of a combined study of the stoichiometry and the steric course of periodate oxidations of carbohydrates:

α-Series

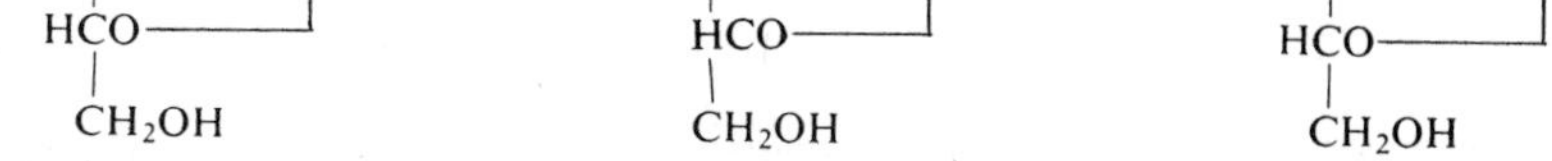

$$\begin{array}{ccccc}
\text{HCOCH}_3 & & \text{HCOCH}_3 & & \text{HCOCH}_3 \\
\text{HOCH} & & \text{HC}{=}\text{O} & & \text{HCOH} \\
\text{HOCH} & \xrightarrow{\;2\,\text{IO}_4^-\;} & & \xleftarrow{\;2\,\text{IO}_4^-\;} & \text{HOCH} \\
\text{HCOH} & & \text{HC}{=}\text{O} & & \text{HCOH} \\
\text{HCO} & & \text{HCO} & & \text{HCO} \\
\text{CH}_2\text{OH} & & \text{CH}_2\text{OH} & & \text{CH}_2\text{OH} \\
\text{(XVa)} & & \text{(XVIIa)} & & \text{(XVIa)} \\
[\alpha]_\text{D}^{20}\ +79° & & [\alpha]_\text{D}^{20}\ +121° & & [\alpha]_\text{D}^{20}\ +159°
\end{array}$$

[72] J. E. Cadotte, G. G. S. Dutton, I. J. Goldstein, B. A. Lewis, F. Smith, and J. W. van Cleve, *J. Am. Chem. Soc.* **79**, 691 (1957).

β-Series

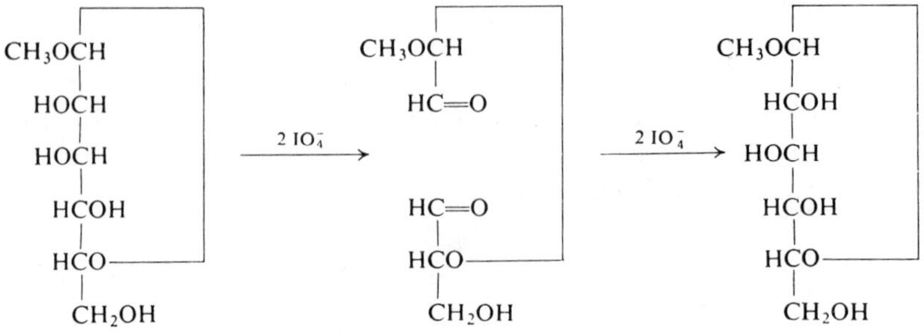

$$\begin{array}{ccc}
\begin{array}{|l}
CH_3OCH \\
HOCH \\
HOCH \\
HCOH \\
HCO \\
CH_2OH
\end{array}
&
\xrightarrow{2\ IO_4^-}
&
\begin{array}{|l}
CH_3OCH \\
HC{=}O \\
HC{=}O \\
HCO \\
CH_2OH
\end{array}
\end{array}$$

(XVb)   (XVIIb)   (XVIb)

$[\alpha]_D^{20} - 69°$ $[\alpha]_D^{20} -151°$ $[\alpha]_D^{20} - 34°$

Honeyman and his co-workers have shown how the rates and products of oxidation of a number of ethylidene and benzylidene derivatives can be understood in terms of the structure of the glycosides.[25a, 33] They studied the oxidation of a number of alkylidene glucosides, and showed that the oxidation products were sometimes not dialdehydes, e.g., XVIII, but were the cyclic hemiacetals formed from them, (cf. ref. 72):

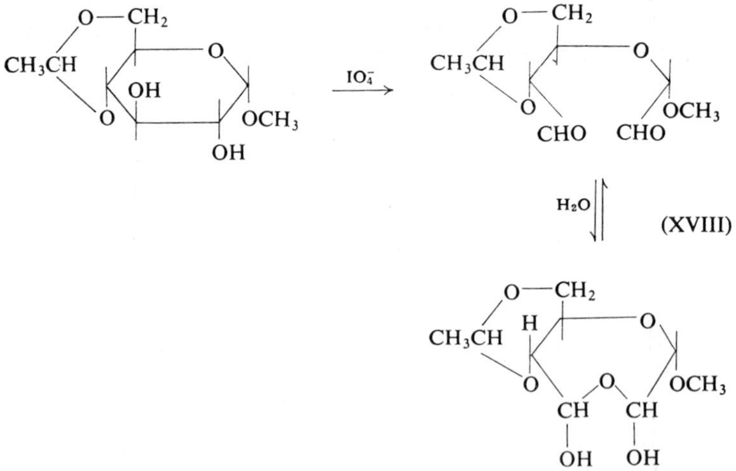

(XVIII)

Some cyclic 1,2-diols are inert to periodate because their geometry prevents their complexing with periodate to form a cyclic periodate ester. Some examples of these, usually *trans*-diols, were given in Section II,B,2.

The rate of periodate uptake can be used to distinguish between *threo*- and *erythro*-diols, provided that both diols are available.[23, 29, 30] The *threo* isomer is the more reactive, because formation of the transition state from it and periodate involves less steric hindrance than from the *erythro* isomer. Relative reactivities depend upon substituents, as well as upon reaction conditions, but generally $k_{threo}/k_{erythro}$ is between 2 and 5.

Somewhat similarly, a *cis*-cyclic diol is more reactive than its *trans* isomer. However, the relative reactivities depend markedly upon the diol as well as upon reaction conditions, in part because cyclohexane-1,2-diols form intermediate complexes at $0°$ C in water,[44] whereas other cyclic diols do not[25a, 37, 38]; the rate-limiting steps are therefore different.

The relative unreactivity of the *trans*-diol increases with increasing methyl substitution and with increasing rigidity of the ring. For the cyclohexane-1,2-diols, k_{cis}/k_{trans} is 3–17, being least at higher temperatures and at pH $\approx$ 4, whereas for its 1,2-dimethyl homolog the ratio is ca. 10^3. For the corresponding cyclopentane diols, $k_{cis}/k_{trans} \approx 20$ for the unsubstituted diols, $\approx 10^2$ for the monomethyl homologs, and very much greater than 10^3 for the 1,2-dimethyl homologs. The difference in reactivities stems largely from differences in activation energies.

Some of these inert *trans*-diols are cleaved by lead tetraacetate (Section III,A), although they are much less reactive than the *cis*-diols toward this reagent; in determining structure it is always useful to study the reactions of the diols with both periodate and lead tetraacetate.

The difficulty of finding a satisfactory solvent for both a high molecular weight organic compound and periodic acid or its salts inevitably restricts the use of periodate as a preparative oxidant, and the slowness of the reaction in organic solvents compounds the difficulty. Therefore lead tetraacetate, with its high solubility in many organic solvents, is generally preferred as a preparative oxidant for water-insoluble organic compounds.

However, when periodate must be used for the oxidation of a compound which is sparingly water soluble, alcohols, dioxan, or acetic acid can be added as cosolvents, or an emulsifying agent can be used. As for the analysis of simple diols, it is also useful to add the periodate as an amine, or tetraalkylammonium salt, e.g., tetramethylammonium periodate is reasonably soluble in aqueous dioxan, whereas the sodium salt is almost insoluble. The isolation of the reaction products is relatively simple. They can be extracted from water by organic solvents, or the iodate and periodate ions can be precipitated from water as the barium salts, and the products isolated by evaporation of the water.

Olefinic double bonds are cleaved by mixtures of periodate and catalytic amounts of potassium permanganate.[73] The first step of the reaction is oxidation of the olefin by permanganate to a hydroxyketone, which is then

---

[73] R. U. Lemieux and E. von Rudloff, *Can. J. Chem.* **33**, 1701 (1955); E. von Rudloff, *ibid.* **34**, 1413 (1956) and references cited therein.

cleaved by periodate. The manganate ion is then reoxidized to permanganate by periodate. This general method is useful both analytically and preparatively.

III. Lead Tetraacetate

Since the general use of lead tetraacetate is discussed in the chapter by Criegee (this volume), only its application to the carbon–carbon cleavage of 1,2-diols and related compounds is discussed here.

A. DIOL CLEAVAGE

The stoichiometry of the cleavage of 1,2-diols by lead tetraacetate is:

$$\begin{array}{c} R_2COH \\ | \\ R_2COH \end{array} + Pb(OAc)_4 \longrightarrow 2\,R_2CO + Pb(OAc)_2 + 2\,HOAc$$

Lead tetraacetate oxidizes iodide ion quantitatively to iodine, which can be titrated against sodium arsenite or thiosulfate in the usual way.

The use of this reagent was pioneered by Criegee, who showed that it would cleave 1,2-diols quantitatively.[8, 32, 74] He used dry solvents, e.g., acetic acid or aprotic solvents such as benzene, but except for unreactive diols, lead tetraacetate can be used in the presence of relatively large amounts of water.[75, 76] Criegee suggested that a cyclic intermediate XIX was formed between diol and lead tetraacetate, and that it decomposed to products:

$$\begin{array}{c} R_2C-OH \\ | \\ R_2C-OH \end{array} + Pb(OAc)_4 \longrightarrow \begin{array}{c} R_2C-OPb(OAc)_3 \\ | \\ R_2C-OH \end{array} \longrightarrow \begin{array}{c} R_2C-O \\ | \\ R_2C-O \end{array}\!\!Pb(OAc)_2$$

$$(XIX)$$

$$2\,R_2C{=}O + Pb(OAc)_2$$

The isolation of stable cyclic osmates gave indirect support to this theory.[77]

This theory explains the generally higher reactivity of *cis*- over *trans*-1,2-diols (up to cycloheptane diols[32]), and of *threo* over *erythro* (cf. Sections II,B and II,D,2). However, lead tetraacetate will oxidize some tertiary *trans*-diols which

[74] R. Criegee, *Ann.* **481**, 275 (1930); *Ber.* **64**, 260 (1931); R. Criegee, E. Büchner, and W. Walther, *ibid.* **73**, 571 (1940); R. Criegee and H. Zogel, *Chem. Ber.* **84**, 215 (1951); R. Criegee, *Angew. Chem.* **70**, 173 (1958).

[75] E. Baer, R. Grosheintz, and H. O. L. Fischer, *J. Am. Chem. Soc.* **61**, 2607 (1939); R. Criegee and E. Büchner, *Ber.* **73**, 563 (1940).

[76] L. K. Dyall and K. H. Pausacker, *J. Chem. Soc.* p. 3950 (1958); J. P. Cordner and K. H. Pausacker, *ibid.* p. 102 (1953).

[77] R. Criegee, *Angew. Chem.* **50**, 153 (1937); R. Criegee, B. Marchand, and H. Wannowins, *Ann.* **550**, 99 (1942).

cannot form a cyclic intermediate and which are inert to periodate, and herein lies much of its value as a diol-cleaving reagent.

It will cleave *trans*-decalin-9,10-diol (II) and other *trans*-diols of similar structure which cannot form cyclic intermediates, and *trans*-1,2-dimethyl-cyclohexane- and *trans*-1,2-dimethylcyclopentane-1,2-diol (IV) where formation of a cyclic intermediate would require considerable distortion of the carbocyclic system, or considerable compression of nearby groups.[32, 38]

However, the rate of oxidation of these simple *trans*-diols is always less than that of the *cis*-diol, e.g., the ratio k_{cis}/k_{trans} is ca. 20 for the cyclohexane and 1,2-dimethylcyclohexane-1,2-diols; ca. 200 for the 1,2-dimethylcyclopentane-1,2-diols; ca. 3000 for the cyclopentane-1,2-diols; and ca. 4000 for the decalin-9,10-diols. Also, the rate of oxidation of some rigid disecondary *trans*-diols is very slow [e.g., for the camphane-2,3-diols the *endo-endo-cis*-diol (XX) is very reactive toward lead tetraacetate, and toward phenyliodosoacetate and periodate, while the *trans*-diol (XXI) is very unreactive to all three oxidants[9]] and in fact oxidation of rigid *trans*-diols occurs most readily in ditertiary systems. These unreactive diols are, however, cleaved quantitatively by lead tetraacetate in pyridine.[78]

(XX)   (XXI)

There is no direct kinetic evidence for formation of a cyclic intermediate in any appreciable concentration between diol and lead tetraacetate, e.g., in acetic acid oxidation is of first order with respect to each reagent, for a number of 1,2-diols.[79] The only evidence for formation of a cyclic intermediate therefore depends upon the relation between reaction rate and configuration of the diol; complicating the problem is the observation that the *trans* isomer is more reactive than the *cis* in the dihydrophenanthrene diols (XXII), when R = H or alkyl, whereas the "normal" behavior of the *cis* isomer being more reactive than the *trans* is observed when R = aryl.[32, 80]

Increasing the alkylation increases the reactivity of the diol.[32] The main effect of alkyl groups seems to be steric, rather than electronic, because the

[78] R. C. Hockett and D. F. Mowery, *J. Am. Chem. Soc.* **65**, 403 (1943); H. R. Goldschmid and A. S. Perlin, *Can. J. Chem.* **38**, 2280 (1960).

[79] R. P. Bell, J. R. Sturrock, and R. L. St. D. Whitehead, *J. Chem. Soc.* p. 82 (1940).

[80] E. Boyland and G. Wolf, *Biochem. J.* **47**, 64 (1940).

more bulky the substituent the more reactive the diol. Bulky groups should favor formation of the transition state for any reaction in which a tetrahedral carbon atom goes to a trigonal, as in the decomposition of an ester of lead

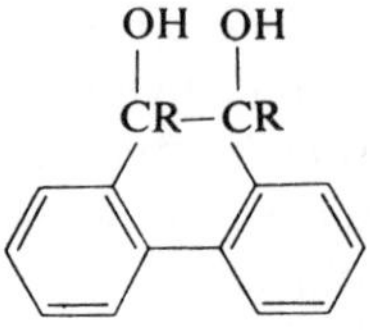

(XXII)

tetraacetate and a diol to a carbonyl compound. But clear-cut electronic effects are observed for the oxidation of substituted benzpinacols by lead tetraacetate.[76] Electron-releasing substituents in the 4-position speed, and electron-attracting substituents retard, reaction. Electron release should assist formation of an intermediate ester by attack of a hydroxyl group upon the lead atom, and assist the breakdown of such an intermediate to the carbonyl compound. The effects of electron-releasing groups upon the rate of periodate oxidation have been discussed in Section II,B,2,a and b.

Monosaccharides are oxidized almost exclusively in their cyclic, rather than in their open-chain, form.[81, 82] Reaction in acetic acid occurs first at the hydroxy-hemiacetal group, because electron release from the ethereal oxygen atom can stabilize the transition state which presumably contains a forming carbonyl group.

The first product is the monoformate of a lower sugar, which may be oxidized in its turn to give the diformate of a still lower sugar.[82] There is some evidence that oxidation of α-D-glucose occurs by conversion of the pyranose form into the more reactive furanose form which, having a five-membered ring, is rapidly oxidized, and that this interconversion may be partially rate limiting. It may therefore be possible to estimate the rate of conversion of a pyranose into a furanose form by measuring the rate of its reaction with lead tetraacetate.

There seems to be a general correlation between the rate of oxidation by lead tetraacetate and the proximity of the hydroxyl groups [26, 32, 83] but it is far from exact, and sometimes breaks down completely, as in the oxidations of dihydrophenanthrene diols.[32, 80]

[81] R. Criegee, *Ann.* **495**, 211 (1932); R. C. Hockett, M. T. Dienes, and H. E. Ramsden, *J. Am. Chem. Soc.* **65**, 1474 (1943).

[82] A. S. Perlin and C. Brice, *Can. J. Chem.* **34**, 541 (1956); A. S. Perlin, personal communication.

[83] V. Prelog, K. Schenker, and W. Kung, *Helv. Chim. Acta* **36**, 471 (1953).

Most of these results suggest that the preferred mechanism for the lead tetraacetate cleavage of a diol involves a cyclic transition state. The original Criegee mechanism was of this type; an alternative cyclic mechanism involves coordination of one hydroxyl group to the lead atom, followed by an intra-molecular proton transfer[32]:

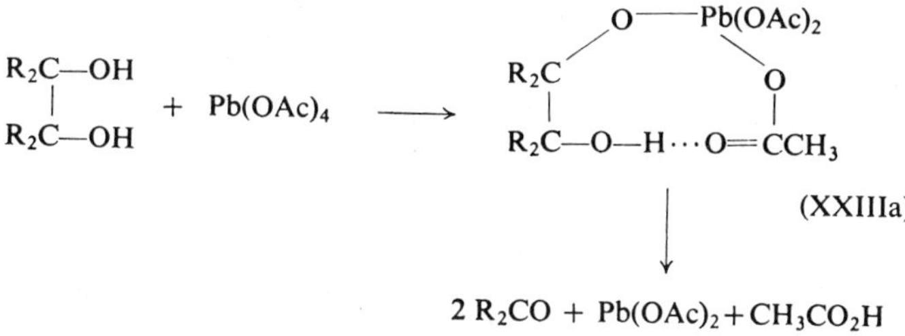

$$
\begin{array}{ccc}
R_2C\!-\!OH & & O\!\!-\!\!\!-\!\!Pb(OAc)_2 \\
| & + \ Pb(OAc)_4 \longrightarrow & R_2C \diagup \qquad \diagdown O \\
R_2C\!-\!OH & & R_2C\!-\!O\!-\!H\cdots O\!\!=\!\!CCH_3 \\
& & \text{(XXIIIa)}
\end{array}
$$

$$
\downarrow
$$

$$
2\,R_2CO + Pb(OAc)_2 + CH_3CO_2H
$$

The intermediate XXIIIb might also break down with proton transfer to an external base[32]:

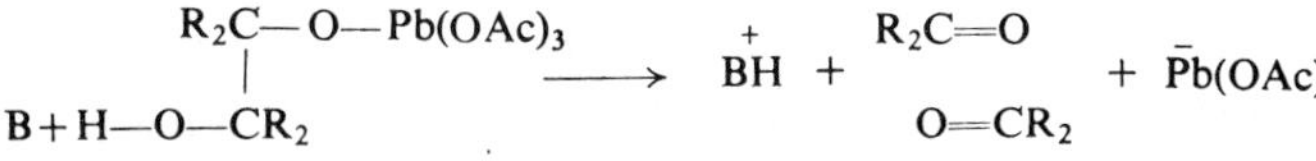

$$
\begin{array}{ccc}
R_2C\!-\!O\!-\!Pb(OAc)_3 & & \overset{+}{B}H \ + \quad R_2C\!\!=\!\!O \\
| & \longrightarrow & \qquad\qquad\qquad + \ \overset{-}{P}b(OAc)_3 \\
B+H\!-\!O\!-\!CR_2 & & \qquad\qquad O\!\!=\!\!CR_2
\end{array}
$$

(XXIIIb)

Such a mechanism should be a favorable one for a *trans*-diol which cannot readily generate a cyclic transition state. Bases, e.g., the acetate ion, will catalyze oxidation of 1,2-diols and α-hydroxy acids, and formic acid.[32,84] They could function by assisting ring closure, as in some oxidations by periodate (Section II,B,2,c), as well as by assisting the breakdown of XXIIIb. The high rates of reaction in pyridine may arise from the high basicity of the solvent, but it is possible that pyridine displaces acetate to generate a more reactive lead(IV) compound.[78]

The oxidation of pinacol and the cyclohexane-1,2-diols is acid catalyzed and a strong acid, e.g., sulfuric or methanesulfonic acid, is a better catalyst than trichloroacetic acid.[85] Acids could catalyze the reaction in various ways. They could protonate lead tetraacetate, and so increase its electrophilicity and its rate of coordination to the diol:

$$
Pb(OAc)_4 + \overset{+}{H} \ \rightleftharpoons \ Pb(OAc)_3\overset{+}{O}AcH
$$

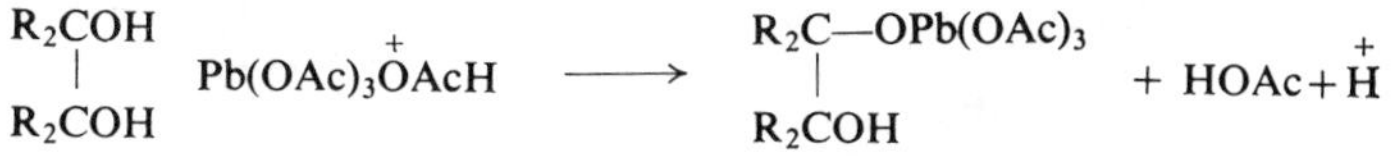

$$
\begin{array}{ccc}
R_2COH & & R_2C\!-\!OPb(OAc)_3 \\
| \quad Pb(OAc)_3\overset{+}{O}AcH & \longrightarrow & | \qquad\qquad + \ HOAc + \overset{+}{H} \\
R_2COH & & R_2COH
\end{array}
$$

(XXIIIb)

[84] A. S. Perlin, *J. Am. Chem. Soc.* **76**, 5505 (1954).

[85] R. P. Bell, V. G. Rivlin, and W. A. Waters, *J. Chem. Soc.* p. 1696 (1958).

Or they could catalyze either the ring closure of XXIIIb or its direct decomposition to products:

$$
\begin{array}{ccc}
R_2C-O-Pb(OAc)_3 & & R_2C-O-Pb(OAc)_2\overset{+}{O}AcH \\
\vert & +\ \overset{+}{H} \rightleftharpoons & \vert \\
R_2COH & & R_2C-OH \\
\text{(XXIIIb)} & &
\end{array}
$$

$$
2\,R_2CO + Pb(OAc)_2 + HOAc + \overset{+}{H} \longleftarrow \begin{array}{c} R_2C-O \\ \vert \quad\quad > Pb(OAc)_2 + HOAc + \overset{+}{H} \\ R_2C-O \end{array}
$$

The present evidence does not allow us to differentiate between these possibilities, nor to decide whether catalysis is specifically by the proton or by general acids.

The rate of oxidation of diols by lead tetraacetate in acetic acid is increased by the addition of moderate amounts of water or an alcohol[75]; water in high concentration retards oxidation[76] and hydrolyzes lead tetraacetate. The water or alcohol may act by displacing one or more of the acetate residues from the lead atom, and so generating a more reactive oxidant; it might also act as a general acid or base and assist a proton transfer.

The addition of aprotic solvents to the acetic acid solvent should favor any equilibrium in which acetic acid is eliminated,[74] e.g.,

$$
\begin{array}{ccc}
R_2COH & & R_2C-Pb(OAc)_3 \\
\vert \quad + Pb(OAc)_4 & \rightleftharpoons & \vert \quad\quad + HOAc \\
R_2COH & & R_2COH
\end{array}
$$

and so catalyze oxidation.

Probably no single reaction mechanism can explain all these results, and there is no reason to believe that there should be only one mechanism for diol cleavage by lead tetraacetate, indeed the versatility of this reagent (see Chapter V by Criegee, in this volume) suggests that it can react in a variety of ways. Many of the *trans*-diols which react with lead tetraacetate, even though they cannot form a cyclic intermediate with it, have hydroxyl groups attached to tertiary carbon atoms and may react by an entirely different mechanism involving complexes with carbonium ion character,[55] e.g., XXIV:

$$
\begin{array}{ccc}
R_2C-O \\
\vert \quad\quad Pb(OAc)_3 \longrightarrow \\
R_2COH \\
\text{(XXIIIb)}
\end{array}
\qquad
\begin{array}{c}
R_2C-O-Pb(OAc)_2 \\
\vert \quad\quad\quad\quad \vert \\
R_2C\cdots\cdots O \\
+ \quad\quad\quad\quad\ \ \diagdown C\cdot CH_3 \\
O^{\diagup} \\
\text{(XXIV)}
\end{array}
$$

$$
\text{products} \longleftarrow \begin{array}{c} R_2C-O \\ \vert \quad\quad > Pb(OAc)_2 + HOAc \\ R_2C-O \end{array}
$$

However, the steric and electronic effects of methyl groups should assist any reaction in which a tetrahedral carbon atom changes to a trigonal (Section II,B,2,b).

The available evidence suggests that for most diol cleavages by lead tetraacetate the rate-limiting step is cyclization of an open-chain ester (XXIII), and that carbon–carbon bond cleavage then occurs rapidly. But these two steps could occur concurrently, and this modification of the original Criegee mechanism, in which the carbon–carbon bond is partially broken and a lead–oxygen bond is partially formed in the transition state, could be applied to the relatively unreactive, rigid, *trans*-diols as an alternative to the "carbonium ion" mechanism discussed earlier. In oxidations of 1,2-diols by periodate it seems that carbon–carbon bond cleavage always follows formation of a cyclic intermediate.

B. α-HYDROXY ACIDS

Lead tetraacetate will cleave α-hydroxy acids.[74, 75] A variety of reaction paths can be written: obvious ones involve coordination of the hydroxyl group to the lead atom, followed by loss of carbon dioxide:

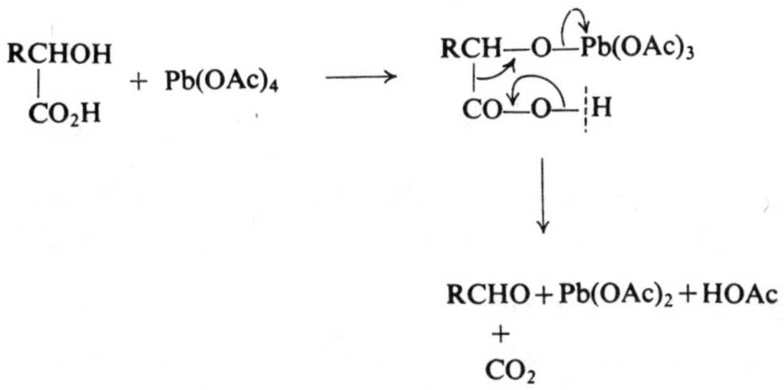

$$\text{RCHOH} \atop \text{CO}_2\text{H} \quad + \text{Pb(OAc)}_4 \longrightarrow \quad \text{RCH-O-Pb(OAc)}_3 \atop \text{CO-O-H}$$

$$\downarrow$$

$$\text{RCHO} + \text{Pb(OAc)}_2 + \text{HOAc}$$
$$+$$
$$\text{CO}_2$$

or coordination of both hydroxyl and carboxyl groups to the lead atom followed by decomposition of a cyclic intermediate, XXV:

$$\text{RCH-O} \atop \text{CO-O} \Big\rangle \text{Pb(OAc)}_2 \longrightarrow \quad \text{RCHO} \atop \text{CO}_2 \quad + \text{Pb(OAc)}_2$$

(XXV)

C. 1,2-DICARBONYL AND 1,2-HYDROXYCARBONYL COMPOUNDS

Lead tetraacetate, like periodate, will generally cleave 1,2-dicarbonyl or hydroxycarbonyl compounds. Baer has shown that the reaction depends upon the presence of protic solvents, usually water or an alcohol, which can add to the carbonyl group.[86] He suggests that the protic solvent converts the organic

[86] E. Baer, *J. Am. Chem. Soc.* **62**, 1597 (1940).

compound into a pseudo-glycol, e.g., XXVI, which is oxidized by lead tetra-acetate:

$$RCO \cdot CO_2H + H_2O \rightleftharpoons R-\underset{\underset{OH}{|}}{\overset{\overset{OH}{|}}{C}}-CO_2H \xrightarrow{Pb(OAc)_4} RCO_2H + CO_2$$

(XXVI)

Evidence for this mechanism is that oxidation is slow, and incomplete, in aprotic solvents. (It should be noted that there is evidence that the periodate cleavage of 1,2-diketones proceeds by an entirely different mechanism—see Section II,B,3.)

For some keto acids, e.g., phenylpyruvic, the reaction is more complex because both oxidative cleavage and acetylation occur, and after saponification mandelic acid can be isolated:

$$PhCH_2CO \cdot CO_2H \xrightarrow{Pb(OAc)_4} \underset{\underset{OAc}{|}}{PhCHCO} \cdot CO_2H \longrightarrow \underset{\underset{OAc}{|}}{PhCHCO_2H} + CO_2$$

$$\downarrow O\bar{H}$$

$$PhCH(OH)CO_2H$$

Lead tetraacetate in an aprotic solvent is a useful acetylating agent for compounds such as phenylpyruvic acid, which have labile hydrogen atoms.

D. EXPERIMENTAL METHODS

Acetic acid is the usual solvent. It should be purified by leaving it with chromium trioxide for some time, then refluxing it, and finally fractionally distilling it through a good column. If rate measurements are to be made, the water content of the acetic acid should be calculated from its melting point,[87] and adjusted by addition of either acetic anhydride or water. Addition of water speeds reaction except in high concentration, but can cause trouble by hydrolyzing the oxidant (Section III,A). Alternatively, aprotic solvents can be added to speed reaction; pyridine is particularly effective in this respect.[78]

After oxidation is complete, a portion of the reaction solution is added to an aqueous solution of potassium iodide and sodium acetate, and the liberated iodine is titrated with either sodium arsenite or thiosulfate. (The sodium acetate keeps the lead iodide in solution.) It is desirable to make a control test upon the solution of lead tetraacetate, particularly if oxidation of the organic compound is slow.

[87] H. D. Richmond and E. A. England, *Analyst* 51, 283 (1926).

Reaction can also be followed spectrophotometrically,[88] or by potentiometric titration with standard hydroquinone.[89] These methods can be used with very dilute solutions, and make it possible to use lead tetraacetate for the quantitative oxidation of relatively insoluble organic compounds, e.g., some amino sugars.[88]

Lead tetraacetate complements periodate, in that it will oxidize many of the diols which are inert to periodate, or which are insoluble in water, and by using both reagents one can often analyze mixtures of isomeric diols.[38] It is extremely useful for the preparative oxidation of water-insoluble compounds because it can be used in many solvents, ranging from aqueous acetic acid to benzene. Addition of water or an alcohol to acetic acid makes lead tetraacetate an excellent reagent for cleavage of diketones and related compounds. The great limitations of lead tetraacetate are that it is much less specific than periodate, e.g., it will oxidize or acetylate many organic compounds (see Chapter V by Criegee), and that its solutions are unstable if much water is present. Although periodate is in many respects the more useful reagent for the oxidation of water-soluble carbohydrates, lead tetraacetate has been used very successfully for the stepwise oxidation of sugars, and for the preparation of some rare sugars.[82]

IV. Iodoso Compounds

Aryl iodosoacetates and benzoates (XXVII) will cleave 1,2-diols and related compounds[90]; however, like lead tetraacetate, they are considerably less specific than periodate, and will act as general oxidants for many organic compounds.[91] The reaction between benzpinacol and phenyl iodosoacetate in acetic acid is of the first order with respect to each reagent, and addition of aprotic solvents speeds reaction.[92] Free acetoxy radicals are not reaction intermediates, and mechanisms can be written analogous to those suggested for lead tetraacetate:

$$
\begin{array}{c}
\begin{array}{c} R_2COH \\ | \\ R_2COH \end{array} + ArI(OCOR)_2 \longrightarrow \begin{array}{c} R_2C\!-\!\!-O\!-\!\!-IAr \\ | \qquad\qquad\ O \\ R_2COH \qquad O\!\!=\!\!CR \end{array} + RCO_2H \\[2em]
(XXVII) \qquad\qquad\qquad\qquad \downarrow \\[1em]
2\,R_2CO + ArI + RCO_2H
\end{array}
$$

[88] A. S. Perlin and S. Suzucki, *Can. J. Chem.* **40**, 1226 (1962).
[89] A. Berka, V. Dvorak, and J. Zyka, *Mikrochim. Acta* p. 541 (1962).
[90] H. Beucker and R. Criegee, *Ber.* **541**, 218 (1939).
[91] L. K. Dyall and K. H. Pausacker, *Australian J. Chem.* **11**, 485 (1958).
[92] K. H. Pausacker, *J. Chem. Soc.* p. 107 (1953).

Electron-attracting substituents in the aryl group of the oxidant increase its reactivity, suggesting that coordination of one or both nucleophilic hydroxyl groups with iodine is important in the formation of the transition state.

Aryl iodosoacetates are best prepared by the oxidation of aryl iodides by hydrogen peroxide in acetic anhydride, to give the iodoso compounds, which are then acetylated *in situ*.[92]

$$H_2O_2 + (CH_3 \cdot CO)_2O \longrightarrow CH_3 \cdot CO \cdot O_2H + CH_3CO_2H$$

$$CH_3 \cdot CO \cdot O_2H + ArI \longrightarrow ArIO + CH_3CO_2H$$

$$\downarrow$$

$$ArI(OCO \cdot CH_3)_2$$

Acetic acid is a convenient solvent for the oxidation of 1,2-diols by iodosoacetates. Reaction is followed by adding the reaction mixture to a solution of potassium iodide, and titrating the iodine produced.

These iodoso compounds are less reactive than lead tetraacetate toward diols and seem to have no advantages over the other reagents for cleaving diols; indeed, their ability to oxidize primary and secondary alcohols makes them unsatisfactory as specific oxidants, and their value is as general oxidants and acetylating agents.[91]

V. Sodium Bismuthate

Rigby has shown that sodium bismuthate will cleave 1,2-diols cleanly to carbonyl compounds; it will also oxidize α-hydroxy acids and formic acid, and is therefore a less specific reagent than periodate.[93] Its main advantage is that it is effective in many solvents, e.g., in water, aqueous dioxan, or acetic acid. There is no compelling evidence for any particular reaction mechanism; any of the various mechanisms suggested for the other glycol-cleaving reagents could be applied to sodium bismuthate. The *cis*- and *trans*-cyclohexane-1,2-diols have similar reactivities toward sodium bismuthate, contrasting sharply with their behavior toward the other oxidants, but the reaction is probably occurring on the surface of the sparingly soluble sodium bismuthate, and its rate could then depend little upon the structure of the diol.

VI. Xenic Acid

Xenic acid will oxidize 1,2-diols and aldehydes, primary and secondary alcohols, and oxalic acid.[94] The first formed products are frequently oxidized

[93] W. Rigby, *J. Chem. Soc.* p. 1907 (1950).
[94] B. Jaselskis and S. Vas, *J. Am. Chem. Soc.* **86**, 2078 (1964).

further to carbon dioxide or a carboxylic acid. Xenic acid is reduced to xenon, and this fact may make it a useful organic reagent. Because the only by-products are xenon and water, isolation of the oxidation products is very simple.

Acknowledgment

The writer is grateful to Prof. R. Criegee, and Drs. G. J. Buist and A. S. Perlin for helpful discussions and communication of their unpublished results.

Author Index

Numbers in parentheses are reference numbers and indicate that an author's work is referred to although his name is not cited in the text.

A

Abel, E., 32, 65, 66
Abell, R. D., 83, 84
Abernethy, J. L., 151
Accountius, O. E., 70, 153
Ackerman, J., 312, 313(139)
Acott, B., 353
Acree, F., 350
Acree, S. F., 51(215), 52
Adams, R., 355
Adamson, A. W., 9, 25, 187, 196(3), 228, 229, 232(3)
Adamson, T., 43, 44(182)
Adkins, H., 147, 148
Adler, E., 391, 392
Adler, S. J., 66, 187, 212(4)
Aebi, H., 56, 57(232)
Afonskii, N. S., 71
Ahmed, R., 7
Ahrens, W., 83
Akimoto, H., 86, 99, 100(77)
Aldag, H. J., 158
Alder, K., 297, 342
Alexander, B. H., 374
Alexander, E. A., 60, 237
Alexander, O. R., 23
Aliew, A., 85
Alimarin, S. P., 270
Alkonyi, J., 339(219), 340
Allen, W. S., 156
Allphin, N. L., 92, 102(48)
Alm, R. M., 151
Altman, C., 81
Amendolla, C., 7
Ames, S. R., 388
Amorosa, M., 285, 286(36)
Anantakrishnan, S. V., 159
Anbar, M., 370
Anderson, C. B., 365
Anderson, J. L., 355
Anderson, J. M., 312, 313(138)

Anderson, J. S., 246
Anderson, R. C., 246
Andrejević, V., 353
Andrelowicz, M., 74, 75
Andrews, L. V., 11
Angyal, S. J., 369, 374(9), 380, 399(9)
Anner, G., 150, 156, 321, 322(163, 168), 323(163, 168, 172, 177, 178, 180, 181, 181, 182), 324(180)
Anschutz, R., 137
Anson, P. C., 112
Antoni, V., 159, 173
Antonow, W. K., 312
Antony, F., 365
Aratani, T., 339(215), 340
Arcand, G. M., 245
Archer, D. P., 93, 94(52), 115, 116(117), 117(117), 124(117)
Ardon, M., 245, 247, 248(27), 249(27), 252(27), 253(11), 261(27), 267, 276(63)
Arigoni, D., 150, 156, 279, 285, 286(36), 321 (9), 233(9, 166, 178)
Arnett, E. M., 233, 275
Arth, G. E., 153, 155
Arzoumanian, H., 301
Aschoff, H. J., 22
Ashurst, K. G., 192
Asselt, W. J., 239
Aston, J. G., 220, 259, 260(49)
Aumüller, W., 308, 310(126)
Austin, P. R., 280, 281(15)
Avram, M., 297, 300(90)
Ayres, G. H., 198
Aznáres, J. I., 180

B

Babcock, J. C., 128, 140(15)
Babko, A. K., 267, 276(63)
Bach, S. J., 240
Bachman, G. B., 296

Bacon, R. G. R., 269
Badcock, G. G., 306(114), 307
Badger, G. M., 312, 314(142)
Badin, E. J., 151
Baer, E., 335, 354, 398, 402(75), 403(75, 84)
Baer, S., 267, 276(63)
Baertschi, P., 31
Bahl, R. K., 370
Bailar, J. C., 279
Bailey, N., 22, 71, 73, 74
Baker, F. B., 244
Baker, H. R., 246
Baker, J. W., 167
Baker, R., 51(211), 52, 68, 143, 147
Baker, R. H., 147
Baker, S. B., 353
Bakore, G. V., 65
Balaban, A. T., 95, 96(65), 98(65), 104(65)
Ballhausen, C. J., 12, 73
Balsohn, M., 84
Banks, C. V., 370, 372(14), 378(14), 394(14)
Baranowska, M., 21
Barbier, P., 127, 132(12)
Barchielli, R., 39
Bardoneschi, R., 323(184)
Barker, G. R., 380
Barlin, G. B., 366
Barnighausen, H., 246
Barraclough, C. G., 72
Barron, H. E., 283, 291(31a), 352(31a)
Bartecki, A., 20
Bartlett, M. F., 183
Bartlett, N., 73
Bartlett, P. D., 43, 44(182), 45, 129, 304
Barton, D. H. R., 128, 164, 296, 325
Basolo, F., 250, 275(35)
Bass, R. G., 183
Bassi, D., 72
Bast, H., 108
Bateman, D. E., 53(221), 54
Batres, E., 155
Baumgarten, H. E., 353, 356
Bavley, A., 7, 43, 44(182)
Bawn, C. E. H., 197, 218(82, 84), 219(112), 221, 222, 235
Baxendale, J. H., 26, 192, 197(22), 198(22), 219(114), 236
Beal, P. F., 323(183)
Beard, R. F., 82
Beck, M. T., 60

Becke, J., 302, 303(99)
Becker, W. J., 159, 163(117)
Beckmann, E. O., 63
Beckwith, A. J. L., 325, 353
Bedi, S. N., 28
Begemann, P. H., 45, 53(190)
Behr, A., 125, 135(1)
Behrend, R., 62
Beilstein, F., 83, 84, 137
Belcher, R., 8, 9, 20, 30, 48
Bell, D. H., 371, 388(20)
Bell, R. P., 384, 386, 399, 401
Benard, J., 74
Bennett, G. W., 146
Bennett, L. E., 197
Bennett, R. M., 11, 12
Benrath, A., 265, 274(60a)
Benson, C., 76, 80
Benson, D., 281, 282(20), 294
Bentley, F. F., 12
Bentley, W. H., 12
Bergmann, E., 133, 317, 318(150, 152)
Bergmann, F., 317, 318(152)
Berka, A., 281, 405
Berkheimer, H. E., 23
Berlin, A. A., 129
Berlin, T., 317, 318(150)
Bernáth, G., 244
Bernhauer, K., 85, 137
Bernstein, S., 156
Berry, R. E., 147
Bert, L., 46
Berthelot, M., 132(29), 133
Best, P. A., 178, 224, 225(91)
Beucker, H., 365, 366(291), 405
Beyers, A., 131(32), 132(32), 133
Beyler, R. E., 153, 155
Bhagwat, W. V., 216(100), 228
Bhattacharya, A. K., 181
Bickel, A. F., 225, 228(94), 234(94), 238(94)
Bielecki, J., 94
Biemann, K., 325
Billman, J. H., 51(213), 52
Biradar, N. S., 191
Birch, A. J., 296, 317, 318(147), 327(148)
Bíró, K., 71
Bischoff, B., 267
Bistrzycki, A., 87
Black, A. H., 265
Black, G., 40

Blaustein, B. D., 246
Blitz, H., 125, 135(1)
Blohm, M., 70
Blomquist, A. T., 45
Bloom, B. M., 43, 44(187)
Bobbitt, J. M., 372, 390, 394(24), 395(24)
Bobovich, Ya. S., 72
Bobtelsky, M., 82, 196, 220(42), 239(42)
Bock, W., 353
Bockemuller, W., 125, 135(1)
Bodea, C., 349
Boden, H., 90
Boedtker, E., 84, 85
Böhme, H., 352
Boekenoogen, H. A., 45, 53(190)
Boeseken, A., 380
Boeseken, J., 42, 140
Bogdanov, G. N., 288, 289(41)
Bogdanov, S. V., 68
Bokadia, M. M., 312, 313(137), 314(137), 320(137), 332(137)
Bollenback, G. N., 106, 126
Bollinger, J., 353
Bonner, N. A., 197
Booth, M. H., 198
Borchers, C. E., 273
Borćić, S., 297
Bordwell, F. G., 63
Borisow, A. E., 363
Bose, J. L., 389
Bosshard, W., 127
Bottini, A. T., 183
Bottomley, C. G., 45
Bourgeois, E., 63
Bourne, E. J., 352
Bourns, A. N., 166
Bouveault, L., 151
Bowden, K., 148
Bower, J. D., 291(61), 292
Bowers, A., 323(165, 169, 170, 173)
Bowman, M. I., 152, 153(80)
Boyd, R. H., 22
Boyer, M. H., 195
Boyland, E., 399, 400(80)
Bradley, A., 110(109), 112, 113(109), 119(109), 178
Bradley, D. C., 249
Brandenberger, S. G., 84, 90(10), 130, 136(47), 138(47)
Brannon, D. R., 297

Brass, K., 292
Braude, E. A., 148, 285
Bray, W. C., 196
Bredt, J., 110(108, 115), 112, 135, 136, 145(41)
Bremer, R. F., 251, 252(39a), 253(39a)
Bremmer, J. G. H., 275
Brennan, H., 73
Breslaver, H., 108
Brice, C., 400, 405(82)
Brill, W. F., 268
Brito, F., 189
Britt, A. D., 24
Broda, E., 25
Brodskii, A. I., 370
Bromby, N. G., 137
Brown, B. R., 312, 313(137), 314(137), 320(137), 332(137)
Brown, D. C., 135
Brown, D. J., 11
Brown, G. B., 63
Brown, H. C., 164, 184
Browne, A. W., 25, 26
Brownell, R., 160, 175
Bruce, J., 64
Brückner, C., 278
Brutcher, F. V., 346
Bubl, E. C., 388
Büchi, G., 294
Büchner, E., 374, 398, 402(74, 75), 403(74, 75)
Buist, G. J., 171, 370, 373, 375, 376(30, 43, 44, 47), 377(30, 43), 378(30, 43), 379(30, 48), 380(49), 381(30, 43) 382(49), 383(30, 43, 48), 385(48), 386(17a), 396(30), 397(44),
Bulgrin, V. C., 373, 374, 377(29), 378(29), 379(29), 380(37), 381(29), 383(29), 385(29), 396(37), 396(29,) 397(37)
Buncel, E., 166
Bunton, C. A., 171, 373, 374, 375(38, 43), 376(30, 43, 44, 47), 377(30, 43), 378(30, 43), 379(30), 380(38, 49), 381(30, 43), 382(49, 55), 383(30, 43), 386, 387(59), 394(59), 396(30), 397(38, 44), 399(38), 402(55), 405(38)
Burdon, J., 45
Burger, M., 288, 290(57)
Burnop, V. C. E., 339(220), 340
Burns, J. W., 102

Burton, C. I., 87
Buscarons, F., 270
Busch, D. H., 70
Buser, W., 56, 57(232)
Bush, J. D., 70, 153
Butleroff, A., 129, 132(22, 30), 133
Buzby, G. C., Jr., 68
Byström, A., 69

C

Cabezas, M. E., 323(169, 170)
Cadotte, J. E., 395
Caglioti, L., 285, 286(36)
Cahill, A. E., 31
Cainelli, G., 150, 156, 279, 285, 286(36), 321(9), 323(9)
Caland, P., 64
Cama, H. R., 7
Campbell, C. D., 357
Campbell, W. P., 91, 92(46)
Candlin, J. P., 57, 197, 221, 221(81)
Cantley, M., 388
Canvin, D. J., 65
Carlson, G. L., 12, 73
Carnelley, T., 86
Carpio, H., 155
Carr, M. D., 374, 380(38), 397(38), 399(38), 405(38)
Carrington, A., 2, 3, 5, 10, 12, 22, 71, 73, 74
Carstanjen, E., 94
Cartledge, G. H., 229
Casanova, J., 294, 297(73), 298(73), 301(73)
Casassas, E., 270
Cason, J., 147
Castro, A. J., 68
Cavelieri, L. F., 63
Cavill, G. W. K., 228, 283, 291(31a, 60), 306 (114, 118), 307(111, 114, 118), 311(111), 312, 313(134), 315(144a), 330, 352(31a)
Cawley, J. J., 143, 169
Čeković, Ž., 285
Celeste, J. R., 119, 120(122)
Cerda, E., 356
Chang, F. C., 279, 329(8)
Chang, T.-L., 32
Chang, Y. W., 160, 162, 171, 175
Chapman, E. T., 182

Chapman, N. B., 297
Chargaff, E., 388
Charlton, F. S., 20
Chatamra, B., 62
Chatterjee, A. K., 249
Chatterji, A. K., 159, 170, 173
Chawla, I. D., 192
Chen, F. Y., 360
Chinard, F. P., 366
Chisholm, D., 135
Chou, S. M., 249
Chrmielowska, M., 20
Churacek, J., 84, 113(15)
Citterio, C., 240
Clapp, R. C., 326, 329(189)
Clarke, H. T., 39
Clarke, M. F., 43, 44(183)
Clarke, R. L., 308, 310(124)
Claus, A., 53
Clausson-Kass, N., 333
Clement, R. A., 358
Clifford, A. A., 209(109), 217(109), 218(109) 234(109), 235(109), 237(109)
Clutterbuck, P. W., 368
Cobble, J. W., 189, 195(12)
Cocker, W., 228, 306
Coffman, D. D., 273
Cohen, M., 72, 153, 159, 160
Colby, T. H., 110(107), 112
Cole, E. R., 280, 283, 291(31a, 60), 330(18), 352(31a)
Collison, E., 188
Colson, A., 278, 279(4), 280(4)
Commarmont, A., 151
Conant, J. B., 129, 132(22), 148, 220, 259, 260(49)
Condary, J., 288, 290(58)
Conforth, J. W., 327
Connick, R. E., 244
Connor, R., 94
Cook, J. W., 312, 314(142)
Cook, S. E., 364
Cookson, E., 327
Cooper, G. D., 63
Cooper, T. A., 209(85), 222
Copestake, T. B., 216(99), 228
Corbett, W. M., 352
Cordner, J. P., 398, 400(76), 402(76)
Corey, E. J., 294, 297(73), 298(73), 301(73), 306

Corey, G. C., 166
Cornforth, J. W., 160, 173
Corson, B. B., 40
Coulombeau, J., 66
Covington, A. K., 187, 210(2)
Cramer, P. L., 146
Cressey, T., 187, 210(2)
Criegee, R., 64, 171, 207, 210(72), 279, 280, 284, 288(32), 290, 302, 303(99, 100, 101), 306(115), 307, 313(13), 317(13), 318(13), 334, 335(13, 14), 336(13, 14, 59), 337(13, 59), 339(13, 59), 340(13, 59), 344(14), 345(13), 346(13), 363, 364(280), 365, 366(291), 369, 373(8, 32), 374, 398(8, 74, 77), 399(32), 400(32, 81), 401(32), 402(74, 75), 403(74, 75), 405
Criner, G. X., 356
Cristol, S. J., 119, 121(123), 130, 135
Critchfield, F. E., 269
Crombie, L., 51(214), 52
Cross, B., 349
Crouthamel, C. E., 370, 372(14), 378(14), 394(14)
Cullis, C. F., 10, 39, 65, 67(168), 214(116), 236
Cummings, W., 312, 313(137), 314(137), 320(137), 332(137)
Cuy, E. J., 196

D

Dahlen, J., 391
Dahlgren, G., 374, 380(37), 386(37), 397(37)
Dainton, F. S., 188, 216(104), 229
Dale, J. I., 183
Dalvi, P. D., 7
Dane, E., 148, 150, 339(214), 340
Dann, O., 63
Darapsky, A., 152, 172
Darrin, M., 73, 95, 97(64)
Daubert, B. F., 151
Daudt, W. H., 326, 329(189)
Davenkov, A. B., 129
David, A., 320
Davidson, A. W., 280, 281(17), 282(17)
Davidson, N., 193
Davies, D. I., 228, 316
Davies, W. G., 71
Davis, D. C., 372, 394(22)

Davis, H. A., 374
Davis, M., 149
Davis, M. A., 138
Day, G. A., 218(127), 239
Dayal, R., 65
De, K., 73
Dean, F. M., 306(118), 307
Dean, G. A., 198
Dean, M. H., 219(134), 239
Dean, P. M., 40
Deasy, C. L., 279
Deffner, J. F., 87
Dehmelt, H. G., 73
Delaby, R., 151
de la Mare, P. B. D., 138
DeLury, R. E., 77, 82
Demjanov, N. J., 151
Deno, N. C., 23
Denot, E., 323(165, 170, 173)
Depp, E., 40
DePuy, C. H., 147
Desaulles, P., 149
Desideri, P. G., 21, 192
de Souza, B. C., 197
Detilleux, E., 306(112), 307, 311(112), 312, 313(135), 335(112), 339(135), 340(135)
Deutsch, H. R., 152, 153(80)
de Vries, G., 93, 94(51)
Dewar, J., 137
Dewar, M. J. S., 264, 296, 312
Dey, A. N., 180
Dhar, N. R., 81, 180, 216(100), 228
Diaper, D. G. H., 135
Dickey, J. B., 62
Diebler, H., 192
Diehl, J. W., 169
Dien, C. K., 333
Dienes, M. T., 400
Dilling, M., 72
Dimler, R. J., 372, 374, 400(26)
Dimroth, K., 355, 363
Dimroth, O., 279, 282(5, 6), 292(5, 63), 307(6), 311(6), 313(6), 362
Dimroth, P., 280, 312(6), 335(14), 336(14), 344(14), 363, 364(280)
Dixon, W. T., 198, 267
Djerassi, C., 149, 150(53), 157
Dobriner, K., 308, 310(124)
Dobrjanski, A., 85
D'Ocón, A., 317

Dodson, V. H., 265
Doering, W. v. E., 83, 137, 297
Dollfus, W., 96, 97(71)
Dorfman, M. K., 246
Doskočil, J., 276
Douglass, R. M., 74
Dressler, R. L., 353
Drickamer, H. G., 12
Drummond, A. Y., 2, 8, 32, 53, 188, 195(8, 39), 206, 211, 213(8, 71), 220, 223(75, 78), 226(8, 75), 227(75), 234(39), 238(39)
Drye, D. J., 196
Ducret, L. P., 189
Duffey, G. H., 247
Duke, F. R., 2, 212(142), 245, 247, 250, 251(39a), 252(39a), 253(39a, b), 254(36) 261(26), 264(36b), 273, 373, 375, 377(29), 378(29), 379(29), 381(29), 383(29), 385(29), 395(29)
Dulon, R., 312, 314(140)
Dulou, R., 107
Dupont, G., 107, 312, 314(140)
Dupuis, T., 72
Dutta, R., 65
Dutton, G. G. S., 395
Dvorak, V., 281, 405
Dvoretzky, I., 84, 90(10), 130, 136(47), 138(47)
Dyall, L. K., 366, 398, 400(76), 402(76), 405, 406(91)
Dyksterhuis, L., 182

Elder, F., 146
Elderfield, R. C., 148
Elian, M., 95, 96(65), 98(65), 104(65)
Eliel, E. L., 164, 165(124)
El-Jadir, N., 70
Elks, J., 128
Elliot, W. J., 95, 97(60)
Ellis, B., 149
Ellis, J. W., 339(221a), 340
Elming, N., 333
Elofson, R. M., 148
Emanuel, N. M., 288, 289(41)
Emerson, W. S., 151
Emmons, W. D., 169
Engels, W., 152, 172
England, E. A., 404
Ephraim, F., 22
Erber, J., 25
Erdtman, H., 317
Ericks, W. B., 229
Erickson, R. E., 294
Eschenmoser, A., 159, 162, 164, 325
Escudero, P., 373, 385(35b)
Espenson, J. H., 80(14)
Essers, W., 34
Étard, A., 94, 95(58, 59), 96(58), 97(59), 102(58), 135
Ettel, V., 21
Evans, E. A., 281, 282(28)
Evans, R. J., 99, 100(78)
Evans, R. M., 7, 128
Evans, W. L., 23, 43, 44(186), 64
Ewerlöf, F., 182

E

Eastman, R. H., 38
Eberhard, R., 40
Ebnöther, A., 288, 290(56)
Edens, R., 294
Eder, K., 339(214), 340
Edwards, J. A., 323(173)
Edwards, J. O., 20, 77, 79(6), 82(6), 194, 219(32)
Edwards, O. E., 339(221), 340
Ege, G., 296
Ehrhart, G., 308, 310(126)
Eilar, K. R., 119, 121(123), 130, 135, 355
Eisenthal, R., 100, 115(80), 118(80), 121(80)
Elbs, K., 137

F

Fackler, J. P., 192
Falkehag, I., 392
Farber, M., 297
Fărcasin, M., 297, 300(90)
Farinacci, N. T., 86
Faro, H. P., 296
Favre, H., 164
Fedneva, E. M., 27
Feher, F., 23
Feldmann, L., 335
Felix, D., 325
Fenn, E. F., 218(127), 239
Fenselav, A. H., 296
Fenton, A. J., 193, 195(28)

Fenton, G. W., 63
Fernelius, W. C., 246
Field, L., 351, 353
Fieser, L. F., 85, 91, 92(46), 112, 115(21, 113), 126, 127, 128, 140(15), 147, 152, 153(81), 161(81), 279, 308, 310(119, 123), 312, 314(141), 315(143), 326, 329(8, 141, 143, 189, 193, 194, 195), 331(141, 143, 194)
Fieser, M., 127
Finch, N., 283, 359(30, 268)
Fineman, M. A., 77
Finkelstein, M., 344
Fiosin, M. J., 279
Fischer, G., 195
Fischer, H., 352, 357
Fischer, H. O. L., 335, 398, 402(75), 403(75)
Fischer, O., 137
Fishel, D. L., 90, 92(45), 136(46), 138(46)
Fishman, J., 308
Fittig, R., 83, 84
Fleming, D. G., 54
Flesch, G. D., 73
Fletcher, R. S., 164
Fleury, P., 368, 371(4), 388(21), 394
Flock, H. F., 342
Fluchaire, M., 146
Flygare, H., 302
Föttinger, W., 73, 135
Fono, A., 267
Ford, J. A., Jr., 166
Forist, A. A., 251, 253(39b)
Fortunator, K., 151
Fossek, W., 151
Foster, A. B., 380, 389
Foster, G., 96, 97(72), 104(72), 105(72), 112, 114(112), 115, 116(118), 117(118), 119(112), 122(112), 123(112, 127), 124(112, 118), 136
Foster, W., 30
Fouinat, F., 32
Fox, A. R., 365
Fox, A. S., 36
Francesconi, L., 85
Francis, P. S., 159, 163, 164, 165(122)
Frank, G., 246
Frank, R., 352
Frank, R. B., 147
Franke, B., 22
Franz, J. E., 239

Franzen, V., 294, 350
Fraser, G. L., 45
Fraser, R. T. M., 196, 221, 222(81), 231(81)
Frass, W., 297, 299(87), 300(87), 320, 333(159)
Frazer, G. L., 129
Fredricks, P. S., 112
Freedman, M. L., 71
Freidlina, R. C., 363, 364
Freiser, H., 275
Freund, T., 27, 28(126, 127), 33, 67(157)
Freure, B. T., 275
Frey, F. W., 364
Friedel, C., 84
Friedemann, O., 279, 282(5), 292(5)
Friedländer, H. N., 293, 368
Friedman, H. L., 188(18), 191
Friedman, L., 90, 92(45), 136(46), 138(46), 191
Frister, F., 362
Fritsch, K. H., 357
Fritzsche, J., 83, 137, 208(86)
Fromageot, I. C., 208(86), 223
Fry, E. M., 91, 92(46)
Fry, H. S., 70
Fujita, K., 107, 108
Fukui, A., 99, 100(77)
Fukunaga, T., 287
Funck, D. L., 51(211), 52, 68, 143, 147
Funk, H., 226, 237(95)
Furman, N. H., 193, 195(28), 265, 272(59)
Fuson, R. C., 86, 305

G

Gale, D. M., 357
Galkowski, T. T., 371, 388(20)
Ganellin, C. R., 264, 296
Gardner, P. D., 306(117), 307, 317, 318(157)
Garg, C. P., 184
Garner, C. S., 191, 244
Garrett, J. W., 172
Gašić, M., 286
Gastambide, B., 336
Gates, M. D., 91, 92(46)
Gatzke, A. L., 135, 141, 180
Gaudefroy, G., 195, 226(36), 227, 231(36), 234(36)
Gaugin, R., 32

Gaur, J. N., 237, 250, 254(36), 264, 274(58)
Gawrilow, G. J., 357
Geier, G., 189
Geissler, W., 21
Geitner, P., 84
Gemenden, C. W., 283, 359(30, 268)
Genequand, P., 70
Gersdorff, W. A., 311
Gerstein, M., 164
Getz, C. A., 244, 245(4a)
Giddings, W. P., 168
Gibault, G. G., 246
Gibson, N. A., 35
Gilham, P. T., 283, 291(31a, 60), 352(31a)
Gillespie, R. J., 246
Gillman, H., 184
Gindraux, L., 151(74)
Ginsburg, S. R., 73
Ginsburg, W. A., 357
Gjertsen, L., 24, 25(110)
Gladding, E. K., 368
Gladding, G., 86
Gladstone, W. A. F., 356
Glasner, A., 82, 196, 220(42), 239(42)
Glemser, O., 74, 75(34)
Glotter, E., 308, 309(121)
Gluschkova, V. P., 365
Gnatz, G., 81
Godchot, M., 85
Goeb, A., 110(108), 112
Goerner, G. L., 250, 254(36)
Goetz, C. A., 245
Gold, A. M., 288, 290(53)
Goldschmid, H. R., 399, 401(78)
Goldstein, I. J., 395
Gorbacher, S. V., 249, 271
Gorgeau, P., 9
Gortner, R. A., 80
Gould, C. W., 183
Goyal, U., 65
Gragerov, I. P., 95, 96(62), 98(62), 102
Graham, G. T. E., 172, 174(4)
Grant, A. J., 273
Grant, G. A., 20
Gray, T., 135
Gredy, B., 146
Green, A. J., 208(90), 209(90), 213(90), 217(90), 223
Green, F. O., 45
Green, N., 311

Greenspan, F. P., 269
Greville, G. D., 371, 388(20)
Griffiths, A. B., 240
Grignard, V., 146
Grigorév, M. Y., 60
Grimmer, G., 164
Grinstead, R. R., 365
Grob, C. A., 297, 299(82), 300(82)
Grosheintz, R., 398, 402(75), 403(75)
Grossman, A. J., 73
Grossman, J., 229
Grossman, P., 306(116), 307
Grovenstein, E., 297, 298(86)
Groves, C. E., 83, 137
Grube, G., 10, 187, 210(1)
Gruber, V. N., 68
Grunewald, L. E., 340
Grundmann, C., 151
Gryder, J. W., 246
Gryszkiewicz-Trochimowski, E., 152
Guelbault, G. G., 251(40), 252, 253(40)
Gugliotta, F., 72
Guiliano, C. R., 195
Guillemonat, A., 108
Guillot-Allégrè, S., 151
Gunstone, F. D., 46
Gupta, Y. K., 29, 65
Guth, V., 288, 289(47)
Guthrie, J., 288, 290(58)
Guthrie, R. D., 372, 373, 396(33)
Gutt, J., 151
Guttmann, S., 370
Guyard, A., 9
Guyot, J., 83
György, H. H., 250, 254(36)
Gyr, J., 87

H

Hager, G. F., 147
Hagihara, N., 75
Hahl, E., 339(213), 340, 345, 347(231), 348(213, 231)
Hahn, G., 359
Haider, S. Z., 73
Haim, A., 197
Halasz, A., 151(73)
Hall, G. A., 376, 383(46)
Hall, N. F., 23

Halperin, J., 29

Halpern, J., 11, 25, 26, 30, 31, 33, 34(159, 161), 56, 57(231, 234), 67(143, 159, 231), 197, 220, 221(81)

Halpern Oo., 323(173)

Hamm, R. E., 238

Hampton, J., 74, 143, 168(5)

Hanic, F., 69

Hanroit, M., 87

Happe, J. A., 25

Hardwick, T. J., 245

Harfenist, M., 7

Hargreaves, G., 195, 218(38), 260, 261(50)

Harkness, A. C., 11, 33, 34(159), 67(159)

Harper, S. H., 51(214), 52

Harries, C., 43, 44(188)

Harrison, E., 239

Harrison, I. T., 7

Harrod, J. F., 31

Hartford, W. H., 73, 95, 97(64)

Hartman, J. L., 152, 153(80)

Hartman, W. H., 62

Hartmann, K., 342

Harvey, D. R., 327

Hashimoto, H., 90

Hass, H., 43, 44(186)

Hauser, D., 285

Haworth, R. D., 317, 319

Hawthorne, M. F., 169

Hayakawa, T., 66

Hayes, A. M., 370, 372(14), 378(14), 394(14)

Hazlewood, E. A., 370

Head, F. S. H., 371, 388(20, 60, 63), 393(60)

Hecker, E., 288, 289(52), 290(51, 52, 54, 55), 365(52)

Heckner, K.-H., 21

Hecksteden, W., 292

Hedberg, K., 269

Heidt, L. J., 245, 274, 368

Heilbron, I. M., 135, 137, 138(45), 148, 152

Heintzelman, W., 146, 147(24)

Hellberg, K. H., 74, 75(34)

Heller, G., 358

Heller, M. S., 287

Hellerman, L., 366

Hellmuth, R., 292

Hellwege, K. H., 73

Helmholz, L., 12, 73, 370

Hemestarn, S., 391

Hemilain, W., 87

Henbest, H. B., 306, 308, 309(120)

Henderson, G. G., 135

Henne, A. L., 151

Henrion, J., 63

Hensel, R. H., 357

Hensinger, W., 56

Henze, M., 240

Hepler, L. G., 71

Herber, J. F., 239

Hershberg, E. B., 312, 314(141), 315(143), 329(141, 143, 194), 331(141, 143, 194)

Herz, J. E., 128, 140(15)

Herzenberg, J., 136, 137(43)

Hessaby, A., 371

Heusler, K., 150, 156, 281, 285, 321, 322(163, 168), 323(163, 167, 168, 171, 172, 176, 177, 178, 180, 181), 324(180)

Hevesy, G. V., 281

Hey, D. H., 329, 365

Hickinbottom, W. J., 93, 94(52), 115, 116(117, 118), 117(117, 118), 124(117, 118), 129, 130, 131(18, 20, 23, 26, 27, 31, 32), 132(31, 32), 133(27, 31, 32), 138(27, 64)

Higginson, W. C. E., 26, 187, 192, 196(6, 7, 41), 197

Hilbert, G. E., 374

Hilcken, V., 292

Hilditch, T. P., 63

Hill, J. A., 241

Hill, L. M., 56

Hine, J., 256

Hinshelwood, C. N., 60, 67(239), 223(86), 255, 256(45a), 257(45a), 258(45a)

Hirota, E., 74

Hirsch, B., 357

Hoard, J. L., 246

Hoare, D. G., 192, 194, 200, 202(33), 209(23, 33, 60), 217(23, 33, 60), 218(33)

Hobbs, C. C., Jr., 119, 120(121), 121(121, 124)

Hobbs, W. E., 73

Hobin, T. P., 218(84), 222

Hock, H., 302, 303, 304(104), 344(104)

Hockett, R. C., 399, 400, 401(78)

Hodnett, E. M., 172

Hoehn, H. H., 288, 289(50), 290(50)

Hoehn, W. M., 128

Hoelzel, C. B., 353

Hönig, M., 28

Hoffmann, R. W., 358
Hoger, E., 373, 398(32), 399(32), 400(32), 401(32)
Hogg, D. R., 129, 131(20)
Holleman, A. F., 64
Holloway, F., 72, 153
Holluta, J., 56, 58
Holmes, O. G., 11, 12
Holmes, R. R., 288, 290(58), 355
Holmes-Siedle, A. G., 269
Holness, N. J., 164
Holum, J. R., 154
Honeyman, J., 372, 373, 374(25a), 380(25a, 50), 394(25a), 395(25a), 396(33), 397(25a)
Hopkins, A. J., 6, 20
Hopkins, H. B., 167
Horeau, A., 295
Horner, L., 355
Hosking, J. W., 35
Hough, L., 388
Houk, B. W., 273
House, H. O., 147
Houston, B., 119, 120(121), 121(121, 124)
Howard, H. C., 47, 91
Howard, J. R., 71
Howell, O. R., 198
Hsu, J. H., 283, 359(30, 268)
Huang, J. Y. S., 137
Huang, W. Y., 126, 128, 140(15)
Huber, G., 373, 398(32), 399(32), 400(32), 401(32)
Huber, J. E., 296
Huber, W. F., 147
Huberich, K., 187, 210(1)
Huebner, C. F., 353, 388
Hückel, W., 70, 339(216), 340, 342, 345(216)
Hünig, S., 357
Hughes, G., 371, 376, 388(20, 60, 63), 393(60)
Hunt, J. P., 188(18), 191, 197
Hurd, C. D., 45, 51(216), 52, 65(216), 144, 151(10, 72), 172, 280, 281(15), 339(221), 340
Hurley, F. R., 70
Hussey, A. S., 147
Huston, J. L., 281, 282(28)
Huston, R. C., 250, 254(36)
Hutchinson, A., 278
Huyser, E. S., 249, 254(33), 261(33), 274

I

Ibáñez, L. C., 323(169, 170)
Ibers, J. A., 193
Ichikawa, K., 306
Iffland, D. C., 356
Immer, H., 285, 286(36), 323(166, 178)
Ingold, C. K., 63
Ingold, K. U., 237
Ingram, D. J. E., 73, 74
Ingri, N., 189
Inhoffen, H. H., 158
Ipatieff, V. N., 41
Iriarte, J., 149, 150(53), 157
Ivanova, M. F., 371

J

Jablczynski, K., 180
Jackson, D. H., 30
Jackson, E. L., 369, 372(7), 373(7), 388(7), 394(7), 395(7)
Jacobson, M., 151
Jacobson, P., 86
Jacoby, R., 127, 132(12), 247, 261(25)
Jacquelain, A., 278
Jacques, J., 295
Jadot, J., 306(112), 307, 312, 313(135), 320, 330, 332(197), 335(112), 339(135), 340(135), 350, 351(240)
Jaffé, H. H., 163, 264
Jagelki, W., 135, 136, 145(41)
Jakubowitsch, A. J., 357
James, A. T., 45
James, B. R., 191
James, C., 273
Janculev, J., 311
Janshen, J., 281, 332(23, 198)
Janssen, R., 125, 135(1)
Japp, F. R., 87
Jaselskis, B., 406(94)
Jeger, O., 150, 156, 279, 285, 286(36), 287, 321(9), 323(9, 166, 178), 325
Jenner, E. L., 273
Jensen, E. H., 27
Jerchel, D., 357
Jeremić, D., 285, 286, 325
Jezowska-Trzebiatowska, B., 6, 20, 21
Jörg, J., 288, 289(45, 46)
Joergensen, Ch. K., 12

Johannesen, R. B., 164
Johns, W. F., 312, 313(139)
Johnson, A. W., 241
Johnson, C. R., 390
Johnson, D. C., 340
Johnson, W. S., 146, 148, 156, 312, 313(138, 139), 336
Jolley, J. E., 218(84), 222
Jones, A. S., 62
Jones, D. G., 275
Jones, D. N., 306, 308, 309(120)
Jones, E. G., 246
Jones, E. R. H., 148, 152
Jones, H. O., 137
Jones, J. R., 199, 201, 202, 210(74) 214(66, 106), 215(59, 66, 74), 216(66, 79, 80), 220, 227, 229, 236(96)
Jones, R. E., 45
Jones, R. G., 147, 201(59)
Jones, W. H., 12, 191
Jones, W. J., 61
Jorison, W. J., 182
Julia, M., 151(75)
Julian, K., 195, 198, 200(34), 207(34), 238(34), 239(34)
Jurecek, M., 84, 113(15)
Just, G., 30, 33, 67(143, 158)
Juveland, O. O., 249, 254(33), 261(33)

K

Kabbe, H. J., 339(222), 340, 365(222)
Kämmerer, H., 279, 282(5), 292(5)
Kagan, F., 323(179)
Kagarise, R. E., 246
Kahn, M., 244
Kainer, H., 362
Kaiser, E. T., 393
Kaizerman, S., 188, 250, 251(37), 266(37)
Kakabadse, G., 198, 238
Kalecinski, J., 6, 21
Kalk, F., 355
Kalliopin, L. E., 129
Kalvoda, J., 150, 156, 281, 285, 321, 322(163, 168), 323(163, 167, 168, 171, 172, 176, 177, 178, 180, 181, 182), 324(180)
Kamm, O., 87
Kantzer, M., 73
Kapadia, K., 343
Kaplan, L., 160, 168, 173

Kappes, E., 359
Karabines, J. V., 147
Karplus, R., 193, 210(29)
Kasperczyck, J., 320
Kato, S., 90
Katz, M., 20
Kaufmann, S., 308, 310(125)
Kauko, Y., 30, 33, 67(143, 158)
Kazakova, J. J., 279
Keen, N., 370
Kehr, C. L., 282, 286, 293(29), 294(29), 320
Keller, J., 285, 286(36)
Kelly, R. C., 287
Kelly, W., 319
Kemp, A. D., 312, 313(139)
Kemp, T. J., 208(63, 80, 90), 209(62, 80, 90), 213(80, 90, 107), 214(80, 107), 216(62, 80, 107), 217(90), 218(62), 219(107), 220, 221(62), 223, 230(107), 232, 233(80), 234(80, 107)
Kendall, E. C., 146
Kenyon, J., 21, 36, 51(210), 52, 53(210)
Keppler, J. G., 45, 53(190)
Kessler, F., 76
Kettle, S. F. A., 34
Khan, N. A., 47
Kharasch, M. S., 267, 268(68), 293, 368
Khundkar, M. H., 73
Kimball, G. E., 247
King, C. G., 244, 245(4b)
King, E. L., 71, 80, 81, 273
King, F. L., 245
Kirk, R. E., 25
Kirner, W. R., 47, 91
Kirschner, H. G., 342
Kiss, Á., 71
Kitahonoki, K., 297, 299(89), 325
Kläning, U., 73, 161
Klaning, U., 22
Kleiderer, E. C., 53(223), 54
Klemm, W., 5, 74
Kling, O., 60
Klinger, H., 133
Klöcking, H. P., 353
Klonk, K., 306(115), 307
Klosterman, H., 374
Knapp, K. H., 355
Knell, M. J., 373, 383(35a)
Knowles, P., 196
Knowles, W. S., 239

Kocheshkov, K. A., 332, 363, 364, 365
Kochi, J. K., 267, 293
Kögler, H., 108
Koelsch, C. F., 40, 53, 133
König, J., 84
König, K. H., 292
Kolthoff, I. M., 8, 9, 20, 30, 48, 77, 193, 210(29)
Kon, G. A. R., 312, 315(144)
Kon, H., 74
Kooyman, E. C., 225, 228(94), 234(94), 238(94)
Kornblum, N., 61
Kornfeld, E. C., 147
Kornilova, Yu. I., 207, 210(72)
Kotlan, J., 288, 289(42, 44, 47), 290(42, 44), 332(42)
Kotoucek, M., 13
Koubek, E., 194, 219(32)
Kourim, P., 110(111), 112, 114(111)
Kovács, O., 244
Kowalak, A. D., 78
Kraft, L., 171, 207, 210(72), 284, 288(32), 312, 313(136), 369, 373(8), 398(8)
Kramer, E. C., 101
Krampitz, L. O., 311
Krasso, A. F., 184
Kraus, K. A., 194
Krauss, H. L., 70, 73, 81, 161
Kreiser, W., 51(211), 52, 68, 143, 147
Krespan, C. G., 357
Kreulen, D. J. W., 181
Krishna, B., 265, 266(62)
Kroll, T. J., 373, 383(34), 385(34)
Kropf, H., 303, 304(104), 344(104)
Kruber, O., 137
Kruck, P., 373, 398(32), 399(32), 400(32), 401(32)
Krupička, J., 159, 162, 163(111), 164, 372, 373(23), 383(23), 394(23), 395(23)
Kümmerle, K., 339(216), 340, 345(216)
Kuhlberg, A., 84
Kuhn, H., 30, 67(143)
Kuhn, R., 151, 357, 362
Kuivila, H. G., 159, 163(117)
Kung, W., 400
Kunz, A. H., 244
Kuraoka, T., 108
Kurbatow, A., 83, 137
Kurihara, H., 229

Kurtenacker, A., 27
Kurz, J. L., 50
Kuzenetsov, D. I., 270
Kwart, H., 38, 159, 163, 164, 165(122, 125), 166

L

Lábler, L., 157
Ladbury, J. W., 10, 39, 65, 67(168), 214(116), 236
LaForge, F. B., 311, 350
LaLonde, J., 83, 137
Lambert, A., 241
Lambert, B. F., 183
LaMer, V. K., 224
Land, H., 201, 213(63), 222
Landsberg, R., 21
Lang, R., 76
Lang, S., 302
Lange, J., 368, 371(4), 394
Langerak, E. O., 143, 164(2)
Langkammerer, C. M., 273
Lankshear, F. R., 6
Lanning, W. C., 280, 281(17), 282(17)
Lansbury, P. T., 135, 169
Lapworth, A., 43, 44(180)
LaSalle, M. J., 189, 195(12)
Latimer, W. M., 10, 11, 187, 210(2), 271, 273(80), 275(80)
Lattrell, R., 288, 289(52), 290(52), 365(52)
Laver, W. M., 146
Laughlin, K. C., 129, 132(22)
Launer, H. F., 8
Launer, H. J., 66
Lavas, M., 335
Lavie, D., 308, 309(121)
Law, H. D., 95, 96, 97(68), 98(68)
Lawrence, G. S., 216(104), 229
Laws, G. F., 128
Lawson, J. E., 351, 353
Lazier, W. A., 7
Lea, T. R., 148
LeBel, N. A., 296
Ledingham, G. A., 46
Lee, D. G., 72, 161, 163, 166(116)
Lee, J. B., 365
Leech, J. L., 148
Leekley, R. M., 146

Leete, E., 360
Lejeune, G., 223
Lemieux, R. U., 46, 397
Leo, A., 74, 143, 160, 168(5), 175
Leonard, N. J., 147, 390
Lepin, A., 87
Lepse, P. A., 75, 93, 102(50), 178, 182
Lerch, B., 363
Le Rossignol, R., 64
Leuchs, H., 62
Lever, B. G., 187, 210(2)
Levesley, P., 9, 206, 207, 213(73), 373
Levitt, L. S., 68, 283
Lewis, B. A., 395
Lewis, C. E., 146
Lewis, J., 72
Lewis, J. D., 370, 386(17a)
Libby, W. F., 196
Lieberman, S. V., 94
Liehr, A. D., 73
Limón, D. C., 155
Lingane, J. J., 8, 193, 195(28), 210(29)
Link, K. P., 353
Linstead, R. P., 83, 137, 339(220), 340
Lipp, A., 110(116), 112
Lisci, J., 155
Lister, M. W., 4
Littell, R., 156
Littler, J. S., 179, 189, 194, 197, 199(15, 30), 200(53, 61), 202, 204, 205, 208(15, 53, 68, 90), 209(68, 90), 210(15), 211, 213(90), 214(53, 66), 215(15, 66, 67, 76, 119), 216(66, 76), 217(90), 223, 224, 225(91), 226(30), 227(30), 234(30), 237(30, 119), 238(119), 248, 249(29), 251(29), 253(29), 254(29, 30), 255(29, 46), 256, 257(46)
Lock, G., 147
Locke, J. M., 353
Locquin, R., 127, 132(12)
Lodha, T. R., 264, 274(58)
Lodochnikowa, V. J., 363
Long, A. G., 128
Long, F. A., 100, 224
Lonnes, C., 133
Looker, J. H., 355
Lorenc, L., 285, 286
Lott, K. A. K., 21, 22, 73
Louder, H. U., 146
Lowry, B. R., 110(107), 112

Lucchi, E., 172
Lucius, G., 108
Ludutsky, A., 147
Ludewig, H., 359
Ludwig, A., 334
Ludwig, W., 355
Lüthi, Ch., 56, 57(232)
Lützow, D., 73
Lukkari, O., 72
Lundberg, W. O., 274
Lundgren, G., 246
Lunge, G., 29
Luther, R., 76
Lutz, R. E., 183, 333
Lux, H., 5
Lynch, B. M., 365
Lyons, J. R., 191

M

Maas, L. W., 84, 90(10), 130, 136(47), 138(47)
Macbeth, A. K., 146
McCallum, K. S., 169
McConnell, H. M., 195
McCormack, W. B., 365
McCoy, L. L., 301
McCurdy, W. H., Jr., 246, 250(40), 252, 253(40)
MacDonald, C. G., 380
McDonald, H. O., 4, 24
McDougall, A. O., 386
MacDougall, M., 389
McElhill, E. A., 263
McElvain, S. M., 40
McGookin, A., 306(118), 307
McHugh, D. J., 291, 380
McKay, R., 288, 290(58)
MacKellar, D. G., 269
McLaren, A. D., 146, 147(25)
McNamee, R. W., 45, 51(216), 52, 65(216)
McReynolds, J. P., 246
Madaeff-Ssitscheff, O., 62
Mader, P. M., 147
Magat, M., 32
Magnusson, R., 391
Mahajani, A. V., 181
Makarow, S. P., 357
Maksimović, Z., 285
Malan, R. L., 40

Malaprade, L., 66, 368, 369(3), 373(3), 376(3), 394(3)
Mallet, A. I., 204, 215(67)
Mal'tseva, N. N., 27
Mamuzič, R. J., 286, 325
Mancera, O., 308, 310(128)
Manchot, W., 82
Manecke, G., 187, 210(1)
Mann, D. R., 56
Mann, F. G., 144, 146(9)
Marchand, B., 398
Marckwald, W., 152
Mareš, F., 109, 112, 114(104, 106), 115(114), 118(104), 119(104, 106), 121(104, 106), 122(104), 124(104, 178, 179(2), 235
Margrave, J. L., 71
Mariella, R. P., 148
Marktscheffel, F., 350, 373, 398(32), 399(32), 400(32), 401(32)
Marshall, B. M., 96, 97(72), 104(72), 105(72), 136, 306(118), 307
Marshall, J. W., 26, 187, 196(7)
Martin, C. J., 151
Martin, D. G., 146
Martin, D. S., 25, 370, 372(14), 378(14), 394(14)
Martin, G., 60
Martinez, H., 308, 310(125)
Martini, C. M., 308, 310(124)
Maruta, S., 158
Marvel, C. S., 53(221), 54, 148
Maschitelli-Coriandoli, E., 240
Mason, H. L., 128
Mason, J. G., 78
Mateescu, G. D., 297, 300(90)
Matrka, M., 270
Matsubara, Y., 339(217, 218), 340, 342
Matsuura, A., 325
Matsuura, T., 107, 108, 158
Mattheides, L., 83
Matthews, A. O., 87
Matuszek, J. M., Jr., 16
May, R., 239
Maynert, E. W., 305
Mayor, P. A., 150
Mazurek, M., 380
Meakins, G. D., 150
Meek, H. V., 370, 372(14), 378(14), 394(14)
Meerwein, H., 140, 317, 347
Mehltretter, C. L., 374

Mehrota, R. C., 273(85b)
Meier, J., 71, 189
Meijer, T. M., 288, 290(56)
Meinert, R. N., 144, 151(10)
Mellor, J. M., 239
Mendelsohn, M. A., 233, 275
Menzel, R., 332
Merkulowa, J. N., 357
Merritt, L. L., 30
Mervyn, L., 241
Merz, J. H., 48
Metlesics, W., 288, 289(42, 43), 290(42), 332(42)
Metter, E., 70
Metz, K., 303
Metz, O., 181
Metzger, H., 10
Meyer, H., 85, 137
Meyer, J., 137
Meyer, R., 38
Meyers, R. J., 247, 261(25)
Meystre, C., 150, 156, 321, 322(163), 323 (163, 182), 323(172, 177)
Michael, A., 74
Mićović, V. M., 284, 286, 325
Middleton, W. J., 357
Migacheva, I. B., 68
Mihailović, M. L., 279, 284, 285, 286(36, 36b), 321(9), 323(9, 166, 178), 325, 353
Mikheeva, V. I., 27
Milas, N. A., 218(127), 239
Mile, B., 188
Miles, J. H., 373, 376(30, 44), 377(30), 378(30), 379(30, 48), 380, 381(30), 382(49), 383(30), 396(30), 397(44)
Mill, T., 72, 172, 173(5), 174(5)
Miller, F. A., 12, 73
Miller, E. M., 356
Mills, G. A., 23
Mills, J. A., 146
Milovanović, A., 285
Minato, H., 122
Ming, W. C. L., 70
Mingazzini, M., 137
Mino, G., 188, 250, 251(37), 266(37)
Mishra, H. C., 6, 7, 23, 73, 189
Mitchell, J., 366
Mladenovic, S., 325
Mocek, M. M., 6, 22, 50, 57(207), 59, 67(236)

Möller, E. F., 63
Möller, G., 292
Möller, H., 362
Moelwyn-Hughes, E. A., 60
Moffet, E. W., 62
Mohammad, S., 28
Moldoványí, L., 162
Mondou, O., 107
Monroy, G., 155
Montigel, C., 308, 310(127)
Moon, S., 335
Mooradian, A., 308, 310(124)
Moore, C. E., 152, 153(80)
Moore, J. A., 146
Moore, M., 126
Moore, R. L., 246
Moore, W. R., 301
Morette, A., 195, 226(36), 231(36), 234(36)
Morgan, K. J., 369
Moriarty, R. M., 325, 343
Morse, H. N., 6, 20
Morton, R. A., 7
Moschner, J., 64
Mosher, W. A., 135, 143, 146(2), 282, 286, 287, 293(29), 294(29), 320
Mottram, E. N., 43, 44(180)
Moussa, G. E. M., 130, 131(27), 133(27), 138(27)
Mowery, D. F., 399, 401(78)
Mowry, D. T., 147
Müller, H., 137
Müller, R., 306(113), 307, 335, 336(207)
Mueller, S., 21
Mugdan, M., 239
Mukherjee, S. K., 170, 173
Mukherji, S. M., 317, 327(148)
Mukhina, L. S., 68
Muldrow, C. N., Jr., 71
Muller, G., 323(184)
Murchi, L. E., 246
Murgulescu, I. C., 216(100), 228
Murray, A. R., 317, 318(147)
Musgrave, F. F., 60
Mutschin, A., 58
Myers, O. E., 24

N

Nad', M. M., 363
Naffa, P., 342

Nagarkatti, A. S., 355
Nair, V. S. K., 71
Nakanishi, K., 126
Naldini, L., 2
Nametkin, S., 62
Nancollas, G. H., 71
Narasimhasastri, M., 237
Nasanen, R., 371
Nawojska, J., 21
Necoechea, E., 155
Necsoiu, I., 87, 95, 96(65), 98(65), 101(33), 104(65), 120
Neher, R., 149
Neidig, H. A., 51(211), 52, 68, 143, 147, 287
Neiland, O. J., 365
Neiman, M. B., 371
Nelson, F., 194
Nemec, J., 281
Nenitzescu, C. D., 87, 95, 96(65), 98(65), 101(33), 104(65), 120, 297, 300(90)
Neptune, J. A., 20, 81
Nessmejanow, A. N., 363
Neubauer, G., 355
Neugebauer, C. A., 71
Neukranz, W., 53
Neumann, F. W., 183
Neumüller, O. A., 302
Neuray, M., 330, 332(197), 350, 351(240)
Neuss, J. D., 71
Neusser, R., 27
Neustädter, V., 151
Nevell, T. P., 376, 380
Newbury, R., 229
Newman, M. S., 47, 90, 317, 318(151)
Newton, T. W., 244, 245
Nicholas, R. D., 117(119), 118, 122(119)
Nickels, J. E., 146, 147(24)
Nicoara, E., 349
Nicol, M. J., 196
Nicolaides, N., 160
Nicolet, B. M., 368, 387(6)
Nielsen, S. D., 109, 339(215a), 340
Nielson, S., 127
Nishimura, T., 93, 94(53)
Nohe, H., 297
Noll, A., 21
Noll, K., 280, 335(14), 336(14), 344(14)
Norman, R. O. C., 198, 267, 327, 356
Norris, T. H., 281, 282(28)
Northcote, D. H., 371, 388(20)

Novick, A., 142, 159
Noyes, A. A., 244
Noyes, R. M., 65, 66, 187, 212(4)
Nozaki, T., 229
Nudenberg, W., 267
Nuenke, N., 27, 28
Null, G. D., 38
Nyholms, R. S., 72
Nyilasi, J., 275

O

Oberhauser, F., 56
Oberrauch, H., 106, 158, 159(96)
O'Brien, T. D., 246
Ochwat, P., 292
Oesper, R. E., 279
Ogard, A. E., 196
Ogata, Y., 86, 99, 100(77), 229, 244,
Ogelvie, J., 90
Ohta, M., 297, 299(82), 300(82)
Okuda, T., 343
Oldfield, D., 241
Olsen, R. E., 183
Oncescu, T., 216(100), 228
O'Neill, A. N., 371, 388(20)
Oppenauer, R. V., 106, 158, 159(96)
O'Rear, J. G., 246
Orgel, L. E., 191
Orlow, N. A., 137
Osborne, E. N., 172
Osterberg, A. E., 146
Ouelette, R. J., 335
Ourisson, G., 312, 314(140), 342
Owen, L. N., 43, 44(183)

P

Padwa, A., 267
Palluy, E., 325
Pandow, M. L., 245, 273
Pankova, M., 181, 182(12)
Pankratz, R. A., 353
Panov, E. M., 332, 363
Panwar, K. S., 237
Pappas, S. P., 297, 298(85)
Pappo, R., 312, 313(139), 336
Pappos, X., 43, 44(188)
Paris, R., 368, 371(4)
Parke, T. V., 147
Parker, E. E., 51(213), 52

Partch, R. E., 284
Partington, J. R., 281, 370
Pascal, P., 74
Pascaru, I., 95, 96(65), 98(65), 104(65)
Pascu, E., 151
Patrick, T. M., Jr., 151
Pattison, V. A., 169
Paude, K. C., 365
Paul, M. A., 100
Paulig, G., 303
Pauling, L., 246
Pausacker, K. H., 353, 354(250), 365, 366,
    398, 400(76), 402(76), 405, 406(91, 92)
Pearson, R. G., 250, 275(35)
Pedlow, G. W., 105
Pelley, R. L., 151
Penny, W. G., 246
Perkin, F. M., 95, 96, 97(68), 98(68)
Perlin, A. S., 281, 293, 320(69), 372, 380,
    399, 400, 401(78, 84), 405(82, 88)
Perrier, G., 86
Peschanski, D., 194, 219(32)
Pesina, A. G., 207, 210(72)
Peters, A. T., 137
Peters, D., 129, 130, 131(20, 26)
Petersen, J., 26
Peterson, H. J., 23
Petit, G., 179, 223
Petro, V. A., 126
Petrow, V., 149
Pettit, R., 264, 296
Phillips, F. C., 33, 34(159)
Phillips, J. N., 22
Pictet, A., 70
Pike, J. E., 148, 156, 323(183)
Pilato, L. A., 164, 165(124)
Pilz, H., 302
Pines, H., 41
Pink, J. M., 65
Pinnow, J., 28
Pinten, P., 110(115), 112
Pistorius, C. W. F. T., 72
Pittet, A. O., 388
Plane, R. A., 188(18), 191
Platt, B. C., 51(210), 52, 53(210)
Plieninger, H., 296, 306(113), 307, 335,
    336(207)
Plump, R. E., 275
Pocker, Y., 224
Pode, J. S. F., 2, 3, 4(3), 5, 32, 65(3)

Podolesov, B., 311
Pogany, J. J., 297, 300(90)
Poittevin, A., 323(184)
Pokrovskaya, O. G., 60
Polissar, M. J., 9, 25
Pollard, W., 278
Pommer, H., 158
Ponomarchuk, M. P., 102
Poos, G. I., 153, 155
Popják, G., 160, 173
Porret, D., 274
Porter, G., 50
Porter, J. W. G., 144, 146(9)
Posdnjakova, E. I., 62
Poskočil, J., 270
Posternak, Th., 43, 44(182)
Postnikova, M. S., 288, 289(41)
Powell, S. G., 51(212), 52, 146
Prakash, S., 73
Pratt, E. F., 7
Pratt, J. M., 241
Preiss, D. M., 143
Preiss, W., 80
Prelog, V., 400
Preuss, F. R., 281, 320, 332(23, 161, 198, 199)
Price, C. C., 147, 373, 383(34, 35a), 385(34)
Price, M. J., 365
Pritzkow, W., 303
Prue, J. E., 71
Pschorr, R., 136(44), 137, 138(44)
Pungor, E., 75, 181
Purves, C. B., 368
Putnam, S. T., 329(193, 195)

Q

Quayle, O. R., 148
Quinn, R. A., 38

R

Rabinowitch, E., 269
Rabzewitsch-Subkowski, J., 86
Radkowsky, A., 143, 168(4)
Raga, J. B. V., 180
Ramanjaneyulu, J. V. S., 237
Ramaswamy, R., 214(116), 236, 271
Ramos, L., 65
Ramsden, H. E., 400
Ramsey, J. B., 195
Rank, B., 171, 207, 210(72), 284, 288(32), 369, 373(8), 398(8)

Ranow, E. M., 363
Rao, C. N. R., 72, 274(58)
Rao, D. V., 297, 298(86)
Rao, G. G., 237
Rao, P. N., 322
Rao, S. P., 250, 254(36), 264
Rao, V. B., 237
Raphael, L., 218(84), 222
Rasmussen, E., 250, 251(37), 266(37)
Rasmusson, G. H., 147, 188
Rautenstrauch, C., 148
Ravens, D. A. S., 237, 238(117)
Rawalay, S. S., 61
Rees, C. W., 357
Regner, A., 21
Reich, W., 87
Reichstein, T., 40, 184, 308, 310(122, 127)
Reid, E. B., 68
Reitsema, R. H., 92, 102(48)
Renger, F., 84, 113(15)
Renk, E., 297
Renoll, M., 147
Ressler, C., 148
Reuter, F., 368
Richardson, T., 317
Richardson, W. H., 175, 176(12, 14), 262, 263, 267
Richer, J. C., 164, 165(124)
Richmond, H. D., 404
Richter, H. J., 353
Rieger, W. H., 327
Riehl, Sr. A., 180
Rieman, W., 71
Riemann, U., 336, 350
Riesenfeld, E. H., 32
Rigby, W., 3, 4(11), 406
Riggs, N. V., 366
Riiber, C. N., 43, 44(181)
Rimmelin, A., 334
Ringold, H. J., 155, 157, 323(169, 170)
Ritter, F. O., 48
Rivett, D. E. A., 182
Rivlin, V. G., 401
Roberts, J. D., 146, 297
Robertson, A., 306(114, 118), 307, 312, 315(144a)
Robertson, E., 245
Robertson, G. R., 143
Robertson, J. M., 135
Robinson, C. C., 148

Robinson, P. L., 73
Robinson, R., 148
Robinson, S. A., 45
Roček, J., 64, 70, 72, 98, 109, 110(110), 112, 113(110), 114(104, 106), 115(114), 118(104), 119(104, 106), 121(104, 106, 110), 122(104), 123, 124(104), 143, 159, 162, 163(111), 164, 166(111, 131), 168(4), 169, 170, 171(4), 173, 178, 179(2), 180, 206, 235, 368
Rodrigo, R., 241
Roe, E. M. F., 312, 315(144)
Roesky, R., 74, 75(34)
Rohde, G., 96, 97(70)
Rokowsky, A., 73
Rollefson, G. K., 274
Romero, M. A., 308, 310(123)
Romo, J., 308, 310(125)
Rosenberg, A., 82
Rosenberg, H. R., 40
Rosenberg, M. E., 196
Rosenkranz, G., 7, 308, 310(125)
Ross, G. W., 62
Ross, S. D., 265
Ross, W. C. J., 127
Rosseinsky, D. R., 8, 192, 196(25, 43), 197
Rossotti, F. J. C., 189
Rossotti, H., 189
Rossow, A. G., 147, 148
Rouhi-Laridjani, M., 311
Rousset, L., 151
Rowe, F. M., 137
Royer, D. J., 23
Rudakoff, G., 280
Ruhemann, S., 136, 137(43)
Ruhoff, J. R., 53(222), 54
Ruland, K., 265, 274(60a)
Rule, C. K., 224
Rumberg, L., 303
Ruschig, H., 308, 310(126)
Russell, G. A., 167, 267, 276(70)
Russell, H., Jr., 244
Rutter, T. F., 76
Ruzicka, E., 13
Ruzicka, L., 127, 137
Rygh, O., 240

S

Sable, H. Z., 43, 44(182)
Sacco, A., 2

Saegebarth, K. A., 42, 140
Saffer, L., 151
Saffir, P., 197, 265
Sager, W. F., 110(109), 112, 113(109), 119(109), 169, 178
Ságner, Z., 270
Sah, P. P. T., 91, 137
Saint-Pierre, O., 87
Saito, K., 108
Sakai, M., 280, 335(16), 348(16)
Sala, O., 72
Salah, M. K., 7
Salisbury, L., 356
Salontai, R., 349
Sandin, R. S., 365
Santappa, M., 256(45c)
Sanz-Garcia, H., 65
Sapper, A., 137
Sarett, L. H., 153, 155
Sasaki, Y., 71
Sastri, M. N., 237
Sato, T., 340
Sauer, J., 151
Saunders, B. C., 269
Sayigh, A., 297
Scagliarini, G., 246
Schaeffer, C., 84
Schafer, W. R., 356
Schaffner, K., 285, 286(36), 287, 323(166, 178), 325
Schall, C., 281
Schechter, H., 90, 92(45), 136(46), 138(46)
Scheidegger, U., 325
Schellenberger, H., 373, 398(32), 399(32), 400(32), 401(32)
Schmejakin, M. M., 312
Schempf, R., 363, 364(280)
Schenck, G. O., 302
Schenker, K., 400
Schepartz, A. I., 151
Schildknecht, H., 73, 135
Schinzel, E., 288, 289(43)
Schlenk, W., 133
Schlesinger, H. I., 3
Schleyer, P. v. R., 117(119), 118, 122(119)
Schlichting, O., 127, 132(12)
Schmid, H., 288, 290(56, 57)
Schmidlin, J., 156
Schmidt, H., 105

Schmeisser, M., 73
Schmitt, J., 148
Schneider, S., 297
Schneider, W., 216(104), 229
Schneider, W. P., 323(179)
Schnorrenberg, W., 302, 303(99)
Schoeller, W., 34
Schönbein, C. F., 76
Scholder, R., 5, 74, 75
Schonland, D. S., 2, 12, 73, 74
Schramm, J., 85
Schrauth, W., 34
Schreckeneder, R., 147
Schreiber, J., 159, 162, 164
Schroeder, E. F., 43, 44(186)
Schröder, K., 29, 238
Schroeter, G., 85, 137
Schrötter, H., 110(108), 112
Schultz, B., 40
Schultz, G., 83
Schulze, W., 292
Schwab, G. M., 73
Schwaebel, G., 62
Schwarz, J. C. P., 228, 306, 389
Schwarzbach, F., 73
Schwarzenbach, G., 71, 189, 238
Schweizer, R., 279, 282(6), 307(6), 311(6), 312(6), 313(6)
Schwenk, E., 288, 290(53)
Schwicker, A., 29
Scroggie, J. G., 353, 354(250), 366
Seebeck, E., 308, 310(122)
Segaller, D., 29
Seidel, C. F., 325
Seki, M., 297, 298(84)
Selim, R. G., 8, 193, 195(28)
Senent-Perez, S., 65
Serebryakov, E. P., 296
Sevent-Perez, S., 373, 385(35b)
Sexton, M., 166
Shankar, J., 197
Shanker, R., 65, 215(144)
Sharma, S. K., 250, 254(36), 272, 273(85b)
Sharp, J. A., 194, 219(32, 112, 134), 235, 239
Shaw, C. J. G., 372, 374(25a), 380(25a, 50), 394(25a), 397(25a)
Shaw, D. F., 380
Shaw, D. L., 335
Shaw, N., 241
Shchukina, M. N., 94

Shecan, J. C., 43, 44(187)
Shechter, H., 61(245a, 247), 62
Shelberg, W. E., 312, 313(138)
Sheldrick, G., 317
Sheppard, J. C., 24, 197
Sherrill, M. L., 146
Sherrill, M. S., 244, 245(4b)
Shetterly, F. F., 26
Shimakawa, Y., 108
Shiner, V. J., 386, 387(57, 59), 393(57), 394(59)
Shinn, L. A., 368, 387(6)
Shklyaruk, E. A., 60
Shoo, Y., 308, 309(121)
Shoolery, J. N., 149, 150(53)
Short, F. W., 86
Shorter, J., 208(86), 223, 255, 256(45a), 257(45a, b, d), 258(45a, b, d), 259 (45b, d)
Shotwell, O. L., 147
Shriner, R. L., 53(223), 54, 182
Shunk, C. H., 147
Sicher, J., 112, 114(106), 119(106), 121(106), 164, 178, 179(2), 181, 182(12), 372, 373(23), 383(23), 394(23), 395(23)
Siebert, H., 370
Siedel, W., 360, 362
Siegel, A., 365
Siems, H. B., 3
Signaigo, F. K., 146
Silverton, J. V., 246
Simon, A., 23
Simon, L. J., 83
Simon, R., 280, 335(14), 336(14), 344(14), 345
Singer, A. W., 40
Sinwel, F., 288, 289(40, 44), 290(44)
Šipoš, F., 164, 181, 182(12)
Sisler, H. H., 70, 73, 153
Skeen, J. W., 281
Skirrow, G., 219(134), 239
Slack, R., 86, 98, 170, 172(1)
Slater, G. P., 306, 308, 309(120)
Sliam, E., 95, 96(65), 98(65), 104(65)
Smid, J., 274
Smiles, S., 64
Smirnov, V. S., 60
Smith, B., 392
Smith, D. R., 188
Smith, F., 374, 395

Smith, G. A., 146
Smith, G. E., 244, 245(4a)
Smith, G. F., 244, 246, 247, 250, 254(36), 261(26), 264(1a, 36b), 266(1a)
Smith, G. W., 194
Smith, H., 317, 318(147)
Smith, J. H., 29
Smith, L. E., 241
Smith, L. I., 83, 137, 146
Smith, L. J., 288, 289(50), 290(50)
Smith, M., 12
Smith, M. E., 245, 274
Smith, M. H., 182
Smith, R. W., 135
Smyth, C. P., 73
Snethlage, H. C. S., 180, 181
Sniegaski, P. J., 246
Soldano, B., 376, 383(46)
Sollman, P. B., 323(175)
Solomon, D. H., 228, 283, 291(31a), 306, 307(111), 311(111), 312, 313(134), 330, 352(31a)
Sondheimer, F., 7, 148, 152, 308, 310(125)
Soper, F. G., 246
Sŏrm, F., 70, 98, 157
Sorum, C. H., 20
Sotheeswaran, S., 297
Soucek, M., 84, 113(15)
Souchay, P., 371
Speakman, P. T., 223
Spencer, H. E., 274
Sperka, G., 75
Spero, G. B., 323(179)
Speroni, G., 39
Spitsyn, V. I., 71
Spooner, R. C., 244, 245(4b)
Sprinson, D. B., 388
Srivastava, T. N., 212(143)
Stacey, F. W., 249, 254(33), 261(33)
Stacey, M., 352
Stadler, J., 292
Staesche, M., 187, 210(1)
Stafford, G., 48
Stahley, E. E., 146
Stairs, R. A., 102, 135
Staklis, A., 353, 356
Stamm, H., 2, 3, 21, 29, 32
Stammreich, H., 72
Staritzky, E., 74
Starling, W. N., 126

Starnes, W. H., 295
Stavely, H. E., 106, 126
Stefanović, M., 286, 325
Steffgen, F. W., 135
Stein, G., 245, 267, 276(63)
Steinberg, G. R., 7
Stempelova, D., 69
Stenhouse, J., 182
Stephen, H., 86
Stephens, F. F., 291(61), 292
Stephens, R. W., 352, 389
Stĕrba, Z., 270
Stevens, H. M., 14
Stevenson, R., 308, 309(119)
Stewart, R., 4, 9, 18, 22, 33, 48, 49(204, 205), 50(206, 207), 51(204), 54, 55(226), 56, 57(207, 230), 59, 60, 65, 67(156, 204, 205, 226, 236), 72, 161, 163, 166(116)
Stirling, C. J. M., 329, 365
Stoddard, E. M., 43, 44(184)
Stojcić, S., 325
Stojiljković, A., 353
Stoll, M., 151, 325
Stone, T. J., 238
Strang, A., 275
Stranks, D. R., 191, 216(104), 229
Streitwieser, A., 102
Struck, H. C., 182
Stuart, C. M., 95, 97(60)
Stubbs, A. L., 7
Sturm, H., 288, 289(48, 49)
Sturrock, J. R., 399
Suchomelova, L., 351
Süllmann, H., 250, 254(36)
Süs, O., 295, 352(74), 366(74)
Suga, K., 107
Suga, T., 107, 158
Sugihara, T. T., 16
Sugiyama, H., 90
Sulima, L. V., 95, 96(62), 98(62)
Sullivan, V. R., 246
Surmatis, J. D., 129, 132(22)
Suskind, S. P., 7
Sussman, S., 239
Sutcliffe, L. H., 192, 195, 197(22, 48, 52), 198(22), 218(38), 260, 261(50), 271, 281, 282(20), 294
Suter, C. M., 64
Sutin, N., 192
Sutton, D., 26, 187, 196(6)

Suzuki, H., 45
Suzuki, S., 281, 405
Suzuki, Y., 158
Svatos, G., 234
Svec, H. J., 73
Svoboda, M., 372, 373(23), 383(23), 394(23), 395(23)
Swain, C. G., 265, 269
Swami, S. N., 215(144)
Swann, S., 236
Swoboda, J., 288, 289(47)
Sword, J., 135
Sworski, T. J., 274
Sycheva, T. P., 94
Sykes, A. G., 196, 220(42), 239(42)
Sykes, P. J., 46
Symons, M. C. R., 2, 3(6, 13), 5, 6, 7, 10, 11, 12(60, 63), 21, 22, 23, 24, 36, 71, 72, 73, 74, 189, 206, 370
Szmant, H. H., 87, 366
Szmuszkovicz, J., 85, 115(21)
Szwarc, M., 274

T

Tabushi, I., 244
Tadanier, J., 323(174)
Takacs, F., 288, 289(44), 290(44)
Takano, Y., 297, 299(89)
Takekazu, B., 74
Takemura, S., 62
Tamas, V., 349
Tamayo, M. L., 317
Tan, L., 320
Tan, T., 305, 332(161)
Tanaka, M., 30, 292
Tarama, K., 179
Tatlow, J. C., 45
Taube, H., 29, 31, 66, 188(18), 191, 193, 196, 197, 212(26, 102), 221, 222(81), 229, 231(81), 234, 265
Tavassenkov, D., 73
Taylor, E. R., 39
Taylor, J. E., 376, 383(46)
Taylor, J. W., 297, 298(86)
Taylor, N. W., 82
Taylor, S. M., 56, 57(231), 67(231)
Taylor, W. I., 183
Taylor, W. J., 283, 259(30, 268), 360

Tazuke, S., 188
Tedder, J. M., 112
Teltow, J., 12
TerHorst, D. T. J., 181
Tewari, K. C., 265, 266(62)
Thamer, B. J., 74
Thanalakshmi, R., 72
Thibault, C., 312, 314(140)
Thiele, J., 92, 94(49)
Thiele, R., 21
Thirsk, H. R., 187, 210(2)
Thoene, J. G., 296
Thomas, J. R., 267
Thompson, A., 371, 388(20)
Thompson, J. L., 323(179)
Thompson, R. J., 317, 318(157)
Thompson, T. W., 62
Thompson, W. W., 41
Tichý, M., 164, 181, 182(12)
Tiemann, P., 151
Tillotson, A., 119
Tishler, M., 45
Tocher, M. H., 181
Tolbert, B., 43, 44(182)
Tompkins, F. C., 9, 54, 56, 60, 237
Tong, J. Y. P., 71, 80
Toogood, J. B., 148
Tosoni, A. L., 354
Toyama, O., 66
Toyne, K. J., 297
Traylor, T. G., 122, 184, 304
Treibs, W., 105, 108, 239, 306(116), 307
Trevalion, P. A., 11, 12, 21
Trompler, J., 75, 181
Tronov, B. V., 54, 60
Trumbull, R. E., 305
Tsviel'nikov, V. I., 71
Tubis, M., 61
Tuch, T. G., 184
Tul'chinskii, M. N., 184
Tull, R., 45
Tulloch, A. P., 46
Tykva, R., 110(111), 112, 114(111)

U

Ubbelohde, A. R. J. P., 8, 193, 195(28)
Udupa, H. V. K., 214(116), 236, 271
Udy, M. J., 74
Ueberwasser, H., 323(172)

Uhrich, R., 51(211), 52, 68, 143, 147
Umeda, K., 179
Ungnade, H. E., 146, 147(25, 27, 35)
Unrau, A. M., 65
Urech, J., 157
Uri, N., 216(99), 228, 237, 275
Uroda, J. C., 322
Urry, W. H., 249, 254(33), 261(33), 274, 293, 368

V

Vabel, Ya. I., 271
Vaidya, M. S., 191, 216(104), 229
Vakhrush, A. A., 73
van Cleve, J. W., 395
Van der Castle, J. F., 7
Van der Linden, R., 4, 33, 48, 49(205), 50(206), 67(156, 205)
van der Meulen, J. H., 27
van der Zanden, J. M., 93, 94(51)
van Emster, K., 140
van Helden, R., 225, 228(94), 234(94), 238(94)
van Krevelen, D. W., 239
van Tamelen, E. E., 297, 298(85)
Vara, F. J., 346
Vas, S., 406(94)
Vasil'eva, Vn. N., 72
Velluz, L., 323(184)
Venable, F. P., 30
Venditti, L., 85
Venkatachalapathy, M. S., 214(116), 236, 271
Venkatakrishnan, S., 255, 256(45c)
Venkatasubramanian, N., 159
Venkateswarlu, K., 72
Veprek-Šiška, J., 21
Vetter, K. J., 187, 210(1)
Vilcsek, H., 288, 289(43)
Vilkas, M., 311
Villotti, R., 323(173)
Vischer, E., 149, 157
Vogel, E., 297, 299(87), 300(87)
Volhard, J., 9
Volkova, A. I., 267, 276(63)
von Miller, W., 96, 97(70)
von Richter, V., 95, 96, 97(69)
von Rudloff, E., 46, 397
von Schweinitz, E. A., 84
von Wartenberg, H., 73, 74, 75(33, 34)

Vratney, F., 72
Vredenburgh, W. A., 148, 156
Vysotskaya, N. A., 370

W

Wadsworth, E., 245
Wagner, C., 80
Wagner, G., 42, 43, 44(185)
Wagner, R. B., 146
Wahl, A. C., 24, 25(109, 110)
Wakabayashi, N., 294
Wakabayashi, S., 342
Walk, E., 288, 290(55)
Walker, M. S., 6, 20
Walker, R. T., 62
Walkley, J., 271, 294
Wallach, O., 107(95)
Walling, C., 263, 267, 272
Walsh, H. G., 325
Walters, R. M., 184
Walther, W., 374, 398, 402(74), 403(74)
Walton, W. L., 148
Wanag, G. J., 365
Wankel, R. A., 355
Wannowins, H., 398
Ward, J. J., 47, 91
Wardlaw, W., 249
Ware, J. C., 122, 184
Warnhoff, E. W., 146
Wassmundt, F. W., 305
Wassmuth, C. R., 386, 387(57), 393(57)
Watanabe, M., 68
Watanabe, W., 160, 168(106)
Watanabe, Y., 108
Waters, W. A., 2, 3, 4(3), 5, 8, 9, 32, 41, 48, 53, 65(3), 85, 86, 98, 170, 171(1), 173, 175(9), 179, 181, 188, 189, 192, 194, 195(8, 39), 198, 199(15, 59), 200, 201(59, 62, 63, 64, 65), 202(33, 66), 204, 205, 206, 207, 208(15, 62, 68, 80, 90), 209(23, 33, 60, 62, 68, 80, 85, 90, 109), 210(15, 74), 211, 213(8, 63, 71, 73, 80, 90, 107), 214(66, 80, 107), 215(15, 59, 66, 67, 74, 76, 119), 216(62, 66, 76, 79, 80, 107), 217(23, 33, 60, 90, 109), 218(33, 62, 109), 219(107), 220, 221(62), 222, 223(75, 78, 89, 90), 224, 225(91), 226(8, 75), 227(75), 229, 230(107), 232, 233(80), 234(39, 80, 107, 109), 235(109),

237(64, 109, 118, 119), 238(39, 119, 123), 248, 249(29), 251(29), 253(29), 254(29), 255(29), 368, 373, 401

Waterstradt, H., 5

Watson, D., 224

Watters, J. I., 193, 210(29)

Way, J. W., 355

Webb, J., 45

Weber, J. R., 192, 197(22, 48, 52), 198(22)

Webster, A. H., 30, 31, 67(143)

Webster, I. M., 83, 137

Weedon, B. C. L., 7, 148

Wehrli, H., 285, 286(36), 287

Wei, M.-M., 60

Weidman, S. W., 393

Weidmann, C., 295

Weiler, J., 86, 137

Weiler, M., 96, 97(73)

Weinland, R. F., 195

Weinstein, B., 296

Weis, C., 280, 335(14), 336(14), 337, 338(211), 339(211), 340(211), 344(14), 345(211), 346(211), 348(211), 349(211)

Weiss, A., 297, 299(82), 300(90)

Weiss, E., 184

Weiss, J., 66, 269, 274

Weiss, W., 226, 237(95)

Weissberger, R., 137

Weizmann, C., 317, 318(150)

Wells, C. F., 192, 197(22), 198(227), 219(114), 236

Welstead, W. J., 183

Wendland, R., 83, 137

Wessely, F., 288, 289(40, 42, 44, 45, 46, 47, 48, 49), 290(42, 44), 332(42)

West, B. L., 151

West, T. S., 8

Westheimer, F. H., 64, 72, 74, 76, 77, 79(6), 82(6), 142, 143, 153, 159, 160, 162, 168(5, 106), 169, 170, 171(4, 5), 172, 174(4), 175, 206, 248, 368

Westin, G., 391

Wettstein, A., 149, 150, 156, 157, 321, 322(163, 168), 323(163, 168, 172, 177, 178, 180, 181, 182), 324(190)

Weygand, C., 151

Whalley, W. B., 306(114), 307, 312, 315(144a)

Wheeler, O. H., 95, 96, 97(67), 98(74), 104(63), 285

Wheland, G. W., 129, 132(22)

White, A. C., 219(82), 221

White, A. G., 194, 197, 219(32)

White, A. M., 241

White, R. V., 133

White, W. B., 73

Whitehead, R. L. St. D., 399

Whitehouse, D. B., 240

Whitham, G. H., 108

Whitmore, F. C., 105, 129, 132(22), 146

Wibant, J. P., 275

Wiberg, K. B., 4, 36, 42, 54, 55(226), 56, 57(230), 67(226), 72, 75, 96, 97(72), 99, 100(78, 80), 104(72), 105(72), 109, 110(107), 112, 114(112), 115(80), 118(80), 119(112), 121(80), 122(112), 123(112, 127), 124(112), 127, 136, 140, 168, 172, 173(5), 174(5), 175, 176(12, 14), 178, 180, 182, 255, 262, 263, 333 (215a), 340

Wieczffinki, K., 74, 75

Wieland, H., 127, 132(12), 150

Wieland, P., 149, 150, 156, 321, 322(163, 168), 323(163, 168, 172)

Wienhaus, H., 70, 153

Wiesendanger, H. U. D., 191

Wilcox, C. F., Jr., 166

Wilcox, M. F., 166

Wilder, R. S., 90

Wilds, A. L., 147

Wilhelmi, K. A., 69

Wilke, E., 30, 67(143)

Wilkins, R. G., 238

Wilkinson, D. G., 137, 138(45)

Wilkinson, F., 50

Willard, H. H., 30, 264, 265(56, 59), 266(56), 272(59)

Wille, F., 151

Williams, C. H., 12

Williams, F. T., Jr., 61(247), 62

Williams, G. H., 329, 365

Williams, R. J. P., 191, 241

Wilson, C. D., 129, 132(22)

Wilson, H. J., 198, 238

Windaus, A., 128, 140(14), 336, 350

Winkelmann, E., 355

Winkelmann, K., 158

Winkler, C. A., 60, 67(239)

Winkler, F., 360

Winnick, C. N., 355

Winstein, S., 164, 365
Winter, E., 92, 94(49)
Wintersteiner, O., 126
Wirtz, H., 342
Witham, G. H., 338, 339(212), 340(212), 349
Wittig, G., 358
Wittmann, J. W., 296
Witzemann, E. J., 43, 44(186)
Wolf, G., 399, 400(80)
Wolf, L., 246
Wolfrom, M. L., 371, 388(20), 390
Wolfsberg, M., 12, 73
Wolpers, J., 297, 299(87), 300(87)
Wood, D. G. M., 129, 130, 131(18, 20, 23, 26, 31), 132(31), 133
Woodward, R. B., 45, 129, 287
Woolf, A. A., 72, 73
Woolsey, N. F., 296
Wormser, Y., 194, 219(32)
Wright, A. N., 9, 206, 373
Wright, L. W., 286
Wright, P., 26, 187, 196(6)
Wroblewsky, E., 84
Wronska, M., 21
Wu, T. C., 184
Wunderlich, K., 347
Wynne, W. P., 64

X
Xanthakos, T. S., 236

Y
Yamaguchi, Y., 306
Yamashita, S., 66
Yamazaki, H., 75
Yatsimirskii, K. B., 72, 73
Yen, W. M., 24
Yohe, C. R., 146
Yoshida, T., 343

Yoshino, Y., 4
Yost, D. M., 66, 244
Young, D. P., 239
Young, P., 264, 265(56, 59), 266(56), 272(59)
Young, R. J., 369, 374(9), 399(9)
Young, W. G., 146
Yuguchi, S., 68, 99, 100(77)
Yukawa, Y., 280, 335(16), 348(16)

Z
Zabrodina, A., 62
Zagalo, A., 301
Zahn, K., 292
Zalkow, L. H., 297, 339(221a), 340
Zatzek, E., 28
Zaweski, E. F., 147
Zbiral, E., 288, 289(45, 46, 48, 49)
Zderic, J. A., 155
Zechmeister, L., 281
Zeidler, F., 132(29), 133
Zeidler, O., 132(29), 133
Zeising, M., 226, 237(95)
Zeiss, H. H., 130, 140(28)
Zelinsky, N., 151
Zeller, M. M., 280, 281(17), 282(17)
Zellner, H., 73
Ziegler, K., 151
Zimmerman, G. L., 14, 21
Zincke, T., 86
Zinner, H., 353
Zogel, H., 398, 402(74), 403(74)
Zonis, S. A., 207, 210(72), 236
Zuman, P., 372, 373(23), 383(23), 394(23), 395(23)
Zvenigorodskaya, V. M., 9
Zwanzig, F. R., 130, 140(28)
Zwerina, J., 76
Zyka, J., 281, 351, 405

Subject Index

A

Acetaldehyde, oxidation by cerium(IV), 259
  by chromium(VI), 173
Acetochromate ion, 72
Acetoin, oxidation by vanadium(V), 211
Acetone, oxidation by cerium(IV), 256
  by permanganate, 53
Acetophenone, oxidation by permanganate, 53
Acetoxy radicals, as intermediates in lead(IV) oxidations, 282
α-Acetoxyketones, by oxidation of ketones, 306
Acid anhydrides, oxidation by lead tetraacetate, 305, 311
Acridines, oxidation by lead tetraacetate, 362
Acrylonitrile, polymerization during oxidations, 68, 188, 207, 225
Adamantane, oxidation by chromic acid, 118
tert-Alcohols, oxidation by chromic acid, 170
  by cobalt(III), 202
Alcohols, cleavage in lead tetraacetate oxidation of, 285
  in vanadium(V) oxidation of, 201
  complexes with cerium(IV), 247
  with cobalt(III), 191, 200
  with vanadium(V), 189, 199
  oxidation by cerium(IV), 247
  by chromic acid, 142, 159
  by cobalt(III), 200
  by lead tetraacetate, 321
  by manganese dioxide, 7
  by permanganate, 47, 51
  by permanganate-hydrogen peroxide, 48
  by vanadium(V), 198
  by xenic acid, 406
  reaction with lead tetraacetate, 284
Aldehyde hydrates, oxidation by permanganate, 58
Aldehydes, oxidation by cerium(IV), 255, 259
  by chromic acid, 172
  by chromium(V), 175
  by cobalt(III), 211
  by manganate, 55
  by manganese(III), 220
  by permanganate, 49, 52
  by vanadium(V), 220
  by xenic acid, 406
Alkanes, oxidation by chromic acid, 109, 119
  by lead tetraacetate, 321
  by permanganate, 36
Alkenes, hydroxylation by lead tetraacetate, 335
  by manganate, 4
  by permanganate, 41
  oxidation by cobalt(III), 235
  by chromic acid, 125, 138
  by chromyl acetate, 131
  by chromyl chloride, 135
  by periodate-permanganate, 46, 397
  by vanadium(V), 235
2-Alkylnaphthoquinones, oxidation by chromic acid, 115
Alkynes, oxidation by permanganate, 46
  by lead tetraacetate, 350
Allenes, oxidation by lead tetraacetate, 350
1-Allylcyclohexanol, cleavage in lead tetraacetate oxidation, 285
Allylic oxidation, by di-tert-butyl chromate, 106
  by chromic acid, 105
  by lead tetraacetate, 337
Amides, oxidation by lead tetraacetate, 326
Amines, oxidation by cerium(IV), 269
  by chromic acid, 183
  by lead tetraacetate, 353
  by manganese(III), 238
  by permanganate, 60
  by vanadium(V), 238
Aminoalcohols, cleavage by periodate, 368, 371, 387
Aminophenols, oxidation by lead tetraacetate, 292
Anthracene, oxidation by chromic acid, 83, 137
  by lead tetraacetate, 328

by manganese(III), 236
Antimony(III), oxidation by permanganate, 30
Aromatic rings, oxidation by chromic acid, 136
 by lead tetraacetate, 326, 331
 by permanganate, 47
Aryl alkanes, oxidation by cerium(IV), 271
 by chromic acid, 83, 98
 by chromyl acetate, 92, 102
 by chromyl chloride, 94, 102
 by dichromate ion, 90
 by lead tetraacetate, 312
 by permanganate, 39

B

Barbier-Wieland degradation, 127
Barium chromate(IV), 75
Barium chromate(V), 74
Benzaldehyde, oxidation by cerium(IV), 262
 by chromic acid, 172
 by chromyl acetate, 178
 by cobalt(III), 222
 by permanganate, 54
Benzhydrol, oxidation by permanganate, 48
Benzilic acid, oxidation by permanganate, 65
Benzpinacolyl alcohol, cleavage in lead tetraacetate oxidation of, 287
Benzyl acetate, from oxidation of toluene, 312
Benzyl alcohol, oxidation by lead tetraacetate, 284
N-Benzylglycine, oxidation by lead tetraacetate, 295
a-Benzylindoles, oxidation by lead tetraacetate, 360
Benzyl nitrate, reaction with base, 166
Benzyloxymalondialdehyde, oxidation by periodic acid, 389
Benzyl phenyl ketone, oxidation by manganese(III), 228
Biacetyl, cleavage by periodic acid, 386
Bisbenzenechromium, 75
Borane-pyridine complex, oxidation by permanganate, 27
Boranes, oxidation by chromic acid, 184
Bornyl acetate, oxidation by chromic acid, 112
Borohydride ion, oxidation by permanganate, 27
Boronic acids, oxidation by chromic acid, 184

Bromide ion, oxidation by lead tetraacetate, 282
 by permanganate, 29
 by vanadium(V), 198
 reaction with cerium(IV), 273
Butadiene, reaction with cerium(IV) and bromide ion, 273
2, 3-Butanediol, oxidation by cerium(IV), 252
 by periodate, 378
tert-Butylamine, oxidation by permanganate, 61
o-2-Butylbenzoic acid, oxidation by chromic acid, 107
p-2-Butylbenzoic acid, oxidation by permanganate, 39
tert-Butyl chromate, 83
 allylic oxidation by, 106
 oxidation of alcohols by, 158
tert-Butyl hydroperoxide, reaction with cerium(IV), 268
tert-Butyl orthovanadate, 194

C

Camphene, oxidation to camphor, 129
 oxidation by lead tetraacetate, 340
Carbohydrates, oxidation by lead tetraacetate, 400
 by periodate, 372, 374, 395
Carbon-carbon bonds, oxidation by lead tetraacetate, 334
Carbon-hydrogen bonds, oxidation by chromic acid, 83, 109
 by lead tetraacetate, 305
 by periodate, 388
Carbon monoxide, oxidation by permanganate, 33
Carboxylic acids, oxidation by cerium(IV), 264
 by chromic acid, 180
 by cobalt(III), 234
 by lead tetraacetate and iodine, 296
 by permanganate, 36
 reaction with lead tetraacetate, 293
Carvomenthene, oxidation by di-*tert*-butyl chromate, 107
Catalysis, by vanadium(V) of oxidations, 238
 of autoxidation by ceric ion, 274
Cerium species, oxidation potentials of, 244
Cerium(IV) alkoxides, 249
Cerium(IV), as oxidant, 26, 243
 complexes from, 245, 247
 complexes with alcohols, 247

with diols, 251, 255
with thiols, 270
indirect oxidation by, 272
irradiation of solutions of, 274
oxidation of alcohols by, 247
of aldehydes by, 255, 259
of amines by, 269
of benzaldehyde by, 262
of carboxylic acids by, 264
of cyclohexanone by, 256
of free radicals by, 271
of hydrocarbons by, 271
of hydroperoxides by, 267
of hydroxyacids by, 265
of ketones by, 255
reaction with bromide ion, 273
stereochemistry of, 246
Chloral hydrate, oxidation by permanganate, 58
Chloride ion, oxidation by cerium(IV), 273
by lead tetraacetate, 282
by permanganate, 29
Chlorochromate ion, 72
1-Chloronorcamphane, oxidation by chromic acid, 112
Cholesteryl acetate, oxidation by di-*tert*-butyl chromate, 106
by chromic acid, 126
Chromate esters, from diols, 171
Chromate ion, dimerization of, 71
infrared spectrum, 72
ultraviolet spectrum, 72
Chromic acid, allylic oxidation by, 105
ionization of, 71
oxidation by, 69
of alcohols by, 142, 159
of aldehydes by, 172
of alkanes by, 109, 119
stereochemistry of, 114, 118, 122
of alkenes by, 125, 138
of amines by, 183
of aromatic rings by, 83, 98
of arsenious ion by, 76, 77
of arylalkanes by, 83
of boranes by, 184
of boronic acids by, 184
of bromide ions by, 82
of C—H bonds by, 82
of carboxylic acids by, 180
of cycloalkanes by, 112
of diarylalkanes by, 86, 101
of 1,2-diols by, 170

of ferrous ion by, 76, 80
of hemiacetals by, 143
of hydroxy acids by, 182
of iodide ion by, 76, 82
of ketones by, 178
of phosphorous ion by, 81
of sulfides by, 182
of uranyl ion by, 82
of vanadous ion by, 80
reaction with anions, 72
with chromic ion, 81
Chromium(III), oxidation by permanganate, 30
Chromium(IV), 75
Chromium(V), 74
in alcohol oxidation, 143, 168
in aldehyde oxidation, 175
Chromium(V) oxide, 74
Chromium(VI), *see* Chromic acid, Chromyl chloride, Chromyl acetate
Chromium dioxide, 74
Chromium pentafluoride, 74
Chromium tetrachloride, 75
Chromium tetrafluoride, 75
Chromium tetra-*tert*-butoxide, 75
Chromium trioxide-pyridine, oxidation of alcohols by, 153
Chromium trioxide, reaction with solvents, 70
structure of, 69
Chromyl acetate, 73, 83
allylic oxidation by, 105
oxidation of alkanes by, 115
of alkenes by, 131
of aryl alkanes by, 92, 102
of benzaldehyde by, 178
of sulfides by, 182
Chromyl chloride, 73, 83
oxidation of alkanes by, 119
of alkenes by, 135
of aryl alkanes by, 94, 102
Chromyl compounds, oxidation by, 69
Cleavage, in chromic acid oxidation, 168
in cobalt(III) oxidation, 202
in lead tetraacetate oxidation of alcohols, 285
in oxidation of *3*-phenylethanol with vanadium(V), 201
of phenyl-*tert*-butyl carbinol, 142, 168, 202
of diols, 4, 8, 170, 361, 398, 399, 406
Cobalt, in biological systems, 240

Cobalt(III), aqueous solutions of, 190
  as catalyst in oxidations, 238
  as oxidant, 26, 185
  complexes from, 191, 196
  oxidation of aldehydes by, 211
    of alkenes by, 235
    of benzaldehyde by, 222
    of carboxylic acids by, 234
    of formaldehyde by, 200, 221
    of formic acid by, 231
    of hydrazine by, 196
    of inorganic ions by, 197
    of ketones by, 223
    of malonic acid by, 234
    of oxalic acid by, 229
  oxidative cleavage of alcohols by, 202
Cobalt(III) acetate, 194
Cobalt(III) formate, permanganate oxi-
  dation of, 57
Conformational effects on alcohol oxi-
  dation, 164
Cumyl hydroperoxide, reaction with lead
  tetraacetate, 303
Cyanide ion, oxidation by permanganate, 31
Cyanoalkenes, oxidation by permanga-
  nate, 45
Cyclic cerium(IV) complexes, 255
Cyclic chromate esters, 171
Cyclic lead esters, 401
Cyclic periodate esters, 374, 379, 381
Cyclic vanadium complexes, 205, 207
Cycloalkanes, oxidation by chromic acid, 112
Cycloalkanols, oxidation by chromic
  acid, 163
Cycloheptatrienecarboxylic acid, oxidation
    by cerium(IV), 264
  by lead tetraacetate, 296
Cyclohexadienecarboxylic acids, oxidation
    by lead tetraacetate, 296
Cyclohexadienes, dehydrogenation by lead
  tetraacetate, 317
1,2-Cyclohexanediol, cleavage by lead tetra-
    acetate, 401
  by periodic acid, 373, 375, 380
  by sodium bismuthate, 406
1,3-Cyclohexanedione, oxidation by periodate, 390
Cyclohexanol, oxidation by cerium(IV), 200,
    248
  by chromic acid, 146
  by cobalt(III), 200
  by manganese(III), 200

  by vanadium(V), 199
Cyclohexanone, oxidation by cerium(IV), 256
  by chromic acid, 178
  by cobalt(III), 223
  by manganese(III), 223, 227
  by vanadium(V), 223
Cyclohexanone peroxide, reaction with va-
  nadium(V), 239
Cyclohexene, oxidation by di-*tert*-butyl
    chromate, 106
  by chromic acid, 105, 109
  by lead tetraacetate, 337, 341
Cyclooctatetraene, oxidation by lead tetraacetate, 344
Cyclopentadiene, oxidation by lead tetraacetate, 345
Cyclopropanes, oxidation by lead tetraacetate, 335
Cytosine, oxidation by permanganate, 62

D

Decalin-9,10-diol, cleavage by lead tetra-
  acetate, 399
  by periodic acid, 374
Decalin, oxidation by chromyl acetate, 118
Dehydrogenation, by lead tetraacetate, 316
Diarylalkanes, oxidation by chromic acid, 86,
  101
Diarylethylenes, chromic acid oxidation of,
  130
Diarylmercury, reaction with lead tetraacetate, 363
Diarylmethanes, oxidation by manganese
  dioxide, 7
Diazoalkanes, oxidation by lead tetraacetate, 357
β-Dicarbonyl compounds, oxidation by lead
  tetraacetate, 311
Dicarboxylic acids, degradation to alkenes
  with lead tetraacetate, 297
Dichromate ion, 71
  oxidation of alcohols by, 152
  of arylalkanes by, 90
Dicyclopentadiene, oxidation by lead tetraacetate, 342
Dienes, oxidation by chromic acid, 128, 140
  by lead tetraacetate, 336
Dihydrofurans, formation by lead tetraacetate oxidation, 349
Dihydropyran, oxidation by lead tetraacetate, 340

Dihydro-α-terpineol, oxidation by permanganate, 38
Diisopropyl ether, oxidation by lead tetraacetate, 320
1,2-Diketones, cleavage by lead tetraacetate, 403
· by periodic acid, 368, 371, 386, 393
from permanganate oxidation of alkynes, 47
oxidation by manganese(III), 226
by vanadium(V), 226
1,3-Diketones, oxidation by periodate, 389
1,2-Dimethyl-1,2-cyclopentanediol, cleavage by periodic acid, 374
1,1-Dineopentylethylene, nonreactivity toward permanganate, 45
1,2-Diols, cleavage by lead tetraacetate, 398
by manganate, 4
by manganese(III), 8
by periodate, 368, 371, 373, 393
by phenyliodosoacetate, 399, 405
by sodium bismuthate, 406
complexes with cerium(IV), 251, 255
from lead tetraacetate oxidation of alkenes, 335
from permanganate oxidation of alkenes, 41, 44
oxidation by cerium(IV), 250
by chromic acid, 170
by chromyl chloride, 172
by cobalt(III), 206
by manganese(III), 206
by permanganate, 64
by vanadium(V), 204
by xenic acid, 406
1,1-Diphenylethylene, oxidation by chromic acid, 138
Diphenylmethane, oxidation by chromic acid, 86, 100
by chromyl chloride, 96
Diterpenes, oxidation by lead tetraacetate, 325
Double bonds, oxidation by chromic acid, 125

E

Enol esters, oxidation by lead tetraacetate, 336
Epimerization, during lead tetraacetate oxidation, 324
Epoxides, formation in chromic acid oxidation, 118, 125, 129, 131
in permanganate oxidation, 45
α-Ergosterol acetate, oxidation by chromic acid, 125
Ester intermediates in alcohol oxidation, 161
Esters, oxidation by lead tetraacetate, 305, 311, 312, 320
Etard reaction, 95, 102
Ethers, formation in lead tetraacetate oxidation, 321
oxidation by lead tetraacetate, 319
Ethylbenzene, oxidation by chromic acid, 84
by dichromate ion, 92
by chromyl chloride, 96
Ethylene glycol, cleavage by periodate, 373
oxidation by chromic acid, 170
by cerium(IV), 251
Ethanolamine, cleavage by periodate, 387
3-Ethylpentane, oxidation by chromic acid, 113

F

Ferrocyanide ion, oxidation by permanganate, 30
Ferrous ion, oxidation by permanganate, 30
by vanadium(V), 196
Flavanones, oxidation by lead tetraacetate, 307
Fluoral hydrate, oxidation by permanganate, 48, 58
Formaldehyde, oxidation by chromic acid, 173
by cerium(IV), 260
by cobalt(III), 200, 221
by manganese(III), 221
by permanganate, 58
by vanadium(V), 220
Formate ion, oxidation by permanganate, 15, 56
Formic acid, oxidation by ceric ion, 250
by chromic acid, 181
by cobalt(III), 231
by lead tetraacetate, 293
by manganese(III), 230
by vanadium(V), 231
by permanganate, 56
Free radicals, as intermediates in oxidations, 21, 288
formation during oxidations, 187, 207
oxidation by cerium(IV), 271
Furan, oxidation by lead tetraacetate, 333

G

Glutaric acid, oxidation by lead tetraacetate, 301
Glycolic esters, formation in lead tetraacetate
oxidation, 345
Grob degradation, 297

H

Hemiacetals, oxidation by chromic acid, 143
Heterocyclic compounds, oxidation by permanganate, 62
Hydrazides, dehydrogenation by lead tetraacetate, 358
Hydrazine, oxidation of, 26
by cobalt(III), 196
by manganese(III), 196
by permanganate, 26
by vanadium(V), 195
Hydrogen, oxidation by permanganate, 30
Hydrogen peroxide, oxidation by permanganate, 31
with cerium(IV) as oxidant, 276
Hydroperoxides, oxidation by cerium(IV),
267
reaction with lead tetraacetate, 302
α-Hydroxyacids, cleavage by lead tetraacetate, 403
oxidation by cerium(IV), 265
by manganese(III), 207
by permanganate, 65
by vanadium(V), 207
α-Hydroxyisobutyric acid, oxidation by va-
nadium(V), 207
α-Hydroxyketones, oxidation by manga-
nese(III), 210
by vanadium(V), 210
Hydroxylamine, oxidation by permanganate, 27
Hydroxylation, of alkenes by permanganate, 41, 44
Hydroxyphenols, oxidation by lead tetraacetate, 292
Hypochlorite, as oxidant, 26

I

Imines, dehydrogenation by lead tetraacetate, 356
Induced oxidation, 76

in chromic acid oxidation of alcohols, 160
Iodide ion, oxidation by lead tetraacetate, 282
by periodate, 390
by permanganate, 15, 29
by vanadium(V), 195
Iodides, formation from carboxylic acids, 296
Iodoso acetates, oxidation by, 365
Iodoso compounds, cleavage of 1,2-diols
by, 405
β-Ionone, oxidation by di-*tert*-butyl chromate, 106
Isobutene, oxidation by lead tetraacetate, 347
Isobutyric acid, oxidation by
permanganate, 38
Isopropyl alcohol, oxidation by chromic
acid, 159
Isotope effects, in alcohol oxidation, 208
in chromic acid oxidation of hydrocarbons, 100, 119
of alcohols, 160, 168
of aldehydes, 172, 176
in ketone oxidation, 208
in permanganate oxidation of alcohols, 50
of aldehydes, 55
of fluoral, 59
of formate ion, 57

J

Jones reagent, 145

K

Ketoacids, oxidation by manganese(III), 226
by vanadium(V), 226
Ketohydrazones, oxidation by lead tetraacetate, 356
Ketols, cleavage by lead tetraacetate, 403
by periodic acid, 368, 371, 386, 393
from permanganate oxidation of alkenes,
41, 45
Ketones, from permanganate oxidation of
nitroalkanes, 61
oxidation by cerium(IV), 255
by chromic acid, 178
by cobalt(III), 223
by lead tetraacetate, 305, 307
by manganese(III), 223
by permanganate, 52
by vanadium(V), 223
products of oxidation by cerium(IV), 258
by manganese(III), 227

by vanadium(V), 227
Kohler peroxides reaction with lead tetraacetate, 303

L

Lactic acid, oxidation by chromic acid, 182
γ-Lactones, formation in lead tetraacetate
oxidation, 348
Lead(IV) salts, preparation of, 280
Lead tetraacetate, acetoxylation of methyl-
pyrrole by, 360
addition of methyl acetate during oxidations, 348
allylic oxidation by, 337, 339
as electrophile, 282
cleavage of 1,2-diketones by, 403
of diols by, 371, 398
of hydroxyacids by, 403
of ketols by, 403
dehydrogenation by, 316
of hydrazides by, 358
of imines by, 356
hyroxylation of alkenes by, 335
oxidation by, 277, 283
of carbohydrates by, 400
of acetylenes by, 350
of acid anhydrides by, 305, 311
of alkanes by, 321
of allenes by, 350
of amides by, 326
of amines by, 353
of aminophenols by, 292
of aromatic hydrocarbons by, 326, 331
of arylalkanes by, 312
of carbon-carbon bonds by, 334
of diazoalkanes by, 357
of β -dicarbonyl compounds by, 311
of dicarboxylic acids by, 297
of dienes by, 336
of enol esters by, 336
of esters by, 305, 311
of ethers by, 319
of furan by, 333
of hydroxyphenols by, 292
of ketones by, 305, 307
of oximes by, 356
of phenol ethers by, 330
of phenols by, 288
of phosphites by, 363
of sulfides by, 352
of thiols by, 351

potential of, 281
of unsaturated acids by, 295
oxidative decarboxylation by, 295
physical properties of, 280
preparation of, 278
procedures for oxidation by, 404
reaction with alcohols, 284
with carboxylic acids, 293
with hyroperoxides, 302
with nitrogen heterocycles, 359
with organometallic compounds, 363
rearrangements in oxidation by, 340
solubility of, 280
spectrum of, 281
thermal decomposition of, 281
Limonene, oxidation by di-*tert*-butyl chromate, 107

M

Malapradian oxidation, 368, 371
Malondialdehyde, oxidation by periodate,
389, 391
Malonic acid, oxidation by chromic acid, 181
by cobalt(III), 234
by manganese(III), 231
by vanadium(V), 233
Mandelic acid, oxidation by permanganate, 65
Manganate(V), disproportionation of, 5
oxidation by permanganate, 3
of alcohols by, 5
properties of, 5
spectrum of, 11, 14
Manganate(VI), cleavage of diols by, 4
disproportionation of, 3
exchange with water, 3
formation from permanganate, 21
hydroxylation of alkenes by, 4
oxidation of aromatic aldehydes by, 55
oxidation to permanganate, 4
properties of, 2
reaction with permanganate, 24
spectrum, 11, 14
Manganese, in biological systems, 240
oxidation states of, 2
Manganese(II), oxidation by permanganate, 9
properties of, 9
Manganese(III), aqueous solutions of, 192
as an oxidant, 8
cleavage of diols by, 8
complexes from, 8, 193

disproportionation of, 8
oxidation by, 185
  of aldehydes by, 220
  of amines by, 238
  of aromatic rings by, 236
  of cyclohexanone by, 227
  of diketones by, 226
  of formaldehyde by, 221
  of formic acid by, 230
  of hydrazine by, 196
  of α-hydroxyacids by, 207
  of ketoacids by, 226
  of ketones by, 223
  of malonic acid by, 231
  of oxalic acid by, 228
  of phenols by, 237
Manganese(III), acetate, 195
Manganese(IV), properties of, 6
Manganese dioxide, as oxidant for alcohols, 7
  oxidation of diarylmethanes by, 7
Manganese species, oxidation potentials of, 10
Methyl acetate, addition to double bond in lead tetraacetate oxidation, 348
Methyl cinnamate, permanganate oxidation of, 43
Methylacetoin, cleavage by periodic acid, 387
Methylation by lead tetraacetate, 326
Methylcyclohexane, oxidation by chromic acid, 105, 113
1-Methyl-α-fenchene, oxidation by chromic acid, 130, 140
3-Methylheptane, oxidation by chromic acid, 114
4-Methylhexanoic acid, oxidation by permanganate, 36
Methylpyrroles, acetoxylation by lead tetraacetate, 360
β-Methylstyrene, oxidation with chromyl chloride, 136
p-Methoxystyrene, oxidation by lead tetraacetate, 344

N

Naphthalene, oxidation by cerium(IV), 271
  by chromic acid, 83, 137
  by lead tetraacetate, 329, 354
  by vanadium(V), 236
Naphthoquinones, methylation by lead tetraacetate, 327
Neohexane, oxidation by chromic acid, 114

  by chromyl acetate, 118
Nitroalkanes, oxidation by permanganate, 61
tert-Nitrobutane, from permanganate oxidation of tert-butylamine, 61
Nitrogen heterocycles, dehydrogenation by lead tetraacetate, 359
p-Nitrotoluene, oxidation by chromic acid, 87
  by chromyl acetate, 93
Norbornanecarboxylic acid, oxidation by permanganate, 37
Norbornene, oxidation by lead tetraacetate, 342
Norborneol, oxidation by chromic acid, 166

O

Octene-4, oxidation by lead tetraacetate, 349
Oleic acid, oxidation by permanganate, 43
One-equivalent oxidations, 25, 186
Organoaluminum compounds, reaction with lead tetraacetate, 364
Organolead compounds, in lead tetraacetate oxidation, 332
  reaction with lead tetraacetate, 364
Organolead derivatives, as intermediates, 283
Organomercury compounds, reaction with lead tetraacetate, 364
Organometallic compounds, reaction with lead tetraacetate, 363
Oxalic acid, oxidation by cerium(IV), 265
  by cobalt(III), 229
  by lead tetraacetate, 297
  by manganese(III), 228
  by permanganate, 65
  by vanadium(V), 229
  by xenic acid, 406
Oximes, oxidation by lead tetraacetate, 356
Oxygen transfer, in permanganate oxidation, 29, 33, 37, 42

P

Periodate, aminoalcohol cleavage by, 368, 371
  analysis for, 368
  cleavage of aminoalcohols by, 368, 371, 387
    of diketones by, 368, 371, 386, 393
    of ketols by, 368, 371, 386
  diol cleavage by, 368, 371, 373, 393
  oxidation of carbohydrates by, 372, 374, 395

of carbon hydrogen bonds by, 388
of iodide ion by, 390
of sulfides by, 390
procedure for oxidations by, 393
properties of, 369
Periodate-permanganate, as oxidant, 46
oxidation of alkenes by, 397
Permanganate, acidity changes during oxidation by, 19
analysis for, 13, 15
exchange with manganese dioxide, 25
oxidation by, 1, 35
of alcohols by, 47, 51
of aldehyde hydrates by, 58
of aldehydes by, 49, 52
of alkanes by, 36
of alkenes by, 41
of alkynes by, 46
of amines by, 60
of aromatic aldehydes by, 54
of aromatic rings by, 47
of arylalkanes by, 39
of borane derivatives by, 27
of carbon monoxide by, 33
of carboxylic acids by, 36
of cyanide ion by, 31
of diols by, 64
of formic acid by, 56
of halide ions by, 29
of heterocyclic compounds by, 62
of hydrazine by, 26
of hydrogen by, 30
of hydrogen peroxide by, 31
of hydroxyacids by, 65
of hydroxylamine by, 27
of ketones by, 52
of metal ions by, 30
of nitroalkanes by, 61
of oxalic acid by, 65
of phenols by, 59, 237
of sulfides by, 63
of sulfinic acids by, 64
of sulfur ions by, 28
of thiols by, 64
oxygen exchange with water, 23
photolytic decomposition of, 21
rates of oxidation by, 67
reaction with formate ion, 15
with iodide ion, 15
with manganate, 24
with manganese(II), 9
silver catalysis of oxidation by, 31, 34

solvents for oxidation by, 35
spectrum of, 11, 14
stoichiometry of oxidations by, 17
thermal decomposition of, 20
Permanganic acid, 22
Permanganic anhydride, 22
Phenanthrene, oxidation by chromic acid, 83, 137
Phenols, oxidation by Fremy's salt, 391
by lead tetraacetate, 288, 391
by manganese(III), 237
by periodate, 391
by permanganate, 59, 237
by potassium nitrosodisulfonate, 391
by sodium bismuthate, 391
by vanadium(V), 237
Phenylation, by lead tetrabenzoate, 329
Phenyl *tert*-butyl carbinol, chromic acid oxidation of, 142, 168
vanadium(V) oxidation of, 202
Phenyliodosoacetate, cleavage of diols by, 399, 405
β-Phenylethanol, oxidation by vanadium(V), 201
Phenyl ethers, oxidation by bismuthate, 391
by lead tetraacetate, 330
by periodate, 391
Phenylglyoxylic acids, by oxidation of phenyl alkyl ketones, 53
Phosphites, oxidation by lead tetraacetate, 363
Pinacol, cleavage by lead tetraacetate, 401
by periodic acid, 373, 383
oxidation by ceric ion, 250
by chromic acid, 170
by cobalt(III), 206
by manganese(III), 207
by vanadium(V), 205
Pinacolyl alcohol, cleavage in lead tetraacetate oxidation of, 286
α-Pinene, oxidation by di-*tert*-butyl chromate, 107
by lead tetraacetate, 338
Platinum(II), oxidation by permanganate, 30
Polychromates, 71
Potassium chromium oxypentachloride, 74
Propylbenzene, oxidation by chromic acid, 84
by chromyl chloride, 104
by dichromate ion, 92
Pyrogallol, oxidation by periodate, 392
Pyrroles, oxidation by lead tetraacetate, 362

Q

Quinol, oxidation by periodate, 392
Quinol acetates, by oxidation of phenols, 290
Quinones, by oxidation of phenols, 290

R

Rearrangements, in lead tetraacetate oxidation, 340
Redox potentials, cerium species, 244
  cobalt species, 210
  lead species, 281
  manganese species, 10, 210
  vanadium species, 210

S

Sarett reagent, 153
Silver catalysis, of permanganate oxidation, 31, 34
Sodium bismuthate, cleavage of 1,2-diols by, 406
Steroidal alcohols, lead tetraacetate oxidation of, 322
  oxidation by chromic acid, 148
Steroidal ketones, oxidation by lead tetraacetate, 309
Strontium chromate(IV), 75
Styrene, oxidation by permanganate, 45
Sulfide ion, oxidation by permanganate, 28
Sulfides, oxidation by chromic acid, 182
  by lead tetraacetate, 352
  by periodate, 390
  by permanganate, 63
Sulfinic acids, oxidation by permanganate, 64
Sulfite, oxidation by permanganate, 28
Sulfoxides, oxidation by permanganate, 63

T

Tartaric acid, oxidation by manganese(III), 210
α-Terpineol, oxidation by di-*tert*-butyl chromate, 107
Tetraarylethylenes, oxidation by chromic acid, 140
  by chromyl acetate, 141
Tetrahydrofuran(s), formation in lead tetraacetate oxidation, 321, 325
  oxidation by cerium(IV) and oxygen, 275
Tetraphenylarsonium permanganate, 16

Tetraphenylethylene, oxidation by chromic acid, 125
  by chromyl acetate, 135
  by permanganate, 45
Tetraphenylfuran, oxidation by chromic acid, 183
Thallic acetate, oxidation by, 365
Thallium(I), oxidation by permanganate, 30
Thallium(III), as oxidant, 26
Thiocyanate, oxidation by permanganate, 29
Thiols, complexes with cerium(IV), 270
  oxidation by lead tetraacetate, 351
  by permanganate, 64
Thiosulfate, oxidation by permanganate, 29
Tin(II), oxidation by permanganate, 30
Toluene, oxidation by chromic acid, 83
  by lead tetraacetate, 312
  by permanganate, 39
Triphenylacetaldehyde, oxidation by chromic acid, 176
  by permanganate, 178
Triphenylmethane, oxidation by chromic acid, 87
  reaction with chromyl chloride, 95
Tungsten(IV), oxidation by permanganate, 30
Two equivalent oxidation, 25, 186

U

Unsaturated acids, oxidation by lead tetraacetate, 295
Uranium(IV), oxidation by permanganate, 30
Uric acid, oxidation by permanganate, 62

V

Vanadium, in biological systems, 240
Vanadium(IV), oxidation by permanganate, 30
Vanadium(V), aqueous solutions of, 189
  as catalyst in oxidations, 238
  complex formation, 190
  oxidation by, 185
    of alcohols by, 198
    of aldehydes by, 220
    of alkenes by, 235
    of amines by, 238
    of cyclohexanone by, 227
    of diketones by, 226
    of diols by, 204

of formaldehyde by, 220
of formic acid by, 231
of hydrazine by, 195
of α-hydroxyacids by, 207
of iodide ion by, 195
of ketoacids by, 226
of ketones by, 223
of malonic acid by, 233
of oxalic acid by, 229
of phenols by, 237
oxidative cleavage of alcohols by, 201
Vanadium oxychloride, 194
Vitamin B_{12}, 240

X

Xenic acid, oxidation of organic compounds
by, 406

Y

Yohimbine, dehydrogenation by lead tetraacetate, 359